# Advanced Level Mathematics

## Second Edition

**R.C. Solomon** M.A., Ph.D.
Dean of Working Men's College

**DP PUBLICATIONS LTD.**
Aldine Place
142/144 Uxbridge Road
London W12 8AW

1992

# Acknowledgements

*I am very grateful to the following examination authorities for their permission to reproduce past examination questions.*

*The source of the question is denoted by the letters in square brackets: questions from Additional Mathematics papers are indicated by add after the letters of the board.*

> *The Associated Examining Board (AEB)*
> *University of Cambridge Local Examinations Syndicate (C)*
> *The Joint Matriculation Board (JMB)*
> *University of London School Examinations Board (L)*
> *Northern Ireland Schools Examinations Council (NI)*
> *University of Oxford Delegacy of Local Examinations (O)*
> *Oxford and Cambridge Schools Examination Board (O&C)*
> *The School Mathematics Project (SMP)*
> *The Mathematics in Education and Industry Project (MEI)*
> *Southern Universities Joint Board (SUJB)*
> *Welsh Joint Education Committee (W)*

*The solutions at the back of the book are the responsibility of the author, and have neither been provided nor approved by the boards.*

*A CIP catalogue record for this book is available from the British Library*

*ISBN 1 870941 24 4*

*Copyright R.C. Solomon © 1992*

*First Edition 1988*
*Reprinted 1990*
*Second Edition 1992*

*Printed in Great Britain by*
>   *Loader Jackson Printers*
>   *Arlesey, Bedfordshire*

# Contents

# STATISTICS

# Preface

## AIM

The aim of this book is to provide all the support needed for a course in Advanced Level Mathematics. The book covers, in one volume, the Pure Mathematics, Mechanics and Statistics that are included in the syllabi for single subject Mathematics at Advanced Level.

It is assumed that the principles of the subject have been taught, and the book contains all the extra material needed, such as course notes, examples, exercises, examination questions and answers.

Note: Candidates for AS-level will be able to select those topics and questions which are required for their exam.

## NEED

Many Advanced Level examination questions cover at least two topics. In the author's experience candidates have difficulty tackling these questions, both through a lack of a full understanding of the topics in the syllabus, and from inability to recognize combinations of topics.

The need was seen for a book which helped to achieve the required full understanding by:

a. assuming the teacher to have explained the principles etc.,

b. reminding candidates of the principles/formulae involved,

c. giving graded examples and graded drill exercises in each of the syllabus topics, as well as examination level questions involving combinations of topics,

d. pointing out common errors made by candidates.

## APPROACH

The main body of the text consists of 46 chapters, divided into four sections as follows:

(a)  The Common Core at A-level   (b)   Extra Topics in Pure Mathematics

(c)  Mechanics                    (d)   Statistics.

Each chapter is divided into topics, each of which includes a statement of principles and formulae, worked examples and graded *routine* exercises.

At the end of each chapter there is a list of common errors in each topic, and several questions taken from recent examination papers of the examination boards. Candidates for AS-level Mathematics should find that the questions from Additional Mathematics papers are at a suitable level of difficulty. Hints for the solution of some of these questions appear in the answer section of the book.

Information to show which topics are required for the various examining boards will be provided, both in a chart at the start of the book and at the beginning of each chapter.

At the end of the book there are 4 test papers in the style of AS exams, and 9 papers in the style of A-level exams.

Complete answers are provided.

# Preface for the Second Edition

I am very grateful for the suggestions provided by users of this book. One suggestion, for a section on algebra, has been incorporated as an appendix.

Several boards now offer modular A and AS level syllabuses, and four exam papers in the modular style have been included.

R C Solomon
May 1992

# Study and Examination Hints

## 1 Study Hints

This book has been written to help you pass A-level or AS-level in Mathematics. Of course it must be used in an efficient way. The following hints will help you to make good use of your study time.

A good rule to follow is: *Little but often.* An hour a day for seven days is more useful than seven hours of work on a single day.

Make sure you get a full 60 minutes out of every hour. Do your study in as quiet a room as possible, with all your equipment to hand, and with as few distractions as possible. Do not try to combine study with watching television or eating.

Write as well as read. There is little to be gained from simply reading Mathematics. Read the topic outlines and the worked examples, and then try the exercises. Write down the solutions, do not try to convince yourself that you can do them in your head.

Do not give in too soon. There are answers at the back of the book, but use them for checking that you are right, rather than for finding out how to do a problem.

The test papers at the back of the book should be done under test conditions, with a time limit and no reference books. In all exams you are allowed to use a calculator - make sure that you are confident in its use.

In A-level work it is assumed that you are familiar with O-level or GCSE work. In particular, you must be confident and accurate with algebraic operations. Questions are not set directly on this, but fairly complicated algebra is used in all parts of A-level Mathematics.

## 2 Examination Hints

How well you do in an examination depends mainly on how well you have prepared for it. But many candidates do poorly because of bad examination technique. The following hints will help you make the most out of your examination time.

Read the question carefully. Very many marks are lost by candidates who have misunderstood a question. Not only do they lose the marks for that question, but they also lose time because the question is often made more complicated by their mistake.

Do not spend too much time on any one question. There is no point in spending a third of the time on a question which carries a twentieth of the marks. Leave that question, and come back to it later if you have time at the end of the exam.

Show your working. If you obtain the wrong answer just because of a slight slip, then you will not lose many marks provided that you show all your working. If you put down the wrong answer without any explanation then you will get no marks at all.

Try to make your solutions neat. Use enough paper to ensure that your answer can be read easily. But do not spend too much time on this - there is no point in spending five minutes on a beautiful diagram for a question which is only worth two marks.

Recognize what each question is about. Many candidates find that they can answer a question when they are doing an exercise consisting of several similar problems, but could not answer the same question when it occurs in a test paper surrounded by different questions. Read each question carefully, and identify the topic or topics of the question. The examiner is not trying to "catch you out", but he is trying to test that you have studied each part of the syllabus and are able to answer questions on it.

Recognize combinations of topics. Many questions start with a problem in one area of Mathematics, and then require you to apply your answer to another, but related, area. Make sure that you appreciate what the examiner is looking for.

Above all: *Make good use of your time!* During the months that you are preparing yourself for the examination make sure that each hour of learning or revision is well spent. During the actual examination make sure that you do not waste the precious minutes!

# Syllabus Analysis

The four tables of syllabus analysis follow the division of this book into four sections.

Table 1. The Core Syllabus     Table 2. Extra Pure Topics
Table 3. Mechanics     Table 4. Statistics

A key for the examining boards and their syllabuses follows. Not every syllabus has been covered. The examining authorities describe the contents of their syllabuses in different ways, and the tables are therefore not an exact guide.

## A = Associated Examining Board

**A-levels**   Pure and Applied Mathematics. Tables 1, 2, 3.
Pure Mathematics and Statistics. Tables 1, 2, 4.

**AS-levels**   Pure with Applications – 994. Tables 1, 2.
Calculus and Particle Dynamics – 995. Tables 1, 3.

## C = Cambridge Examination Syndicate

**A-levels**   Syllabus C. Tables 1, 2, 3, 4.

**AS-levels**   Mathematics – 8480. (CA in tables). Tables 1, 2, 3, 4.
Applicable Mathematics – 8485. (CB). Tables 1, 2, 4.

## J = Joint Matriculation Board

**A-levels**   Pure and Applied Mathematics. Tables 1, 2, 3, 4.
Pure Mathematics with Mechanics. Tables 1, 2, 3.
Pure Mathematics with Statistics. Tables 1, 2, 4.

**AS-levels**   Pure Mathematics. The syllabus consists of the Pure Mathematics topics of the A-levels above.
Pure Mathematics with Mechanics. Tables 1, 2, 3.

## L = London Examinations Board

**Modular**   The board offers modular papers P1, P2, M1, M2, S1 etc. Subject to certain restrictions, an A-level is obtained from 4 of these modules, and an AS-level from 2. For example, P1, P2, M1, S1 constitute an A-level in Mathematics. Modules P1 and P2 constitute an AS-level in Pure Mathematics.

### MEI = Mathematics in Education and Industry project

**Modular**    The board offers modular papers P1, P2, M1, M2, S1 etc. Subject to certain restrictions, an A-level is obtained from 6 of these modules, and an AS-level from 3. For example, P1, P2, P3, M1, M2, S1 constitute an A-level in Mathematics. Modules P1, P2, P3 constitute an AS-level in Pure Mathematics.

### NI = Northern Ireland Examinations Council

**A-level**    Pure and Applied Mathematics. Tables 1, 2, 3, 4.

### O = Oxford Delegacy of Local Examinations

**A-levels**    Mathematics – Pure with Mechanics. Tables 1, 2, 3.
Mathematics – Pure with Statistics. Tables 1, 2, 4.

### OC = Oxford and Cambridge Examination Board

**A-levels**    Mathematics. Tables 1, 2, 3, 4.

**AS-levels**    These are the same as the Cambridge Board AS-levels.

### SMP = Schools Mathematics Project

**Modular**    The papers and their topics fall into four groups.
AS. Compulsory for AS-level and A-level.
A1. Compulsory for A-level, forbidden for AS-level.
A2. Compulsory for A-level, optional for AS-level.
O. Optional for AS-level and A-level.

### W = Welsh Joint Education Committee

**A-levels**    Mathematics. Tables 1, 2, 3, 4.

**AS-levels**    Pure Mathematics. (WP in tables). Tables 1, 2.
Mechanics. (WM). Tables 2, 3.
Pure with Mechanics. (WA and WPM). Tables 1, 3.
Pure with Statistics. (WA and WS). Tables 1, 4.

# Table 1. The Core Syllabus

| | A Level | | | | | | | AS Level | | | | | | | Modular | | |
|---|---|---|---|---|---|---|---|---|---|---|---|---|---|---|---|---|---|
| | A | C | J | NI | O | OC | W | AEB 994 | AEB 995 | C A | C B | J | W P | W A | L | MEI | SMP |
| **CHAPTER 1 Polynomials** | | | | | | | | | | | | | | | | | |
| Algebra of Polynomials | ✓ | ✓ | ✓ | ✓ | ✓ | ✓ | ✓ | ✓ | ✓ | ✓ | ✓ | ✓ | ✓ | | P1 | P1 | AS |
| Remainder and Factor Theorems | ✓ | ✓ | ✓ | ✓ | ✓ | ✓ | ✓ | | | | | | ✓ | ✓ | P1 | P1 | AS |
| Partial Fractions | ✓ | ✓ | ✓ | ✓ | ✓ | ✓ | ✓ | ✓ | | | | | ✓ | | P2 | P3 | |
| **CHAPTER 2 APs and GPs** | | | | | | | | | | | | | | | | | |
| Arithmetic Progressions | ✓ | ✓ | ✓ | ✓ | ✓ | ✓ | ✓ | | | | ✓ | | ✓ | ✓ | P1 | P1 | AS |
| Geometric Progs., sum to | ✓ | ✓ | ✓ | ✓ | ✓ | ✓ | ✓ | | | | ✓ | | ✓ | ✓ | P1 | P1 | AS |
| **CHAPTER 3 Binomial Theorem** | | | | | | | | | | | | | | | | | |
| Binomial for +ve Integer n | ✓ | ✓ | ✓ | ✓ | ✓ | ✓ | ✓ | ✓ | | | | | ✓ | ✓ | P1 | P1 | A1 |
| Binomial for Other n | ✓ | ✓ | ✓ | ✓ | ✓ | ✓ | ✓ | | | | | | ✓ | | P2 | P2 | |
| **CHAPTER 4 Quadratics** | | | | | | | | | | | | | | | | | |
| Solution of Quadratics | ✓ | ✓ | ✓ | ✓ | ✓ | ✓ | ✓ | ✓ | ✓ | ✓ | ✓ | ✓ | ✓ | ✓ | P1 | P1 | AS |
| Roots of Quadratics | ✓ | ✓ | | ✓ | ✓ | | | | | | | | | ✓ | P1 | P4 | |
| **CHAPTER 5 Inequalities** | | | | | | | | | | | | | | | | | |
| Inequalities in 1 Variable | ✓ | ✓ | ✓ | ✓ | | ✓ | ✓ | ✓ | | ✓ | ✓ | ✓ | ✓ | | P1 | P3 | AS |
| Inequalities in 2 Variables | | | | | | | | ✓ | | | ✓ | | | | P1 | | |
| **CHAPTER 6 Indices and Logs** | | | | | | | | | | | | | | | | | |
| Indices and Logarithms | ✓ | ✓ | ✓ | ✓ | ✓ | ✓ | ✓ | ✓ | | ✓ | ✓ | ✓ | ✓ | ✓ | P1 | P1 | AS |
| **CHAPTER 7 Coord. Geom.** | | | | | | | | | | | | | | | | | |
| Coordinates of Points | ✓ | ✓ | ✓ | ✓ | ✓ | ✓ | ✓ | ✓ | ✓ | ✓ | ✓ | | ✓ | | P1 | P1 | AS |
| Straight Lines | ✓ | ✓ | ✓ | ✓ | ✓ | ✓ | ✓ | ✓ | ✓ | ✓ | ✓ | | ✓ | ✓ | P1 | | AS |
| Circles | ✓ | ✓ | ✓ | ✓ | ✓ | ✓ | ✓ | | | | | | ✓ | | P2 | | A1 |
| Parameters | ✓ | ✓ | ✓ | ✓ | ✓ | ✓ | ✓ | | | | | | ✓ | | P2 | P2 | A1 |
| **CHAPTER 8 Functs. and Graphs** | | | | | | | | | | | | | | | | | |
| Composition of Functions | ✓ | ✓ | ✓ | ✓ | ✓ | ✓ | ✓ | | | | | ✓ | ✓ | | P1 | P1 | AS |
| Graphs | ✓ | ✓ | ✓ | ✓ | ✓ | ✓ | ✓ | ✓ | ✓ | ✓ | ✓ | ✓ | ✓ | ✓ | P1 | P1 | AS |
| **CHAPTER 9 Sine and Cos Rules** | | | | | | | | | | | | | | | | | |
| Sin and Cos Rules | ✓ | ✓ | ✓ | ✓ | ✓ | ✓ | ✓ | ✓ | | | | | ✓ | | P1 | | A1 |
| Angles betw. Lines and Planes | ✓ | ✓ | ✓ | ✓ | ✓ | ✓ | ✓ | ✓ | | | | | ✓ | | P1 | | A1 |
| **CHAPTER 10 Trig Equations** | | | | | | | | | | | | | | | | | |
| The Six Ratios | ✓ | ✓ | ✓ | ✓ | ✓ | ✓ | ✓ | ✓ | ✓ | | | | ✓ | ✓ | P1 | P1 | A1 |
| Angles between 0 and 360 | ✓ | ✓ | ✓ | ✓ | ✓ | ✓ | ✓ | | | | | ✓ | ✓ | ✓ | P1 | P1 | AS |
| Compound Angles | ✓ | ✓ | ✓ | ✓ | ✓ | ✓ | ✓ | ✓ | ✓ | | | | ✓ | ✓ | P2 | P2 | A1 |
| The Form $a \sin\theta + b \cos\theta$ | ✓ | ✓ | ✓ | ✓ | ✓ | ✓ | ✓ | ✓ | | | | | ✓ | | P2 | P2 | A1 |
| General Solution | ✓ | ✓ | ✓ | ✓ | ✓ | ✓ | ✓ | ✓ | | | | | ✓ | | P2 | P2 | A1 |
| **CHAPTER 11 Radians** | | | | | | | | | | | | | | | | | |
| Radians | ✓ | ✓ | ✓ | ✓ | ✓ | ✓ | ✓ | ✓ | ✓ | | | ✓ | ✓ | ✓ | P2 | P2 | AS |
| Small Angles | ✓ | ✓ | ✓ | ✓ | ✓ | ✓ | ✓ | ✓ | ✓ | | | | ✓ | | P2 | P2 | |
| **CHAPTER 12 Vectors** | | | | | | | | | | | | | | | | | |
| Vector Geometry | ✓ | ✓ | ✓ | ✓ | ✓ | ✓ | ✓ | | | | ✓ | | ✓ | | P2 | P1 | A1 |
| Scalar Product | ✓ | ✓ | ✓ | ✓ | ✓ | ✓ | ✓ | | | | ✓ | | ✓ | | P2 | P3 | A1 |
| **CHAPTER 13 Differentiation** | | | | | | | | | | | | | | | | | |
| Derivatives of Powers of x | ✓ | ✓ | ✓ | ✓ | ✓ | ✓ | ✓ | ✓ | ✓ | ✓ | ✓ | ✓ | ✓ | ✓ | P1 | P1 | AS |
| Tangents and Normals | ✓ | ✓ | ✓ | ✓ | ✓ | ✓ | ✓ | ✓ | ✓ | ✓ | ✓ | ✓ | ✓ | ✓ | P1 | P1 | AS |
| Maxima and Minima | ✓ | ✓ | ✓ | ✓ | ✓ | ✓ | ✓ | ✓ | ✓ | ✓ | ✓ | ✓ | ✓ | ✓ | P1 | P1 | AS |
| **CHAPTER 14 Further Diff.** | | | | | | | | | | | | | | | | | |
| Product and Quotient Rules | ✓ | ✓ | ✓ | ✓ | ✓ | ✓ | ✓ | ✓ | ✓ | ✓ | ✓ | ✓ | ✓ | ✓ | P2 | P2 | A1 |
| Chain Rule | ✓ | ✓ | ✓ | ✓ | ✓ | ✓ | ✓ | ✓ | ✓ | ✓ | ✓ | ✓ | ✓ | ✓ | P2 | P2 | A1 |
| Trig and Exponential Fns. | ✓ | ✓ | ✓ | ✓ | ✓ | ✓ | ✓ | ✓ | ✓ | ✓ | ✓ | ✓ | ✓ | ✓ | P2 | P2 | AS |
| **CHAPTER 15 Integration** | | | | | | | | | | | | | | | | | |
| Integration of Powers of x | ✓ | ✓ | ✓ | ✓ | ✓ | ✓ | ✓ | ✓ | ✓ | ✓ | ✓ | ✓ | ✓ | ✓ | P1 | P1 | AS |
| Areas | ✓ | ✓ | ✓ | ✓ | ✓ | ✓ | ✓ | ✓ | ✓ | ✓ | ✓ | ✓ | ✓ | ✓ | P1 | P1 | AS |
| Volumes | ✓ | ✓ | ✓ | ✓ | ✓ | ✓ | ✓ | | | ✓ | ✓ | | ✓ | | P1 | P1 | A1 |
| **CHAPTER 16 Methods of Int.** | | | | | | | | | | | | | | | | | |
| Trig and Exponential Fns. | ✓ | ✓ | ✓ | ✓ | ✓ | ✓ | ✓ | ✓ | ✓ | ✓ | ✓ | ✓ | ✓ | ✓ | P2 | P2 | A1 |
| Substitution | ✓ | ✓ | ✓ | ✓ | ✓ | ✓ | ✓ | ✓ | ✓ | | | | ✓ | | P2 | P2 | A1 |
| Standard Functions | ✓ | ✓ | ✓ | ✓ | ✓ | ✓ | ✓ | ✓ | | | | | ✓ | | P2 | P2 | A1 |
| Integration by Parts | ✓ | ✓ | ✓ | ✓ | ✓ | ✓ | ✓ | ✓ | ✓ | | | | ✓ | | P2 | P2 | A1 |

# Table 2. Extra Pure Topics

Throughout this table, the symbol √✳ shows that the topic occurs in an optional part of the syllabus.

For the AEB and Welsh syllabuses, the symbol √M shows that the topic occurs in the Mechanics paper. For the JMB syllabuses, the symbol √A shows that the topic occurs in the Applied Mathematics paper. In all other cases the topic occurs in the Pure Maths paper.

| | A Level | | | | | | | AS Level | | | | | | Modular | | |
|---|---|---|---|---|---|---|---|---|---|---|---|---|---|---|---|---|
| | A | C | J | NI | O | OC | W | AEB 994 | C A | C B | J | W P | W M | L | MEI | SMP |
| **CHAPTER 17 Numerical Methods** | | | | | | | | | | | | | | | | |
| Numerical Solutions | | √✳ | √A | | √✳ | √ | | √ | √ | √ | | √ | | | P3 | AS |
| Trapezium Rule | √ | √ | √A | √ | | √✳ | √ | √ | | √ | | √ | | P2 | P1 | AS |
| Simpson's Rule | √ | | √A | √ | | √✳ | | √ | | | | | | P3 | | |
| **CHAPTER 18 Series and Induction** | | | | | | | | | | | | | | | | |
| Trig and Exponential Series | | √ | | | √ | | | | | | | | | P3 | | |
| Maclaurin Series | | √ | | | √✳ | √✳ | | | | | | | | P3 | | A1 |
| Induction | | √ | | | √ | √ | | | | | | | | | | |
| **CHAPTER 19 Complex Numbers** | | | | | | | | | | | | | | | | |
| Arithmetic of Complex Numbers | √ | √✳ | √ | √ | √ | | √ | | | | | | | P2 | P3 | |
| Argand Diagram, Mod. and Arg. | √ | √✳ | √ | √ | √ | | √ | | | | | | | P2 | P3 | |
| De Moivre's Theorem | | √✳ | | | √ | | | | | | | | | | | |
| Polar Coordinates | | √✳ | | | | √ | | | | | | | | | | |
| **CHAPTER 20 Differential Equations** | | | | | | | | | | | | | | | | |
| Separable Variables | √ | √✳ | √ | √ | √ | √ | √M | √ | | √ | √ | | √ | P2 | P3 | A1 |
| Integrating Factor | √M | | | | | | √M | | | | | | √ | | | |
| Second Order, Linear | √M | √✳ | | | √ | √ | √M | | | | | | √ | P3 | | 0 |
| **CHAPTER 21 Geometry** | | | | | | | | | | | | | | | | |
| Lines and Planes | | √✳ | | | | | | | | | | | | | P3 | |
| Matrix Transformations | √ | | | | √ | √ | | √ | | | | | | | | |

## Table 3. Mechanics

The symbol √✳ indicates that the topic occurs in an optional part of the syllabus.

Note 1: the topic of non-constant acceleration occurs in the Pure part of the syllabus for JMB A-level and JMB AS-level (Pure).

| | A Level | | | | | | | | AS Level | | | | | Modular | | |
| --- | --- | --- | --- | --- | --- | --- | --- | --- | --- | --- | --- | --- | --- | --- | --- | --- |
| | A | C | J M | J AM | NI | O | OC | W | AEB 995 | C A | J | W M | W PM | L | MEI | SMP |
| **CHAPTER 22 Displ. Vel. Acc.** | | | | | | | | | | | | | | | | |
| Constant Acceleration | √ | √✳ | √ | √ | √ | √ | √ | √ | √ | √ | √ | √ | √ | M1 | M1 | A2 |
| Non-Const. Acc. | √ | √✳ | √1 | √1 | √ | √ | √1 | √ | √ | √ | √ | √ | √ | P1 | M1 | A2 |
| Vector Quantities | √ | √✳ | √ | √ | √ | √ | √ | √ | √ | | | √ | √ | M1 | M1 | A2 |
| **CHAPTER 23 Force and Acceleration** | | | | | | | | | | | | | | | | |
| Newton's First and Second Laws | √ | √✳ | √ | √ | √ | √ | √ | √ | √ | √ | √ | √ | √ | M1 | M1 | A2 |
| Action and Reaction | √ | | √ | √ | √ | √ | √ | √ | √ | √ | √ | √ | √ | M1 | M1 | A2 |
| **CHAPTER 24 Resolving Forces** | | | | | | | | | | | | | | | | |
| Forces at an angle | √ | √✳ | √ | √ | √ | √ | √ | √ | √ | √ | √ | √ | √ | M1 | M1 | O |
| Problems involving weight | √ | √✳ | √ | √ | √ | √ | √ | √ | √ | √ | √ | √ | √ | M1 | M1 | O |
| **CHAPTER 25 Friction** | | | | | | | | | | | | | | | | |
| Friction | √ | √✳ | √ | | | √ | √ | √ | | √ | | √ | √ | M1 | M2 | O |
| **CHAPTER 26 Moments** | | | | | | | | | | | | | | | | |
| Perpendicular Forces | √ | | √ | | √ | √ | √ | | | | | √ | | M1 | M2 | O |
| Moments of Forces at an Angle | √ | | √ | | √ | √ | √ | | | | | √ | √ | M1 | M1 | O |
| **CHAPTER 27 Centre of Gravity** | | | | | | | | | | | | | | | | |
| One Dimensional Problems | √ | | √ | | √ | √ | √ | | | | | √ | √ | M1 | M2 | O |
| Two and Three Dimensional Problems | √ | | √ | | √ | √ | √ | | | | | √ | √ | M1 | M2 | O |
| Calculus Problems | √ | | √ | | √ | √ | √ | | | | | √ | | M1 | | O |
| Statics Problems | √ | | √ | | √ | √ | √ | √ | | | | √ | | M2 | M2 | O |
| **CHAPTER 28 Miscellaneous Statics** | | | | | | | | | | | | | | | | |
| Couples | √ | | √ | | √ | √ | √ | √ | | | | √ | | | M2 | O |
| Equivalent Systems | √ | | √ | | | √ | √ | √ | | | | √ | | | | O |
| Three Forces on a Body | √ | | √ | | √ | √ | √ | √ | | | | √ | | | M2 | O |
| Frameworks | √ | | √ | | | √ | | | | | | | | | M2 | |
| **CHAPTER 29 Work, Energy, Power** | | | | | | | | | | | | | | | | |
| Work and Energy | √ | √✳ | √ | √ | √ | √ | √ | √ | √ | √ | √ | √ | √ | M1 | M2 | O |
| Power | √ | √✳ | √ | √ | √ | √ | √ | √ | √ | √ | √ | √ | √ | M1 | M2 | |
| **CHAPTER 30 Relative Velocity** | | | | | | | | | | | | | | | | |
| Relative Velocity | √ | | | | | √ | √ | √ | | | | √ | | M1 | | |
| **CHAPTER 31 Projectiles** | | | | | | | | | | | | | | | | |
| Projectiles | √ | √✳ | √ | √ | | √ | √ | √ | √ | | √ | √ | √ | M1 | M1 | O |
| **CHAPTER 32 Momentum** | | | | | | | | | | | | | | | | |
| Momentum and Impulse | √ | √✳ | √ | √ | √ | √ | √ | √ | √ | √ | √ | √ | √ | M1 | M2 | A2 |
| Coefficient of Restitution | √ | | √ | | | √ | | √ | √ | | | √ | √ | M2 | M2 | O |
| **CHAPTER 33 Variable Acceleration** | | | | | | | | | | | | | | | | |
| Force as Funct. of Dist. or Vel. | √ | √✳ | √ | √ | √ | √ | √ | √ | √ | | √ | √ | | M2 | | |
| **CHAPTER 34 Circular Motion** | | | | | | | | | | | | | | | | |
| Circular Motion with Constant Speed | √ | √✳ | √ | √ | | √ | √ | √ | | | √ | √ | | M2 | M3 | O |
| Motion in a Vertical Circle | | | √ | √ | | √ | √ | | | | √ | √ | | M2 | | |
| **CHAPTER 35 Elasticity and Oscill.** | | | | | | | | | | | | | | | | |
| Elasticity | √ | √✳ | √ | √ | √ | √ | √ | √ | √ | | √ | √ | | M2 | M3 | |
| S H M and Oscillating Systems | √ | | √ | √ | | √ | √ | √ | √ | | | √ | | M2 | M3 | O |

## Table 4. Statistics

The symbol √✱ shows that the topic occurs in an optional part of the syllabus.

Note 1: *Permutations and Combinations* occur in the Pure papers for the Cambridge board.

Note 2: The topic of *fitting straight lines* occurs in the Pure papers for AEB and JMB.

| | A Level | | | | | | | | AS Level | | | Modular | | |
|---|---|---|---|---|---|---|---|---|---|---|---|---|---|---|
| | A | C | JS | JAM | NI | O | OC | W | CA | CB | WS | L | MEI | SMP |
| **CHAPTER 36 Probability** | | | | | | | | | | | | | | |
| Simple and Conditional Probability | √ | √✱ | √ | √ | √ | √ | √ | √ | √ | √ | √ | S1 | S1 | A2 |
| **CHAPTER 37 Perms. and Combs.** | | | | | | | | | | | | | | |
| Perms. and Combs. | √ | √1 | √ | √ | | √ | √ | √ | √ | √ | | S1 | S1 | |
| **CHAPTER 38 Representation of Data** | | | | | | | | | | | | | | |
| Mean. Variance etc | √ | √✱ | √ | √ | √ | √ | √ | √ | √ | | √ | S1 | S1 | A2 |
| Histograms and Cumulative Frequency | | | √ | √ | | √ | √ | | √ | | √ | S2 | S1 | A2 |
| **CHAPTER 39 Discrete Random Variables** | | | | | | | | | | | | | | |
| Distributions | √ | √✱ | √ | √ | √ | √ | √ | √ | √ | | √ | S1 | S2 | A2 |
| Mean | √ | √✱ | √ | √ | √ | √ | √ | √ | √ | | √ | S1 | S2 | A2 |
| Variance | √ | √✱ | √ | √ | √ | √ | √ | √ | √ | | √ | S1 | S2 | A2 |
| **CHAPTER 40 Binomial and Poisson** | | | | | | | | | | | | | | |
| Binomial Distribution | √ | √✱ | | √ | √ | √ | √ | √ | √ | √ | √ | S1 | S1 | A2 |
| Poisson Distribution | √ | √✱ | √ | | √ | √ | √ | √ | | √ | √ | S1 | S2 | O |
| **CHAPTER 41 Continuous Variables** | | | | | | | | | | | | | | |
| P.D.F. mean and variance | √ | √✱ | √ | √ | √ | √ | √ | √ | | | √ | S1 | S3 | O |
| C.D.F. | √ | √✱ | √ | √ | √ | √ | √ | √ | | | | S1 | S3 | O |
| **CHAPTER 42 Sampling and Estimation** | | | | | | | | | | | | | | |
| Sums of RVs | √ | √✱ | √ | √ | √ | √ | √ | √ | | | | S1 | S3 | O |
| Estimation of $M$ | √ | √✱ | √ | √ | √ | √ | √ | √ | | | | S1 | S3 | O |
| Estimation of $\sigma^2$ | √ | √✱ | √ | | | √ | √ | √ | | | | S1 | S3 | O |
| Use of Random Numbers | √ | | | | | √ | | | | | | | | |
| **CHAPTER 43 The Normal Distribution** | | | | | | | | | | | | | | |
| Normal Calculations | √ | √✱ | √ | √ | √ | √ | √ | √ | √ | | √ | S1 | S2 | O |
| Central Limit Theorem | √ | √✱ | √ | √ | √ | √ | √ | √ | √ | | √ | S1 | S2 | O |
| **CHAPTER 44 Hypothesis Tests** | | | | | | | | | | | | | | |
| Hypothesis Tests | √ | √✱ | √ | | √ | √ | √ | √ | √ | | | S1 | S1 | O |
| Confidence Intervals | √ | √✱ | √ | | √ | √ | | √ | | | | S1 | S3 | O |
| **CHAPTER 45 t and $x^2$ Distributions** | | | | | | | | | | | | | | |
| The t-test | | | | | | | | √ | | | | | S3 | O |
| Goodness of Fit | √ | | | | | √ | | | | | | | S3 | O |
| Testing Association | √ | | | | | | | | | | | | S4 | O |
| **CHAPTER 46 Regression and Correlation** | | | | | | | | | | | | | | |
| Fitting Straight Lines | √2 | | √2 | | | | | √ | | | | P2 | S2 | |
| Linear Regression | √ | √ | | | | | | √ | | | | S2 | S2 | O |
| Tests on Regression Coefficients | | | √ | | | | | √ | | | | | | O |
| Correlation and Rank Correlation | √ | | | | | √ | | - | | | | S2 | S2 | O |

# CORE SYLLABUS

# 1 Polynomials

The function $P(x)$ below is an example of a *polynomial:*

$$P(x) = 3x^4 - 2x^2 + 2\tfrac{1}{2}x - 8.$$

In general, polynomial functions of $x$ are made up only of positive whole number powers of $x$, multiplied by constants and added together.

Examples of functions which are not polynomials are:

$$x^{\frac{1}{2}}, \quad \frac{1}{x+3}, \quad \cos x \text{ and } \log_{10} x$$

The *order* of a polynomial is the highest power of $x$. So the order of the polynomial above is 4.

If the variable $x$ in $P(x)$ is replaced by a number $\alpha$, the result is written $P(\alpha)$. In the example above:

$$P(2) = 3 \times 2^4 - 2 \times 2^2 + 2\tfrac{1}{2} \times 2 - 8 = 37.$$

Polynomials can be added, subtracted and multiplied by using ordinary algebraic methods. The results can be simplified by the collection of terms with the same power of $x$.

$$(3x^2 - 2x + 1) + (x^3 - 4x + \tfrac{1}{2}) = x^3 + 3x^2 - 6x + 1\tfrac{1}{2}$$

$$(3x^2 - 2x + 1) \times (x - 3) = 3x^3 - 11x^2 + 7x - 3$$

When one polynomial is divided by another, long division is used. To divide $(3x^2 - 2x + 1)$ by $(x - 3)$:

$$
\begin{array}{r}
3x \quad + \quad 7 \qquad\qquad \\
\hline
x - 3) \overline{\smash{)}\, 3x^2 \quad - \quad 2x \quad + \quad 1} \\
3x^2 \quad - \quad 9x \qquad\qquad \\
\hline
7x \quad + \quad 1 \\
7x \quad - \quad 21 \\
\hline
22
\end{array}
$$

So the quotient when $3x^2 - 2x + 1$ is divided by $x - 3$ is $3x + 7$, and the remainder is 22.

## 1.1 Remainder and Factor Theorems

The *Remainder Theorem* states:

The remainder when $P(x)$ is divided by $x - \alpha$ is $P(\alpha)$.

So the remainder when $3x^2 - 2x + 1$ is divided by $x - 3$ is $3 \times 3^2 - 2 \times 3 + 1 = 22$. This confirms the result above.

A particular case of this is the *Factor theorem*:

$$x - \alpha \text{ divides } P(x) \text{ if and only if } P(\alpha) = 0$$

When trying to find factors of $P(x)$, the first values of $\alpha$ to try are the divisors of the constant term in $P(x)$.

### 1.1.1 Examples

(1)      Find the remainder when $x^5 + x^3 - 2x + 2$ is divided by $x + 2$.

Solution    Use the Remainder Theorem above, putting $\alpha = -2$.
The remainder is $(-2)^5 + (-2)^3 - 2 \times (-2) + 2$

**The remainder is $-34$**

(2)      $x^3 - 2x^2 + ax - b$ is divisible by $(x-1)(x+2)$. Find the values of $a$ and $b$.

Solution    Use the Factor Theorem twice, putting $\alpha = 1$ and $\alpha = -2$.

$$1 - 2 + a - b = 0 \text{ and } -8 - 8 - 2a - b = 0$$

$$a - b = 1 \text{ and } 2a + b = -16$$

Solve these simultaneously to obtain:

**$a = -5$ and $b = -6$**

(3)      Factorise $x^3 - 4x^2 + x + 6$.

Solution    Use the Factor Theorem, trying first the divisors of 6.

$$\text{For } \alpha = 1, P(\alpha) = 4 \quad \text{For } \alpha = -1, P(\alpha) = 0$$
$$\text{For } \alpha = 2, P(\alpha) = 0 \quad \text{For } \alpha = -2, P(\alpha) = -20$$
$$\text{For } \alpha = 3, P(\alpha) = 0$$

Three factors have been found, so there is no need to try $-3$, 6 or $-6$.

$$\mathbf{x^3 - 4x^2 + x + 6 \equiv (x + 1)(x - 2)(x - 3)}$$

### 1.1.2 Exercises

1. Which of the following are polynomials? Write down the order of those which are.

     (a)   $3x^2 + 7/x$        (b)   $2x^3 + 5$

     (c)   $2\sin x - 4\cos x$    (d)   $(x + 3)(x^2 - 7x^3 + 1)$

2. Evaluate the following polynomial sums and products:

    (a) $(2x^3 - 3x + 1) + (2x^3 + 4x - 4)$    (b) $(2x^2 + 3x) \times (x^3 - 1)$

    (c) $(x^3 + 2x) - (x^2 - 5)$                  (d) $(x^4 + x^2 + 1) \times (x^3 - x)$

3. Find the quotient and remainder in each of the following division problems.

    (a) $(x^3 + 2x^2 + x - 3) \div (x - 4)$    (b) $(x^3 + x^2 - 3x + 1) \div (x^2 + 5x - 1)$

    (c) $(x^3 + 2x - 1) \div (x + 4)$          (d) $(4x^4 - 3x^2 + 1) \div (2x - 3)$

4. Find the remainder in each of the following divisions.

    (a) $(x^2 + 3x - 2) \div (x - 5)$        (b) $(3x^3 + x^2 + x - 1) \div (x - 2)$

    (c) $(x^3 + 7x^2 - 2x - 1) \div (x + 1)$   (d) $(x^4 + 2) \div (x + 2)$

5. The remainder when $x^3 - 3x^2 + ax - 1$ is divided by $x - 2$ is 5. Find the value of $a$.

6. The remainder when $ax^3 + 3x^2 + 3x + 5$ is divided by $x + 3$ is 8. Find the value of $a$.

7. When $x^3 + 2x^2 + ax + b$ is divided by $x - 1$ the remainder is 3, and when it is divided by $x + 2$ the remainder is $-1$. Find $a$ and $b$.

8. When $ax^3 - 2x^2 - 3x + b$ is divided by $x + 1$ the remainder is 3, and when it is divided by $x + 2$ the remainder is 1. Find $a$ and $b$.

9. $x - 3$ divides $x^3 - 2x^2 + x - a$. Find $a$.

10. Find $k$, given that $x + 2$ is a factor of $x^3 + 2x^2 - kx - 1$.

11. $x^3 - 3x^2 + ax + b$ is divisible by both $x - 2$ and $x + 3$. Find $a$ and $b$.

12. $ax^3 + bx^2 - 2x + 5$ is divisible by $(x + 1)(x - 2)$. Find $a$ and $b$.

13. $x^2 - 4$ divides $x^3 + ax^2 + bx + 20$. Find $a$ and $b$, and find the third factor.

14. Factorise the following:

    (a) $x^3 - 2x^2 - x + 2$      (b) $x^3 + 3x^2 - 4x - 12$

    (c) $x^3 - 2x^2 - 5x + 6$     (d) $2x^3 + 11x^2 + 17x + 6$

    (e) $2x^3 - 9x^2 + 7x + 6$    (f) $x^4 - x^2 + 4x - 4$

    (g) $x^3 - x^2 - x + 1$       (h) $x^3 + 5x^2 + 8x + 4$

15. Solve the following equations:

(a) $x^3 + 4x^2 + x - 6 = 0$    (b) $x^3 - 4x^2 + x + 6 = 0$

(c) $2x^3 + 5x^2 + x - 2 = 0$    (d) $6x^3 - 11x^2 + 6x - 1 = 0$

## 1.2 Partial Fractions

A *Rational Function* is a function obtained by dividing one polynomial by another.

$$R(x) \equiv \frac{Q(x)}{P(x)}$$

The following simple rational functions are known as *Partial Fractions*.

$$\frac{A}{(x - \alpha)}, \qquad \frac{Bx + C}{(ax^2 + bx + c)}, \qquad \frac{D}{(x - \alpha)^n}$$

Here A, B, C, D are constants, and $ax^2 + bx + c$ is a quadratic which cannot be factorised.

Any rational function $Q(x)/P(x)$ can be written as the sum of a polynomial and partial fractions. The polynomial is the quotient when $Q(x)$ is divided by $P(x)$. The partial fractions are found as follows:

For each linear factor $(x - \alpha)$ of $P(x)$, include $\dfrac{A}{x - \alpha}$

For each quadratic factor $(ax^2 + bx + c)$ of $P(x)$, include $\dfrac{Bx + C}{ax^2 + bx + c}$

For each repeated linear factor $(x - \alpha)^2$, include $\dfrac{D}{(x - \alpha)^2} + \dfrac{E}{x - \alpha}$

The constants $A, B, C, D, E$ are found by putting in values for $x$, or by equating coefficients of powers of $x$.

### 1.2.1 Example

Express in partial fractions:

(a) $\dfrac{3}{(x - 1)(x + 2)}$    (b) $\dfrac{x + 4}{x(x^2 + 4)}$

(c) $\dfrac{3x + 1}{(x + 1)(x - 1)^2}$    (d) $\dfrac{3x^2 + 11x - 9}{(x - 2)(x + 3)}$

**Solution**

a. Write $\dfrac{3}{(x - 1)(x + 2)} \equiv \dfrac{A}{x - 1} + \dfrac{B}{x + 2}$

Multiply across by $(x - 1)(x + 2)$

$$3 \equiv A(x+2) + B(x-1)$$

Put $x = 1$, to obtain $3 = 3A$. Put $x = -2$, to obtain $3 = -3B$.

$$\frac{3}{(x-1)(x+2)} \equiv \frac{1}{x-1} - \frac{1}{x+2}$$

b.  Write $\dfrac{x+4}{x(x^2+4)} \equiv \dfrac{A}{x} + \dfrac{Bx+C}{x^2+4}$

$$x + 4 \equiv A(x^2 + 4) + (Bx + C)x$$

Put $x = 0$, to obtain $A = 1$.
Equate the $x^2$ coefficients, to obtain $0 = A + B$. Hence $B = -1$
Equate the $x$ coefficient, to obtain $1 = C$.

$$\frac{x+4}{x(x^2+4)} \equiv \frac{1}{x} + \frac{1-x}{x^2+4}$$

c.  Write $\dfrac{3x+1}{(x+1)(x-1)^2} \equiv \dfrac{A}{x+1} + \dfrac{B}{x-1} + \dfrac{C}{(x-1)^2}$

$$3x + 1 \equiv A(x-1)^2 + B(x+1)(x-1) + C(x+1)$$

Put $x = 1$, to obtain $C = 2$. Put $x = -1$, to obtain $A = -\frac{1}{2}$ .
Equate the $x^2$ coefficient, to obtain $B = -A = \frac{1}{2}$

$$\frac{3x+1}{(x+1)(x-1)^2} \equiv \frac{-\frac{1}{2}}{x+1} + \frac{\frac{1}{2}}{x-1} + \frac{2}{(x-1)^2}$$

d.  Before putting this into partial fractions, divide through so that the order of the top is less than the order of the bottom.

$$
\begin{array}{r}
3 \\
x^2 + x - 6 \overline{)\; 3x^2 + 11x - 9} \\
3x^2 + 3x - 18 \\
\hline
8x + 9
\end{array}
$$

It follows that:

$$\frac{3x^2 + 11x - 9}{(x-2)(x+3)} \equiv 3 + \frac{8x+9}{(x-2)(x+3)}$$

Now proceed as in part (a).

$$\frac{3x^2 + 11x - 9}{(x-2)(x+3)} \equiv 3 + \frac{5}{x-2} + \frac{3}{x+3}$$

## 1.2.2 Exercises

(1) Express the following as single fractions:

(a) $\dfrac{1}{x+1} + \dfrac{1}{x-1}$  (b) $\dfrac{1}{x} - \dfrac{2}{x+3}$

(c) $\dfrac{1}{x^2} + \dfrac{2}{2-x}$  (d) $\dfrac{2}{x} - \dfrac{1}{x^2+1}$

(e) $\dfrac{4}{x+1} + 1$  (f) $x + \dfrac{3}{5-x}$

Express the following rational functions in terms of partial fractions:

(2) $\dfrac{2}{(x+1)(x-1)}$  (3) $\dfrac{8}{(x-1)(x+3)}$

(4) $\dfrac{x+3}{(x-1)x}$  (5) $\dfrac{2x-1}{(x+1)(x-3)}$

(6) $\dfrac{2}{(x+1)(2x-1)}$  (7) $\dfrac{3x-2}{(3x+1)(x-2)}$

(8) $\dfrac{2x}{(x+1)(x^2+1)}$  (9) $\dfrac{3}{x(x^2+x+1)}$

(10) $\dfrac{x^2-1}{(x+2)(x^2+1)}$  (11) $\dfrac{3-2x}{(2x^2+3)(x+1)}$

(12) $\dfrac{2}{(x-1)(x-2)^2}$  (13) $\dfrac{3x-1}{x^2(x+1)}$

(14) $\dfrac{x^2}{(x+1)^2(2x-1)}$  (15) $\dfrac{5}{(2x+1)^2(x-1)}$

(16) $\dfrac{x^2-2}{(x-3)(x+4)}$  (17) $\dfrac{4x^2}{(x+1)(x-1)}$

(18) $\dfrac{x^3+x^2+2x-1}{(x-1)(x+2)}$  (19) $\dfrac{x^4}{(x-1)(x+1)}$

(20) $\dfrac{6}{(x-1)(x-2)(x-3)}$  (21) $\dfrac{4x-3}{x(x-1)(x+2)}$

(22) Express $\dfrac{1}{n(n+1)}$ in partial fractions. By writing each term in partial fractions find the sum of the series:

$$\frac{1}{1 \times 2} + \frac{1}{2 \times 3} + \frac{1}{3 \times 4} + \dots + \frac{1}{n(n+1)}$$

(23) Find the sum to infinity of the series in Question 22.

(24) By methods similar to that of Question 22, find the sums of the following series:

a. $\dfrac{1}{1 \times 3} + \dfrac{1}{3 \times 5} + \dfrac{1}{5 \times 7} + \dots + \dfrac{1}{(2n-1)(2n+1)}$

b. $\dfrac{1}{2 \times 4} + \dfrac{1}{4 \times 6} + \dfrac{1}{6 \times 8} + \dots + \dfrac{1}{2n(2n+2)}$

9

## 1.3 Examination Questions

(1)

i. Write down one factor of the expression

$$(x+4)(2x^2+5x+5) - (x+4)(x+1)(x-1)$$

By factorising, or otherwise, show that $(x+3)$ is also a factor, and find the third factor.

Find the coefficient of $x^2$ in the expression.

ii. $\dfrac{3x^2 - x + 5}{x - 1}$ may be expressed in the form $ax + b + \dfrac{r}{x-1}$

Show that $b = 2$ and find the values of $a$ and $r$.

[SMP add]

(2) Given the expression $6x^4 - 23x^3 + 11x^2 + 12x$,

a. find the remainder when this expression is divided by $(x-1)$

b. find the remainder when this expression is divided by $(x-3)$

c. factorise this expression completely,

d. solve the equation $6x^4 - 23x^3 + 11x^2 + 12x = 0$.

[AEB add 1987]

(3)

a. Find the values of $a$ and $b$ so that $x^4 + x^3 + x^2 + ax + b$ may be exactly divisible by $(x-3)(x+2)$.

b. If $2u^2 - 9u + 10 = 0$ and $u = x + 1/x$, prove that

$$2x^4 - 9x^3 + 14x^2 - 9x + 2 = 0.$$

Solve the equation $2x^4 - 9x^3 + 14x^2 - 9x + 2 = 0$.

[SUJB]

(4) Given that

$$f(x) \equiv \frac{1}{(x+1)(x+3)}$$

Express $f(x)$ in partial fractions and find

$$\sum_{r=1}^{n} \frac{1}{(2r+1)(2r+3)}$$

[L]

# COMMON ERRORS
## (1) Division of Polynomials

a. When performing long division, be careful of negative signs. When subtracting $-3x$ from $5x$, the result is $8x$. (Not $2x$).

b. Do not be confused when you are dividing into a polynomial, such as $x^4 - 2x^2 + x$, which misses out some of the powers. Write it as $x^4 + 0x^3 - 2x^2 + x + 0$, and then perform the long division.

## (2) Remainder and Factor Theorems

a. When you are finding the remainder after division by $x + 3$, you must put $\alpha = -3$. A common mistake is to put $\alpha = +3$.

b. These theorems only apply to polynomials. You cannot use them to factorise something like $\sin x - \sin 30°$.

## (3) Partial Fractions

a. Before putting a function into partial fractions you must ensure that the top has a lower order than the bottom. If this is not the case then you must divide first.

b. The partial fraction corresponding to a quadratic factor is of the form $(Bx + C)/(ax^2 + bx + c)$. Do not forget to put in either the $B$ term or the $C$ term.
If your partial fractions include say $(Bx + C)/(x^2 + 4)$, then you cannot always find the values of $B$ and $C$ by putting in values for $x$. You may have to find them by equating coefficients.

c. The partial fractions corresponding to a repeated factor is of the form $D/(x - \alpha) + E/(x - \alpha)^2$. Both these terms must be put in. If your partial fractions include $D/(x - \alpha) + E/(x - \alpha)^2$, then multiply by $(x - \alpha)^2$. There is no need to multiply by $(x - \alpha)^3$.

# 2 Arithmetic and Geometric Progressions

A *sequence or progression* is any list of numbers.

A sequence can be written as $u_1, u_2, u_3, \ldots$ The $n$'th term of the sequence is $u_n$.

## 2.1 ARITHMETIC PROGRESSIONS

If the differences between successive terms of a sequence are constant, then the sequence is an *Arithmetic Progression* (an A.P.). The difference is called the *common difference*.

1, 4, 7, 10 is an Arithmetic Progression with common difference 3.

$1, \frac{1}{2}, 0, -\frac{1}{2}, -1, -1\frac{1}{2}$ is an A.P. with common difference $-\frac{1}{2}$.

If an Arithmetic progression has first term $a$ and common difference $d$,

then the $n$'th term is:

$$u_n = a + (n-1)d$$

The sum of the first $n$ terms is:

$$\sum_{r=1}^{r=n} u_r = u_1 + u_2 + \ldots + u_n = \frac{1}{2}n(2a + (n-1)d)$$

### 2.1.1 Examples

(1)    Find the 10'th term and the sum to 40 terms of the sequence 3, 5, 7, 9, ...

Solution    The first term is 3 and the common difference is 2.
**The tenth term is** $3 + (10 - 1)2 = 21$.
Put $n = 40$, $a = 3$ and $d = 2$ into the formula for the sum of an A.P.
**The sum of 40 terms is** $\frac{1}{2}40(2 \times 3 + (40 - 1)2) = 1680$

(2)    The first two terms of an A.P. are 5 and 8. How many terms are less than 1,000?

Solution    Here $a = 5$ and $d = 3$.    The $n$'th term is $5 + (n - 1)3 = 2 + 3n$.
If $2 + 3n < 1000$, then $n < 998/3 = 332\frac{2}{3}$
**332 terms are less than 1,000.**

(3)    The fifth term of an A.P. is 13 and the eighth term is 19. Find the first term and the $n$'th term.

Solution    The $n$'th term is $a + (n - 1)d$. Use the information above:
$13 = a + 4d$ and $19 = a + 7d$
Solve these equations to obtain $d = 2$ and $a = 5$.
**The first term is 5 and the $n$'th term is** $5 + (n - 1)2$.

### 2.1.2 Exercises

(1)    Find the eleventh term of the following sequences:

(a)   1, 4, 7, 10    (b)   13, 17, 21, 25

(c)   4.2, 4.4, 4.6   (d)   11, 8, 5, 2

(2)    Find the sum of the first 12 terms for the sequences in question 1.

(3)    Find the $n$'th term and the sum of the first $n$ terms for the sequences in question 1.

(4)    Find the first term and the $n$'th term for the sequences which have:

a.        5'th term 12 and common difference 3

b.        4'th term 14 and 9'th term 29

c.     6'th term 2.1 and 10'th term 2.9

d.     Third term 13 and seventh term $-3$.

(5)   The $n$'th term of an Arithmetic Progression is $5 + 3n$. Find the common difference and the first term.

(6)   Find the common difference and first term for the sequences which have $n$'th term:

   (a)   $2 + 5n$   (b)   $7n - 3$

   (c)   $2 + \frac{n}{5}$   (d)   $3 - 2n$

(7)   The sum of the first $n$ terms of an Arithmetic Progression is $2n^2 + n$. Find the first 3 terms, and hence find the common difference.

(8)   Find the first term and the common difference for the A.P.s for which the sum of the first $n$ terms is:

   (a)   $n^2 + n$     (b) $3n - n^2$

   (c)   $2n + 3n^2$   (d) $n - \frac{1}{4}n^2$

(9)   Find the first term of the sequence 1, 7, 13, 19 which is greater than 100.

(10)  Which is the first negative term of the sequence 98, 93, 88, 83,....? How many terms must be taken before their sum is negative?

(11)  Find the sum of the first $n$ integers.

(12)  Find the sum of the first $n$ odd numbers.

(13)  Find the sum of the first ten multiples of 7 which are bigger than 100.

(14)  3, $x$, 7 form an Arithmetic Progression. Find $x$.

(15)  53, $x, y$, 25 form an A.P. Find $x$ and $y$.

## 2.2 GEOMETRIC PROGRESSIONS

If the ratio between successive terms of sequence is constant, then the sequence is a *Geometric Progression* (G.P.) The ratio is the *Common Ratio*.

2, 6, 18, 54, 162 is a Geometric Progression with common ratio 3.

1, $-\frac{1}{2}, \frac{1}{4}, -\frac{1}{8}$ is a Geometric Progression with common ratio $-\frac{1}{2}$.

If the first term of a Geometric Progression is $a$ and the common ratio is $r$, then the $n$'th term is:

$$u_n = ar^{n-1}$$

The sum of the first $n$ terms of the sequence is:

$$\sum_{i=1}^{i=n} u_i = u_1 + u_2 + \cdots + u_n = \frac{a(r^n - 1)}{r - 1}$$

If $-1 < r < 1$, then the *sum to infinity* of the sequence is:

$$\sum_{r=1}^{\infty} u_r = u_1 + u_2 + \cdots + u_n + \cdots = \frac{a}{1 - r}$$

### 2.2.1 Examples

(1)  Find the sixth term and the sum of the first 10 terms for the sequence 3, 6, 12, 24, ...

Solution  The first term is 3 and the common ratio is 2. Hence the sixth term is:

$$3 \times 2^{6-1} = 96$$

The sum to 10 term is:

$$\frac{3 \times (2^{10} - 1)}{2 - 1} = 3069$$

(2)  How many terms of the sequence 1, 3, 9, 27, ... must be taken for the sum to exceed 1,000?

Solution  The sum to $n$ terms is $\frac{1(3^n - 1)}{3 - 1}$. If this is to be greater than 1,000, then:

$$3^n > 2001$$

By logs or by trial and error find that $n > 6.9$
**7 terms of the sequence must be taken.**

(3)  A ball is thrown upwards, and returns to the ground after 5 seconds. After each bounce the time until it returns to earth is multiplied by a factor of $\frac{2}{3}$. Find the total time which passes before it stops bouncing.

Solution    The time of the first bounce is 5 secs. The time for the second bounce is $5 \times \frac{2}{3}$. The time for the third bounce is $5 \times \frac{2}{3}^2$. And so on. The total time is the sum to infinity of the G.P. with first term 5 and common ration $\frac{2}{3}$.

$$\textbf{Total time} = \frac{5}{1 - \frac{2}{3}} = \textbf{15 seconds.}$$

## 2.2.2 Exercises

(1) Find the seventh term and the sum of the first 5 terms for the following Geometric Progressions:

(a)   2, 4, 8, 16, ..          (b)   4, 2, 1, $\frac{1}{2}, \frac{1}{4}, \cdots$

(c)   $2, -6, 18, -54, \cdots$   (d)   -2, $\frac{1}{2}, -\frac{1}{8}, \frac{1}{32}, \cdots$

(2) Find the $n$'th term for each of the sequences in question 1.

(3) Find the sum to $n$ terms of each of the sequences in question 1.

(4) Find, where possible, the sum to infinity of the sequences in question 1.

(5) Find the first term and the common ratio for the geometric progressions with:

a.   Second term 3 and fifth term 24.

b.   Third term 8 and sixth term 1.

c.   Third term 5 and sixth term $-40$

d.   Second term 4 and sum to infinity 16.

(6) The fourth term of a G.P. is 4 and the sixth is 100. Find two possible values for the common ratio, and hence find two possible values for the first term.

(7) A G.P. has first term 5 and common ratio 4. How many terms of the sequence are less than 9,000?

(8) A G.P. has first term 2 and common ratio 1.5. How many terms of the sequence must be taken before their sum is greater than 100?

(9) A G.P. has first term 6 and common ratio 0.7. Which is the first term of the sequence less than 1?

(10) 3, $x$, 75 are terms of a G.P. Find the values of $x$.

(11) 8, $x, y, -1$ are terms of a G.P. Find $x$ and $y$.

(12) Find the common ratios and the first terms of the sequences whose sum to $n$ terms is:

(a)   $2 \times 3^n - 2$   (b)   $4 - \frac{1}{4}^{n-1}$

### 2.3.1 Miscellaneous Examples

(1)      The first, second and fifth terms of an A.P. form consecutive terms of a G.P. Find the common ratio.

Solution     Let the first term be $a$, the common difference be $d$ and the common ratio be $r$. Then:

$$a + d = ar \text{ and } a + 4d = ar^2$$

Eliminate $d$ between these equations:

$$4(ar - a) = ar^2 - a$$

$$4r - 4 = r^2 - 1$$

$$0 = r^2 - 4r + 3$$

$$0 = (r - 3)(r - 1)$$

$$\mathbf{r = 3 \text{ or } r = 1}$$

(2)      The first term of a G.P. is two thirds of the sum to infinity. Find the common ratio.

Solution     Let the first term be $a$ and the common ratio $r$.

$$a = \frac{\frac{2}{3}a}{1 - r}$$

$$1 - r = \frac{2}{3}$$

$$\mathbf{r = \frac{1}{3}}$$

(3)      At the beginning of each year a man invests £100 at 10% compound interest. How much will he have at the end of 12 years?

Solution     The £100 which was originally invested will have increased to £100 $\times 1.1^{12}$. The £100 which was invested at the beginning of the second year will have increased to £100 $\times 1.1^{11}$. And so on. The total sum of money will be the sum of a G.P. with first term 110 and common ratio 1.1.

$$\textbf{Total} = \frac{110 \times (1.1^{12} - 1)}{1.1 - 1} = \pounds\mathbf{2,352}$$

## 2.3.2 Miscellaneous Exercises

(1) The third term of an A.P. is $x$, and the seventh term is $y$. Express the common difference and the first term as functions of $x$ and $y$.

(2) $x - 3$, $2x - 3$, $6x + 1$ are consecutive terms of a G.P. Find the possible values of $x$.

(3) Find the sum of all the numbers less than 100 whose last digit is 5.

(4) A man invests £50 each year at 9% compound interest. How much will he have in the bank just before his tenth investment?

(5) A job is advertised at a starting salary of £8,500 with annual increments of £600. How much will the salary be during the 10th year? How much will be the total sum earned after 10 years?

(6) A job is advertised at a starting salary of £8,000 with an annual increase of 5%. What will the salary be during the 10th year? What will the total sum earned after 10 years?

(7) A child builds a triangular wall of bricks, with 1 brick on the top row, 2 bricks on the second, and so on. If the wall is 8 bricks high, how many bricks does it contain? If the child has only 70 bricks, what is the tallest wall she can build?

(8) A large sheet of paper is 0.04 mm thick. How thick is it after it has been folded ten times? (Assuming that this is possible). How many times must it be folded before it is 1 metre thick?

(9) A king was so pleased with the game of chess that he granted its inventor any prize she desired. The inventor asked for one grain of wheat on the first square, two grains on the second square, four grains on the third square and so on for all 64 squares. How many grains is she asking for in total?

(10) How many terms of the series $2 + 1 + \frac{1}{2} + \frac{1}{4} + \frac{1}{8} + \cdots$ must be taken so that the sum is within 0.001 of its sum to infinity?

(11) Let $x$ be the recurring decimal $0.12121212\cdots$ Show that $x$ can be written as $^{12}/_{100} + {}^{12}/_{10000} + {}^{12}/_{1000000} + \cdots$. Write this as the sum of a geometric series and hence find $x$ as a fraction in its simplest form.

(12) By the method of Question 11 express the following as fractions in their simplest form:

   (a)  $0.72727272\cdots$   (b)  $0.3209090909\cdots$

   (c)  $0.037037037\cdots$   (d)  $23.314214214\cdots$

(13) Achilles can run at 10 feet per second, and the Tortoise at 1 foot per second. They have a race, and the Tortoise is given a 10 feet start. After 1 second T is 1 foot ahead. When A has run that extra foot, T is still ahead by 0.1 foot. When $A$ has run that extra 0.1 ft, $T$ is 0.01 ft ahead. Find how long it takes for $A$ to catch up with $T$.

## 2.4 Examination Questions

(1) The first term of a geometric series is 1 and the sum of the first 3 terms is $^7/_9$. Find the two possible values of the common ratio of this series.

[L add]

(2)

i. The sum of an arithmetic progression is $-600$. The first term is 12, and the common difference is $-3$. How many terms are there in the series?

ii. The second and fourth terms of a geometric series are 2 and $\frac{1}{18}$. Calculate the first term and the values of the common ratio. Write down the first four terms of each of the two possible series.

iii. Calculate the smallest number of terms of the geometric series $1 + 4 + 16 + \cdots$ that will give a total greater than $2 \times 10^6$.

[O add]

(3)

i. If a salary is increased during each year by 12% of its value at the start of the year, by what factor is it multiplied each year? By what factor will the original salary have been multiplied after five years and by what percentage has it increased in this time?

ii. If the cost of repairs to a new car is £20 in the first year and this cost increases thereafter by £25 each year, write down and simplify a formula for the cost of repairs in the $n$th year. Find also the total amount paid in repair bills up to the end of the $n$th year.

The owner decides to keep the car until the end of the year in which the total repair bill passes £1,000. How old will the car be when he sells it?

[MEI add]

(4) The sum $S_n$ of the first $n$ terms of a series is given by $S_n = \frac{1}{4}(5n^2 + 11n)$. Write down an expression for $S_{n-1}$. Deduce the value of $u_n$, the $n^{th}$ term of the series. Hence show that the series is an arithmetic series, and state the values of the first term and of the common difference.

[C]

(5) The first term of a geometric series is 10 and the second term is $10 - x$. Show that the set of values for which the series is convergent is given by

$$0 < x < 20$$

Show also that, for these values, the series converges to a sum greater than 5.

Given that the series converges to sum 100, find the smallest positive integer $n$ such that the sum of the first $n$ terms is greater than 99.

[L]

## COMMON ERRORS

(1) Be certain whether you are dealing with an Arithmetic or a Geometric progression. Some sequences are neither of these.

(2) Do not confuse the $n$'th *term* with the $n$'th *sum*.

(3) Sometimes the term you want to deal with is not the $n$'th but the $n - 1$'th or the $n+1$'th. Make sure you know the number of the term.

(4) Be very careful with problems which involve investment or salaries. Read the question carefully to make sure whether it is the beginning or the end of the year which is being dealt with.

(5) Be careful with signs. If an A.P. is decreasing, then the common difference is negative. If the common ratio of a G.P. is negative, then the terms are alternately positive and negative.

(6) Be careful when taking square roots. Problems involving G.P.'s often require you to solve an equation like $r^2 = 4$. There are two solutions: $r = 2$ or $r = -2$. Often the question will help you by requiring the values of $r$.

# 3 The Binomial Theorem

## 3.1 Positive Integer Powers

*Pascal's Triangle* is the triangle of numbers shown below, in which each term is obtained by adding the two terms above it.

| | | | | | | | | | | | | | |
|---|---|---|---|---|---|---|---|---|---|---|---|---|---|
| | | | | | | 1 | | | | | | | $n = 0$ |
| | | | | | 1 | | 1 | | | | | | $n = 1$ |
| | | | | 1 | | 2 | | 1 | | | | | $n = 2$ |
| | | | 1 | | 3 | | 3 | | 1 | | | | $n = 3$ |
| | | 1 | | 4 | | 6 | | 4 | | 1 | | | $n = 4$ |
| | 1 | | 5 | | 10 | | 10 | | 5 | | 1 | | $n = 5$ |
| 1 | | 6 | | 15 | | 20 | | 15 | | 6 | | 1 | $n = 6$ |

The *Binomial Coefficient* $^nC_r$ is the $r$'th term of the $n$'th row of Pascal's Triangle, (counting from 0 instead of from 1). So for example:

$$^5C_0 = 1.^4 \; C_2 = 6.\; ^6 \; C_6 = 1$$

These coefficients are also given by the formula:

$$^nC_r = \frac{n!}{r!(n-r)!}$$

The binomial coefficients are sometimes written as $\binom{n}{r}$ .
The *Binomial Theorem* states that:

$$(a+b)^n \equiv a^n +^n C_1 a^{n-1}b + \cdots +^n C_r a^{n-r}b^r + \cdots + b^n.$$

So for example $(a+b)^5 \equiv a^5 + 5a^4b + 10a^3b^2 + 10a^2b^3 + 5ab^4 + b^5$.

### 3.1.1 Examples

(1)        Expand $(x+2y)^4$.

Solution    Use the Binomial Theorem, using the fourth row of Pascal's triangle. Put $a = x$ and $b = 2y$.

$$(x+2y)^4 \equiv x^4 + 4x^3(2y) + 6x^2(2y)^2 + 4x(2y)^3 + (2y)^4$$

$$\mathbf{(x+2y)^4 \equiv x^4 + 8x^3y + 24x^2y^2 + 32xy^3 + 16y^4.}$$

(2)        Use the binomial theorem to find an approximation for $(0.997)^7$, taking the first three terms of the expansion.

Solution    The first three terms of $(1+x)^7$ are:
$1 +^7 C_1 x +^7 C_2 x^2$.
Put $x = -0.003$ to obtain $1 - 7 \times 0.003 + 21 \times 0.003^2$

$$\mathbf{(0.997)^7 \simeq 0.979189.}$$

### 3.1.2 Exercises

(1) Expand the following using the binomial theorem, and simplify as far as possible.

$$\text{(a)} \quad (2+b)^5 \qquad \text{(b)} \quad (1+3b)^4$$

$$\text{(c)} \quad (2x+3y)^4 \quad \text{(d)} \quad (1-2z)^6$$

$$\text{(e)} \quad (2a-b)^7 \qquad \text{(f)} \quad (2-\tfrac{1}{2}x)^7$$

(2) In the following expansions, write down the appropriate terms. Simplify your answers as far as possible.

(a) $(1+x)^8$    $x^3$ term.    (b) $(1-y)^9$    $y^5$ term.

(c) $(2+x)^{10}$    $x^8$ term.    (d) $(1+2x)^8$    $x^3$ term.

(e) $(3+2y)^5$    $y^3$ term.    (f) $(3x-5)^5$    $x^2$ term.

(g) $(x+y)^{16}$    $x^5y^{11}$ term.    (h) $(2a-3b)^7$    $a^5b^2$ term.

(i) $(x+1/x)^8$    $x^4$ term    (j) $(y-2/y)^7$    $y^{-3}$ term.

(k) $(x^2+1/x)^7$   $x^8$ term.    (l) $(y-1/y^2)^9$   constant term.

(3) Find the greatest coefficient of $x$ in the following expansions:

$$\text{(a)} \quad (1+x)^{17} \quad \text{(b)} \quad (1+2x)^7$$

$$\text{(c)} \quad (1-3x)^8 \quad \text{(d)} \quad (2+3x)^9$$

(4) Expand and simplify $(1+\sqrt{3})^6+(1-\sqrt{3})^6$, without using a calculator.

(5) Expand $(1+x)^{12}$ up to the term in $x^3$. Hence find approximations for:

(a) $1.02^{12}$   (b) $0.96^{12}$

(6) Use the binomial theorem to find approximations for:

(a) $1.01^8$   (b) $0.95^7$

(c) $2.01^9$   (d) $2.96^5$

(7) The first two terms of the expansion of $(2+ax)^n$ are $1024 + 15360x$. Find $a$ and $n$.

(8) The constant term in the expansion of $(ax+b/x)^{10}$ is 8064. Find $a$ in terms of $b$.

(9) There is no $x^2$ term in the expansion of $(1+ax)^6 - (2+bx)^7$. Find the ratio of $a$ to $b$.

(10) Use the expansion of $(1+y)^{10}$ to find $(1+(x+x^2))^{10}$, up to the term in $x^2$.

(11) Expand the following, up to the term indicated:

(a) $(1 - x + x^2)^7$  $x^2$ term  (b) $(1 + x^2)^8$  $x^6$ term

(c) $(1 + 2x + 3x^2)^6$  $x^2$ term  (d) $(2 - x + 2x^2)^7$  $x^2$ term

## 3.2 BINOMIAL THEOREM FOR OTHER POWERS

If $n$ is not a positive integer, the binomial theorem is still true, with certain restrictions. Provided that $-1 < x < 1$:

$$(1 + x)^n = 1 + nx + \frac{n(n - 1)x^2}{2!} + \frac{n(n - 1)(n - 2)x^3}{3!} + \cdots$$

In general, this series continues to infinity. So if only the first few terms are taken then the result is only an approximation.

### 3.2.1 Examples

(1)  Find an expansion for $\sqrt{(1 + x)}$, up to the term in $x^2$.
Hence find an approximation for $\sqrt{17}$.

Solution  Write $\sqrt{(1 + x)}$ as $(1 + x)^{\frac{1}{2}}$. Writing $n = \frac{1}{2}$ in the binomial expansion:

$$(1 + x)^{\frac{1}{2}} \simeq 1 + \frac{1}{2}x + \frac{\frac{1}{2}(\frac{1}{2} - 1)}{2!}x^2 = 1 + \frac{1}{2}x - \frac{1}{8}x^2$$

Write $\sqrt{17}$ as $(16 + 1)^{\frac{1}{2}} = 4(1 + \frac{1}{16})^{\frac{1}{2}}$.
Put $x = \frac{1}{16}$ in the expansion above:

$$\sqrt{17} \simeq 4(1 + \frac{1}{2} \times (\frac{1}{16}) - \frac{1}{8} \times (\frac{1}{16})^2) = 4.1230.$$

(2)  Expand $\frac{1 + 3x}{1 - 2x}$ up to the term in $x^2$. For which values of $x$ is the expansion valid?

Solution  Write $\frac{1 + 3x}{1 - 2x}$ as $(1 + 3x)(1 - 2x)^{-1}$.
$(1 - 2x)^{-1} \simeq 1 + -1 \times (-2x) + -1 \times -2 \times (-2x)^2/2! = 1 + 2x + 4x^2$.

$\frac{1 + 3x}{1 - 2x} \simeq (1 + 3x)(1 + 2x + 4x^2)$. Expand this, ignoring terms in $x^3$:

$$\frac{1 + 3x}{1 - 2x} \simeq 1 + 5x + 10x^2.$$

The expansion is valid if $-1 < 2x < 1$.
**The expansion is valid for $-\frac{1}{2} < x < \frac{1}{2}$**

## 3.2.2 Exercises

(1) Expand the following up to the term in $x^2$.

$$\text{(a)} \quad (1+x)^{\frac{1}{4}} \qquad \text{(b)} \quad \sqrt{(1+3x)}$$

$$\text{(c)} \quad (1-x)^{1\frac{1}{2}} \qquad \text{(d)} \quad (1-2x)^{1\frac{1}{3}}$$

$$\text{(e)} \quad (1+x)^{-2} \qquad \text{(f)} \quad \frac{1}{1+2x}$$

$$\text{(g)} \quad \frac{1}{1-x^2} \qquad \text{(h)} \quad \frac{3}{1+x^2}$$

(2) For which values of $x$ are the expansions in Question 1 valid?

(3) Use the binomial expansion to find approximations for:

(a)  $1.01^{\frac{1}{2}}$  (b)  $\sqrt{1.05}$

(c)  $0.98^{\frac{1}{2}}$  (d)  $\sqrt{0.96}$

(4) Without using a calculator or tables find $\sqrt{1.01} + \sqrt{0.99}$ correct to 5 decimal places.

(5) Using the binomial expansion of $(1+x)^{\frac{1}{2}}$, and writing 50 as $49 + 1$, find an approximation for $\sqrt{50}$.

(6) Use the method of question 5 to find approximations for:

(a)  $\sqrt{101}$  (b)  $\sqrt{98}$

(c)  $28^{\frac{1}{3}}$  (d)  $63^{\frac{1}{3}}$

(7) Expand the following up to the term in $x^2$:

(a)  $\dfrac{1+x}{1-x}$ $\qquad$ (b)  $\dfrac{1+x^2}{1+2x}$

(c)  $\dfrac{1+2x-x^2}{1+3x}$ $\qquad$ (d)  $\dfrac{1+x}{1+x^2}$

(8) Show that the expansion of $\sqrt{(1+x)} + \sqrt{(1-x)}$ up to the term in $x^3$ is of the form $a + bx^2$. Find $a$ and $b$.

(9) $\dfrac{1+ax+bx^2}{(1-x)^2}$ has no term in either $x$ or $x^2$. Find $a$ and $b$.

## 3.3 Examination Questions

(1) Find the first three terms in the expansion, in ascending powers of $x$, of

(i)   $(1-3x)^5$

(ii)   $(2+x)^4$

Hence find the coefficient of $x^2$ in the expansion of $(1-3x)^5(2+x)^4$.

[C add]

(2)

i.   Write down the expansion of $(1-x)^5$. Deduce that the first three terms in the expansion of $(1-3x)(1-x)^5$ are $1-8x+25x^2$ and find the term in $x^3$.

ii.  Find an approximation to $(1-3x)(1-x)^5$ when $x = \frac{1}{100}$ by taking the first three terms of the expansion. Show that the inclusion of the term in $x^3$ does not affect the approximation when working to 4 decimal places.

[O&C add]

(3) Obtain the expansion in ascending powers of $x$ of $(1-x)^8$. Hence calculate the value of $(0.95)^8$ correct to three decimal places.

When a ball is dropped on to level ground it always rebounds to a height of 0.95 times the height from which it fell. If it is dropped from a height of 10 metres, calculate, correct to three significant figures, the height to which it rebounds after eight bounces.

[L add]

(4) (a) Evaluate the term which is independent of $x$ in the expansion of

$$(x - 1/x^2)^{12}$$

(b) Expand

$$(1-x)^2\sqrt{(1+2x)}$$

in ascending powers of $x$ as far as the term in $x^3$. For which values of $x$ is this expansion valid?

[NI]

(5) The first three terms in ascending powers of $x$ of $\frac{1+px}{1+qx}$ and of $(1+x)^{\frac{1}{10}}$ are identical. Find the values of $p$ and $q$, assuming that $x$ is sufficiently small for both expansions to be valid.

Use this result to show that the tenth root of 33 is approximately $\dfrac{651\sqrt{2}}{649}$.

[C]

(6) (a) Express $\dfrac{1}{(1+x)(2+x)}$ in partial fractions.

Hence or otherwise, given that $x$ is sufficiently small for powers of $x$ above the second to be neglected, show that

$$\frac{1}{(1+x)(2+x)} = \frac{1}{8}(4 - 6x + 7x^2)$$

(b) Show that the first three non-zero terms in the series expansion of

$$(1 - 1/n)^{1/n}$$

in ascending powers of $1/n$ are

$$1 - (1/n)^2 - \frac{1}{2}(1/n)^3$$

and find the term in $(1/n)^4$.

By giving $n$ a suitable value, use the first four non-zero terms of the series to find a value for $(0.9)^{1/10}$, giving your answer to five decimal places.

[C]

(7) Use the binomial series to expand $(1 - x)^{\frac{1}{4}}$ in ascending powers of $x$ as far as the term in $x^3$.

By putting $x = \frac{1}{81}$ in the expression and in the series, calculate the value of $5^{\frac{1}{4}}$ correct to five decimal places, explaining why your working ensures this degree of accuracy.

[AEB 1986]

## COMMON ERRORS

### (1) Positive Integer Powers

a. When writing out the expansion of $(a + b)^n$ do not forget the binomial coefficients.

b. When expanding something like $(a + 2b)^5$, then do not forget to take powers of 2 as well as of $b$. For example, the third term is $10a^3(2b)^2 = 40a^3b^2$, not $10a^32b^2 = 20a^3b^2$.

c. Similarly, be careful of negative numbers. If you are expanding $(a - 2b)^5$, then the terms will be alternately positive and negative.

### (2) **Other Powers**

If $n$ is not a positive integer, then the binomial theorem only holds for expressions of the form $(1+x)^n$, where $-1 < x < 1$. Do not try to expand $\sqrt{5}$ as $(1+4)^{\frac{1}{2}}$, using $x = 4$.

Similarly, the first term inside the bracket must be 1. Do not write $\sqrt{5}$ as $(4\frac{1}{2} + \frac{1}{2})^{\frac{1}{2}}$ and attempt to expand.

The correct way to find $\sqrt{5}$ is to write it as $(4+1)^{\frac{1}{2}} = 2(1+\frac{1}{4})^{\frac{1}{2}}$. This can now be expanded using the Binomial theorem.

# 4 Quadratics

A *quadratic* function has the form $y = ax^2 + bx + c$, where $a, b, c$ are constants.

A *quadratic* equation has the form $ax^2 + bx + c = 0$.

## 4.1 SOLVING QUADRATIC EQUATIONS

Quadratic equations can be solved by factorizing, by completing the square, or by use of the following formula:

$$x = \frac{-b \pm \sqrt{(b^2 - 4ac)}}{2a}$$

Simultaneous equations, one linear and the other quadratic, can often be solved by substitution.

### 4.1.1 Examples

(1)  The length of a rectangle is 1 m greater than the width. If the area is 150 m$^2$, find the length.

Solution  If the length is $x$ m, then the width is $(x - 1)$. Using the fact that the area is 150:

$$x(x - 1) = 150$$

$$x^2 - x - 150 = 0$$

$$x = \frac{+1 \pm \sqrt{(1^2 - 4 \times 1 \times (-150))}}{2 \times 1}$$

**The length is 12.76 m.**

(2)  Write $2x^2 - 4x - 5$ in the form $a(x + b)^2 + c$, and hence solve the equation $2x^2 - 4x - 5 = 0$, leaving your answer in square root form.

Solution  Expanding, $2x^2 - 4x - 5 \equiv ax^2 + 2abx + ab^2 + c$
Equating coefficients of $x^2, a = 2$
Equating coefficients of $x, -4 = 2ab$. Hence $b = -1$
Equating constants, $-5 = ab^2 + c$. Hence $c = -7$

$$2x^2 - 4x - 5 \equiv 2(x - 1)^2 - 7$$

Put $2(x - 1)^2 - 7 = 0$

$$\mathbf{x = \sqrt{\left(\frac{7}{2}\right)} + 1}$$

(3)  Find where the line $y = x + 3$ crosses the circle $x^2 + y^2 = 20$.
Solution Substitute the first equation into the second.

$$x^2 + (x + 3)^2 = 20$$

$$2x^2 + 6x - 11 = 0$$

$$x = 1.284 \text{ or } -4.284$$

**They cross at (1.284, 4.284) and at (−4.284, −1.284)**

## 4.1.2 Exercises

(1) Solve the following equations:

(a) $x^2 + 4x - 77 = 0$          (b) $2y^2 - 7y - 15 = 0$

(c) $x^2 + 8x + 3 = 0$          (d) $5z^2 + 3z - 2 = 0$

(e) $x^4 - 3x^2 + 1 = 0$         (f) $3y^4 - 2y^2 - 7 = 0$

(g) $x^6 + 4x^3 + 2 = 0$         (h) $x^2 = 1 + 1/x^2$

(i) $(2x + 1)^2 + 3(2x + 1) - 9 = 0$    (j) $3/y^2 - 7/y + 2 = 0$

(2) A rectangle is 3 ft longer than it is broad. If its area is 33 sq. ft. find the width.

(3) The area of a circle in cm$^2$ is 4 greater than its perimeter in cm. Find the radius of the circle.

(4) A man rows upstream 5 miles against a current, and then rows back with the current. He can row at 4 m.p.h., and the total time taken is 3 hours. Find the speed of the current.

(5) Complete the square for the following equations by writing the left hand side in the form $a(x + b)^2 + c$, and hence solve the equations.

(a) $x^2 + 2x - 3 = 0$     (b) $x^2 - 7x + 2 = 0$

(c) $3x^2 + 6x + 1 = 0$     (d) $2x^2 - 3x - 8 = 0$

(6) Solve the following pairs of equations:

(a)   $y = x + 1$      (b)   $y = 2x - 3$
      $y = x^2 - 3$         $x^2 + y^2 = 18$

(c)   $x + y = 3$      (d)   $2x + 3y = 5$
     $x^2 - y^2 = 1$         $xy = 1$

(7) The sum of two numbers is 23 and their product is 20. Find the numbers.

(8) Find the points where the line $y = x + 2$ crosses the parabola $y = 4x^2$.

(9) Find where the line $x + y = 1$ crosses the circle $x^2 + y^2 = 8$.

(10) The sum of two numbers is 17, and the sum of their squares is 170. Find the two numbers.

(11) By subtracting one equation from the other, find the line which goes through the points of intersection of the circles $x^2 + y^2 = 10$ and $x^2 + y^2 - 9x + y = 0$. Hence find the co-ordinates of the points of intersection.

## 4.2 DISCRIMINANT

The *discriminant* of the equation $ax^2 + bx + c = 0$ is the expression $\Delta = b^2 - 4ac$.

If $\Delta > 0$ then the equation has 2 solutions. If $\Delta = 0$ then the equation has 1 solution. If $\Delta < 0$ then the equation has no solutions.

### 4.2.1 Examples

(1)      Find the range of values of $m$ for which $mx^2 + 3x + 5 = 0$ can be solved.

Solution      The equation can be solved if the discriminant is not negative.

$$3^2 - 4 \times m \times 5 \geq 0$$

$$\mathbf{m} \leq \frac{9}{20}$$

(2)      Find the values of $\lambda$ if the line $y = \lambda x$ is a tangent to the parabola $y = x^2 + 3$.

Solution      Solving the equations simultaneously:

$$x^2 - \lambda x + 3 = 0.$$

If the line is a tangent, this equation must have exactly one solution. The discriminant is 0.

$$\lambda^2 - 12 = 0$$

$$\lambda = \pm\sqrt{12}$$

### 4.2.2 Exercises

(1) How many solutions do the following equations have?

(a)   $x^2 + x + 3 = 0$      (b)   $x^2 - 4x + 4 = 0$

(c)   $2x^2 - 3x - 7 = 0$   (d)   $101x^2 + 99x + 24 = 0$

(2) For the following equations, find the range of values of $\lambda$ if there is to be a solution.

(a)   $\lambda x^2 + 2x + 3 = 0$   (b)   $x^2 - 3x - \lambda = 0$

(c)   $x^2 + \lambda x + 4 = 0$   (d)   $\lambda x^2 + x + 2\lambda = 0$

(3) Show that for all values of $\lambda$ and $\mu$ the equation $\lambda x^2 + \mu x - \lambda = 0$ has a solution.

(4) Find the value of $k$ which will ensure that $x^2 + kx - k - 1 = 0$ has equal roots.

(5) Show that $\lambda x^2 - (\lambda + \mu)x + \mu = 0$ always has solutions, for all values of $\lambda$ and $\mu$ .

(6) Find the range of values of $\lambda$ if the line $y = \lambda x$ meets the circle $x^2 + y^2 + 4y + 1 = 0$.

(7) Find the values of $\lambda$ if $y = \lambda x$ is a tangent to $y = x^2 + 2$.

(8) Find the values of $\mu$ if $y = \mu x - 3$ is a tangent to $y = x^2$ .

(9) Find the values of $\nu$ if $y = \nu x - 4$ is a tangent to $x^2 + y^2 = 1$.

(10) Find the values of $\rho$ if $y = \rho x$ is a tangent to $x^2 + y^2 + 8y + 15 = 0$.

## 4.3 ROOTS OF QUADRATIC EQUATIONS

If $\alpha$ and $\beta$ are the roots of the equation $ax^2 + bx + c = 0$, then:

$$\alpha + \beta = -b/a \text{ and } \alpha\beta = c/a.$$

The quadratic equation with roots $\alpha$ and $\beta$ must be of the form $x^2 - (\alpha + \beta)x + \alpha\beta = 0$.

### 4.3.1 Example

(1)     Let the equation $ax^2 + bx + c = 0$ have roots $\alpha$ and $\beta$ .
(a) Find an expression for $\alpha^2 + \beta^2$.
(b) Find the equation which has roots $\alpha^2$ and $\beta^2$.

Solution

a.     Use the identity $\alpha^2 + \beta^2 \equiv (\alpha + \beta)^2 - 2\alpha\beta$.

$$\alpha^2 + \beta^2 \equiv (\tfrac{-b}{a})^2 - \tfrac{2c}{a} \equiv \tfrac{b^2}{a^2} - \tfrac{2c}{a}$$

b.     The sum of the roots of the new equation is $\alpha^2 + \beta^2$, and the product is $\alpha^2\beta^2$. The new equation can be written down:

$$y^2 - (\alpha^2 + \beta^2)y + \alpha^2\beta^2 = 0.$$

$$\mathbf{y^2} - \left( \frac{b^2}{a^2} - \frac{2c}{a} \right) \mathbf{y} + \frac{c^2}{a^2} = 0$$

## 4.3.2 Exercises

(1) Without solving the following equations find the sum and the product of their roots.

    (a)  $2x^2 - 3x + 5 = 0$  (b)  $x^2 + 3 = 0$

    (c)  $x^2 + 5x + 1 = 0$    (d)  $3x^2 + x - 4 = 0$.

(2) Check that your results in Question 1 are correct by solving the equations, where possible.

(3) Write down and simplify the equations which have as roots:

  (a)  2 and 1     (b)  $-3$ and $4\frac{1}{2}$

  (c)  $k$ and $l/k$  (d)  $2 + \sqrt{3}$ and $2 - \sqrt{3}$

(4) The roots of $2x^2 + x + 7 = 0$ are $\alpha$ and $\beta$. Without solving the equation find the values of:

  (a)  $\alpha^2 + \beta^2$     (b)  $1/\alpha + 1/\beta$

  (c)  $\alpha/\beta + \beta/\alpha$  (d)  $\alpha^2\beta + \beta^2\alpha$

(5) The roots of $ax^2 + bx + c = 0$ are $\alpha$ and $\beta$. Express in terms of $a$, $b$ and $c$ the following:

  (a)  $\alpha^2 + \beta^2$     (b)  $1/\alpha + 1/\beta$

  (c)  $\alpha/\beta + \beta/\alpha$  (d)  $\alpha^2\beta + \beta^2\alpha$

  (e)  $\alpha^3 + \beta^3$      (f)  $(\alpha - \beta)^2$

(6) The roots of $ax^2 + bx + c = 0$ are $\alpha$ and $\beta$. Form the equation whose roots are:

  (a)  $1/\alpha$ and $1/\beta$    (b)  $\alpha + 1$ and $\beta + 1$

  (c)  $\alpha^3$ and $\beta^3$      (d)  $\alpha^2\beta$ and $\beta^2\alpha$

  (e)  $\alpha - \beta$ and $\beta - \alpha$  (f)  $\alpha\beta + \alpha - 2$ and $\beta\alpha + \beta - 2$

(7) The roots of the equation $x^2 + 2x + k = 0$ are $\alpha$ and $\alpha + 1$. Find the value of $k$.

(8) One root of $x^2 + 6x + c = 0$ is twice the other. Find the value of $c$.

(9) If one root of $x^2 + bx + c = 0$ is twice the other find a relation between $b$ and $c$.

(10) If the roots of the cubic $ax^3 + bx^2 + cx + d = 0$ are $\alpha, \beta$, and $\gamma$, show that:

$$ax^3 + bx^2 + cx + d \equiv a(x - \alpha)(x - \beta)(x - \gamma)$$

By expanding out show that:

$$\alpha + \beta + \gamma = -b/a : \beta\gamma + \gamma\alpha + \alpha\beta = c/a : \alpha\beta\gamma = -d/a$$

## 4.4 Examination Questions

(1) Given that $f(x) \equiv 3x^2 + 12x + 17$, find constants $a, b, c$ such that

$$f(x) \equiv a(x + b)^2 + c.$$

a.      Show that $f(x)$ is always positive.

b.      Find the least value of $f(x)$.

c.      Solve the equation $f(x) = 7$, giving your answers to one decimal place.

d.      Sketch the graph of $f(x)$.

[L add]

(2)

a.      Find the values of $p$ for which the equation

$$(p + 1)x^2 + 4px + 9 = 0$$

has equal roots.

b.      Find the range of values of $m$ for which the straight line $y = mx - 5$ intersects the curve $y = x^2 - 1$ in two distinct points.

[C add]

(3) Given that the roots of the equation $ax^2 + bx + c = 0$ are $\beta$ and $n\beta$, show that

$$(n + 1)^2 ac = nb^2.$$

[L]

(4) Given that $\alpha$ and $\beta$ are the roots of the equation

$$x^2 - px + 2 = 0$$

express $\alpha^2 + \beta^2$ in terms of $p$.

Without solving the given equation, find a quadratic equation whose roots are

$$\alpha^2 + \alpha/\beta \text{ and } \beta^2 + \beta/\alpha$$

giving the coefficients in a simplified form not involving $\alpha$ or $\beta$.

[JMB]

## COMMON ERRORS
### (1) Use of formula
When using the formula to solve a quadratic equation, be sure that you do not ignore the signs. For the equation $x^2 - 3x - 4 = 0$ the constants are:

$$a = 1 \text{ (not 0)} : b = -3 \text{ (not 3)} : c = -4 \text{ (not 4)}$$

### (2) Completing the square
Be careful when completing the square of a quadratic. It is often a good idea to expand your result to ensure that you have the correct values. In particular:

$$x^2 + 3x + c \text{ begins } (x + 1\tfrac{1}{2})^2, \text{ not } (x + 3)^2.$$

### (3) Simultaneous equations
When you solve a linear and a quadratic equation, you will usually get two values of $x$ and two values of $y$. Make sure that the correct value of $y$ goes with the correct value of $x$.

### (4) Roots of quadratics
If $\alpha$ and $\beta$ are the roots of $ax^2 + bx + c = 0$, then do not forget the minus sign in $\alpha + \beta = -b/a$.

# 5 Inequalities

An *inequality* asserts that one expression is less than another.

$x + 1 < 3, 3x - 2y < 4, x^2 + 3x - 7 < 0$ are examples of inequalities.

To *solve* an inequality is to find the range of values for which it is true.

When multiplying or dividing an inequality by a negative number the inequality changes round.

$$\text{If } x < y \text{ then } -2x > -2y.$$

## 5.1 Inequalities in one variable

The *modulus* function $|x|$ gives the positive value of $x$.

$$|x| = \begin{cases} x \text{ if } x \geq 0 \\ -x \text{ if } x < 0 \end{cases}$$

## 5.1.1 Example

(1)     Solve the following inequalities:

(a)  $x^2 + 3x - 10 < 0$    (b)  $|2x - 1| > 2$

(c)  $\frac{1+x}{3-x} \geq 1$         (d)  $\frac{1}{|x|-1} \geq 1$

**Solution**

a.        Factorize the quadratic.

$$(x + 5)(x - 2) < 0$$

The quadratic is zero at $-5$ and $2$. These values divide the number line into three regions. Compile a table to show when the factors are positive and when negative.

|               | $x < -5$ | $-5 < x < 2$ | $2 < x$ |
|---------------|:--------:|:------------:|:-------:|
| $x + 5$       | -        | +            | +       |
| $x - 2$       | -        | -            | +       |
| $(x+5)(x-2)$  | +        | -            | +       |

The inequality is satisfied in the middle region.

$$-5 < \mathbf{x} < 2$$

b.        Square both sides, to eliminate the modulus sign.

$$4x^2 - 4x + 1 > 4$$
$$4x^2 - 4x - 3 > 0$$

$(2x - 3)(2x + 1) > 0$. Now proceed as in (a).

$$\mathbf{x} < -\frac{1}{2} \ \text{ or } \ \mathbf{x} > 1\frac{1}{2}$$

c.        Take the 1 over to the left hand side.

$$\frac{1+x}{3-x} - 1 \geq 0$$

$$\frac{1 + x - (3 - x)}{3 - x} \geq 0$$

$$\frac{2(x - 1)}{3 - x} \geq 0$$

The method of (a), when expressions are multiplied, applies when they are divided. Proceed as in (a). The solution is:

$$1 \leq x < 3$$

d.  Consider two cases; when $|x|-1$ is positive and when it is negative.

If $|x| - 1$ is positive, i.e. $|x| > 1$, then $1 \geq |x| - 1$.

$$\text{Hence } |x| \leq 2$$

If $|x| - 1$ is negative, i.e. $|x| < 1$, then $1 \leq |x| - 1$.

$$|x| \geq 2.$$

But this contradicts the fact that $|x| < 1$. The solutions come only from the first case:

$$1 < |x| \leq 2. \text{ i.e.} - 2 \leq x < -1 \text{ or } 1 < x \leq 2$$

## 5.1.2 Exercises

Solve the following inequalities:

(1)  $3x + 1 > 4$  (2)  $1 - 2x \geq 2$

(3)  $1 + x < 6 - 2x$  (4)  $3(1 + 2x) \leq 2(x - 3)$

(5)  $x^2 + 8x + 12 < 0$  (6)  $x^2 - 3x - 18 > 0$

(7)  $2x^2 - 3x + 2 \geq 0$  (8)  $x^2 + x - 3 \leq 0$

(9)  $x^2 + x < 2$  (10)  $x^2 > 2x + 35$

(11)  $(x + 1)(x + 2)(x + 3) < 0$  (12)  $(2x - 1)(x - 3)(3 - 2x) > 0$

(13)  $(x + 1)^2(x - 1) \leq 0$  (14)  $x^2(2x + 1) > 0$

(15)  $|2x| < 1$  (16)  $|x + 3| > 2$

(17)  $|x + 1| \leq |x - 2|$  (18)  $|2x| \geq |1 - x|$

(19)  $\dfrac{(x - 1)(x + 2)}{(x + 3)} < 0$  (20)  $\dfrac{(x + 3)(1 - 2x)}{(x + 2)^2} > 0$

(21)  $x + 3 < \dfrac{10}{x}$  (22)  $\dfrac{x + 1}{2 - x} > 1$

(23)  $\dfrac{x}{3} < \dfrac{12}{x}$  (24)  $\dfrac{x - 2}{x} > \dfrac{x - 1}{x}$

(25)  $x < |x|$  (26)  $x > |\tfrac{1}{2}x|$

(27)  $x + 1 \geq |2x|$  (28)  $|2x| - |x| \geq 2$

## 5.2 Inequalities in two variables

Inequalities in two variables correspond to areas on a graph. It is usual to illustrate the required region by shading the areas which are *not* wanted.

### 5.2.1 Example

(1)        Illustrate on a graph the region corresponding to the inequalities:

$$x \geq 0 : y \geq 0 : 3x + 2y \leq 6 : 2x + 5y \leq 10.$$

Find the point in the region which gives the greatest value of $x + y$.

Solution        The boundaries of all the regions involved are straight lines. Shade the areas outside the wanted region.

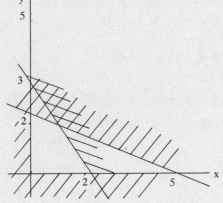

$x + y$ will have its greatest value at one of the corners of the region. The corners are:

$$(0,0) : (0,2) : (\frac{10}{11}, \frac{18}{11}) : (2,0)$$

$x + y$ has its greatest value at the third of these points.

**The greatest value is $2\frac{6}{11}$**

### 5.2.2 Exercises

(1) Illustrate on a graph the region corresponding to the inequalities:

$$x \geq 0 : x + y \leq 3 : y \geq 2x$$

(2) Illustrate on a graph the region corresponding to the inequalities:

$$3y + x \geq 2 : 2y + 3x \leq 6 : y \leq 3x + 4$$

(3) Illustrate on a graph the region corresponding to the inequalities:

$$y \leq x + 2 : 2x + y \leq 5 : 3y + x + 1 \geq 0$$

(4) In the region of Question 1 find the maximum value of (a) $x + 2y$ (b) $2x + y$.

(5) In the region of Question 2 find the maximum value of (a) $x + y$ (b) $2x - y$.

(6) In the region of Question 3 find the (a) maximum value of $x + y$ (b) the minimum value of $x + y$.

(7) Find the ranges of values taken in the region of Question 3 by (a) $x$ (b) $y$.

## 5.3 Examination Questions

(1) Find (a) the range of values of $x$ for which $2x^2 + 5x - 12 < 0$

(b) the range of values of $x$ for which $\dfrac{3}{2 - x} < 1$

[AEB add 1987]

(2) (a) Express $x^3 + x^2 - 8x - 12$ as $(x - 3)g(x)$, where $g(x)$ is a polynomial.
(b) Factorise $g(x)$.
(c) Solve the inequality $x^3 + x^2 - 8x - 12 > 0$.

[SMP add]

(3) With the same axes, draw accurately on graph paper the straight lines

$$2x + y = 6, \; y - x = 3, \; y + x = 3$$

Indicate clearly the boundary of the region A defined by the three inequalities

$$2x + y \leq 6, \; y - x \leq 3, \; y + x \geq 3$$

State the coordinates of the point in the region $A$ at which $2y - 3x$ takes its largest value.

Calculate the area of the region $A$.

[L add]

(4)

a.  In each of the following cases find the set of values of $x$ which satisfy the given inequality

  (i)  $(x-2)(4-x) < 0$   (ii)  $\frac{3x}{1-x} \geq 2$

b.  Show by means of a sketch and shading that there are values of $x$ and $y$ which satisfy $x + y \geq 7, 3x - y \leq 13$, and $y^2 = 2x - 1$.

Write down one pair of values of $x$ and $y$ which satisfy all three relationships.

[O add]

(5) Solve the following inequalities:

  (i)  $\frac{x+1}{x-1} < 4$   (ii)  $\frac{|x|+1}{|x|-1} < 4$   (iii)  $\left| \frac{x+1}{x-1} \right| < 4$

[C]

(6)

a.  Illustrate the solution set of the simultaneous inequalities

$$9 \leq y + 3x \leq 18, 0 \leq 2y - 3x \leq 18$$

by means of a diagram, and write down the sets of values to which $x$ and $y$ are separately restricted.

b.  Find the solution set of the inequality

$$\frac{2}{x-3} > \frac{3}{x-2}$$

where $x \epsilon R$, $x \neq 2$, $x \neq 3$.

[C]

## COMMON ERRORS

### (1) Solving Inequalities

a.  Do not multiply or divide an inequality by a term unless you are sure that the term is positive.

b.  If the solution to a quadratic inequality consists of two regions, then leave it like that. Write $x < 1$  or  $x > 3$, do not write $1 > x > 3$.

### (2) Inequalities in Two dimensions

If you are dealing with say the inequality $3x + 2y \leq 6$, then the region is enclosed by the line $3x + 2y = 6$. It is not enclosed by the lines $x = 2$ and $y = 3$.

# 6 Indices and Logarithms

## 6.1 Laws of Indices and Logarithms

Indices obey the following laws:

$$a^n \times a^m = a^{n+m}$$

$$a^n \div a^m = a^{n-m}$$

$$(a^n)^m = a^{nm}$$

$$a^{-n} = 1/a^n$$

$$a^{m/n} = {}^n\sqrt{(a^m)} = ({}^n\sqrt{a})^m$$

The *exponential* function is defined as $e^x$, where $e \simeq 2.71828$.

The *logarithm* function is the inverse of the index function. i.e.:

$$\text{If } a^n = x, \text{ then } n = \log_a x.$$

This is read: "log to the base $a$ of $x$". If the base is not mentioned then by convention it is 10.

$$\log x = \log_{10} x.$$

Logarithms to the base $e$ are called *natural logarithms*. They are written as $\ln x$.

$$\ln x = \log_e x$$

Logarithms obey the following laws:

$$\log_a x + \log_a y = \log_a xy$$

$$\log_a x - \log_a y = \log_a x/y$$

$$\log_a x^n = n \log_a x$$

To change the base of logarithms use the following:

$$\log_b x = \frac{\log_a x}{\log_a b}$$

In particular,

$$\log_a x = \frac{\log x}{\log a} = \frac{\ln x}{\ln a}$$

To convert to powers of 10 or of $e$ use the following:

$$a^x = 10^{x \log a} = e^{x \ln a}$$

### 6.1.1 Examples

(1)        Simplify the expression $\log_2 x + \log_2 3 + 2$ by writing it as a single log.

Solution     First write 2 as $\log_2 4$. Then use the rule for addition of logs.

$$\log_2 x + \log_2 3 + 2 = \log_2 x + \log_2 3 + \log_2 4 = \log_2(x \times 3 \times 4)$$

$$\log_2 \mathbf{x} + \log_2 \mathbf{3} + \mathbf{2} = \log_2 \mathbf{12x}$$

(2)    Solve the equation $e^{2x} + 2e^x - 15 = 0$

Solution    Note that $e^{2x} = (e^x)^2$. Write the equation as a quadratic in $e^x$.

$$(e^x)^2 + 2e^x - 15 = 0$$

$$e^x = -5 \text{ or } 3.$$

$e^x = -5$ has no root. The solution for $e^x = 3$ is:

$$\mathbf{x = \ln 3 = 1.0986}$$

(3)    The population of a country is increasing at 3% per annum. At this rate of growth how long will it be before the population doubles?

Solution    Every year the population is multiplied by $103/100 = 1.03$. After $x$ years the population will be multiplied by $1.03^x$. If it has doubled after $x$ years, this gives the equation:

$$2 = 1.03^x$$

Take logs of both sides.

$$\log 2 = \log 1.03^x = x \log 1.03$$

$$x = \frac{\log 2}{\log 1.03} = 23.45$$

**The population doubles after 23.45 years**

## 6.1.2 Exercises

(1) Without use of a calculator evaluate the following:

(a)  $16^{\frac{1}{2}}$                  (b)  $100^{1\frac{1}{2}}$

(c)  $\frac{1}{4}^{-2}$                   (d)  $8^{4/3}$

(e)  $5 \times 25^{\frac{1}{4}} \times 125^{1/6}$  (f)  $3^{\frac{1}{2}} \div 9^{-\frac{1}{4}}$

(2) Simplify the following as far as possible:

(a)  $x^3 \times x^{-2} \div x^5$          (b)  $y^{\frac{1}{2}} \times y^{1\frac{1}{2}} \div y^{-1}$

(c)  $5^x \times 25^x \times 125^{2x}$     (d)  $2^{2n} \times 4^{3n} \div 16^{-3n}$

(3) Write the following in logarithmic form:

(a) $2^4 = 16$    (b) $10^3 = 1000$

(c) $9^{1\frac{1}{2}} = 27$    (d) $25^{-\frac{1}{2}} = 1/5$

(e) $e^2 = 7.34$    (f) $e^{2.0258} = 10$

(4) Write the following in index form:

(a) $\log_2 8 = 3$    (b) $\log_9 3 = \frac{1}{2}$

(c) $\log 0.1 = -1$    (d) $\log_{16} 8 = \frac{3}{4}$

(e) $\ln 6 = 1.792$    (f) $\ln 12.18 = 2.5$

(5) Without the use of a calculator evaluate the following:

(a) $\log_2 16$   (b) $\log_5 125$

(c) $\log_9 3$    (d) $\log 0.001$

(e) $\log_2 \frac{1}{8}$    (f) $\log_a a$

(g) $\log_a a^2$    (h) $\log_a 1/\sqrt{a}$

(6) Use a calculator to find the following:

(a) $\log_2 3$   (b) $\log_4 9$

(c) $\log_5 2$   (d) $\log_3 0.002$

(7) Simplify the following expressions by writing them as single logarithms:

(a) $\log x + \log 2$    (b) $\log_2 x - \log_2 3x$

(c) $\log_2 x + 3\log_2 x$    (d) $\log x + 2\log 3x$

(e) $\log x + 1$    (f) $\log_2 x + 2$

(8) Solve the following equations:

(a) $2^x = 3$        (b) $10^x = 6$

(c) $3^{x+1} = 4$       (d) $2^{2x-1} = 4^{1-3x}$

(e) $4^x - 5 \times 2^x + 6 = 0$    (f) $3^x = 5^{x-1}$

(g) $2^x \times 3^{x+1} = 10$    (h) $2^x = 5/3^x$

(i) $e^{2x} - 7e^x + 10 = 0$    (j) $e^x + e^{-x} = 4$

(9) Write the following equations so that $y$ is the subject.

(a) $\log x + \log y = 1000$    (b) $\log_y x = 3$

(10) Solve the following equations:

(a) $\log_2 x = 7$

(b) $\log_2 x + \log_2(x+1) = \log_2 6$

(c) $\log x - \log(x-2) = 2$

(d) $2\log_3 x = 5$

(e) $\log_3 x - \log_9 x = 2$

(f) $\log_x 4 = 5$

(g) $\ln x = 3$

(h) $\ln x + \ln \sqrt{x} = -3$

(11) A population is growing at 5% each year. How long will it be before the population has tripled?

(12) A man invests £1,200 in a building society at 9% compound interest. When will he have £2,000?

(13) A radio-active isotope decays so that each year it loses $\frac{1}{5}$ of its mass. What is its half-life? (How long before it has lost half its mass?)

(14) The half-life of an isotope is 8 years. How much is lost after 1 year? How long does it take to lose $\frac{9}{10}$ of its mass?

## 6.2 Examination Questions

(1)

i. Write the cube root of 4 as a power of 2. Hence evaluate $(^3\sqrt{4})^{4.5}$ without using a calculator or tables, showing the steps of your working.

ii. Simplify $(\frac{x^3 y}{z})^{-2} \times \frac{x^4 y^2}{z}$

iii. Simplify $\log_b(ab^2) - \log_b a$.

[MEI add]

(2)

i. Express as a single logarithm in its simplest form

$$\log_{10} 5 - 3\log_{10} 25 + 2\log_{10} 50.$$

ii. Solve the equation $3 \times 2^{2x} - 7 \times 2^x + 2 = 0$

[O add]

(3)

a. Express as powers of 2:

$$\frac{1}{16}, \quad 64^a, \quad 8^b/4^c$$

b. If $x^x = 30$, without attempting to evaluate $x$, find the values of $x^{\frac{1}{2}x}$ and $x^{3x}$.

47

c.   Solve the equation $(17.1)^x = 9$

[O&C add]

(4)

a.   Solve the equation

$$2 \log_3 x = 1 + \log_3(18 - x)$$

b.   Given that $3 = a^k$, express in terms of $k$,

   (i)   $\log_a {}^3/_a$   (ii)   $\log_9 3a$

[AEB 1986]

(5) Solve each of the following equations, to find $x$ in terms of $a$, where $a > 0$ and $a \neq e^2$ :

   i.   $a^x = e^{2x+1}$,

   ii.   $2 \ln (2x) = 1 + \ln a$.

[C]

(6) Evaluate in terms of $\ln 2$

   i.   $\ln 2 + \ln (2^2) + \cdots + \ln (2^n) + \cdots + \ln (2^{100})$

   ii.   $\sum_{n=1}^{\infty} (\ln 2)^n$

[JMB]

## COMMON ERRORS

### (1) Indices

Algebraic and arithmetic mistakes are very common when dealing with indices. Pay regard to the following:

$$a^n \times a^m \neq a^{mn}$$

$$a^{1/n} \neq a/n$$

$$a^{-n} \neq -a^n$$

### (2) Logarithms

Similar mistakes arise when dealing with logarithms. Pay regard to the following:

$$\log a + \log b \neq \log(a + b)$$

$$\log a \times \log b \neq \log ab$$

## (3) Compound Interest

In problems involving compound interest, or percentage growth or decay, remember that the original number is *multiplied* by the same amount each year. Do not *add* a constant amount.

# 7 Coordinate Geometry

## 7.1 Co-ordinates of points

Suppose $(x_1, y_1)$ and $(x_2, y_2)$ are points in a plane.

The *distance* between $(x_1, y_1)$ and $(x_2, y_2)$ is $\sqrt{((x_1 - x_2)^2 + (y_1 - y_2)^2)}$

The *midpoint* of $(x_1, y_1)$ and $(x_2, y_2)$ is $(\frac{1}{2}(x_1 + x_2), \frac{1}{2}(y_1 + y_2))$

The point which divides the line between $(x_1, y_1)$ and $(x_2, y_2)$ in

the ratio $\lambda : \mu$ is $\left( \dfrac{\mu x_1 + \lambda x_2}{\lambda + \mu}, \dfrac{\mu y_1 + \lambda y_2}{\lambda + \mu} \right)$

### 7.1.1 Examples

(1)         Find the distance between (3, 4) and (−1, 8).

Solution    Use the formula above, being careful with minus signs.

$$\text{Distance} = \sqrt{((3 - (-1))^2 + (4 - 8)^2)} = \sqrt{32} = 5.66$$

50

(2)        Find the point which divides (3, 4) and (−1, 8) in the
ration 2:3.

Solution        Use the formula above.
$$\left( \frac{3 \times 3 + 2 \times -1}{2+3} , \frac{3 \times 4 + 2 \times 8}{2+3} \right) = \left( \frac{7}{5} , \frac{28}{5} \right)$$

## 7.1.2 Exercises

(1) Find the distances between the following pairs of points:

    (a)   (2,1) and (4,7)        (b)   (0,0) and (2,5)

    (c)   (4,6) and (2,9)        (d)   (2,−3) and (−2,8)

    (e)   (−3, −2) and (1,−5)   (f)   (2,−6) and (−5, −3)

(2) By finding the lengths of its sides show that the quadrilateral formed
by the points (1,1), (4,5), (4,10) and (1,6) is a rhombus.

(3) Show that the points (1,1), (4,3) and (−1,4) form a right-angled
triangle. What is its area?

(4) Find the midpoints of the pairs of points in Question 1.

(5) For the following pairs of points, find the point which divides them
in the ratio shown.

    (a)   (1,3) and (2,7), ratio 1:3      (b)   (4,2) and (3,9), ratio 4:1

    (c)   (3,4) and (−1,5), ratio 2:3    (d)   (−2,-4) and (4,−3), ratio 5:6

(6) By showing that its diagonals bisect each other, show that the quadrilateral formed by the points (1,1), (3,5), (9,7) and (7,3) is a parallelogram.

(7) Is the quadrilateral of Question 6 a rhombus?

(8) Show that the points (0,0), $(m, 1)$, $(-1, m)$ form a right-angled triangle.

(9) Show that the points $(x, y)$, $(x + \lambda, y + \mu)$, $(x + \mu, y - \lambda)$ form a
right-angled triangle.

(10) Let $A, B,$ and $C$ be at $(x_1, y_1)$, $(x_2, y_2)$ and $(x_3, y_3)$. Find the coordinates of the point $D$ which is the midpoint of $BC$. Find the coordinates
of the point $G$ which divides $AD$ in the ratio 2:1. Simplify your answer as
far as possible. What do you notice? what can you say about $G$?

## 7.2 Equations of straight lines

The *gradient* of a straight line is the ratio of its $y$-change to its $x$-change. The equation of a straight line can be written in the following forms:

$ax + by + c = 0$, where $a, b, c$ are constants.

$y = mx + c$, where $m$ is the gradient and $(0, c)$ the intercept on the $y$-axis.

$y - y_0 = m \times (x - x_0)$, where the gradient is $m$ and the line goes through $(x_0, y_0)$.

$x/a + y/b = 1$, where $(a, 0)$ and $(0, b)$ are the intercepts on the $x$ and $y$ axes respectively.

$y = mx + c$ and $y = nx + d$ are *parallel* if $m = n$.

$y = mx + c$ and $y = nx + d$ are *perpendicular* if $m \times n = -1$.

The shortest (i.e. perpendicular) distance from the point $(x_0, y_0)$ to the line $ax + by + c = 0$ is:

$$\frac{|ax_0 + by_0 + c|}{\sqrt{(a^2 + b^2)}}$$

### 7.2.1 Examples

(1)     Find the equation of the line through $(1,4)$ and $(2,6)$.

Solution     The ratio of the $y$-change to the $x$-change is $(6 - 4)/(2 - 1) = 2$. Use the third form of the equation of a line.

$$y - 4 = 2 \times (x - 1)$$

$$\mathbf{y = 2x + 2}$$

(2)     A triangle has its vertices at $A(6,1)$, $B(1,6)$ and $C(-3, -2)$. Find the equations of the perpendicular bisectors of $BC$ and $AB$. Find the coordinates of the point $D$ where these lines meet, and verify that $D$ is the circumcentre of the triangle, i.e. is the same distance from $A$, $B$, and $C$.

Solution     The midpoint of $BC$ is $(-1,2)$. The gradient of $BC$ is 2, hence the gradient of the perpendicular is $-\frac{1}{2}$. The equation of the perpendicular is therefore:

$$\mathbf{y = -\frac{1}{2}x + 1\frac{1}{2}.}$$

Similarly, the equation of the perpendicular bisector of $AB$ is:

$$\mathbf{y = x}$$

Solve these equations simultaneously:

**D is at $(1, 1)$**

Use the definition of distance in 7.1:

$$AD = BD = CD = 5$$

### 7.2.2 Exercises

(1) Find the equations of the following straight lines.

a.  Through $(1,1)$ and $(2,5)$
b.  Through $(2,4)$ and $(5,5)$
c.  Through $(2,3)$ and $(3,1)$
d.  Through $(6,3)$ and $(2,6)$
e.  With gradient 2 and through $(3,4)$
f.  With gradient $\frac{1}{2}$ and through $(2,1)$
g.  With gradient $-3$ and through $(1,5)$
h.  With gradient $-\frac{3}{4}$, through $(1,-3)$
i.  Through $(2,3)$, parallel to $y = 4x$
j.  Through $(2,1)$, parallel to $y = 2 - x$
k.  Through $(5,7)$, perpendicular to $y = x - 3$
l.  Through $(2,-3)$, perpendicular to $y = 2x + 1$

(2) Find the perpendicular distances between the following points and lines.

(a)  $(1,2)$ and $2y + 3x - 1 = 0$    (b)  $(3,4)$ and $y + x + 3 = 0$

(c)  $(2,3)$ and $y = 2x - 4$    (d)  $(0,0)$ and $2y = 3x - 1$

(3) Show that opposite sides of the quadrilaterals in Questions 2 and 6 of 7.1.2 are parallel.

(4) Show that the diagonals of the quadrilateral in Question 2 of 7.1.2 are perpendicular.

(5) Show that the quadrilateral formed by the points $(1,1)$, $(5,5)$, $(8,2)$ and $(4,-2)$ is a rectangle. Is it a square?

(6) By the method of Question 2 of 7.2.1 find the circumcentre of the triangle formed by $(1,4)$, $(0,1)$ and $(4,1)$. Find the radius of the circumcircle.

(7) $ABC$ is the triangle whose vertices are $(2,3)$, $(1,-1)$, $(4,3)$. Find the equations of the sides. Find the equations of the lines through $A, B, C$ perpendicular to $BC, AC, AB$ respectively. Find the point where these three lines intersect. (The *orthocentre* of $\triangle ABC$).

(8) Verify that (1,3) is the same distance from $4x + 3y - 1 = 0$ as from $5y - 3 = 0$. Hence find the equation of the bisector of the angle between these two lines.

## 7.3 Circles

If a circle has radius $r$ and centre $(h, k)$, then its equation is:

$$(x - h)^2 + (y - k)^2 = r^2$$

### 7.3.1 Examples

(1) Find the centre and radius of the circle with equation $x^2 + y^2 + 2x - 4y - 15 = 0$. Find the equation of the tangent at $(1, -2)$.

Solution   Complete the square for $x$ and $y$.

$$(x + 1)^2 + (y - 2)^2 = 1 + 4 + 15 = 20$$

**The centre is at $(-1, 2)$ and the radius is $\sqrt{20}$**

The radius from the centre to $(1, -2)$ has gradient $-2$.
Hence the gradient of the tangent is $\frac{1}{2}$.
The tangent has equation $y + 2 = \frac{1}{2}(x - 1)$.

**The equation is $y = \dfrac{1}{2}x - 2\dfrac{1}{2}$**

(2) $A$ is at $(0,3)$ and $B$ is at $(6,0)$. $P$ is such that $PA = 2PB$. Show that the locus of $P$ is a circle, and find its centre and radius.

Solution   Let P be at $(x, y)$. Use the formula for distance:

$$PA = \sqrt{(x^2 + (y - 3)^2)} \quad PB = \sqrt{((x - 6)^2 + y^2)}$$

Use the fact that $PA = 2PB$, and hence $PA^2 = 4PB^2$:

$$x^2 + (y - 3)^2 = 4((x - 6)^2 + y^2)$$

Expand and collect like terms.

$$0 = 3x^2 + 3y^2 - 48x + 6y + 135$$

$$x^2 + y^2 - 16x + 2y + 45 = 0$$

$$(x - 8)^2 + (y + 1)^2 = 20$$

**The locus is a circle, with centre $(8, -1)$ and radius $\sqrt{20}$**

## 7.3.2 Exercises

(1) Write down the equations of the following circles:

(a) With centre (1,2) and radius 5    (b) with centre (1,−3) and radius 8

(2) Find the centres and radii of the following circles:

(a) $x^2 + y^2 + 4x - 2y - 3 = 0$    (b) $x^2 + y^2 - 3x - y + 1 = 0$

(c) $x^2 + y^2 - 6y + 2 = 0$        (d) $x^2 + y^2 + 3x = 0$

(3) Find the equation of the circle with centre (1,3) which goes through the point (2,7).

(4) Find the equation of the circle whose diameter is the line between (1,4) and (-3,6).

(5) Find the distance from (1,−1) to the line $3x + 4y = 2$. Hence find the equation of the circle with centre (1,−1) which touches $3x + 4y = 2$.

(6) Find the equation of the circle which has centre (2,3) and which touches the line $x - 3y + 5 = 0$.

(7) Find the equation of the tangent to $x^2 + y^2 + 2x - 6y + 2 = 0$ at the point (1,1).

(8) Find where the circle $x^2 + y^2 - 3x + 2y + 2 = 0$ cuts the $x$-axis. Find the equations of the tangents to the circle at these points.

(9) Find the points where the circle $x^2 + y^2 + 3x + 1 = 0$ cuts the line $y = x$. Find the equations of the tangents at these points.

(10) P moves so that its distance from the origin is twice its distance from (3,−9). Prove that $P$ moves in a circle, and find its centre and radius.

(11) The centre of a circle is on the line $x = 3$, and both the axes are tangents to the circle. Find the equation of the circle.

(12) $A$ is at (2,−3) and $B$ is at (4,5). $P$ moves so that $PA$ is perpendicular to $PB$. Show that $P$ moves in a circle, and find its centre and radius.

(13) With $A$ and $B$ as in Question 12, let $P$ move so that $PA^2 + PB^2 = 100$. Show that the locus of $P$ is a circle, and find its centre and radius.

(14) Let a circle have centre at C(1,1) and radius 3. Find the distance from $P(4,5)$ to $C$. Does $P$ lie inside or outside the circle? Find the length of the tangent from $P$ to $C$.

(15) Find the values of $m$ so that $y = mx$ is a tangent to the circle $x^2 + y^2 + 3x - 2y + 1 = 0$.

(16) Find the values of $k$ so that the line $y + x = k$ is a tangent to the circle $x^2 + y^2 + 4x - 3 = 0$.

## 7.4 Parameters

If a curve is defined by an equation relating $x$ and $y$ then the equation is the *Cartesian* form of the curve.

If $x$ and $y$ are expressed in terms of a third variable $t$ then $t$ is a *parameter* for the curve. The equations which define $x$ and $y$ in terms of $t$ are the *parametric* equations of the curve.

### 7.4.1 Examples

(1)      Let the parametric equations of a curve be $x = t^2 + 1$ and $y = t^3$. Obtain the Cartesian equation of the curve.

Solution      Re-write the equations as $t^2 = x - 1$ and $t^3 = y$. Cube the first equation and square the second.

$$t^6 = (x - 1)^3 = y^2$$

**The equation is $(x - 1)^3 = y^2$**

(2)      Verify that the point $(t^2, 2t)$ lies on the curve $y^2 = 4x$. Find the equation of the chord from $(t^2, 2t)$ to $(1, 2)$. By letting $t$ tend to one find the equation of the tangent at $(1,2)$.

Solution      If $y = 2t$, then $y^2 = 4t^2 = 4x$.

**$(t^2, 2t)$ lies on the curve.**

The gradient of the chord is
$$\frac{2t - 2}{t^2 - 1} = \frac{2(t - 1)}{(t - 1)(t + 1)} = \frac{2}{t + 1}$$
The equation of the chord is:

$$y - 2 = \frac{2}{t + 1}(x - 1)$$

$$(y - 2)(t + 1) = 2(x - 1)$$

**The equation is $ty + y - 2x = 2t$**

Now put $t = 1$.

**The equation of the tangent is $y - x = 1$**

### 7.4.2 Exercises

(1) The parametric equations of curves are given below. Obtain the equations of the curves in a form which does not mention the parameter.

(a) $x = t^2, y = t^3$           (b) $x = t, y = 5/t$

(c) $x = t + 1, y = 3t - 2$     (d) $x = 2t, y = t^2 - 1$

(e) $x = t^3, y = \frac{1}{t}$           (f) $x = t^2, y = \frac{1}{1+t}$

(g) $x = \frac{1}{2}(t + \frac{1}{t}), y = \frac{1}{2}(t - \frac{1}{t})$    (h) $x = \frac{1}{1+2t}, y = \frac{t}{1+2t}$

(2) Verify that the point $(t, 3/t)$ lies on the curve $xy = 3$. Find the equation of the chord joining the points with parameters $p$ and $q$.

(3) Verify that the point $(4t, t^2)$ lies on the curve $16y = x^2$. Find the equation of the chord joining the points with parameters 2 and $p$. By letting $p$ tend to 2 find the equation of the tangent to the curve at $t = 2$.

(4) Show that the point $(\frac{1}{1+t^2}, \frac{t}{1+t^2})$ lies on a circle, and find its centre and radius.

### 7.5 Examination Questions

(1) Find the gradient of the line through $A(-4, -1)$ and $C(8, 7)$ and write down the coordinates of $E$, the middle point of $AC$.

Find the equation of the line through $E$ perpendicular to $AC$ and the coordinates of $B$ where this line meets the $y$-axis.

Find the equation of the line through $C$ parallel to $AB$ and calculate the coordinates of the point $D$ where this line meets $BE$ produced.

[MEI add]

(2) *Note: A solution to this question by scale drawing will not be accepted.*

$ABCD$ is a trapezium with $AD$ parallel to $BC$. $A$ and $B$ lie on the $x$-axis, and the $x$-coordinate of $A$ is less than the $x$-coordinate of $B$.

The equation of the side $BC$ is $y - 3x + 15 = 0$.

  i.   Find the coordinates of $B$.

       The diagonals $AC$ and $BD$ intersect at the point $M(1,2)$ which divides $DB$ internally in the ratio 1:2.

 ii.   Find the coordinates of $D$.

iii.   Hence find the coordinates of $A$ and $C$.

       $CD$ produced cuts the $x$-axis at $E$.

 iv.   Find the coordinates of $E$.

  v.   Hence or otherwise calculate the area of the trapezium $ABCD$.

[NI add]

(3) The line $x/a + y/b = 1$ meets the $x$-axis at A and the $y$-axis at $B$. $G$ is the mid-point of $AB$ and $H$ is the point which divides $AB$ in the ratio $2:3$.

Find, in terms of $a$ and $b$,

  i.  the coordinates of $G$,

 ii.  the coordinates of $H$.

If the line moves so that the length of $AB$ is always 10 units,

iii.  show that the locus of $G$ is a circle, stating its centre and radius,

iv.  *verify* that the locus of $H$ is the curve whose equation is $x^2/36 + y^2/16 = 1$.

[O&C add]

(4) Points $A$ and $B$ in a plane have co-ordinates $(1,0)$ and $(0,1)$ respectively. A point $P$ divides $OB$ in the ratio $\lambda : 1 - \lambda$, and a point $Q$ divides $PA$ in the same ratio. Find the coordinates of $P$, and show that the coordinates of $Q$ are $(\lambda, \lambda - \lambda^2)$.

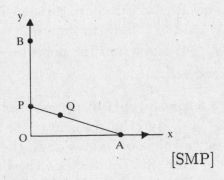

[SMP]

(5) Find the points of intersection of the circle

$$x^2 + y^2 - 6x + 2y - 17 = 0$$

and the line $x - y + 2 = 0$. Show that an equation of the circle which has these points as the ends of a diameter is

$$x^2 + y^2 - 4y - 5 = 0$$

Show also that this circle and the circle

$$x^2 + y^2 - 8x + 2y + 13 = 0$$

touch externally.

[L]

(6) (a) Calculate the coordinates of the centres $C_1, C_2$ and the radii of the two circles whose equations are

$$x^2 + y^2 + 2x - 4y - 5 = 0$$

and  $x^2 + y^2 - 2x - 6y + 5 = 0$

Find the coordinates of the points of intersection A, B of the two circles, and show that AB is perpendicular to $C_1C_2$.

(b) Show that the point $P(ap^2, 2ap)$ lies on the curve having equation $y^2 = 4ax$ for all values of $p$.

The point $Q(aq^2, 2aq)$ is another point on the curve. Show that the equation of PQ is

$$(p+q)y - 2x = 2apq$$

If PQ passes through the point $S(a,0)$, show that

$$q = -1/p,$$

and in this case deduce the coordinates of $R$, the mid-point of $PQ$, in terms of $p$. Hence show that the equation of the locus of $R$ as $p$ varies is

$$y^2 = 2a(x - a)$$

[W]

## COMMON ERRORS

### (1) Suffices

Do not confuse $x_3$ (the third variable) with $x^3$ ($x$ cubed).

### (2) Arithmetic

Throughout coordinate geometry, be very careful of negative signs. The difference between 5 and $-3$ is 8, not 2.

When finding distances, do not oversimplify the expression.

$$\sqrt{(x^2 + y^2)} \neq x + y$$

### (3) Gradients

The gradient of the line between two points is the $y - change$ over the $x - change$. It is not the $y - value$ over the $x - value$.

When finding the gradient of a line from its equation, it must first be written in the form $y = mx + c$. The gradient of $2y = 3x + 4$ is $1\frac{1}{2}$. It is not 3.

### (4) Division of lines

Notice that when a line $AB$ is divided in the ratio $\lambda : \mu$, then the coordinates of $A$ are multiplied by $\mu$ and the coordinates of $B$ are multiplied by $\lambda$. Do not get this the wrong way round.

# 8 Functions and Graphs

## 8.1 Composition and Inverses of Functions

A function $y = f(x)$ can be written in the form $f : x \rightarrow y$. The set of possible $x$ values is called the *domain*, and the set of possible $y$ values is the *range* or *image* or *co-domain*.

The *composition* $f°g$ or $fg$ of two functions $f$ and $g$ is defined by:

$$f°g(x) = f(g(x))$$

The *identity* function $i(x)$ is such that $i(x) = x$ for all $x$.

The *inverse* of a function $f$ is the function $f^{-1}$ such that:

$$f(f^{-1}(x)) = f^{-1}(f(x)) = x$$

Equivalently, $f°f^{-1} = f^{-1}°f = i$.

## 8.1.1 Examples

(1)     Let $f$ and $g$ be defined by $f : x \to 3x - 1, g : x \to 2 - 5x$.
Find (i) $f°g(2)$ (ii) $g°f(2)$ (iii) $f°g$ (iv) $f^{-1}$.

Solution     (i) Apply $g$ first and then $f$ . $g(2) = -8, f(-8) = -25.$

$$\mathbf{f°g(2) = -25}$$

(ii) Apply $f$ first and then $g$. $f(2) = 5, g(5) = -23$.

$$\mathbf{g°f(2) = -23}$$

(iii) $g(x) = 2 - 5x$. Apply $f$; $f(2 - 5x) = 3(2 - 5x) - 1$.

$$\mathbf{f°g : x \to 5 - 15x}$$

(iv) f is obtained by multiplying by 3 and subtracting 1. The inverse is obtained by adding 1 and dividing by 3.

$$\mathbf{f^{-1} : x \to \frac{1}{3}(x + 1)}$$

(2)     The function $h$ is defined by $h : x \to 4 - x^2$. Its domain is the set of all real numbers. Find the range of $h$, and explain why it has no inverse. Restrict the domain of $h$ so that it does have an inverse.

Solution     $x^2$ is always at least 0. Hence $4 - x^2$ is always at most 4.

$$\textbf{The range of h is } \mathbf{\{y : y \leq 4\}}$$

$h(1) = h(-1) = 3$. Hence $h^{-1}$ cannot be defined on 3, for example.

$$\mathbf{h^{-1}(3) \textbf{ does not exist.}}$$

If the domain of $h$ is restricted to positive values of $x$, then the inverse is $h^{-1} : x \to \sqrt{(4 - x)}$.

$$\textbf{Restrict h to the domain } \mathbf{\{x : x \geq 0\}}$$

## 8.1.2 Exercises

(1) With $f$ and $g$ as in Example 1 above, find:

    (a)  $g \circ f(-3)$  (b)  $f \circ g(-3)$

    (c)  $g \circ f$      (d)  $g^{-1}$

(2) Let $j : x \to 2x + 3$ and $k : 3x - 4$. Find:

    (a)  $j \circ k(-2)$  (b)  $k \circ j(-2)$

    (c)  $j \circ k$      (d)  $k \circ j$

    (e)  $j^{-1}$      (f)  $k^{-1}$

    (g)  $(j \circ k)^{-1}$  (h)  $(k \circ j)^{-1}$

    (i)  $j^{-1} \circ k^{-1}$  (j)  $k^{-1} \circ j^{-1}$

(3) For the functions $f$ and $g$ of Example ·1 above show that:

$$(f \circ g)^{-1} = g^{-1} \circ f^{-1} \text{ and } (g \circ f)^{-1} = f^{-1} \circ g^{-1}$$

(4) The function $m$ is defined by $m : x \to 2 + 5x$, for $x \geq 1$. Find the range of $m$.

(5) Find the inverse of $m$ of Question 4, and find its domain and range.

(6) Find the ranges of the following functions:

    (a)  $\sin x$        (b)  $x^2$

    (c)  $\cos x + 3$    (d)  $10^x$

    (e)  $2 \sin x - 1$    (f)  $(x + 1)^2 + 5$

    (g)  $x^2 + 4x + 1$  (h)  $(x + 1)^3$

(7) For the following functions, state whether or not they have an inverse. Find the inverse if it does exist, and for those functions without an inverse restrict the domain so that an inverse exists.

    (a)  $x^2 + 3$       (b)  $3x - 4$

    (c)  $x^3$          (d)  $\sin x$

    (e)  $x^2 - 2x - 3$  (f)  $(x + 1)^3$

## 8.2 Graphs of Functions

Some standard graphs are as shown

| $\sin x$ | $\cos x$ | $\tan x$ | $|x|$ | $1\ /\ x$ |

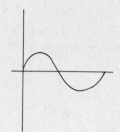 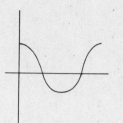  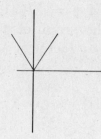 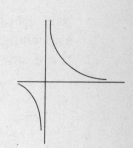

The effect of simple transformations on graphs is as follows.

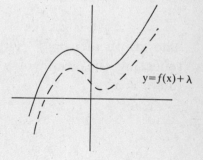

The graph of $y = f(x) + \lambda$ is obtained by shifting up the graph of $y = f(x)$ by $\lambda$ units.

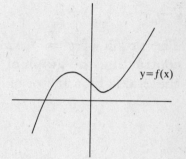

The graph of $y = f(x + \lambda)$ is obtained by shifting the graph of $y = f(x)$ $\lambda$ units to the left.

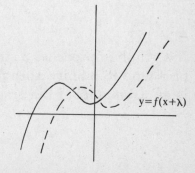

The graph of $y = \lambda f(x)$ is obtained by stretching the graph of $y = f(x)$, along the $y$-axis by a factor of $\lambda$.

The graph of $y = f(\lambda x)$ is obtained by contracting the graph of $y = f(x)$, along the $x$-axis by a factor of $\lambda$.

The graph of $y = f^{-1}(x)$ is obtained by reflecting the graph of $y = f(x)$, in the line $y = x$.

If a graph approaches a straight line, as $y$ or $x$ tend to infinity, then the straight line is an *asymptote* of the graph.

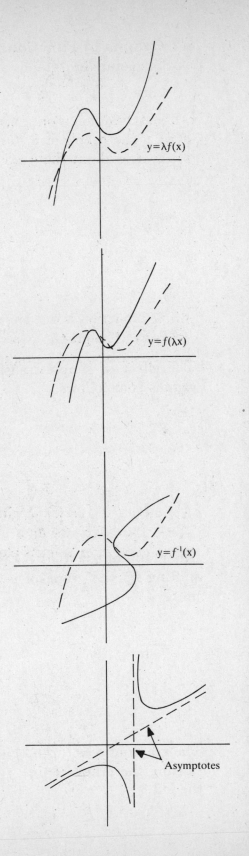

An even function is one for which $f(-x) = f(x)$. The graph of an even function is symmetric about the $y$-axis.

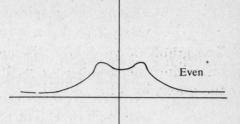

An *odd* function is one for which $f(-x) = -f(-x)$. The graph of an odd function is symmetric about the origin.

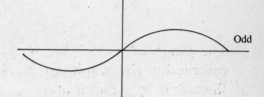

A function is *periodic* with period $\mu$ if $f(x + \mu) = f(x)$ for all $x$. The graph repeats itself after $\mu$ units along the $x$ axis.

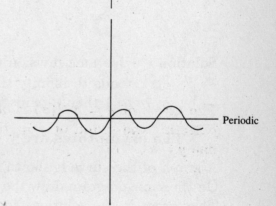

## 8.2.1 Examples

(1)      Using the graph of $y = \sin x$ sketch the graph of $y = 3\sin 2x - 1$, for $x$ in the range $0° \leq x \leq 360°$.

Solution    The graph of $\sin x$ is the dotted line of fig 8.3. Enlarge it by 3 in the $y$ direction, contract it by 2 in the $x$ direction and shift it down by 1. The result is the filled in line of fig 8.3.

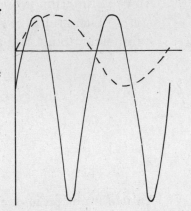

(2)      Let a function be defined by $y = \dfrac{x^2 - 2x}{x - 1}$. Find the equations of its asymptotes. Draw the graph. Solve the equation

$$x^2 - 2x = x - 1.$$

Solution    Use long-division to rewrite $y$ as $x - 1 - \dfrac{1}{x - 1}$. As $x$ tends to infinity then $y$ tends to $x - 1$, and as $x$ tends to 1 then $y$ tends to infinity.

**The asymptotes are y = x − 1 and  x = 1**

A graph of the curve is shown in fig 8.4.
On the same diagram draw the line $y = 1$.
They cross at the solutions to $x^2 - 2x = x - 1$.

**The solutions are x = 2.6 and  x = 0.4**

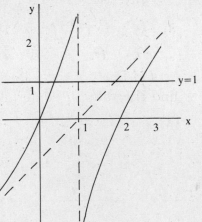

### 8.2.2 Exercises

(1) Sketch the graphs of the following functions, for $x$ in the range $0° \leq x \leq 360°$ :

(a) $\cos 2x$      (b) $2 \sin x$

(c) $\cos x + 2$      (d) $3 \sin x - 1$

(e) $\sin(x - 180°)$    (f) $2 \cos(x + 45°)$

(g) $\tan(x + 90°)$    (h) $3 \sin 2x - 1$

(2) Sketch the graphs of the following:

(a) $\frac{2}{x}$      (b) $\frac{3}{x-1}$

(c) $\frac{1}{1-x}$      (d) $3 + \frac{1}{x}$

(e) $2 + \frac{1}{x+3}$    (f) $1 - \frac{3}{x+2}$

(3) Find, where relevant, the equations of the asymptotes of the graphs in Question 2.

(4) Sketch, on the same paper, the graphs of $e^x$ and $\ln x$. What is the relationship between the two graphs?

(5) Sketch the following graphs:

(a) $|2x|$      (b) $|x + 1|$

(c) $|2x - 1|$    (d) $|x^2 - 1|$

(e) $|\sin x|$     (f) $|x| - 1$

(g) $|x| - x$     (h) $|x + 1| - |x|$

(6) Sketch the following graphs, and in each case write down the equation of the line of symmetry:

(a) $x^2 + 3$      (b) $2x^2 + 4$

(c) $(x - 2)^2 - 5$    (d) $x^2 + 4x - 3$

(e) $x^2 - 3x - 1$    (f) $3x^2 + x - 4$

(7) Each of the following graphs is of the form $(x + b)^2 + c$. In each case find the values of $b$ and $c$.

(a) 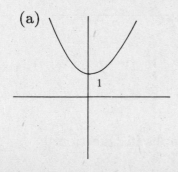    (b) 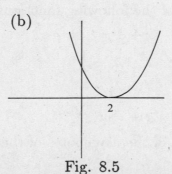    (c)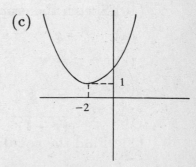

Fig. 8.5

(8) Each of the following graphs is of the form $x^2 + bx + c$. In each case find the values of $b$ and $c$.

(a)                          (b)                         (c)

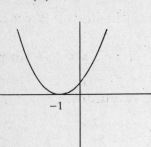
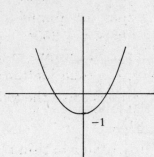
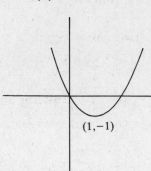

(9) Each of the following graphs is of the form $a + \dfrac{1}{x + b}$. In each case find the values of $a$ and $b$.

(a)                          (b)                         (c)

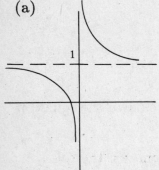
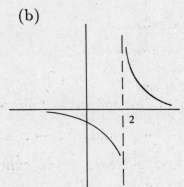
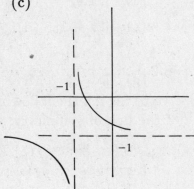

(10) Sketch the graphs of the following functions:

(a)  $x^3 - x$           (b)  $x + \dfrac{1}{x}$

(c)  $x - \dfrac{2}{x}$         (d)  $x^2 + x - \dfrac{1}{x}$

(e)  $x + \dfrac{3}{x + 3}$     (f)  $1 - \dfrac{1}{x^2}$

(g)  $1 + \dfrac{2}{(x + 1)^2}$    (h)  $x - \dfrac{1}{x^2}$

(11) Find the equations of the asympotes of the graphs in Question 9.

(12) Draw the graph of $y = x^3 + 2x^2 - 1$. By drawing a suitable line solve the equation $x^3 + 2x^2 + x - 1 = 0$.

(13) Draw the graph of $y = x^2 + 1/x$. By drawing a suitable line solve the equation $x^3 - x^2 + 2x + 1 = 0$.

(14) Draw on the same paper the graphs of $y = \sin 2x$ and $y = \cos x$. Hence solve $\sin 2x = \cos x$, for $0° \leq x \leq 360°$.

(15) Draw on the same paper the graphs of $y = \tan x$ and $y = 2 - \sin x$, for $0° \leq x \leq 180°$. Hence solve the equation $\tan x + \sin x = 2$.

(16) By drawing suitable graphs solve the following equations:

(a) $\cos x = 2 \sin x$ (b) $e^x = 2 - x$

(c) $\sin x = \frac{1}{2} + \cos x$ (d) $\tan x = 2 \sin x$

(17) For each of the following functions, state whether they are odd, even or periodic. If they are periodic give the period.

(a) $x^2$ (b) $1/x$

(c) $\sin x$ (d) $\cos x$

(e) $x + \sin x$ (f) $\cos^2 x$

(g) $x + 1$ (h) $\tan x$

(i) $e^x$ (j) $\tan 3x$

(k) $\sin \frac{1}{2}x$ (l) $\cos(2x - 45°)$

## 8.3 Examination Questions

(1) The functions $f$ and $g$ are defined as follows:

$$f : x \to x^2 \text{ and } g : x \to x + 3$$

i. Show that $gf(5) = 28$, and write down expressions for the following: (a) $gf(x)$; (b) $fg(x)$.
ii. If the domain is the set of real numbers, state the range of $gf$.
iii. Say whether the inverse of $gf$ is a function, and justify your answer.

[SMP add]

(2)

a. A function is defined by $f : x \to \dfrac{2x - 3}{x + 1}$ for all real values of $x$ except $x = -1$.

i. Express $f^{-1}$ and $ff$ in similar form and state the values of $x$ for which these functions are not defined.

ii. Express the equation $f(x) = x$ in the form $ax^2 + bx + c = 0$ and hence show that there are no values of $x$ which map on to themselves under the function $f$.

b. The function $g$ is defined by $g :\to \dfrac{ax - 4}{x + 1}$ for all real values of $x$ except $x = -1$. Find the positive value of $a$ for which there is only one value of $x$ satisfying $g(x) = x$.

[C add]

(3) Using the same scales and axes draw the graphs of $y = 2\sin x$ and $y = \cos(x - 60°)$ between the values $x = 0°$ and $x = 360°$. Take a scale of 2 cm for 30° on the $x$-axis and 4 cm for 1 unit on the $y$-axis and plot points corresponding to 30° intervals on the $x$-axis.

Use your graph to

a. solve the equation $2\sin x = \cos(x - 60°)$, for $0° < x < 360°$,

b. estimate the range of values of $x$, between $x = 0°$ and $x = 360°$, for which $2\sin x < \cos(x - 60°)$.

[AEB add 1987]

(4) Draw separate sketches of the curves

(a) $y = x^2 + 1$, (b) $y = (x + 1)^2$, (c) $y^2 = x + 1$.

[AEB add 1987]

(5) Sketch the graph of $y = |2x - 1|$

Determine the set of values of $x$ for which $|2x - 1| > 1/x$.

[C]

(6) Express $2x^2 - 12x + 9$ in the form $a[(x - r)^2 + s]$, where $a$, $r$ and $s$ are constants.

The graph of $y = 2x^2 - 12x + 9$ may be obtained from the graph of $y = x^2$ by means of appropriate translations and scalings (stretches). Describe suitable transformations in detail and in the order in which they are to be used.

The function is defined for the domain $x \geq 3$ by $f(x) = 2x^2 - 12x + 9$. Sketch the graph of $y = f(x)$.

State the domain and range of $f^{-1}$ and determine $f^{-1}$.

[JMB]

(7)

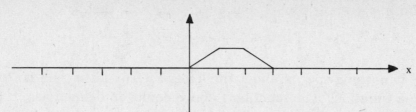

The diagram shows the graph of a function $x \to f(x)$ over the interval $0 \le x \le 3$. You are given that f is an odd, periodic function with period 6. Draw the graph of $f$ over the interval $-6 \le x \le 6$.

What is the smallest positive value of $a$ for which the function defined by $x \to f(x-a)$ is an even function?

[SMP]

(8) The figure shows a sketch of the part of the graph of $y = f(x)$ for $0 \le x \le 2a$.

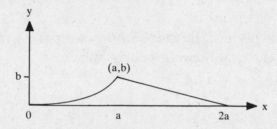

The line $x = 2a$ is a line of symmetry of the graph.

Sketch on separate axes the graphs of

(a)  $y = f(x)$ for $0 \le x \le 4a$,    (b)  $y = -f(2x)$ for $0 \le x \le a$,

(c)  $y = 3f(\frac{1}{2}x)$ for $0 \le x \le 2a$   (d)  $y = f(x-a)$ for $2a \le x \le 4a$.

[AEB 1987]

## COMMON ERRORS

### (1) Composition and Inverses

a.  Do not confuse composition with multiplication, or inverses with dividing.

$$f \circ g(x) \ne f(x) \times g(x), \text{ and } f^{-1}(x) \ne 1/f(x).$$

b. When finding $f°g(x)$, $f$ must be applied to the *whole* of $g(x)$. If for example $f : x \to 3x + 1$ and $g : x \to 2x - 3$, then:

$$f°g : x \to 3(2x - 3) + 1 = 6x - 8.$$

c. There is nothing special about the letter $x$. Any letter will do to define a function. The function f above could be defined as:

$$f : y \to 3y + 1, \text{ or as } f : Z \to 3Z + 1$$

d. $f°g$ means: do $g$ first and then $f$. Do not get this the wrong way round.

## (2) Graphs

a. When plotting a curve do not join up the points with straight line segments. Make as smooth a curve as you can between them.

b. Changing $y = f(x)$ to $y = f(x + a)$ moves the graph $a$ units to the *left*, not to the right.

c. Changing $y = f(x)$ to $y = f(ax)$ *shrinks* the graph by a factor of $a$. It does not expand it.

d. An asymptote divides the graph into two separate pieces. Do not try to make the graph cross the asymptote.

# 9 The Sine and Cosine Rules

## 9.1 The Sine and Cosine Rules

The *sine rule* and the *cosine rule* extend trigonometry to triangles which are not necessarily right-angled.

When labelling the sides and angles of the triangle ABC, the convention is that each side is labelled with the same letter as the opposite angle. So side $c$ is opposite $\hat{C}$ etc.

**The sine rule is:**

$$\frac{\sin \hat{A}}{a} = \frac{\sin \hat{B}}{b} = \frac{\sin \hat{C}}{c}$$

The rule can be written the other way up:

$$\frac{a}{\sin \hat{A}} = \frac{b}{\sin \hat{B}} = \frac{c}{\sin \hat{C}}$$

**The cosine rule is:**

$$c^2 = a^2 + b^2 - 2ab \cos \hat{C}$$

73

In this form it gives a side in terms of the other sides and the opposite angle. To find an angle in terms of the sides it can be re-written in the form:

$$\cos \hat{C} = \frac{a^2 + b^2 - c^2}{2ab}$$

A useful formula for the area $\Delta$ of a triangle is:

$$\Delta = \frac{1}{2}bc \sin \hat{A}$$

### 9.1.1 Examples

(1)   From the point $A$, a church spire is on a bearing of 020°. I walk 200 m due North to $B$, and the spire is now on a bearing of 098° . How far is $B$ from the church?

Solution   Fig 9.2 is a diagram of the situation.
$c = 200$, $\hat{A} = 20°$, $\hat{B} = 82°$. Use of the sine rule gives:

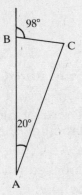

$$BC/\sin 20° = 200/\sin 78°.$$

$$BC = 69.9m.$$

(2)   In the triangle $ABC$, $c = 3, a = 4$ and $\hat{C} = 43°$. Find the possible values of $\hat{B}$.

Solution   Use of the sine rule gives:

$$\sin \hat{A} = \sin 43° \times 4/3 = 0.909$$

$\hat{A}$ could either be acute or obtuse.

$$\hat{A} = 65.4° \text{ or } 180° - 65.4° = 114.6°$$

$$\mathbf{\hat{B} = 71.6° \text{ or } 22.4°}$$

(3)        In the triangle $ABC$, $AB = 5$, $BC = 6$, $CA = 7$. Find $\hat{A}$.

Solution    Use the second form of the cosine rule.

$$\cos \hat{A} = \frac{5^2 + 7^2 - 6^2}{2 \times 5 \times 7} = 0.543$$

$$\hat{A} = 57°$$

(4)        A tower is 2 miles away on a bearing of 345°, and a spire is 1.4 miles away on a bearing of 036°. How far is the tower from the spire?

Solution    The angle between the two directions is 51°. Use the first form of the cosine rule:

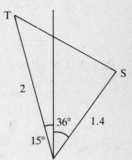

$$TS^2 = 2^2 + 1.4^2 - 2 \times 2 \times 1.4 \times \cos 51°$$

**The distance is 1.56 miles**

### 9.1.2 Exercises

(1) Find the unknown sides in the following triangles.
Fig. 9.4

(a)                                (b)

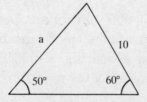
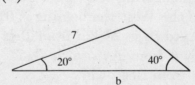

(2) Find the unknown angles in the following triangles, given that they are acute.
Fig. 9.5 (a)                            (b)

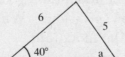

(3) Find the unknown angles in the following triangles, given that they are obtuse.

Fig. 9.6 (a)                                           (b)

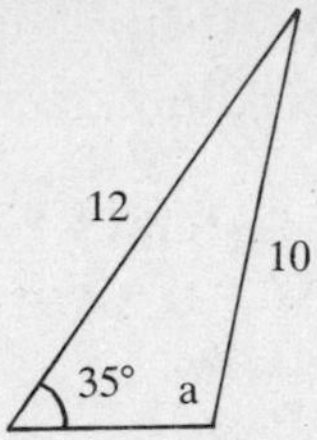

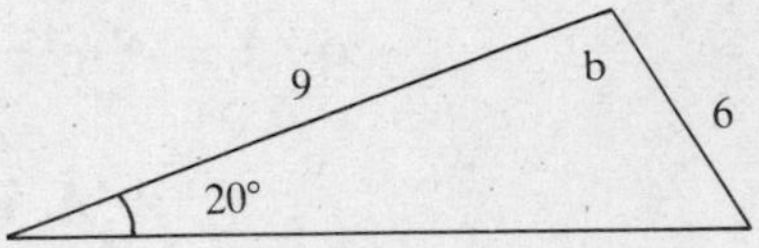

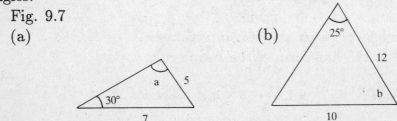

(4) Find the possible values of the unknown angles in the following triangles.

Fig. 9.7

(a)                                           (b)

(5) In the triangle $ABC$, $AB = 5$, $\hat{A} = 45°$ and $B = 56°$. Find $AC$ and $BC$.

(6) In the triangle $ABC$, $AB = 12$, $BC = 14$ and $\hat{C} = 54°$. Find the possible values of $\hat{A}$ and of $\hat{B}$.

(7) The bearing of a target from a gun is 006°. From an observation point 300 m to the West the bearing is 012°. How far is the target from the gun?

(8) Aytown is 20 km from Beetown on a bearing of 080°. The bearing of Ceetown from Aytown is 345°, and from Beetown is 027°. How far is Ceetown from Beetown?

(9) A surveyor measures the angle of elevation of a tower as 23°. He then walks 50 m towards the tower, and the elevation is now 35°. How high is the tower?

(10) A mountain is on a bearing of 035°. After walking 2 km due North, I am told that I am now 1.8 km from the mountain. What are the possible bearings of the mountain from my new position? What are the possible distances from my original position to the mountain?

(11) Find the unknown sides in the triangles below.

Fig. 9.8

(a)                                           (b)

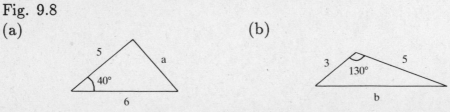

(12) Find the unknown angles in the triangles below.

Fig. 9.9

(a)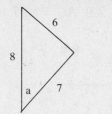

(b)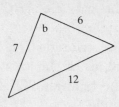

(13) In the triangle $ABC, AB = 12, BC = 14, CA = 13.7$. Find the angles of the triangle.

(14) In the triangle $DEF, DE = 23, DF = 17, \hat{D} = 76°$. Find $EF$.

(15) I drive 50 miles due North, then turn through 57° and drive a further 43 miles. How far away am I from my starting point?

(16) A ship sails 15 km on a bearing of 123°, then for 12 km on a bearing of 284°. How far is it away from its starting point?

(17) The hands of a clock are 5 cm and 8 cm long. What is the distance between the tips of the hands at 7 o'clock?

(18) The diagonals of a parallelogram are of length 12 cm and 17 cm, and the longer side is 13 cm. Find the angle between the diagonals, and the length of the shorter side.

(19) Two guns are 200 m apart, and are 1500 and 1600 m from a target. What is the difference between the bearings of the target from the guns?

(20) Find the unknown angles of the triangles below.

Fig. 9.10

(a)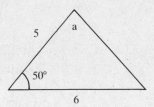

(b)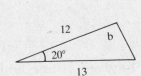

(21) Find the areas of the triangles below.

Fig. 9.11

(a)

(b)

(22) The triangle $ABC$ has $AB = 4$, $AC = 7$, $\hat{A} = 43°$. Find $\hat{C}$.

(23) The triangle $DEF$ has $DE = 8$, $DF = 7.3$, $\hat{D} = 102°$. Find $\hat{E}$.

(24) The triangle $ABC$ has $AB = 3$, $BC = 2.9$, $AC = 3.7$. Find the area of the triangle.

(25) The triangle $DEF$ has $DE = 7$, $DF = 8.4$, $\hat{F} = 47°$. Find the possible values of the area of the triangle.

(26) The triangle $XYZ$ has $XY = 12$, $\hat{X} = 57°$, $Z = 76°$. Find the area of the triangle.

(27) The triangle $ABC$ has $AB = 12.7$, $AC = 6.3$, $BC = 6.2$. Find $\hat{C}$. What has gone wrong?

(28) Two circles, of radius 12 and 17 cm, are in the same plane with their centres 25 cm apart. Find the length of the chord common to both circles.

## 9.2 Angles between Lines and Planes

Straight lines which are not parallel yet which do not meet are skew lines.

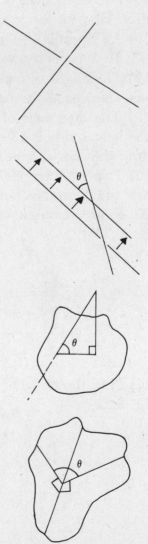

The angle between two *skew* lines is found by translating one of the lines until they do meet.

The angle between a line and a plane is the angle between the line and its perpendicular projection in the plane.

The angle between two planes is the angle between two lines in the planes perpendicular to the line of intersection of the planes.

### 9.2.1 Example

*ADCDEFGH* is a cuboid, in which *ABCD* is a rectangle vertically above *EFGH*. *AB* = 4, *AD* = 4, *AE* = 12. Find the following angles:
(a) Between *AH* and *CF*.
(b) Between *AG* and the plane *ABCD*.
(c) Between the planes *BDE* and *BDG*.

Solution    (a) Translate *CF* to *DE*. *DE* crosses *AH* at *X* say. The angle between *AH* and *CF* is *AXD*.

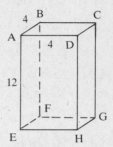

**The angle between *AH* and *CF* is**
$$2 \times \tan^{-1} \tfrac{2}{6} = 37°$$

(b) First use Pythagoras to find the length of the diagonal of ABCD.

$$AC = \sqrt{(4^2 + 4^2)} = \sqrt{32}$$

The perpendicular projection of *AG* in the plane *ABCD* is *AC*. The angle between *AG* and *ABCD* is *CÂG*.
**The angle between *AG* and *ABCD* is** $\tan^{-1} \frac{12}{\sqrt{32}} =$ **65°.**

(c) The line of intersection of *BDE* and *BDG* is *BD*. If *Y* is the midpoint of *BD*, then by symmetry *YE* and *YG* are both perpendicular to *BD*. The angle between the two planes is *EŶG*.
**The angle between *BDE* and *BDG* is** $2 \times \tan^{-1} \frac{\sqrt{8}}{12} =$ **26.5°.**

### 9.2.2 Exercises

(1) *ABCDEFGH* is a cube of side 8 units, in which the square *ABCD* is vertically above *EFGH*. Find the angles between:

(a)   *AC* and *FH*    (b)   *AD* and *BE*

(c)   *AC* and *BE*    (d)   *AG* and *BF*.

(2) In the cube of Question 1, find the angles between the following:

(a) $AH$ and $DCGH$    (b) $AC$ and $BCGF$

(c) $AG$ and $ABCD$    (d) $AG$ and $ABGH$

(3) In the cube of Question 1, find the angles between the following:

(a) $ABCD$ and $ABGH$    (b) $ABCD$ and $BDG$

(c) $BDG$ and $BDHF$    (d) $BDG$ and $CAEG$.

(4) $PQSRWXYZ$ is a cuboid, in which $PQRS$ is directly above $WXYZ$. $PQ = 6, PS = 5, PW = 7$. Find the following angles:

(a) Between $PZ$ and $RX$    (b) Between $PY$ and $RQ$

(c) Between $PY$ and $QRYX$    (d) Between $QRZW$ and $PSYX$.

(5) $VABCD$ is a pyramid, in which $ABCD$ is a square base of side 8 units. $VA = VB = VC = VD = 12$ units. Find the following angles:

(a) Between $VA$ and $VD$    (b) Between $VA$ and $BC$

(c) Between $VA$ and $ABCD$    (d) Between $VAB$ and $ABCD$.

(6) $ABCDEF$ is a wedge, in which $ABCD$ is a horizontal square base of side 10 units, and $E$ and $F$ are 4 units vertically above $C$ and $D$ respectively. Find the following angles:

(a) Between $AC$ and $FE$    (b) Between $AE$ and $CD$

(c) Between $AE$ and $ABCD$    (d) Between $ABEF$ and $ABCD$.

(7) $ABCD$ is a regular tetrahedron of side 4 units. Find the following angles:

(a) Between $AC$ and $BCD$    (b) Between $ABC$ and $ACD$.

## 9.3 Examination Questions

(1) An observer standing on a cliff 50 m high observes a ship due East at an angle of depression of 5°. Seven minutes later he observes the ship on a bearing of 040° at an angle of depression of 3°. Calculate the speed of the ship in knots and the course which it is taking. [1 nautical mile = 1.853 km.]

[O add]

(2) The triangle $ABC$ lies in a *horizontal* plane; $AB$ = 3cm, $BC$ = 8cm, $AC$ = 7cm.

(a) Prove that $A\hat{B}C$ = 60°. (b) Find, in cm$^2$, the area of $\triangle ABC$. The point $P$ is 9 cm *vertically* above $A$. Calculate, to the nearest 0.5°,

(c) the acute angle between $PB$ and the horizontal, (d) the acute angle between the plane $PBC$ and the horizontal.

[L add]

(3) Find the smallest angle and the area of a triangle whose sides are measured as 6.3 m, 7.2 m and 8.1 m.

[MEI]

(4) In the triangle $ABC$, the point $D$ is the foot of the perpendicular from $A$ to $BC$. Show that

$$AD = \frac{BC \sin \hat{B} \sin \hat{C}}{\sin \hat{A}}$$

The triangle $ABC$ lies in a horizontal plane. A vertical pole $FT$ stands with its foot $F$ on $AD$ and between $A$ and $D$. The top $T$ of the pole is at a height 3 m above the plane, and the angle of elevation of $T$ from $D$ is 65°. Given that $BC$ = 7m, angle $B$ = 62° and angle $C$ = 34°, calculate $AF$ correct to two decimal places.

Find, to the nearest degree, the angle between the planes $ATC$ and $ABC$.

[JMB]

## COMMON ERRORS

### (1) General

Make sure that you label the triangle correctly. The formulae are true only if side $a$ is opposite angle $A$ etc.

### (2) Sine Rule

When using the sine rule to find an angle, do not forget the ambiguity of the sine function. If $\sin \theta = \frac{1}{2}$, then $\theta$ could be either 30° or 150°. Questions are set deliberately to test knowledge of this point.

### (3) Cosine Rule

Arithmetic errors are very common, especially when using the cosine rule to find an angle. After working out the top line of the formula, be sure to press the = button. If you do not do so, then only the $c^2$ term will be divided by $2ab$.

Be sure that you *divide* the top line by 2 and by $a$ and by $b$. If your formula is $\cos \hat{C} = (5^2 + 6^2 - 7^2)/2 \times 5 \times 6$, then you should obtain $\cos \hat{C} = 0.2$. If instead you obtain $\cos \hat{C} = 180$, then you have multiplied by 5 and by 6.

### (4) Angles between lines and planes

Make sure you use the correct lines when finding the angle between a line $L$ and a plane $P$. The line within the plane must be the *perpendicular* projection of $L$ on $P$.

Make sure you use the correct lines when finding the angle between two planes $P$ and $Q$. The lines must be perpendicular to the line of intersection of $P$ and $Q$.

# 10 Trigonometric Equations

## 10.1 The Six Trigonometric Ratios

The right-angled triangle is labelled as shown. The six ratios between the sides are:

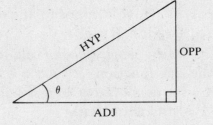

$$\sin \theta = \frac{OPP}{HYP} \quad \cos \theta = \frac{ADJ}{HYP} \quad \tan \theta = \frac{OPP}{ADJ}$$

$$\cot \theta = \frac{ADJ}{OPP} \quad \sec \theta = \frac{HYP}{ADJ} \quad \operatorname{cosec} \theta = \frac{HYP}{OPP}$$

Some relations between these functions are as follows:

$$\tan \theta \equiv \frac{\sin \theta}{\cos \theta} \quad \cot \theta \equiv \frac{\cos \theta}{\sin \theta}$$

$$\sec \theta \equiv \frac{1}{\cos \theta} \quad \operatorname{cosec} \theta \equiv \frac{1}{\sin \theta}$$

Pythagoras's Theorem gives rise to the three identities:

$$\cos^2 \theta + \sin^2 \theta \equiv 1$$

$$\sec^2 \theta \equiv 1 + \tan^2 \theta$$

$$\operatorname{cosec}^2 \theta \equiv 1 + \cot^2 \theta$$

(Here $\cos^2 \theta$ means $(\cos \theta)^2$ etc.)

## 10.1.1 Example

Prove the identity: $\tan \theta + \cot \theta \equiv \dfrac{1}{\sin \theta \cos \theta}$

Solution Write the left hand side in terms of sin and cos, and add.

$$\tan \theta + \cot \theta \equiv \frac{\sin \theta}{\cos \theta} + \frac{\cos \theta}{\sin \theta} \equiv \frac{\sin^2 \theta + \cos^2 \theta}{\sin \theta \cos \theta}$$

Use the identity: $\cos^2 \theta + \sin^2 \theta \equiv 1$

$$\tan \theta + \cot \theta \equiv \frac{1}{\sin \theta \cos \theta}$$

## 10.1.2 Exercises

(1) Prove the following identities.

(a) $\cos^2 \theta - \sin^2 \theta \equiv 2\cos^2 \theta - 1$

(b) $\cos^4 \theta - \sin^4 \theta \equiv \cos^2 \theta - \sin^2 \theta$     (c) $\sec^4 \theta - \tan^4 \theta \equiv sec^2\theta + \tan^2 \theta$

(d) $\sec^2 \theta + \operatorname{cosec}^2 \theta \equiv \sec^2 \theta \operatorname{cosec}^2 \theta$

(e) $\dfrac{\tan^2 \theta - 1}{\tan^2 \theta + 1} \equiv 2\sin^2 \theta - 1$     (f) $\dfrac{1}{1 - \sin \theta} + \dfrac{1}{1 + \sin \theta} \equiv 2\sec^2 \theta$

(g) $\dfrac{\cos \theta}{1 - \sin \theta} - \tan \theta \equiv \sec \theta$

(2) If $\sin x = \frac{3}{5}$ find, without using tables or a calculator, the values of $\operatorname{cosec} x, \cos x, \tan x$.

(3) If $\tan x = 2$ find, in square root form, the values of $\sec x$, $\cos x$, $\sin x$.

(4) If $\sin x = 2t/(1 + t^2)$ find $\cos x$ and $\tan x$ in terms of $t$.

(5) Simplify the following expressions:

(a) $1 - \cos^2 x$   (b) $2\tan^2 x + 2$

(c) $\dfrac{1 - \sin^2 x}{\cot x}$   (d) $\dfrac{\cot x}{1 + \cot^2 x}$

(6) If $x = 2\cos\theta$ and $y = 2\sin\theta$ show that $x^2 + y^2 = 4$.

(7) Find an equation involving $x$ and $y$, without $\theta$, from the following.

(a)   $x = 3\cos\theta, y = 3\sin\theta$          (b)   $x = 2\cos\theta, y = 3\sin\theta$

(c)   $x = \tan\theta, y = \sec\theta$             (d)   $x = \tfrac{1}{2}\cot\theta, y = 2\mathrm{cosec}\,\theta$

(e)   $x = 1 + \cos\theta, y = 2 + \sin\theta$     (f)   $x = 3 + 2\cos\theta, y = 2 + 3\sin\theta$

(g)   $x = \cos\theta + \sin\theta, y = \cos\theta - \sin\theta$

(h)   $x = \sec\theta + \tan\theta, y = \sec\theta - \tan\theta$.

## 10.2 Trigonometric Functions between $0°$ and $360°$

The definition of the trigonometric functions can be extended to angles other than acute angles.

### For $90° \le \theta \le 180°$

$$\sin\theta = \sin(180° - \theta), \cos\theta = -\cos(180° - \theta), \tan\theta = -\tan(180° - \theta).$$

### For $180° \le \theta \le 270°$

$$\sin\theta = -\sin(\theta - 180°), \cos\theta = -\cos(\theta - 180°), \tan\theta = \tan(\theta - 180°)$$

### For $270° \le \theta \le 360°$

$$\sin\theta = -\sin(360° - \theta), \cos\theta = \cos(360° - \theta), \tan\theta = -\tan(360° - \theta).$$

cosec , sec and cot obey the same rules as sin, cos and tan respectively.

### 10.2.1 Examples

(1)         Solve for $0° \le \theta \le 180°, \cos 2\theta = 0.25$.

Solution     Using the inv cos button, $2\theta = 76°$. By the formulae above, there is also a value in the range $270°$ to $360°$.

$$2\theta = 76° \text{ or } 360° - 76° = 284°$$

$$\theta = 38° \text{ or } 142°$$

(2)         Solve for $0° \leq \theta \leq 360°, 2\cos^2\theta + \sin\theta - 1 = 0$.

Solution     Write $\cos^2\theta$ as $1 - \sin^2\theta$ and rearrange.

$$1 + \sin\theta - 2\sin^2\theta = 0.$$

This factorizes, giving:

$$(1 - \sin\theta)(2\sin\theta + 1) = 0$$

The first bracket gives $\sin\theta = 1$, so $\theta = 90°$. The second bracket gives $\sin\theta = -\frac{1}{2}$, which has solutions in the ranges $180°$ to $270°$ and $270°$ to $360°$.

$$\theta = 90° \text{ or } 210° \text{ or } 330°$$

## 10.2.2 Exercises

(1) Express the following in terms of ratios of acute angles.

(a)   $\sin 156°$    (b)   $\cos 220°$

(c)   $\tan 325°$    (d)   $\cot 130°$

(2) Solve the following equations, giving all the solutions in the range $0°$ to $360°$.

(a)   $\sin\frac{1}{2}x = 0.3$            (b)   $\tan 2x = 3$

(c)   $\sin(x + 60°) = 0.3$        (d)   $\cos(x - 20°) = 0.4$

(e)   $\sec x = 4$                  (f)   $\operatorname{cosec}(x - 50°) = 1.5$

(g)   $\cot\frac{1}{2}x = 2.5$           (h)   $\cos\frac{1}{2}x = -0.3$

(i)   $\sin(x - 30°) = -0.1$    (j)   $\tan(50° - x) = 1.9$

(3) Find $x$ in the range $0° \leq x \leq 360°$, if $\sin x = \frac{3}{5}$ and $\cos x = -\frac{4}{5}$.

(4) Find $x$ in the range $0° \leq x \leq 360°$, if $\cos x = -\frac{5}{13}$ and $\sin x = -\frac{12}{13}$.

(5) If $\sin x = \frac{8}{17}$ find $\cos x$, given that $x$ is between $90°$ and $180°$.

(6) If $\tan x = -\frac{7}{24}$ find $\operatorname{cosec} x$, given that $x$ is between $90°$ and $180°$.

(7) Solve the following equations, giving all the solutions in the range $0°$ to $180°$.

(a)   $\sin^2 x = 0.5$              (b)   $\tan^2 x = 3$

(c)   $3\cos x = \sec x$          (d)   $\tan x = 2\cot x$

(e)   $5\cos x = \sin x$          (f)   $\sin x = \tan x$

(g)   $\tan^2 x - 5\sec x + 7 = 0$   (h)   $4\cos x + \sec x = 4$

(i)   $\tan x + \cot x = 2$

## 10.3 General Solutions of Trigonometric Equations

The trigonometric functions can be defined for angles bigger than 360° or smaller than 0°. The functions repeat themselves after adding or subtracting 360°. For example:

$$\sin (x \pm 360°) = \sin x$$

So if $x = \alpha$ is a solution of $\sin x = k$, then $\alpha + 360°$ is also a solution. In fact, for any integer $n$, $\alpha + n360°$ is also a solution.

### 10.3.1 Examples

(1) Express sec 730° in terms of the sec of an acute angle.

Solution    Subtract 360° twice, to obtain 10°.
$$\sec 730° = \sec 10°$$

(2) Find the general solution of $\sin 2x = 0.5$.

Solution    Between 0° and 360°, both 30° and 150° have a sine of 0.5. But we can add or subtract 360° as many times as we like.
$$2x = 30° + n360° \text{ or } 2x = 150° + n360°.$$
$$x = 15° + n180° \text{ or } 75° + n180°.$$

### 10.3.2 Exercises

(1) Express in terms of functions of acute angles:
  (a) sin 380°          (b) cos 1100°         (c) cot 500°
  (d) sec 470°          (e) tan 2000°         (f) cosec −100°

(2) Find the general solutions of the following:
  (a) $\cos x = 0.5$        (b) $\tan x = 1$          (c) $\sin x = 1$

(3) Find the general solutions of the following. In (d), (e) and (f) $k$ denotes a constant angle.
  (a) $\cos 2x = 0.4$       (b) $\operatorname{cosec} 3x = 2$       (c) $\tan (2x + 35°) = 1$
  (d) $\sin x = \sin k$       (e) $\cos 2x = \cos k$       (f) $\tan (2x - 30°) = \tan k$

## 10.4 Compound Angles

Trigonometric functions of sums and differences of angles can be found by the following formulae.

$$\sin(A + B) = \sin A \cos B + \cos A \sin B$$

$$\sin(A - B) = \sin A \cos B - \cos A \sin B$$

$$\cos(A + B) = \cos A \cos B - \sin A \sin B$$

$$\cos(A - B) = \cos A \cos B + \sin A \sin B$$

$$\tan(A + B) = \frac{\tan A + \tan B}{1 - \tan A \tan B}$$

$$\tan(A - B) = \frac{\tan A - \tan B}{1 + \tan A \tan B}$$

Two important cases occur when $A = B$.

$$\sin 2A = 2 \sin A \cos A$$

$$\cos 2A = \cos^2 A - \sin^2 A = 2 \cos^2 A - 1 = 1 - 2 \sin^2 A$$

The following are known as *factor formulae*:

$$\sin C + \sin D = 2 \sin \frac{1}{2}(C + D) \cos \frac{1}{2}(C - D)$$

$$\sin C - \sin D = 2 \sin \frac{1}{2}(C - D) \cos \frac{1}{2}(C + D)$$

$$\cos C + \cos D = 2 \cos \frac{1}{2}(C + D) \cos \frac{1}{2}(C - D)$$

$$\cos C - \cos D = 2 \sin \frac{1}{2}(C + D) \sin \frac{1}{2}(D - C)$$

### 10.4.1 Examples

(1) If $\theta$ and $\varphi$ are acute angles, for which $\sin \theta = \frac{3}{5}$ and $\sin \varphi = \frac{5}{13}$, find $\sin(\theta + \varphi)$ without using tables or a calculator.

Solution Using the identity $\cos^2 A + \sin^2 A \equiv 1, \cos \theta = \frac{4}{5}$ and $\cos \varphi = \frac{12}{13}$. Apply the formula above:

$$\sin(\theta + \varphi) = \sin \theta \cos \varphi + \cos \theta \sin \varphi = \frac{3}{5} \times \frac{12}{13} + \frac{4}{5} \times \frac{5}{13}$$

$$\sin(\theta + \varphi) = \frac{56}{65}$$

(2)      Use the fact that $\cos 30° = \frac{1}{2}\sqrt{3}$ to find an expression for $\cos 15°$, without using tables or a calculator.

Solution    Let $A = 15°$ in the formula for $\cos 2A$ above.

$$\cos 30° = 2\cos^2 15° - 1.$$

Make $\cos 15°$ the subject of this formula.

$$\cos 15° = \sqrt{\left(\frac{1}{2} + \frac{1}{4}\sqrt{3}\right)}$$

(3)      Prove the identity:

$$\frac{\sin 2x + \sin 2y}{\sin 2x - \sin 2y} \equiv \frac{\tan(x+y)}{\tan(x-y)}$$

Solution    Factorize both top and bottom of the left hand side:

$$\frac{\sin 2x + \sin 2y}{\sin 2x - \sin 2y} \equiv \frac{2\sin\frac{1}{2}(2x+2y)\cos\frac{1}{2}(2x-2y)}{2\cos\frac{1}{2}(2x+2y)\sin\frac{1}{2}(2x-2y)} \equiv \frac{\sin(x+y)\cos(x-y)}{\cos(x+y)\sin(x-y)}$$

Use the fact that $\tan\theta \equiv (\sin\theta)/(\cos\theta)$.

$$\frac{\sin 2x + \sin 2y}{\sin 2x - \sin 2y} \equiv \frac{\tan(x+y)}{\tan(x-y)}$$

## 10.4.2 Exercises

(1) Simplify the following expressions, without using tables or a calculator.

(a)   $\sin 10° \cos 30° + \cos 10° \sin 30°$    (b)   $\cos 30° \cos 50° + \sin 30° \sin 50°$

(c)   $\sin A \cos 2A - \cos A \sin 2A$    (d)   $\cos^2 2A - \sin^2 2A$

(2) Simplify (a) $\sin 40° \cos 40°$ (b) $(2\tan 20°)/(1 - \tan^2 20°)$

(3) Letting $\alpha$ be the angle such that $\sin\alpha = \frac{3}{5}$, $\cos\alpha = \frac{4}{5}$, express in terms of $\alpha$ and $\theta$:

(a)   $\frac{4}{5}\sin\theta + \frac{3}{5}\cos\theta$   (b)   $\frac{4}{5}\cos\theta + \frac{3}{5}\sin\theta$

(4) $\cos 45° = \sin 45° = 1/\sqrt{2}$, $\sin 30° = \cos 60° = \frac{1}{2}$, $\sin 60° = \cos 30° = \frac{1}{2}\sqrt{3}$. Use these values to obtain surd expressions for the following. Do not use tables or a calculator.

(a)   $\sin 75°$    (b)   $\sin 15°$

(c)   $\cos 75°$    (d)   $\tan 15°$

(e)   $\cos 22\frac{1}{2}°$   (f)   $\tan 22\frac{1}{2}°$

(5) Without using tables or a calculator find the value of $\tan x$, given that $\tan(45° + x) = 3$

(6) If $\alpha$ and $\beta$ are acute angles so that $\sin \alpha = \frac{3}{5}$ and $\sin \beta = \frac{5}{13}$, find the values of the following.

    (a)   $\sin(\alpha + \beta)$   (b)   $\sin(\alpha - \beta)$

    (c)   $\cos(\alpha - \beta)$   (d)   $\tan(\alpha + \beta)$

(7) Solve the following equations, for values of $\theta$ between $0°$ and $180°$.

    (a)   $\sin 2\theta = 1.7 \sin \theta$           (b)   $\cos 2\theta + \cos \theta = 1$

    (c)   $\sin(\theta + 30°) = \cos(\theta - 60°)$   (d)   $4 \sin(45° - \theta) = \cos(\theta + 45°)$

    (e)   $\tan 2\theta = 3 \tan \theta$           (f)   $\tan(\theta + 45°) = 3 \tan \theta$

(8) Prove the following identities.

(a) $\sin(A + B) + \sin(A - B) \equiv 2 \sin A \cos B$

(b) $\cos(A + B) + \cos(A - B) \equiv 2 \cos A \cos B$

(9) Use the factor formulae to prove the following identities:

    (a)  $\dfrac{\cos A - \cos B}{\sin A + \sin B} \equiv \tan \frac{1}{2}(B - A)$         (b)  $\dfrac{\sin X + \sin Y}{\cos X + \cos Y} \equiv \tan \frac{1}{2}(X + Y)$

    (c)  $\sin x + \sin(x + 120°) + \sin(x + 240°) \equiv 0$.

(10) Use the factor formulae to solve the following equations, for $0° \leq x \leq 180°$:

    (a)   $\sin x + \sin(x - 60°) = 1$         (b)   $\cos x + \cos 3x = 0$

    (c)   $\sin 5x + \sin x = \cos 2x$         (d)   $\cos(x + 10°) + \cos(x - 10°) = \frac{1}{2}$

    (e)   $\sin(x + 30°) \sin(x - 30°) = \frac{1}{2}$   (f)   $\cos x + \cos 3x = \sin x + \sin 3x$

(11) Writing $3A = 2A + A$, find an expression for $\cos 3A$ in terms of $\cos A$ only.

(12) Find an expression for $\sin 3A$ in terms of $\sin A$ only.

## 10.5 The form $\mathbf{a} \sin \theta + \mathbf{b} \cos \theta$

$a \sin \theta + b \cos \theta \equiv \sqrt{(a^2 + b^2)} \sin(\theta + \alpha)$, where $\tan \alpha = b/a$.

$a \sin \theta + b \cos \theta \equiv \sqrt{(a^2 + b^2)} \cos(\theta - \beta)$, where $\tan \beta = a/b$.

## 10.5.1 Examples

(1)         Find the range of the function $y = 8 \sin x + 15 \cos x$.

Solution     Use the formula above.

$$y = \sqrt{(8^2 + 15^2)} \sin(x + \alpha) = 17 \sin(x + \alpha)$$

Whatever the value of $\alpha$, $\sin(x + \alpha)$ lies between $-1$ and $1$.

$$-17 \leq y \leq 17$$

(2)     Solve the equation

$3 \sin x + 4 \cos x = 1$, for $0° \leq x \leq 360°$.

Solution     Use the formula above to rewrite the equation.

$$5 \sin(x + \alpha) = 1, \text{ where } \alpha = \tan^{-1} \frac{4}{3} = 53.1°.$$

$$x + \alpha = \sin^{-1} \frac{1}{5} = 11.5° \text{ or } 168.5° \text{ or } 371.5°.$$

When $\alpha$ is subtracted the first value becomes out of range.

$$\mathbf{x = 115° \text{ or } 318°}$$

## 10.5.2 Exercises

(1) Write the following in the form $r \sin(x + \alpha)$, stating the values of $r$ and $\alpha$.

(a)   $3 \sin x + 4 \cos x$     (b)   $4 \sin x - 5 \cos x$

(c)   $6 \cos x - 3 \sin x$     (d)   $\sin x - \cos x$

(e)   $\frac{1}{2} \sin x + \frac{1}{4} \cos x$     (f)   $1\frac{1}{2} \sin x - \frac{1}{8} \cos x$

(2) Find the greatest value of each of the functions in Question 1, and the value of $x$ which gives the maximum.

(3) Write down the range of values of the functions in Question 1.

(4) Solve the following equations, for values of $x$ between $-180°$ and $180°$.

(a)   $2 \sin x + 3 \cos x = 1$     (b)   $4 \sin x - 5 \cos x = 3$

(c)   $7 \sin x + 8 \cos x = 9$     (d)   $12 \sin x - 11 \cos x = 13$

(5) Write $y = 3 \sin x + 4 \cos x$ in the form $r \sin(x + \alpha)$. Show that $y$ can also be written as $s \cos(x - \beta)$, giving the values of $s$ and $\beta$. Solve the equation $y = 2.5$ in the range $-180° \leq x \leq 180°$, using both forms of $y$. Check that your answers are the same.

## 10.6 Examination Questions

(1) Prove the identity:

$$\frac{1 + \sin x}{\cos x} + \frac{\cos x}{1 + \sin x} \equiv 2 \sec x$$

[C add]

(2) Solve the equations below, giving all the answers in the range $0° \leq x \leq 360°$:

   (i)    $\cos 2x = 0.35$,                   (ii)   $\tan x - 4 \cot x = 3$

   (iii)   $8 \sin^2 x - 8 \sin x + 3 \cos^2 x = 0$

[O&C add]

(3)

  i.  On the same diagram, sketch the graphs of $y = 3 \cos x$ and $y = 2 \sin 2x$ in the interval $0° \leq x \leq 360°$.

  ii.  By using the formula for $\sin 2x$, solve by calculation the equation $2 \sin 2x = 3 \cos x$ in the same interval.

  iii.  Solve the inequality $2 \sin 2x \geq 3 \cos x$ in this interval.

[SMP add]

(4)

  i.  *Without the use of tables or a calculator,* find the values of

    (a)   $\sin 40° \cos 10° - \cos 40° \sin 10°$

    (b)   $\frac{1}{\sqrt{2}} \cos 15° - \frac{1}{\sqrt{2}} \sin 15°$        (c) $\frac{1 - \tan 15°}{1 + \tan 15°}$

  ii.  Find, to one decimal place, the elements of the set $\{x : 0 \leq x \leq 360°\}$ which satisfy the equation

$$2 \sin x° = \cos(x° - 60°)$$

[L add]

(5) Show that $\tan A + \tan B = \dfrac{\sin(A + B)}{\cos A \cos B}$ and use it to find all the angles in the range $0 \leq x \leq 180°$ which satisfy the equation $\tan x + \tan 3x = \tan 4x$.

[O]

(6) Determine all of the angles between $0°$ and $180°$ which satisfy the equation

$$\cos 5\theta + \cos 3\theta = \sin 3\theta + \sin \theta$$

[NI]

(7) Express $3 \cos x + 4 \sin x$ in the form $R \cos(x - \alpha)$, where $R$ is positive and $\alpha$ lies between $0°$ and $90°$.

What are the maximum and minimum values of $3\cos x + 4\sin x$, and for what values of $x$ in the range $0°$ to $360°$ do they occur?

Draw the graph of $y = 3\cos x + 4\sin x$ for values of $x$, at intervals of $30°$, in the range $0°$ to $360°$, taking 1 cm to represent $30°$ on the $x$ axis and 1 cm to represent 1 unit on the $y$ axis.

Using your graph, and giving solutions in the range $0°$ to $360°$:

i. solve the equation $6\cos x + 8\sin x = 7$;

ii. solve the inequality $6\cos x + 8\sin x < 7$.

[SUJB]

## COMMON ERRORS

### (1) Identities

Do not confuse identities and equations. An identity is true for all values of $x$. An equation is only true for some values, and we find these values when we solve the equation.

When proving an identity, do not assume the answer, i.e. do not start with the expression you are asked to show true. Start with one side, and show that it can be reduced to the other side.

### (2) Solving Equations

When you are solving an equation in the range $0°$ to $360°$, you must give all the solutions. The trig functions take each value twice in that range.

When solving say $\sin 2x = 0.5$ in the range $0°$ to $360°$, you must consider the values of $\sin^{-1} 0.5$ up to $720°$. When you divide $2x$ by 2 the value will be less than $360°$.

When solving an equation of the form $\sin(x + \alpha) = 0.5$ in the range $0°$ to $360°$, you may have to consider values of $\sin^{-1} 0.5$ greater than $360°$, for when $\alpha$ is subtracted the result may be within the correct range.

When you solve a quadratic in $\cos x$, you might get the answer $\cos x = 2$ or $\frac{1}{2}$. Only the $\frac{1}{2}$ value is relevant here - do not worry about the impossible value of 2.

### (3) Compound Angles

These formulas must be used when finding sin or cos of compound angles. Be aware of the following:

$$\sin(A + B) \neq \sin A + \sin B$$

# 11 Radians

## 11.1 Radians

Often angles are measured in terms of *radians* rather than degrees. If a sector of a circle with radius $r$ subtends an arc of length $\alpha$, then the angle of the sector measured in radians is $\alpha/r$.

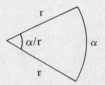

There are $2\pi$ radians in a circle. A right angle is $\frac{1}{2}\pi$ radians.

To convert degrees to radians, multiply by $\pi/180$.

To convert radians to degrees, multiply by $180/\pi$.

Suppose a circle has radius $r$. Then a sector which subtends $\theta$ radians has area $\frac{1}{2}r^2\theta$.

The length of an arc which subtends $\theta$ radians at the centre of a circle radius $r$ is $r\theta$.

*Angular velocity* is measured in radians per second.

## 11.1.1 Examples

(1)     Solve the equation $\tan x = 3$, giving all the solutions in the range 0 to $2\pi$.

Solution    If you have a scientific calculator, then it will work directly in radians.

If your calculator works only in degrees, then multiply $\tan^{-1} 3$ by $\pi/180$. In both cases the answer is $\tan^{-1} 3 = 1.25$.

There is another solution between $\pi$ and $3\pi/2$.

$$x = 1.25 \text{ or } \pi + 1.25 = 4.39$$

(2)     A circle with radius 10 cm is cut by a chord which subtends 0.8 radians at the centre. Find the area of the smaller segment.

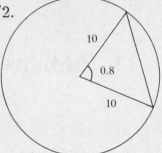

Solution    The area of the sector is $\frac{1}{2} \times 10^2 \times 0.8$. The area of the triangle is $\frac{1}{2} \times 10^2 \times \sin 0.8$. The area of the segment is the difference between these.

$$\textbf{Area } = \frac{1}{2} \times 10^2 (0.8 - \sin 0.8) = 4.13 \text{cm}^2$$

## 11.1.2 Exercises

(1) Convert the following to radians, leaving your answers in terms of $\pi$.

(a)   180°   (b)   60°   (c)   240°   (d)   30°   (e)   10°

(2) Convert the following to degrees.

(a)   $\frac{1}{3}\pi$   (b)   1.3   (c)   3.7   (d)   $4\pi$   (e)   $\frac{1}{4}\pi$

(3) A wheel is spinning at 50 revolutions per minute. What is its angular speed?

(4) Convert an angular speed of 20 radians per second to revolutions per minute.

(5) What are the angular speeds of the minute and hour hands of a clock?

(6) A wheel of radius 2 m rolls along the floor at an angular speed of 35. What is the speed of the centre of the wheel in m/sec?

(7) The wheel of a cycle is of radius 45 cm. What is the angular speed of the wheel when the cycle is moving at 4 m/sec?

(8) What is the angular speed of (a) the earth about its axis (b) the earth about the sun?

(9) A sector of a circle radius 5 cm has angle 0.4. Find the arc length of the sector and the area of the sector.

(10) An arc of length 3 cm lies on a circle of radius 15 cm. What angle does the arc subtend at the centre?

(11) An arc of length 5 cm subtends an angle of 1.1. What is the radius of the circle?

(12) A chord subtends 1.05 at the centre of a circle radius 12 cm. Find the areas of the minor and major segments.

(13) Two circles, each of radius 10 cm, have their centres 15 cm apart. Find the area which is common to both the circles.

(14) A circle of radius $r$ has a sector of which the arc length is $a$. Find the area of the sector in terms of $r$ and $a$.

(15) Solve the following equations, giving the solutions in the range 0 to $2\pi$.

(a) $\sin x = 0.2$              (b) $\cos x = -0.4$

(c) $\tan x = 2$                 (d) $\cot x = -\frac{1}{2}$

(e) $\sec^2 x + \tan x = 1$      (f) $\operatorname{cosec} x = 2\frac{1}{2}\sin x$

(g) $\sin(\frac{1}{3}\pi + x) = 0.1$      (h) $\tan(\frac{1}{2}\pi - x) = 1.8$

(i) $6\sin^2 x - 5\sin x - 1 = 0$

## 11.2 Small Angles

If $\theta$ is a small angle measured in radians, then the following approximations hold.

$$\sin\theta \simeq \theta, \quad \tan\theta \simeq \theta, \quad \cos\theta \simeq 1 - \frac{1}{2}\theta^2$$

### 11.2.1 Example

Find an approximation for $\dfrac{\theta\sin\theta}{1-\cos\theta}$, valid when $\theta$ is small.

Solution Rewrite the function using the approximations above.

$$\frac{\theta\sin\theta}{1-\cos\theta} \simeq \frac{\theta\times\theta}{1-(1-\frac{1}{2}\theta^2)} = \frac{\theta^2}{\frac{1}{2}\theta^2}$$

$$\frac{\theta\sin\theta}{1-\cos\theta} \simeq 2$$

### 11.2.2 Exercises

(1) Find approximations for the following, valid when $\theta$ is small.

(a) $\dfrac{\sin\theta}{\tan\theta}$          (b) $\dfrac{\sin 2\theta}{\theta}$

(c) $\dfrac{1-\cos\theta}{\theta^2}$      (d) $\dfrac{\sec\theta - 1}{\theta^2}$

(e) $\dfrac{\sin\theta\tan 2\theta}{1-\cos 3\theta}$    (f) $\tan(\frac{1}{4}\pi + \theta)$

(g) $\cot(\frac{1}{4}\pi - 2\theta)$

95

(2) Find an expression for $(\tan(\frac{1}{4}\pi+\theta)-\tan\frac{1}{4}\pi)/\theta$, valid when $\theta$ is small.

(3) Use the values $\sin\pi/6 = \frac{1}{2}, \cos\pi/6 = \frac{1}{2}\sqrt{3}$ to find an approximation for $\sin(\pi/6 + \theta)$.

(4) Find an approximation for $(\cos(\frac{1}{3}\pi + \theta) - \cos\frac{1}{3}\pi)/\theta$.

(5) Show that $\sin 1° \simeq \pi/180$. Find a similar approximation for $\cos 2°$.

## 11.3 Examination Questions

(1) The diagram shows two arcs, $AB$ and $CD$, of concentric circles, centre $O$. The radii $OA$ and $OC$ are 11 cm and 14 cm respectively, and $A\hat{O}B = \theta$ radians. Express in terms of $\theta$ the area of

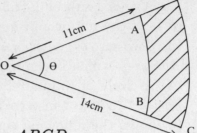

  (i)   sector $AOB$   (ii)   the shaded region $ABCD$.

Given that the area of the shaded region ABCD is $30\,\mathrm{cm}^2$, calculate

  (iii)   the value of $\theta$,   (iv)   the perimeter of the shaded region ABCD.

[C add]

(2) After $t$ seconds the extension of a piston is given by $x = \sin 3t$ and of its crankshaft by $x = \sin^2 t$.

  a.   Sketch these two curves on the same axes for $0 \le t \le 2\pi$.

  b.   Prove that $\sin(t + 2t) = 3\sin t - 4\sin^3 t$.

  c.   Hence verify that the extension of the piston is the same as that of the crankshaft when $S(S + 1)(4S - 3) = 0$, where $S = \sin t$.

  d.   Calculate, corrected to 3 significant figures, all the times in the first five seconds when the extensions are the same.

  e.   Hence find the percentage of the time in each cycle for which the piston is more extended than the crankshaft.

[SMP add]

(3) State the exact principal values, in radians, of

  (i)   $\sin^{-1}(-1)$,   (ii)   $\cos^{-1}(\frac{1}{2})$,   (iii)   $\sin^{-1}(0.4) + \cos^{-1}(0.4)$.

[*Warning.* Because your calculator works to a finite number of figures it may not give you the *exact* values.]

[SMP]

(4)

a.  i.   Express $7\sin\theta - 24\cos\theta$ in the form $R\sin(\theta - \alpha)$, giving the values of $R$ and $\alpha$, where $0 < \alpha < \pi/2$.

ii.  What is the maximum value of $7\sin\theta - 24\cos\theta$, and for what value of $x$ between 0 and $2\pi$ does it occur?

iii.  What is the minimum value of $\dfrac{1}{7\sin\theta - 24\cos\theta + 5}$ for values of $\theta$ between $\pi/2$ and $3\pi/2$, and for what value of $\theta$ does it occur?

b.  i.   A sector of a circle, centre $O$, has radius $r$ and area $A$. If the length of the arc of the sector is $s$, prove that $A = \frac{1}{2}rs$.

ii.  In the diagram, $A$ and $B$ are points on a circle, centre O, such that the length of the arc $AB = x$. The tangent $BC$ of length $x$ is drawn and $OC$ is joined, meeting the circle at $D$. Prove that the shaded area is equal to the area of the sector $OAD$.

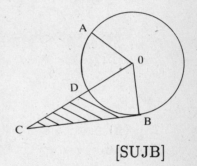

[SUJB]

(5) Use the approximations $\sin x \simeq x; \tan x \simeq x; \cos x \simeq 1 - \frac{1}{2}x^2$ to find the smallest positive root of the equation

$$\sin x + \cos x + \tan x = 1.5$$

giving your answer to 2 decimal places.

[W]

## COMMON ERRORS
### (1) Radians
When working with radians, make sure that your calculator is correctly adjusted.

If a question is about radians, then it will tell you directly, or it will ask you to give the answer in the range 0 to $2\pi$. You will get very few marks if you then give your answers in degrees.

### (2) Small Angles
The approximations for sin, cos and tan of small angles hold only when the angle is measured in radians. They do not apply if the angle is given in degrees.

# 12 Vectors

A quantity with both direction and magnitude is a *vector*. A quantity with magnitude only is a *scalar*.

A vector with magnitude 1 is a *unit* vector.

A two dimensional vector can be written as $\binom{x}{y}$ or as $(x, y)$ or as $x\mathbf{i} + y\mathbf{j}$, where $\mathbf{i}$ and $\mathbf{j}$ are unit vectors in the $x$ and $y$ directions respectively.

The *magnitude* or *modulus* of $(x, y)$ is $|(x, y)| = \surd(x^2 + y^2)$.

Three dimensional vectors can be written as $\begin{pmatrix} x \\ y \\ z \end{pmatrix}$ or as $(x, y, z)$ or as

$x\mathbf{i} + y\mathbf{j} + z\mathbf{k}$, where $\mathbf{i}, \mathbf{j}, \mathbf{k}$ are unit vectors in the $x, y, z$ directions respectively.

The magnitude of $(x, y, z)$ is $|(x, y, z)| = \surd(x^2 + y^2 + z^2)$.

## 12.1 Vector Geometry

If $A$ and $B$ are points, the vector from $A$ to $B$ is written $\underline{AB}$.

The vector from the origin to a point is the *position vector* of that point.

If the position vectors of $A$ and $B$ are $\mathbf{a}$ and $\mathbf{b}$, then $\underline{AB} = \mathbf{b} - \mathbf{a}$.

Vectors can be added by a *vector triangle* or a *vector parallelogram*.

Note that if $OABC$ is a parallelogram, with the position vectors of $A$, $B$, $C$ relative to $O$ being $\mathbf{a}, \mathbf{b}, \mathbf{c}$ respectively, then $\mathbf{b} = \mathbf{a} + \mathbf{c}$.

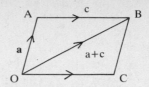

One vector is *parallel* to another if it is a scalar multiple of it. i.e.:
$\mathbf{a}$ is parallel to $\mathbf{b}$ if there is a scalar $\lambda$ so that $\mathbf{a} = \lambda\mathbf{b}$.

If $w\mathbf{a} + x\mathbf{b} = y\mathbf{a} + z\mathbf{b}$, where $\mathbf{a}$ and $\mathbf{b}$ are not parallel to each other, then $w = y$ and $x = z$.

If $A$ has position vector $\mathbf{a}$, then a general point on the line through $A$ parallel to $\mathbf{b}$ has position vector $\mathbf{a} + t\mathbf{b}$, where $t$ is a scalar.

### 12.1.1 Examples

(1) $OABC$ is a parallelogram, $X$ and $Y$ lie on $OC$ and $AC$ respectively, with $OX = \frac{2}{3}OC, AY = \frac{3}{4}AC$. Show that $X, Y, B$ lie on a straight line.

Solution   Let the position vectors relative to $O$ of $A$ and $C$ be $\mathbf{a}$ and $\mathbf{c}$.

The position vector of $B$ is $\mathbf{a} + \mathbf{c}$.
The position vector of $X$ is $\frac{2}{3}\mathbf{c}$.
The position vector of $Y$ is $\mathbf{a} + \frac{3}{4}(\mathbf{c} - \mathbf{a}) = \frac{1}{4}\mathbf{a} + \frac{3}{4}\mathbf{c}$.
$\underline{YB} = \mathbf{a} + \mathbf{c} - (\frac{1}{4}\mathbf{a} + \frac{3}{4}\mathbf{c}) = \frac{3}{4}\mathbf{a} + \frac{1}{4}\mathbf{c}$.
$\underline{XB} = \mathbf{a} + \mathbf{c} - \frac{2}{3}\mathbf{c} = \mathbf{a} + \frac{1}{3}\mathbf{c}$.
$\underline{YB} = \frac{3}{4}\underline{XB}$. It follows that $YB$ is parallel to $XB$.
$X, Y, B$ **lie on a straight line**

(2) $OABC$ is a parallelogram, with the position vectors of $A$ and $C$ relative to $O$ being $\mathbf{a}$ and $\mathbf{c}$. $X$ is the midpoint of $OA$, and $OB$ and $XC$ meet at $Y$. Find the position vector of $Y$.

Solution   As above, the position vector of $B$ is $\mathbf{a} + \mathbf{c}$. The position vector of $X$ is $\frac{1}{2}\mathbf{a}$.
A general point on $OB$ is $t(\mathbf{a} + \mathbf{c})$
A general point on $XC$ is $\mathbf{c} + s(\frac{1}{2}\mathbf{a} - \mathbf{c})$.
$Y$ is on both these lines.

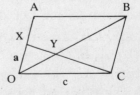

$$ t\mathbf{a} + t\mathbf{c} = \mathbf{c} + \frac{1}{2}s\mathbf{a} - s\mathbf{c} $$

This gives two equations:

$$t = \frac{1}{2}s \text{ and } t = 1 - s.$$

Solve to find that $s = \frac{2}{3}, \quad t = \frac{1}{3}$.

**Y has position vector $\frac{1}{3}(a + c)$**

## 12.1.2 Exercises

(1) Which of the following quantities are vectors and which are scalars?

(a) Velocity        (b) Mass

(c) Magnetic field    (d) Temperature.

(2) Find the magnitudes of the following vectors:

(a) $(3,4)$    (b) $(2,1,-7)$

(c) $i + 3j$    (d) $2i - 3j - 2\frac{1}{2}k$

(3) Find the vectors $\underline{AB}$ for the following points $A$ and $B$:

(a) $A(3,7), B(4,9)$    (b) $A(2,7,4), B(1,2,3)$

(c) $A(x,y), B(p,q)$    (d) $A(2x,-y,3z), B(x+1,y-3,4z)$

(4) $OAB$ is a triangle, and $X$ and $Y$ are the midpoints of $OA$ and $OB$ respectively. Let $\underline{OA} = a$ and $\underline{OB} = b$. Find $XY$ in terms of $a$ and $b$. Show that $XY$ is parallel to $AB$.

(5) $OAB$ is a triangle, with $\underline{OA} = a$ and $\underline{OB} = b$. $X$ and $Y$ are such that $OX = \lambda a$ and $OY = \mu b$. If $XY$ is parallel to $AB$ show that $\lambda = \mu$.

(6) $OABC$ is a parallelogram, with $\underline{OA} = a$ and $\underline{OC} = c$. Find $\underline{OB}$ in terms of $a$ and $c$. Find the position vectors of the midpoints of $OB$ and $AC$ in terms of $a$ and $c$. What can you deduce?

(7) $A, B, C, D$ are four points in space, with position vectors $a, b, c, d$ respectively. $I, J, K, L$ are the midpoints of $AB, BC, CD, DA$ respectively. Find the position vectors of $I, J, K, L$ in terms of $a, b, c, d$. Find the vectors $\underline{IJ}, \underline{JK}, \underline{LK}, \underline{IL}$. What can you say about the figure $IJKL$?

(8) $A, B, C$ have position vectors $a, b, c$ respectively. Find the position vector of $M$, the midpoint of $BC$. $G$ lies on $AM$ with $AG = 2GM$. Show that the position vector of $G$ is $\frac{1}{3}(a + b + c)$. Show that $G$ lies also on the lines from $B$ to the midpoint of $AC$ and from $C$ to the midpoint of $AB$.

(9) The position vectors of $A$ and $B$ relative to $O$ are $a$ and $b$. $X$ is the midpoint of $OA$ and $Y$ lies on $OB$ with $OY = \frac{1}{3}OB$. $XY$ meets $AB$ at $Z$. Find the position vector of $Z$.

(10) **a** and **b** are two non-parallel vectors. The position vectors of $X, Y$ and $Z$ are $\mathbf{a} + 2\mathbf{b}, \frac{1}{2}\mathbf{a} + \frac{3}{4}\mathbf{b}$ and $\lambda\mathbf{a} + \mathbf{b}$. Find the value of $\lambda$ if $X, Y$ and $Z$ lie on a straight line.

(11) $ABCDEF$ is a regular hexagon, with centre at $O$. $OA = \mathbf{a}$ and $OB = \mathbf{b}$. Express, in terms of **a** and **b**, $\underline{FA}, \underline{DE}, \underline{CD}, \underline{CF}$.

## 12.2 Scalar Product

The *scalar*, or *dot* product of two vectors is defined as follows:

$\mathbf{a}.\mathbf{b} = |\mathbf{a}||\mathbf{b}| \cos\theta$, where $\theta$ is the angle between **a** and **b**

In terms of coordinates the scalar product is as follows:

$(a, b).(x, y) = ax + by$ for two-dimensional vectors.

$(a\mathbf{i} + b\mathbf{j} + c\mathbf{k}).(x\mathbf{i} + y\mathbf{j} + z\mathbf{k}) = ax + by + cz$, for three-dimensional vectors.

In particular, $a.b = 0$ if and only if $a$ and $b$ are perpendicular.

In particular, putting $\mathbf{a} = \mathbf{b}, \mathbf{a}.\mathbf{a} = |\mathbf{a}|^2$

The *component* or *projection* of **a** in the direction of **b** is $\dfrac{\mathbf{a}.\mathbf{b}}{|\mathbf{b}|}$.

### 12.2.1 Examples

(1)        Find the angle between the vectors $(1,2,3)$ and $(2,1,-4)$.

Solution     Apply the formula above.

$|(1,2,3)| = \sqrt{14}$ and $|(2,1,-4)| = \sqrt{21}$.

$(1,2,3).(2,1,-4) = 1 \times 2 + 2 \times 1 + 3 \times -4 = -8$.

$\sqrt{14} \times \sqrt{21} \times \cos\theta = -8$.

$$\theta = \cos^{-1}\left(\frac{-8}{\sqrt{14} \times \sqrt{21}}\right) = \mathbf{117.8°}$$

(2)        $A, B, C$ are the vertices of a triangle. Let the perpendiculars from $A$ to $BC$ and from $B$ to $AC$ meet at $D$. Show that $CD$ is perpendicular to $AB$. (Note: $D$ is called the *orthocentre* of $\triangle ABC$.)

Solution     Let $A, B, C, D$ have position vectors **a**, **b**, **c**, **d** respectively. From the information given:

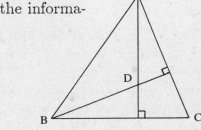

$$(\mathbf{d} - \mathbf{a}).(\mathbf{b} - \mathbf{c}) = 0 \text{ and } (\mathbf{d} - \mathbf{b}).(\mathbf{a} - \mathbf{c}) = 0$$

Expand these out:

$$\mathbf{d.b} - \mathbf{d.c} - \mathbf{a.b} + \mathbf{a.c} = 0$$

$$\mathbf{d.a} - \mathbf{d.c} - \mathbf{b.a} + \mathbf{b.c} = 0$$

Subtract these equations:

$$\mathbf{d.b} - \mathbf{d.a} - \mathbf{b.c} + \mathbf{a.c} = 0$$

$$(\mathbf{d} - \mathbf{c}).(\mathbf{b} - \mathbf{a}) = 0$$

**DC is perpendicular to AB**

### 12.2.2 Exercises

(1) Evaluate the following:

  (a)  $(1,2).(3,4)$       (b) $(2,-4).(7,-1)$

  (c)  $(1,2,5).(2,1,1)$   (d) $(3\mathbf{i} + 2\mathbf{j}).(\mathbf{i} - 5\mathbf{j})$

(2) Find the angles between the pairs of vectors in Question 1.

(3) Find the value of $x$ if $(x, 3)$ is perpendicular to $(3,1)$.

(4) Find a vector which is perpendicular to $(2,7)$.

(5) Find a unit vector which is perpendicular to $(7,24)$.

(6) Find the values of $x$ and $y$ if $(x, y, 3)$ is perpendicular to both $(1,2,4)$ and $(4,-2,-1)$.

(7) Find a vector which is perpendicular to both $(1,0,3)$ and $(2,1,2)$.

(8) Find a unit vector which is perpendicular to both $(3,3,5)$ and $(1,1,1)$.

(9) Find the component of $(2,4)$ in the direction of $(3,1)$.

(10) Find the component of $2\mathbf{i} + 3\mathbf{j} + \mathbf{k}$ in the direction of $3\mathbf{i} - \mathbf{j}$.

(11) Verify that the component of $(x, y)$ in the direction of $(1,0)$ is $x$.

(12) Verify that the component of $x\mathbf{i} + y\mathbf{j} + z\mathbf{k}$ in the $\mathbf{j}$ direction is $y$.

(13) Let $OAB$ be a triangle, with $\underline{OA} = \mathbf{a}$ and $\underline{OB} = \mathbf{b}$. Let $\mathbf{c} = \mathbf{a} - \mathbf{b}$ be the third side of the triangle. By expanding $\mathbf{c.c}$ prove the cosine rule for $\triangle OAB$.

(14) $OABC$ is a parallelogram, with $\underline{OA} = \mathbf{a}$ and $\underline{OC} = \mathbf{c}$. By considering $\underline{OB}.\underline{CA}$ show that $OABC$ is a rhombus if and only if its diagonals are perpendicular.

(15) Let O be the circumcentre of $\triangle ABC$. Let the position vectors of $A, B, C$ relative to O be $\mathbf{a}, \mathbf{b}, \mathbf{c}$. (So that $|\mathbf{a}| = |\mathbf{b}| = |\mathbf{c}|$). Show that $\mathbf{a} + \mathbf{b} + \mathbf{c}$ is the orthocentre of the triangle. (See (2) of 12.2.1)

(16) Find the point $X$ on the line $(2,3)+t(4,3)$ such that $OX$ is perpendicular to the line. Hence find the perpendicular distance from the origin to the line.

(17) Find the point $X$ on the line of Question 16 such that $AX$, where $A$ is at $(2,-7)$, is perpendicular to the line. Hence find the perpendicular distance from $A$ to the line.

## 12.3 Examination Questions

(1) Referred to the point $O$ as origin, the position vectors of the points $A$ and $B$ are $3\mathbf{i}+\mathbf{j}$ and $8\mathbf{i}-4\mathbf{j}$ respectively. The point $P$ lies on the line $OB$, between O and $B$, such that $4\underline{OP}=\underline{OB}$. The point $Q$ lies on the line $AB$, between $A$ and $B$, such that $5\underline{AQ}=2\underline{AB}$. Find, in terms of $\mathbf{i}$ and $\mathbf{j}$, the vectors $\underline{OP},\underline{AB},\underline{AQ},\underline{OQ}$ and $\underline{AP}$.

The lines $AP$ and $OQ$ intersect at the point $R$. Given that $OR:OQ=\lambda$ and $AR:AP=\mu$, express the position vector of $R$ in terms of

(a)  $\lambda,\mathbf{i}$ and $\mathbf{j}$  (b)  $\mu,\mathbf{i}$ and $\mathbf{j}$

Hence find the values of $\lambda$ and $\mu$.

Prove that the length of $OR$ is $(\frac{5}{11})\sqrt{26}$.

[L add]

(2) The position vectors, relative to an origin $O$, of three points $A,B,C$ are $2\mathbf{i}+2\mathbf{j},5\mathbf{i}+11\mathbf{j}$ and $11\mathbf{i}+9\mathbf{j}$ respectively.

(i) Given that $\underline{OB}=m\underline{OA}+n\underline{OC}$, where $m$ and $n$ are scalar constants, find the value of $m$ and of $n$.

(ii) Evaluate $\underline{AB}.\underline{BC}$ and state the deduction which can be made about $A\hat{B}C$.

(iii) Evaluate $\underline{AB}.\underline{AC}$ and hence find $B\hat{A}C$.

[C add]

(3) The position vectors of the points $A,B$ with respect to an origin $O$ are $\mathbf{a}$ and $\mathbf{b}$ respectively, where $A,B$ and $O$ are not collinear. Points $L,M,N$ have position vectors $p\mathbf{a},q\mathbf{b}$ and $2\mathbf{b}-\mathbf{a}$ respectively, where $p$ and $q$ are non-zero constants and $LM$ is not parallel to $AB$. Show that $N$ lies on the line $AB$. Prove that $L,M,N$ are collinear if and only if

$$2p=q(1+p).$$

If $p=\frac{1}{3}$ and $q=\frac{1}{2}$, find $LM:LN$.

If, further, $\mathbf{a}=2\mathbf{i}+3\mathbf{j}+6\mathbf{k}$ and $\mathbf{b}=4\mathbf{i}+\mathbf{j}+4\mathbf{k}$, find the position vector of the foot of the perpendicular from $N$ to $OA$.

[O&C add]

(4) A cartesian frame of reference, having origin O, is defined by the mutually perpendicular unit vectors $\mathbf{i}, \mathbf{j}$ and $\mathbf{k}$.

(i) Find the vector equation of the line which passes through the two points, having position vectors relative to $O, 2\mathbf{i} - \frac{1}{3}\mathbf{j} + 2\mathbf{k}$ and $\mathbf{i} + \frac{1}{3}\mathbf{j}$ in the form $\mathbf{r} = \mathbf{a} + t\mathbf{b}$.

(ii) A second line has vector equation

$$\mathbf{r} = -3\mathbf{i} - 4\mathbf{j} - \frac{1}{2}\mathbf{k} + s(2\mathbf{i} + \mathbf{j} + 1\frac{1}{2}\mathbf{k}).$$

Find the point of intersection of the two lines.

[NI]

(5) Relative to an origin $O$, points $A$ and $B$ have position vectors $2\mathbf{i} + 9\mathbf{j} - 6\mathbf{k}$ and $6\mathbf{i} + 3\mathbf{j} + 6\mathbf{k}$ respectively, $\mathbf{i}, \mathbf{j}$ and $\mathbf{k}$ being orthogonal unit vectors. $C$ is the point such that $OC = 2OA$ and $D$ is the mid-point of $AB$. Find

  i. the position vectors of $C$ and $D$;

  ii. a vector equation of the line $CD$;

  iii. the position vector of the point of intersection of $CD$ and $OB$;

  iv. the angle $AOB$ correct to the nearest degree.

[SUJB]

(6) Calculate unit vectors in the directions $\binom{3}{4}$ and $\binom{4}{-3}$.

By considering the sum of these two vectors, or otherwise, calculate the equation of one of the bisectors of the angles between the lines

$$\binom{x}{y} = s\binom{3}{4} \text{ and } \binom{x}{y} = t\binom{4}{-3}$$

Deduce the equation of one of the bisectors of the angles between the lines

$$\binom{x}{y} = \binom{4}{1} + s\binom{3}{4} \text{ and } \binom{x}{y} = \binom{5}{19} + t\binom{4}{-3}.$$

giving your answer in a similar form.

[O&C]

# COMMON ERRORS

## (1) Points and Vectors

a. The vector from the origin to (3,4) is (3,4). But this vector also goes from say (1,7) to (4,11). Vectors have magnitude and direction, but not position.

b. The vector from (2,5) to (1,10) is (−1,5), not (1,−5).

c. In general, if $A$ and $B$ have position vectors $\mathbf{a}$ and $\mathbf{b}$, then $\underline{AB}$ is $\mathbf{b} - \mathbf{a}$. It is not $\mathbf{b}$, or $\mathbf{a} + \mathbf{b}$, or $\mathbf{a} - \mathbf{b}$.

## (2) Modulus

a. The modulus of (3,4) is $\sqrt{(3^2 + 4^2)} = 5$, not $3 + 4 = 7$.

b. Be careful of negative signs. Any number squared is positive, so the modulus of $(-3, -4)$ is the same as the modulus of (3,4).

## (3) Scalar Product

a. $\mathbf{a}.\mathbf{b}$ is a scalar, not a vector:

$$(2,3).(3,4) \neq (6,12).\text{ It should be } 6 + 12 = 18.$$

b. Do not be confused if there are many possible answers to a problem. There are infinitely many vectors perpendicular to (1,2,3), for example. Just give the simplest one you can find.

# 13 Differentiation

If $y$ is a function of $x$, the rate of change of $y$ with respect to $x$ is called the *derivative* or the *differential coefficient* of $y$. It represents the gradient of the graph of $y$ against $x$.

The derivative of $y$ is written $dy/dx$. If the function is of the form $y = f(x)$, then the derivative is sometimes written as $dy/dx = f'(x)$.

The process of going from $y$ to $dy/dx$ is called *differentiation*.

The result of differentiating twice, i.e. of differentiating the derivative, is the *second derivative*.

$$\frac{d}{dx}\left(\frac{dy}{dx}\right) = \frac{d^2y}{dx^2}$$

## 13.1 Differentiation of Powers of x

Let $y$ be a power of $x$, (even a negative or a fractional power of $x$). Differentiate by multiplying by the power and subtracting 1 from the power.

$$\text{If } y = x^n, \text{ then } dy/dx = nx^{n-1}.$$

If a function is multiplied by a constant, then the derivative is also multiplied by the constant.

$$\text{If } y = ax^n, \text{ then } dy/dx = anx^{n-1}$$

If two functions are added, then their derivatives are also added.

$$\text{If } y = ax^n + bx^m, \text{ then } dy/dx = anx^{n-1} + bmx^{m-1}$$

Two special cases are as follows:
If $y$ is a constant, then $dy/dx = 0$.
If $y$ is the straight line $y = mx + c$, then $dy/dx = m$.

### 13.1.1 Examples

(1)        Differentiate $y = 3x^2 - 2/x + \sqrt{x}$.

Solution    Write $y$ in terms of powers of $x$.

$$y = 3x^2 - 2x^{-1} + x^{\frac{1}{2}}$$

Apply the formulae above, using $n = 2, n = -1$ and $n = \frac{1}{2}$.

$$dy/dx = 3(2)x^{2-1} - 2(-1)x^{-1-1} + \frac{1}{2}x^{\frac{1}{2}-1}$$

$$\mathbf{dy/dx = 6x + 2x^{-2} + \frac{1}{2}x^{-\frac{1}{2}}}$$

(2)        Differentiate $y = \dfrac{(x+3)(x-4)}{x^2}$

Solution    Before differentiating it is necessary to multiply out the expression and divide by $x^2$.

$$y = \frac{x^2 - x - 12}{x^2} = 1 - x^{-1} - 12x^{-2}$$

Now use the formulae above.

$$\mathbf{dy/dx = -(-1)x^{-2} - 12 \times (-2) \times x^{-3} = x^{-2} + 24x^{-3}}$$

## 13.1.2 Exercises

(1) Differentiate the following:

(a) $y = x^3$

(b) $y = 7x^5$

(c) $y = 3x^2 + 2x$

(d) $y = 2 - 2x + 4x^5$

(e) $y = 2x^{-3}$

(f) $y = 2x - 3x^{-4}$

(g) $y = 4x^{\frac{1}{2}}$

(h) $y = 3x^{-3} + 2x^{-\frac{1}{2}} + 17$

(i) $y = 7/x^3$

(j) $y = 2/x - 8/x^3$

(k) $y = \sqrt{x}$

(l) $y = 3\sqrt{x} - 7/\sqrt{x}$

(m) $y = 2x^5 - 5/x^6 + 7/x^{\frac{1}{4}}$

(n) $y = 2 + 2/\sqrt{x} - 9/x$

(2) Differentiate the following:

(a) $y = x(x - 3)$

(b) $y = (x + 1)(x - 6)$

(c) $y = (2 - 3x^2)(4 + x^3)$

(d) $y = x(1 + 1/x)(2 + 3/x^3)$

(e) $y = (x + 2)^2$

(f) $y = (3 + 2x^2)^2$

(g) $y = (2 + 3/x)^2$

(h) $y = (3x - 4/x)^2$

(i) $y = x^{\frac{1}{2}}(x - 4)$

(j) $y = (x^{\frac{1}{2}} + 1)(x^{\frac{1}{2}} - 2)$

(k) $y = \dfrac{x + 17}{x^4}$

(l) $y = \dfrac{2x^2 - 3x + 1}{x}$

(m) $y = \dfrac{x + 8}{\sqrt{x}}$

(n) $y = \dfrac{3\sqrt{x} - 4\sqrt{x} + 3}{\sqrt{x}}$

(3) Find the second derivatives of the following:

(a) $y = x^3$

(b) $y = 2x^2 - 3x + 1$

(c) $y = (x^3 + 1)(x - 4)$

(d) $y = 3\sqrt{x} - 2x^{-2}$

## 13.2 Tangents and Normals

The derivative of a function at a point is the gradient of the tangent of the function at that point.

### 13.2.1 Examples

(1)      Find the equation of the tangent to the curve $y = 3x^2 - 7x + 5$ at the point $(2, 3)$.

Solution     Differentiate to find that $dy/dx = 6x - 7$. When $x = 2$, the gradient of the tangent is $6 \times 2 - 7 = 5$.
The tangent is of the form $y = 5x + c$. The tangent goes through the point $(2, 3)$, hence $c = 3 - 5 \times 2 = -7$.

$$\textbf{The tangent is } \mathbf{y = 5x - 7}$$

(2)      At what points of the curve $y = 4x^3 - 12\frac{1}{2}x$ is the normal parallel to $y = 2x + 4$?

Solution     The gradient of the line $y = 2x + 4$ is 2. The gradient of the curve $y = 4x^3 - 12x$ is $dy/dx = 12x^2 - 12\frac{1}{2}$.
If these are at right angles, then $2 \times (12x^2 - 12\frac{1}{2}) = -1$.

$$24x^2 = 24. \quad x = 1 \text{ or } -1.$$

$$\textbf{The points are } \left(1, -8\tfrac{1}{2}\right) \textbf{ and } \left(-1, 8\tfrac{1}{2}\right)$$

### 13.2.2 Exercises

(1) Find the equations of the tangents to the following curves at the points given.

(a)   $y = x^2$ at $(2, 4)$          (b)   $y = x^3 - 2x$ at $(1, -1)$

(c)   $y = 3x^2 - 7x + 2$ at $(-1, 12)$    (d)   $y = 1 - 2/x$ at $(4, \frac{1}{2})$

(2) Find the normals to the curves in Question 1 at the same points.

(3) Where is the tangent to $y = 3x^2 + 7x - 4$ parallel to $y = 3x + 4$?

(4) Find the points where the tangents to $y = x^3 - x$ are parallel to the $x$-axis.

(5) Show that the tangents to the curve $y = x^3 + 2x$ are never parallel to the $x$-axis.

(6) The line $y = x + 7$ is a tangent to the curve $y = x^2 + a$, where $a$ is a constant. Find the value of $a$.

## 13.3 Maxima and Minima

A point of a curve where $dy/dx = 0$ is called a *stationary point*. A point where $y$ is at the top of a peak is a maximum ($\alpha$). A point where $y$ is at the bottom of a pit is a minimum ($\beta$). A point where the curve is flat but continues to go up or down is a point of inflection ($\gamma$).

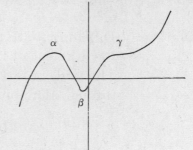

The points can be distinguished either by examining the curve on both sides of the point, or by means of the second derivative.

If $\dfrac{d^2y}{dx^2} > 0$ then it is a minimum.

If $\dfrac{d^2y}{dx^2} < 0$ then it is a maximum.

At a point of inflection $\dfrac{d^2y}{dx^2} = 0$.

### 13.3.1 Examples

(1)  Find the maxima and minima of $y = 2x^3 + 3x^2 - 12x + 4$, distinguishing between them. Sketch the graph of the function.

Solution  Differentiating, $dy/dx = 6x^2 + 6x - 12$. This is zero at a maximum or a minimum.

$$6x^2 + 6x - 12 = 0$$

$$6(x - 1)(x + 2) = 0$$

$$x = 1, y = -3 \text{ and } x = -2, y = 24.$$

To find out whether $(1, -3)$ is a maximum or a minimum, find the value of $y$ on either side of the point. For $x = 0.9, y = -2.9$. For $x = 1.1, y = -2.91$ **(1, –3) is a minimum. Similarly, (–2, 24) is a maximum.**

Sketch the graph as shown, with a peak at $(-2, 24)$ and a pit at $(1, -3)$.

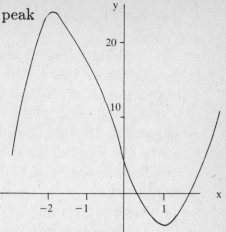

(2)    Thin metal is used to make cylindrical cans which are to hold 1,000 c.c. of soup. What should be the radius of the cans if they are to use as little metal as possible?

Solution    Let the height be $h$ and the base radius $r$.
The volume is 1,000, hence $\pi r^2 h = 1,000$.

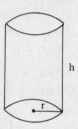

The surface area is $A = 2\pi r^2 + 2\pi rh$. Write $h$ in terms of $r$, so that $A$ is in terms of $r$ only.
$h = 1,000/\pi r^2$, so $A = 2\pi r^2 + 2,000/r$.
Differentiate to find where $A$ is a minimum.
$dA/dr = 4\pi r - 2,000/r^2$.
At a minimum, $dA/dr = 0$.
$4\pi r = 2,000/r^2, r^3 = 2,000/4\pi$.

**The best radius is 5.42 cm.**

### 13.3.2 Exercises

(1) Find the coordinates of the maxima and minima of the following, distinguishing between them.

(a)   $y = x^2 - 2x$    (b)   $y = 2 + 4x - x^2$

(c)   $y = x^3 - 3x$    (d)   $y = 2x^3 - 15x^2 + 36x - 4$

(e)   $y = x + 1/x$    (f)   $y = x + 4/x^2$

(2) The function $y = x^2 - 2x + a$ has a minimum of 5. Find the value of $a$.

111

(3) The function $ax^2 + bx$ has a maximum at (2,3). Find the values of $a$ and of $b$.

(4) A metal basket is made in the form of a cylinder with an open top. Its height is $h$ and its radius $r$. It is to contain 5,000 c.c. What is the radius, if it is to consist of the smallest possible amount of metal?

(5) A cardboard box is to be made in the form of a cuboid with square cross-section. Its volume must be 2,000 c.c. Let $x$ be the side of the square, and $z$ be the length. What value of $x$ will use the least cardboard?

(6) Repeat Question 5, if the squares at the end use a double thickness of cardboard.

(7) Repeat Example 2 of 13.3.1, if the top and bottom of the can use a double thickness of metal.

(8) A cuboid box is to have a volume of 512 c.c. The length is twice the breadth. Find the height, if the surface area is to be as small as possible.

(9) A farmer has 100 m of fencing, with which to make a rectangular sheepfold. One side of the fold is already provided by a stone wall. How should he make his fold if he is to enclose as much area as possible?

(10) A 100 cm length of wire is cut in two pieces, which are then made into two squares. Show that the total area enclosed by the squares is least when they have equal sides.

(11) 100 cm of wire is cut into two pieces, one of which is made into a square and the other into a circle. Find the radius of the circle if the total area is to be as small as possible.

(12) The line through (1,2) with gradient $m$ is $y - 2 = m(x - 1)$. Find where this line crosses the axes. Find the value of $m$ which will make the area enclosed by the line and the two axes as small as possible.

## 13.4 Examination Questions

(1) Find $dy/dx$ when

(i)  $y = x^3 + 1/x^3$,        (ii)  $y = x(x - 1)^2$

(iii)  $y = x^{-1\frac{1}{2}}$ and $x = 9$,  (iv)  $y = (x^2 + 1)/x$ and $x = 2$

[O&C add]

(2) A curve has equation $y = \frac{1}{3}x^3 - 4x^2 + 13x$.

a.  Show that the tangent at the point where $x = 2$ has gradient 1 and find its equation.

b.  Find the $x$-coordinate of another point where the tangent has gradient 1.

c.  Show that there is only one tangent with gradient $-3$.

[SMP add]

(3) The point P(0,2) lies on the curve

$$y = x^3 - 3x + 2.$$

The tangent and normal to the curve at $P$ intersect the $x$-axis at $A$ and $B$ respectively. Calculate the length of $AB$.

[L add]

(4) In making closed cylindrical tins of height $h$ cm and radius $r$ cm the walls can be made from rectangular sheets of width $h$ cm and length $2\pi r$ cm without waste, but stamping out each circular end of area $\pi r^2 \mathrm{cm}^2$ requires an area of $4r^2 \mathrm{cm}^2$ and some is wasted.

If the tins are to contain 1000 $cm^3$,

i. find $h$ in terms of $r$ to give the correct volume;

ii. find the area of tinplate required for each tin in terms of $r$.

If tinplate costs 0.01 p per $\mathrm{cm}^2$, find by a calculus method the radius, height and cost of the tin which will contain the required volume most cheaply.

[MEI add]

(5) At which point (other than the origin) do the parabolas

$$y^2 = 4ax \text{ and } x^2 = 4ay$$

meet?

Write down the equation of the tangent to each parabola at this point.

If the angles which these tangents make with the positive direction of the $x$-axis are $\theta_1$ and $\theta_2$, show that $|\tan(\theta_1 - \theta_2)| = \frac{3}{4}$

[NI]

(6) In the diagram, $CDEF$ is a rectangle with $CD = FE = 2x$ and $CF = DE = y$, and $OAB$ is a triangle with angles at $A$ and $B$ each equal to $\theta$.

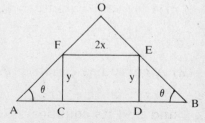

a. Show that the area, $\Delta$, of the triangle $OAB$ is given by

$$\Delta = (x + y/t)(y + tx), \text{ where } t = \tan\theta.$$

Deduce that, as $t$ varies, with $x$ and $y$ remaining fixed, the *least* value of $\Delta$ is $4xy$.

b. Given further that $OA = OB = \ell$, show that $y = \ell \sin \theta - x \tan \theta$, and that the area, $S$, of the rectangle $CDEF$ is given by

$$S = 2[\ell x \sin \theta - x^2 \tan \theta].$$

Deduce that, as $x$ varies with $\ell$ and $\theta$ remaining fixed, the *greatest* value of $S$ is $\frac{1}{2}\ell^2 \sin \theta \cos \theta$.

[C]

## COMMON ERRORS
### (1) Differentiation

There are a number of common mistakes made when differentiating. Be careful of negative powers, of constants, of products and of ratios. Watch out for the following:

If $y = x^{-5}, dy/dx \neq -5x^{-4}$. It should be $-5x^{-6}$.

If $y = x^2 + 7, dy/dx \neq 2x + 7$. It should be $2x$.

If $y = x^2 \times x^3, dy/dx \neq 2x \times 3x^2$. It should be $5x^4$.

If $y = x^6/x^2, dy/dx \neq 6x^5/2x$. It should be $4x^3$.

### (2) Maxima and Minima

When you are asked for the maximum or minimum value, then you must give the $y$ value, not the $x$ value. If you are asked for the point at which it is a maximum, give both the $x$ and the $y$ values.

When you are solving problems about minimum area or length, make sure that your area is expressed in terms of only one variable. If the area is in terms of both the height and the width then it cannot be differentiated.

# 14 Further Differentiation

## 14.1 The Product and Quotient Rules

These rules enable products and quotients of functions to be differentiated.

The *Product Rule*. If $y = uv$, then $\dfrac{dy}{dx} = u\dfrac{dv}{dx} + v\dfrac{du}{dx}$

The *Quotient Rule*. If $y = \dfrac{u}{v}$, then $\dfrac{dy}{dx} = \dfrac{v(du/dx) - u(dv/dx)}{v^2}$

### 14.1.1 Examples

(1)     Differentiate $y = (x^2 + 3x - 2)(4 - x^2)$

Solution     Here $u = x^2 + 3x - 2$ and $v = 4 - x^2$. Apply the Product Rule:

$$dy/dx = (x^2 + 3x - 2)(-2x) + (4 - x^2)(2x + 3)$$

$$\mathbf{dy/dx = -4x^3 - 9x^2 + 12x + 12}$$

115

(2)  Differentiate $y = \dfrac{x}{2x^2 - 3x + 5}$

Solution  Here $u = x$ and $v = 2x^2 - 3x + 5$. Apply the Quotient Rule:

$$\frac{dy}{dx} = \frac{(2x^2 - 3x + 5) \times 1 - x \times (4x - 3)}{(2x^2 - 3x + 5)^2}$$

$$\frac{dy}{dx} = \frac{-2x^2 + 5}{(2x^2 - 3x + 5)^2}$$

### 14.1.2 Exercises

(1) Without multiplying out the brackets, differentiate the following:

(a)  $y = x(x^2 + 7x - 3)$    (b)  $y = (x + 3)(2x^3 + 6x)$

(c)  $y = x^2(3x^5 - 3x^2 + x)$   (d)  $y = (x^2 - 1)(x^2 + 1)$

(2) Differentiate the following:

(a)  $y = \dfrac{x}{x + 3}$   (b)  $y = \dfrac{x^2 + 7x - 2}{x^2 + 3}$

(c)  $y = \dfrac{3x^2}{x - 17}$   (d)  $y = \dfrac{1}{x + 3}$

(3) Find the equation of the tangent to the curve $y = \dfrac{x^2}{x - 1}$ at the point (2,4).

(4) Find the maxima and minima of the following functions

(a)  $y = \dfrac{x^2}{x - 1}$   (b)  $y = \dfrac{x^2 + 1}{x + 1}$

(c)  $y = \dfrac{1}{x^2 + 1}$   (d)  $y = \dfrac{1}{x^2 + 4x + 9}$

## 14.2 The Chain Rule

The *Chain Rule* enables functions of functions to be differentiated. If $y$ is a function of $z$, and $z$ is a function of $x$, then the derivative of $y$ is found by the following:

$$\frac{dy}{dx} = \frac{dy}{dz} \times \frac{dz}{dx}$$

### 14.2.1 Examples

(1)  Differentiate $y = (x^2 + 1)^{\frac{1}{2}}$.

Solution  Substitute for the inside function. Let $z = x^2 + 1$. Then $y = z^{\frac{1}{2}}$.

Use the chain rule above.

$$\frac{dy}{dx} = \frac{dy}{dz} \times \frac{dz}{dx} = \frac{1}{2}z^{-\frac{1}{2}} \times 2x$$

$$\mathbf{dy/dx = x(x^2 + 1)^{-\frac{1}{2}}}$$

(2)  Differentiate $x(x^2 + 1)^{\frac{1}{2}}$

Solution  This is a product. $u = x$ and $v = (x^2 + 1)^{\frac{1}{2}}$. Use the product rule of 14.1, with the derivative of $v$ which was found in Example 1.

$$\frac{dy}{dx} = u\frac{dv}{dx} + v\frac{du}{dx} = x \times x(x^2 + 1)^{-\frac{1}{2}} + (x^2 + 1)^{\frac{1}{2}} \times 1$$

$$\mathbf{dy/dx = x^2(x^2 + 1)^{-\frac{1}{2}} + (x^2 + 1)^{\frac{1}{2}}}$$

### 14.2.2 Exercises

(1) Differentiate the following:

(a)  $y = (3x + 7)^{\frac{1}{2}}$        (b)  $y = (2 - x^2)^5$

(c)  $y = \sqrt{(1 + 2x^2)}$        (d)  $y = 1/\sqrt{(1 + x)}$

(e)  $y = \sqrt{(1 + x + x^2)}$    (f)  $y = (1 + x^2)^{100}$

(2) Differentiate the following:

(a)  $y = x(1 + 2x)^{\frac{1}{2}}$    (b)  $y = (x + 3)(x - 17)^{21}$

(b)  $y = \dfrac{x + 4}{\sqrt{(x^2 + 1)}}$    (d)  $y = \dfrac{\sqrt{x}}{\sqrt{x} + 1}$

### 14.3 Differentiation of Trig and Log Functions

Provided that the angles are measured in radians, the trigonometric functions are differentiated as follows:

If $y = \sin x, \dfrac{dy}{dx} = \cos x$   If $y = \cos x, \dfrac{dy}{dx} = -\sin x$

$$\text{If } y = \tan x, \frac{dy}{dx} = \sec^2 x$$

$e$ is a number approximately equal to 2.718281828. The *exponential function* is defined as $e^x$.

$\ln x$ is defined as $\log_e x$. $e^x$ and $\ln x$ can be differentiated as follows:

If $y = e^x, \dfrac{dy}{dx} = e^x$   If $y = \ln x, \dfrac{dy}{dx} = \dfrac{1}{x}$.

### 14.3.1 Examples

(1)       Differentiate $y = e^x \cos x$.

Solution    This is a product, so the product rule must be used.

$$dy/dx = e^x \cos x + e^x(-\sin x)$$

$$\mathbf{dy/dx = e^x(\cos x - \sin x)}$$

(2)       Differentiate $y = \ln(1 + x^2)$

Solution    This is a function of a function, so the chain rule is used.

$$\frac{dy}{dx} = \frac{1}{1 + x^2} \times 2x$$

$$\mathbf{\frac{dy}{dx} = \frac{2x}{1 + x^2}}$$

### 14.3.2 Exercises

(1) Differentiate the following:

| | | | |
|---|---|---|---|
| (a) | $\sin 3x$ | (b) | $\cos 4x$ |
| (c) | $e^{2x-1}$ | (d) | $\tan(5x - 3)$ |
| (e) | $5\cos 3x - 2\sin 4x$ | (f) | $e^{\cos x}$ |
| (g) | $\ln(2x - 3)$ | (h) | $\ln(\cos x)$ |
| (i) | $x \cos x$ | (j) | $x^2 \sin x$ |
| (k) | $e^x \tan x$ | (l) | $x \ln x$ |
| (m) | $e^x \ln x$ | (n) | $e^{-x} \sin 2x$ |
| (o) | $(\cos 3x)(\sin 2x)$ | (p) | $\cos(1 + x^2)$ |
| (q) | $x \sin(1 + 3x^2)$ | (r) | $\cos^2 x$ |
| (s) | $\sin^3 3x$ | (t) | $x/\cos x$ |
| (u) | $\dfrac{x^2}{\cos x + \sin x}$ | (v) | $\dfrac{\cos^2 x}{\ln x}$ |
| (w) | $\cos \sqrt{(x^2 + 3)}$ | (x) | $e^x(\cos x - \sin x)$ |
| (y) | $\ln 3x - \ln x$ | (z) | $e^{\ln x}$ |

(2) By considering $\tan x = \sin x / \cos x$, use the quotient rule to prove that $d(\tan x)/dx = \sec^2 x$.

(3) Find the derivatives of $\cot x, \sec x, \operatorname{cosec} x$.

(4) Use the fact that $10^x = e^{x \ln 10}$ to differentiate $10^x$.

(5) Use the fact that $\log_{10} x = \ln x / \ln 10$ to differentiate $\log_{10} x$.

(6) Let $a$ be a positive constant. Differentiate $a^x$ and $\log_a x$.

118

## 14.4 Applications of the Chain Rule

An *explicit* function gives $y$ directly in terms of $x$. An *implicit* function connects together $y$ and $x$ by an equation.

$$y = 3x^2 + 7x - 3 \text{ or } y = \cos 3x - 7e^x \text{ are explicit.}$$

$$x^2 + y^2 = 3 \text{ or } \cos xy + 7y^2 = 8x \text{ are implicit.}$$

If $x$ and $y$ are both expressed, not in terms of each other, but in terms of a third variable $t$, then $t$ is called a *parameter*.

A small change in $x$ is often written as $\delta x$. (Pronounced *delta x*). Small changes are connected by the following approximation:

$$\delta y \simeq dy/dx \times \delta x$$

### 14.4.1 Examples

(1)      Find the gradient of the curve $y^2 + 3xy + 2x^2 = 6$ at the point (1,1).

Solution      Here $y$ is an implicit function of $x$. The $y^2$ term and the $3xy$ term are differentiated as follows:

$$\frac{d(y^2)}{dx} = \frac{d(y^2)}{dy} \times \frac{dy}{dx} = 2y\frac{dy}{dx}$$

(Using the Chain Rule)

$$\frac{d(3xy)}{dx} = y\frac{d(3x)}{dx} + 3x\frac{dy}{dx} = 3y + 3x\frac{dy}{dx}$$

(Using the Product Rule)

Go through the equation, differentiating each term.

$$2y\frac{dy}{dx} + 3y + 3x\frac{dy}{dx} + 4x = 0$$

Substitute in the values $x = 1$ and $y = 1$.

$$2\frac{dy}{dx} + 3 + 3\frac{dy}{dx} + 4 = 0$$

$$\mathbf{dy/dx = -7/5}$$

(2)     $x$ and $y$ are given by $x = t^2 + 1, y = t^3 + 2$. Find $dy/dx$ in terms of $t$.

Solution    Use the chain rule:

$$\frac{dy}{dx} = \frac{dy}{dt} \times \frac{dt}{dx} = \frac{dy}{dt} \div \frac{dx}{dt} = 3t^2 \div 2t$$

$$\mathbf{dy/dx = 3t/2}$$

(3)     The radius of a sphere is 12 cm. What is the approximate change in surface area if the radius increases by 0.01 cm?

Solution    The area is given by $A = 4\pi r^2$. Use the small change formula above, with $\delta r = 0.01$.

$$\delta A \simeq dA/dr \times \delta r = 8\pi r \times 0.01 = 8\pi \times 12 \times 0.01$$

**The change is approximately** $3\text{cm}^2$

(4)     Air is pumped into a spherical balloon at $10\text{cm}^3$ per second. How fast is the radius increasing when it is 8 cm?

Solution    The rate of change of the volume is $dV/dt = 10$. The rate of change of the radius is $dr/dt$. The volume is given by $V = 4\pi r^3/3$. Use the chain rule:

$$\frac{dV}{dt} = \frac{dV}{dr} \times \frac{dr}{dt} = 4\pi r^2 \times \frac{dr}{dt}$$

$$dr/dt = 10/4\pi 8^2$$

**The radius is increasing at 0.012 cm per second**

### 14.4.2 Exercises

(1) Find the gradients of the following functions at the points shown.

(a)  $x^2 + y^2 = 5$ at $(1,2)$           (b)  $x^2 - y^3 = 1$ at $(3,2)$

(c)  $y^2 - 3x + 2y + x^2 = 1$ at $(2,1)$   (d)  $x \cos y = 1$ at $(1,0)$

(e)  $y^2 - 2xy = -3$ at $(2,3)$          (f)  $yx^2 + x^3 + 2y = 2$ at $(2,-1)$

(g)  $ye^x + e^y + e^x = 2$ at $(0,0)$      (h)  $y^2x^2 + 2x - 3y = 0$ at $(1,2)$

(2) For each of the following functions, express $dy/dx$ in terms of $x$ and $y$.

(a)  $x^2 + y^2 = 4$          (b)  $x^2 + y^3 - 3x + y = 5$

(c)  $x^2 + 4xy - y^2 = 3$   (d)  $x^2 + 3yx^3 + 4y = 7$

(3) Show that the stationary points of the ellipse $2x^2 + xy + y^2 = 1$ occur when $y + 4x = 0$.

(4) Find the equation of the tangent to $5x^2 - 4y^2 = 1$ at the point $(1,1)$.

(5) Find the maximum and minimum values of $y$ for the curve $x^2 - xy + y^2 = 1$.

(6) Find the maximum and minimum values of $x$ for the curve in Question 5. (Hint: when $x$ is a maximum or minimum, $dx/dy = 0$.)

(7) Find $dy/dx$ in terms of the parameter $t$ for the following functions:

(a)  $x = t^2, y = 2t^3 + 1$               (b)  $y = t^2, x = \dfrac{1}{1+t}$

(c)  $x = t + 2t^2, y = t^2 - t^3$          (d)  $x = \dfrac{1}{1+t}, y = \dfrac{1}{1+t^2}$

(e)  $x = at^2, y = 2at$ ($a$ is constant)  (f)  $x = ct, y = c/t$ ($c$ is constant)

(g)  $x = \cos t, y = \sin t$               (h)  $x = 3\cos t, y = 2\sin t$

(i)  $x = e^t + e^{-t}, y = e^t - e^{-t}$    (j)  $x = 2\tan t, y = 3/\cos t$

(8) If $x$ and $y$ are given parametrically by $x = 3\cos t$ and $y = 4\sin t$, find the equation of the tangent at the point where $t = \pi/4$.

(9) Find the equation of the normal to the curve given by $x = t^2 + 1$, $y = t^3 - 1$, at the point where $t = 2$.

(10) Find the approximate increase in the area of a square when its side changes by 0.02 cm, when the side is 10 cm.

(11) A cube has side 3 cm. Find the approximate change in its volume if its side changes by 0.01 cm.

(12) The radius of a sphere is 5 cm. Find the approximate change in radius if the volume changes by $0.1\text{cm}^3$.

(13) The radius of a sphere is measured as 12.3 cm, with a possible error of 0.05 cm. What is the possible error in the volume?

(14) The surface area of a sphere is measured as $67\text{cm}^2$, with a possible error of $0.5\text{cm}^2$. What is the approximate error in the radius? What is the approximate error in the volume?

(15) The side of a square is measured, with a possible error of 1%. What is the approximate percentage error in the area?

(16) The percentage error when measuring the area of a circle was 4%. What was the approximate percentage error in its radius?

(17) The side of a square is increasing at 0.5 cm per sec. At what rate is the area increasing at a time when the side is 15 cm?

(18) The radius of a sphere is increasing at 0.02 cm/sec. At what rate is the surface area increasing when the radius is 6 cm? At what rate is the volume increasing?

(19) The area of a circle is increasing at $20\,cm^2$/sec. At what rate is the radius increasing, when it is 45 cm?

(20) Water is poured into a cone, of semi-vertical angle 45°, at 10 c.c./sec. When the height of the water is 15 cm, at what rate is it increasing?

(21) The volume of a cube is decreasing at $3\,cm^3$/sec. When the side is 4 cm, what is the rate of decrease of (a) the side (b) the surface area?

(22) At the equinox on the equator the angle $\theta$ of elevation of the sun changes at 0.000073 radians/sec. A flagpole of height 40 m. throws a shadow of length $40/\tan\theta$. Find the rate of decrease of the shadow when $\theta = 0.1$.

## 14.5 Examination Questions

(1)

a.  Differentiate with respect to $x$,

   (i)  $\ln(3x+1)$   (ii)  $x\cos 2x$

b.  Find the equation of the tangent to the curve

$$y = \frac{3+x}{1-2x}$$

at the point where the curve crosses the line $y = -1$.

c.  Given that $x^2 y + y^2 = 10$, find $dy/dx$ in terms of $x$ and $y$.

[C add]

(2)

a.  Sketch the curve $y = \log_e(x+3)$.

b.  Find the gradient of this curve at the point where $x = (e-3)$. Hence show that the equation of the tangent to the curve at this point is $ey = x+3$.

[AEB add 1987]

(3) The surface area of an expanding spherical balloon is increasing at the rate of $16\ cm^2/s$. At the instant when the surface area is $144\ cm^2$, calculate

a.  the rate, in cm/s to 2 significant figures, at which the radius of the balloon is increasing,

b. the rate, in cm³/s to 2 significant figures, at which the volume of the balloon is increasing.

Find, in cm³ to 2 significant figures, the approximate increase in the volume of the balloon when the surface area increases from 144 cm² to 146 cm².

[L add]

(4) Express $\dfrac{13x + 16}{(x - 3)(3x + 2)}$ in partial fractions.

Hence find the value of $\dfrac{d}{dx}\left[ \dfrac{13x + 16}{(x - 3)(3x + 2)} \right]$ when $x = 2$.

[AEB 1986]

(5)

a. A curve has the equation $x^3 - xy + y^3 = k$, where $k$ is a constant. Find $dy/dx$ in terms of $x$ and $y$.
Prove that the curve cannot possess a tangent which is parallel to the $y$-axis if $k < \frac{-1}{27}$.

b. If $y = \dfrac{e^x}{1 + x^2}$, prove that $\dfrac{dy}{dx}$ may be written in the form $\dfrac{(x - 1)^2 e^x}{(1 + x^2)^2}$.
Hence, or otherwise, prove that, for all positive values of $x$,

$$\frac{e^x}{1 + x^2} > 1$$

[SUJB]

(6)

a. The parametric equations of a curve are

$$x = a(1 + 1/t), y = a(t - 1/t^2),$$

Where $a$ is a constant and $t \neq 0$. Find the equation of the normal to the curve at the point where $t = 2$.

b. The equation of a curve is $(y - x)^2 = 2a(y + x)$, where $a$ is a constant. Find an expression for $dy/dx$ in terms of $x, y$ and $a$.

c. The velocity $v$ of a point moving in a straight line is given in terms of the time $t$ by

$$v = e^{-2t} \sin 3t.$$

Find the smallest positive value of $t$ for which the acceleration of the point is zero, giving two significant figures in your answer.

[C]

(7) Apply the small increment formula $f(x + \delta x) - f(x) \approx \delta x f'(x)$ to $\tan x$ to find an approximate value of

$$\tan\left(\frac{100\pi + 4}{400}\right) - \tan\frac{\pi}{4}.$$

[L]

(8) Sketch the curve whose equation is

$$\frac{x^2}{a^2} + \frac{y^2}{b^2} = 1 \, (a, b > 0)$$

Find the gradient of the curve at the point $P(a\cos\theta, b\sin\theta)$. Hence show that the equation of the tangent at $P$ is

$$bx\cos\theta + ay\sin\theta = ab$$

and that the equation of the normal at $P$ is

$$ax\sin\theta - by\cos\theta = (a^2 - b^2)\sin\theta\cos\theta.$$

The tangent at $P$ meets the $x$-axis at $T$ and the $y$-axis at $U$; the normal at $P$ meets the $x$-axis at $M$ and the $y$-axis at $N$. Show that $NT$ is perpendicular to $MU$.

Write down the coordinates of the mid-point $Q$ of $UT$ and hence find the equation of the locus of $Q$ as $\theta$ varies.

[W]

## COMMON ERRORS

### (1) Products and Quotients

The derivative of a product is not the product of the derivatives. Similarly the derivative of a quotient is not the quotient of the derivatives. In both cases the rules must be used.

$$\text{If } y = uv, \text{ then } \frac{dy}{dx} \neq \frac{du}{dx} \times \frac{dy}{dx}$$

$$\text{If } y = \frac{u}{v}, \text{ then } \frac{dy}{dx} \neq \frac{du}{dx} \div \frac{dv}{dx}.$$

### (2) Chain Rule

When using the chain rule $dy/dx = dy/dz \times dz/dx$, make sure you put the value of $z$ in the $dy/dz$ term. Watch out for the following:

For $y = \sin x^2$, $dy/dx \neq 2x\cos x$. It should be $2x\cos x^2$.

Once you have found the derivative, substitute back so that the answer is in terms of $x$. It would be incorrect to leave $z$ in the answer.

### (3) Differentiating Power Functions

$a^x$ is a very different function from $x^a$. Do not differentiate as though they were the same function. In particular:

$$\text{If } y = e^x, \text{ then } dy/dx \neq xe^{x-1}. \text{ It should be } e^x.$$

### (4) Implicit Functions

Many difficulties are found when differentiating implicit functions. For something like $y^2$, use $d(y^2)/dx = d(y^2)/dy \times dy/dx$. For something like $3xy$, use the product rule. And if there is a constant at the right hand side, its derivative is 0. Note the following:

$$\text{If } x^2 + y^2 = 3, \text{ then } 2x + 2y \times dy/dx \neq dy/dx.$$

The right hand side of the last equation should be 0.

# 15 Integration

*Integration* is the opposite operation to differentiation.

$$\text{If } dF(x)/dx = f(x), \text{ then } \int f(x)dx = F(x) + c.$$

The constant $c$ is called the *constant of integration*.

## 15.1 Integration of powers of $x$

Powers of $x$ are integrated by the rule:

$$\int x^n dx = \frac{x^{n+1}}{n+1} + c, \text{ for all } n \text{ except } n = -1.$$

In particular, $\int 0dx = c$; $\int kdx = kx + c$, where $k$ is a constant.

If functions are added or multiplied by constants, then the integrals are added or multiplied by constants.

$$\int (ax^n + bx^m)dx = \frac{ax^{n+1}}{n+1} + \frac{bx^{m+1}}{m+1} + c.$$

## 15.1.1 Examples

(1)      If $dy/dx = 6x^2 + 2$, find $y$ given that $y = 7$ when $x = 1$.

Solution      Integrate $6x^2 + 2$.

$$y = 2x^3 + 2x + c.$$

Substitute $x = 1$ and $y = 7$ to find that $c = 3$.

$$\mathbf{y = 2x^3 + 2x + 3}$$

(2)      Integrate $(\sqrt{x} + 1)(x^2 - 3)$.

Solution      The brackets must be multiplied out before integration.

$$(\sqrt{x} + 1)(x^2 - 3) = x^{2\frac{1}{2}} - 3x^{\frac{1}{2}} + x^2 - 3.$$

$$\int (\sqrt{x} + 1)(x^2 - 3)dx = \frac{x^{3\frac{1}{2}}}{3\frac{1}{2}} - + \frac{3x^{1\frac{1}{2}}}{1\frac{1}{2}} + \frac{x^3}{3} - 3x + c$$

## 15.1.2 Exercises

(1) For each of the following find $y$ as a function of $x$.

a.   $dy/dx = 2x, y = 1$ for $x = 0$
b.   $dy/dx = 3x^2 + x, y = 1$ for $x = 1$
c.   $dy/dx = x^2 + x + 1, y = 3$ for $x = 1$
d.   $dy/dx = 1/x^2, y = 1$ for $x = 1$
e.   $dy/dx = x^{1\frac{1}{2}}, y = 1$ for $x = 4$
f.   $dy/dx = 3/\sqrt{x}, y = 4$ for $x = 16$
g.   $dy/dx = x(x^2 + 1), y = 0$ for $x = 1$
h.   $dy/dx = (x^2 + 3)/\sqrt{x}, y = 3$ for $x = 4$

(2) Evaluate the following integrals:

(a)   $\int 2x dx$          (b)   $\int (3x^2 + 2x + 1)dx$

(c)   $\int (x^2 + 2x^3 + 5)dx$    (d)   $\int (2x^5 - 2\frac{1}{2}x^7)dx$

(e)   $\int x^{1\frac{1}{2}}dx$          (f)   $\int (3 - \sqrt{x})dx$

(g)   $\int 1/x^3 dx$         (h)   $\int (2/x^2 + 7/x^3 + 2)dx$

(i)   $\int x(3x^2 + 7)dx$

(j)   $\int (x-3)(x^2 + 2x)dx$

(k)   $\int x(4x^2 - 2x^3)dx$

(l)   $\int (\sqrt{x} + 1/\sqrt{x})(x^4 - 3)dx$

## 15.2 Definite Integrals and Areas

When $f(x)$ is integrated to find $F(x)$, the result is the *indefinite integral* of $f$.

The difference of $F(x)$ between two values of $x$ is the *definite integral* of $f$.

$$\text{If } \int f(x)dx = F(x), \text{ then } \int_a^b f(x)dx = [F(x)]_a^b = F(b) - F(a)$$

The area bounded by a curve $y = f(x)$, the $x$-axis and the limits $x = a$ and $x = b$ is given by the definite integral of $f(x)$ between $a$ and $b$.

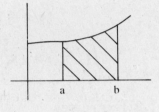

$$\text{Area} = \int_a^b f(x)dx$$

Negative area corresponds to a region *below* the $x$-axis.

If $x$ and $y$ are expressed in terms of a parameter $t$, then integrals can be found from the following:

$$\int y\,dx = \int y(dx/dt)dt.$$

### 15.2.1 Examples

(1)   Evaluate the definite integral $\int_1^2 (x^2 - 3/x^3)dx$.

Solution   First find the indefinite integral.

$$\int (x^2 - 3/x^3)dx = \frac{1}{3}x^3 + 1\frac{1}{2}x^{-2} + c.$$

Evaluate this at the values 1 and 2 and subtract.

$$\int_1^2 (x^2 - 3/x^3)dx = (\frac{1}{3} \times 2^3 + 1\frac{1}{2} \times 2^{-2} + c) - (\frac{1}{3} \times 1^3 + 1\frac{1}{2} \times 1^{-2} + c)$$

$$\int_1^2 (x^2 - 3/x^3)dx = 1.2083$$

(2)      Find the area enclosed by the curve $y = \sqrt{x}$, the $x$-axis and the line $y = x - 2$.

Solution     A rough sketch of the area is shown. The curve and the line cross at (4,2). The area is the difference between the area under the curve and the area under the line.

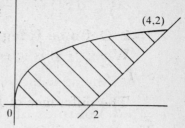

$$\text{Area} = \int_0^4 \sqrt{x}\,dx - \int_2^4 (x-2)\,dx = [\tfrac{2}{3}x^{1\frac{1}{2}}]_0^4 - [\tfrac{1}{2}x^2 - 2x]_2^4$$

$$\textbf{Area} = 3\frac{1}{3}$$

## 15.2.2 Exercises

(1) Evaluate the following definite integrals:

(a)   $\int_0^3 (2x + 3x^2)\,dx$      (b)   $\int_0^1 (x^2 - x^4/4)\,dx$

(c)   $\int_1^9 (\sqrt{x} - 3/x^2)\,dx$   (d)   $\int_1^4 x(x + 3)\,dx$

(e)   $\int_1^4 (x^2 - 1)/\sqrt{x}\,dx$   (f)   $\int_{-1}^2 (x^3 + 2)^2\,dx$

(2) Find the areas enclosed by the following curves and the $x$-axis, between the limits shown:

(a)   $y = x^2, x = 1$ and $x = 3$      (b)   $y = 1/x^2, x = 1$ and $x = 20$

(c)   $y = x^{-\frac{1}{2}}, x = 0$ and $x = 9$   (d)   $y = x^3 - x, x = 0$ and $x = 1$

(3) Sketch the curve $y = 3 - 2x - x^2$. Find the area of the region enclosed by the curve and the $x$-axis.

(4) Sketch the curve $y = x^3 - x$. Find the areas of the regions (a) enclosed by the curve above the $x$-axis (b) enclosed by the curve below the $x$-axis. What do you notice?

(5) On the same graph sketch the curve $y = 1 - x^2$ and the line $y = 1 - x$. Find the areas (a) between the curve and the line (b) enclosed between the curve, the line and the $x$-axis.

(6) Find the area between the $y$-axis, the curve $y = x^3 - 4$ and the line $y = 4$.

(7) Find the areas of the two regions between the $x$-axis and the curve $y = (x + 1)(x - 3)(2x + 1)$.

(8) For each of the following, evaluate the definite integral and sketch the area to which it corresponds.

(a) $\int_0^4 3x^2\,dx$    (b) $\int_1^2 4/x^3\,dx$

(c) $\int_0^2 (4 - x^2)\,dx$    (d) $\int_1^9 x^{-\frac{1}{2}}\,dx$

(9) $x$ and $y$ are given in terms of the parameter $t$ by $x = t^2 + 1, y = t^3 - t$. Find the area enclosed by the curve between $t = 0$ and $t = 1$ and the $x$-axis.

## 15.3 Volumes of revolution

When a curve $y = f(x)$ is rotated through $360°$ about the $x$-axis, it passes through a region of space called a *solid of revolution*. The volume of this solid is the *volume of revolution*. The volume is given by:

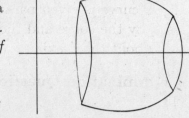

$$V = \int \pi y^2\,dx$$

### 15.3.1 Example

The area enclosed by the curve $y = 4 - x^2$ and the $x$-axis is rotated about the $x$-axis. Find the volume of revolution.

Solution    The curve crosses the $x$-axis at $x = -2$ and $x = 2$. The volume is therefore:

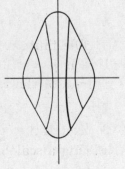

$$V = \int_{-2}^{2} \pi(4 - x^2)^2\,dx = \int_{-2}^{2} \pi(16 - 8x^2 + x^4)\,dx$$

$$V = \pi[16x - 8x^3/3 + x^5/5]_{-2}^{2}$$

$$\mathbf{V = 107.2}$$

### 15.3.2 Exercises

(1) Find the volumes enclosed when the following curves between the limits shown are rotated about the $x$-axis.

(a)  $y = 3x^2, x = 1$ and $x = 2$    (b)  $y = \sqrt{x}, x = 0$ and $x = 3$

(c)  $y = 1/x, x = 1$ and $x = 10$    (d)  $y = 2x - 3, x = 2$ and $x = 4$

(e)  $y = 3x - 2/x, x = 1$ and $x = 4$  (f)  $y = \sqrt{(1 + x^2)}, x = 0$ and $x = 3$

(2) The line $y = 3x$, between $x = 0$ and $x = 4$, is rotated about the $x$-axis. Show that the solid of revolution is a cone. What is its height and its base radius? Find the volume of revolution, and verify that this agrees with the formula $V = \frac{1}{3}\pi r^2 h$.

(3) By rotating the line $y = rx/h$, from $x = 0$ to $x = h$, about the $x$-axis, prove that the volume of a cone of height $h$ and base radius $r$ is $\frac{1}{3}\pi r^2 h$.

(4) The circle with centre at the origin and radius 1 has equation $y = \sqrt{(1 - x^2)}$. What is the solid formed when this curve is rotated about the $x$-axis? Find the volume of revolution, and verify that it agrees with the formula for the volume of this solid.

(5) Find the equation of the straight line through (0,1) and (2,3). When this line is rotated about the $x$-axis, the solid of revolution is a *frustum*, of height 2 and radii 1 and 3. Find the volume of this frustum.

(6) A curve is given parametrically by $x = at^2$, $y = 2at$. Find the area enclosed by the curve and the line $x = a$. Find the volume when this area is rotated about the $x$-axis.

## 15.4 Examination Questions

(1)

a. Integrate with respect to $x$:

   (i) $x^2 - x^{1\frac{1}{2}}$,  (ii) $(x^2 - 1)^2$

b. A curve passes through the point (9,2) and its gradient at the point $(x, y)$ is given by $dy/dx = \sqrt{x} + 3$. Find the equation of the curve and the equation of the tangent at the point (9,2).

[O&C add]

(2) The finite region contained between the $x$-axis and the curve whose equation is $y = x(2 - x)$ is completely rotated about the $x$-axis. Calculate the volume of the solid so formed. (Leave your answer as a multiple of $\pi$.) [L add]

(3)

a. Using a scale of 2 cm to 1 unit on each axis, sketch the graph of

$$y = 3 - 5/x^2, \text{ for } 1 \le x \le 5.$$

b. Shade the area represented by $I$ where $I = \int_2^4 (3 - \frac{5}{x^2})dx$.

c. The rate of flow of water through a drainpipe $t$ minutes after the beginning of a storm is approximated by $100(3 - 5/t^2)$ m/min for $t \ge 2$.
   If the drainpipe remains full and has cross-sectional area $0.2m^2$, calculate the volume of water flowing through the drain during the time from $t = 2$ to $t = 4$.

[SMP add]

(4) Sketch the curve $y = 3x^{2/3}$ for values of $x$ from 1 to 8. A vase is made from thin glass in the shape of the surface obtained by rotating this curve, together with the line segment from (0,3) to (1,3), about the $y$-axis which is vertical. The unit along each axis is 1 cm. Water is poured into the vase at a constant rate of $30\,\mathrm{cm}^3\mathrm{s}^{-1}$. Prove by integration that the volume, $V\,\mathrm{cm}^3$, of water in the vase, when its depth is $h\,\mathrm{cm}$, is given by

$$V = \frac{\pi}{108}[(h + 3)^4 - 3^4].$$

a.  How long does it take for the depth to increase from 0 to 6 cm?
b.  Find, when $h = 6$, the rate at which

i.  the water level is rising,
ii.  the area of the horizontal water surface is increasing.

[AEB 1986]

(5) A curve is defined by the equations $x = t^2 - 1, y = t^3 - t$, where $t$ is a parameter.
  Sketch the curve for all real values of $t$.
  Find the area of the region enclosed by the loop of the curve.

[L]

(6) Sketch the graph of the function $f : x \rightarrow |3x - 2|$ in the interval $0 \le x \le 1$.
  Evaluate $\int_0^1 f(x)dx$. [If you wish, you may use a formula for the area of a triangle.]

[SMP]

## COMMON ERRORS
### (1) Integration

a.  Do not integrate when you are asked to differentiate, or the other way round.

b.  When integrating a negative power of $x$, you still add 1 to the power.
$$\int x^{-3}dx = -\frac{1}{2}x^{-2} + c, \text{ not } -\frac{1}{4}x^{-4} + c.$$

c.  Do not forget to divide by $(n + 1)$ when integrating $x^n$. And divide by $(n + 1)$, not by $n$.

d.  If functions are multiplied, you cannot integrate them individually and multiply the results.

$$\int f(x)g(x)dx \neq \int f(x)dx \times \int g(x)dx.$$

A similar mistake arises when one function is divided by another.

e.  Do not forget the constant of integration $c$.

### (2) Definite Integrals

Make sure that you get the limits of integration the correct way round. Be very careful of negative signs when subtracting the second value from the first.

### (3) Areas

Questions often ask you to find the area between two curves. You must first find out where they intersect.

### (4) Volume

a.  When using the formula $\int \pi y^2 dx$, you must square first and then integrate. Watch out for the following:

$$\int \pi y^2 dx \neq \pi (\int y dx)^2$$

b.  When using the formula $\int \pi y^2 dx$, you must express $y$ as a function of $x$. And the other way round: if a curve is rotated about the $y$-axis, you will use the formula $\int \pi x^2 dy$. Write $x$ as a function of $y$ before integrating.

# 16 Methods of Integration

Trigonometric and exponential functions are integrated as follows:

$$\int \cos x \, dx = \sin x + c \quad \int \sin x \, dx = -\cos x + c$$

$$\int e^x \, dx = e^x + c \qquad \int 1/x \, dx = \ln x + c.$$

## 16.1 Integration by Substitution

Simple functions can often be integrated by inspection.

More complicated functions which cannot be directly integrated can be reduced to a simpler form by *substitution*.

When an expression involves a "function of a function", $f(g(x))$, it is often helpful to substitute for the inside function. That is, put $u = g(x)$.

### 16.1.1 Examples

(1)　　　Find the integral $\int \cos 3x \, dx$.

Solution　　The answer must be of the form $k \sin 3x + c$, where $k$ is a constant. The derivative of $\sin 3x$ is $3 \cos 3x$. This is 3 times too big. Hence to balance out $k$ must be $\frac{1}{3}$.

$$\int \cos 3x \, dx = \frac{1}{3} \sin 3x + c$$

134

(2)    Evaluate the integral $\int_0^{\pi/4} \sin^3 x \cos x dx$.

Solution    Put $u = \sin x$. $du/dx = \cos x$, hence $du = \cos x dx$. The integral becomes:

$$\int u^3 du = [\frac{1}{4}u^4]_{x=0}^{x=\pi/4} = [\frac{1}{4}\sin^4 x]_0^{\pi/4}$$

**The integral is** $\dfrac{1}{4}\sin^4 \pi/4 =^1/_{16}$

(3)    Find the indefinite integral $\int x\sqrt{(1+x)}dx$.

Solution    Put $u = 1+x$. Then $x = u - 1$. Also $du/dx = 1$, hence $du = dx$. The integral becomes:

$$\int (u-1)\sqrt{u}du = \int (u^{1\frac{1}{2}} - u^{\frac{1}{2}})du = \frac{u^{2\frac{1}{2}}}{2\frac{1}{2}} - \frac{u^{1\frac{1}{2}}}{1\frac{1}{2}} + c$$

**The integral is** $\dfrac{2}{5}(1+x)^{2\frac{1}{2}} - \dfrac{2}{3}(1+x)^{1\frac{1}{2}} + c$

## 16.1.2 Exercises

(1) Find the following integrals by inspection:

(a)  $\int \sin 2x dx$          (b)  $\int \cos \frac{1}{2}x dx$

(c)  $\int \sin(3x - 1)dx$      (d)  $\int 4\cos(2x + 3)dx$

(e)  $\int e^{3x} dx$           (f)  $\int e^{2x+1} dx$

(g)  $\int \frac{1}{x+3} dx$     (h)  $\int \frac{1}{2x-5} dx$

Evaluate the following integrals:

(2)  $\int_0^{\pi/2} \cos^4 x \sin x dx$      (3)  $\int_0^4 x\sqrt{(1+x^2)}dx$

(4)  $\int_0^1 e^x \sqrt{(2 + e^x)}dx$       (5)  $\int_1^2 xe^{x^2} dx$

(6)  $\int_0^{\pi/6} \cos x e^{\sin x} dx$    (7)  $\int_0^a \frac{x}{a + x^2}dx$

(8)  $\int_0^{\pi/2} \frac{\cos x}{1 + \sin x} dx$   (9)  $\int_1^2 \frac{2x + 1}{x^2 + x + 1}dx$

(10)  $\int x^2 \sqrt{(x^3 + 4)}dx$      (11)  $\int (\cos \sqrt{x})/\sqrt{x}dx$

(12)   $\int \sec^2 x \tan^3 x\,dx$       (13)   $\int 1/(x \ln x)\,dx$

(14)   $\int x\sqrt{(3+x)}\,dx$       (15)   $\int 2x/\sqrt{(1+3x)}\,dx$

(16)   $\int (x-1)(x+1)^{1\frac{1}{2}}\,dx$   (17)   $\int 1/(3x-1)^3\,dx$

(18)   $\int x(1+4x)^{14}\,dx$       (19)   $\int (x-3)(x+2)^{12}\,dx$

(20) Use the identity $\cos^2 x = 1 - \sin^2 x$ to evaluate $\int \cos^3 dx$

(21)   $\int \sin^5 x\,dx$   (22)   $\int dx/(1-e^x)$ (Multiply top and bottom by $e^{-x}$)

(23) $\int \cos^2 x\,dx$ (Use the identity $\cos 2x \equiv 2\cos^2 x - 1$).

(24) $\int \sin^2 3x\,dx$ (Use the identity $\cos 2x \equiv 1 - 2\sin^2 x$).

(25) Express $\dfrac{1}{(1+x)(2+x)}$ in partial fractions. Hence evaluate

$$\int \frac{1}{(1+x)(2+x)}\,dx$$

(26) By the method of Question 25, evaluate:

(a)   $\displaystyle\int \frac{dx}{(3+x)(2+x)}$

(b)   $\displaystyle\int \frac{x+4}{(2+x)(1+x)^2}\,dx$

(c)   $\displaystyle\int \frac{2-x}{(1+2x)(1-3x)}\,dx$

## 16.2 Standard Integrals

The following integrals can be quoted:

$\int \dfrac{1}{\sqrt{(a^2-x^2)}}\,dx = \sin^{-1}\dfrac{x}{a} + c \quad \int \dfrac{1}{a^2+x^2}\,dx = \dfrac{1}{a}\tan^{-1}\dfrac{x}{a} + c$

### 16.2.1 Examples

(1)       Evaluate $\int_0^1 \dfrac{1}{\sqrt{(4-x^2)}}\,dx$

Solution   Apply the first formula, using $a = 2$.

$$\int_0^1 \frac{1}{\sqrt{(4-x^2)}}\mathbf{dx} = \left[\sin^{-1}\frac{1}{2}\mathbf{x}\right] = \pi/6$$

(2) Evaluate $\int \dfrac{1}{9 + 4(x+2)^2} dx$, by using the substitution $u = 2(x+2)$.

Solution Use the substitution as suggested. $du = 2dx$.

$$\int \frac{1}{9 + 4(x+2)^2} dx = \int \frac{\frac{1}{2}}{9 + u^2} du$$

This is now in the second form. Evaluate the integral:

$$\frac{1}{6} \ \tan^{-1} \frac{1}{3} u + c = \frac{1}{6} \ \tan^{-1} \frac{2}{3}(x+2) + c$$

## 16.2.2 Exercises

Evaluate the following integrals

(1) $\int_0^2 \dfrac{1}{\sqrt{(9 - x^2)}} dx$  (2) $\int_0^8 \dfrac{5}{\sqrt{(64 - x^2)}} dx$

(3) $\int_0^{\frac{1}{2}} \dfrac{4}{\sqrt{(1 - 4x^2)}} dx$  (4) $\int_0^1 \dfrac{1}{1 + \frac{1}{4}x^2} dx$

(5) $\int \dfrac{1}{\sqrt{(1 - x^2/9)}} dx$  (6) $\int \dfrac{1}{4 + 9x^2} dx$

(7) $\int \dfrac{1}{\sqrt{(1 - (x+1)^2)}} dx$  (8) $\int \dfrac{1}{4 + (x-3)^2} dx$

(9) $\int \dfrac{3}{\sqrt{(4 - (2x+1)^2)}} dx$  (10) $\int \dfrac{7}{9 + 16(x-3)^2} dx$

(11) By use of partial fractions, evaluate

$$\int \frac{x^2 + x + 4}{x(x^2 + 4)} \ dx$$

## 16.3 Integration by Parts

A product of two functions can sometimes be integrated by means of *integration by parts*.

$$\int uv\,dx = \left(\int u\,dx\right)v - \int \left(\int u\,dx\right)(dv/dx)\,dx$$

### 16.3.1 Examples

(1) Find $\int xe^x dx$.

Solution Here let $v$ be $x$ and $u$ be $e^x$. Apply the formula:

$$\int xe^x dx = xe^x - \int e^x(dx/dx)dx = xe^x - \int e^x dx$$

$$\int xe^x dx = xe^x - e^x + c$$

137

(2)     Find $\int \ln x \, dx$.

Solution     Regard $\ln x$ as $1 \times \ln x$. Take $u$ as 1 and $v$ as $\ln x$.
Apply the formula:

$$\int 1 \times \ln x \, dx = x \ln x - \int x (d \ln x / dx) \, dx = x \ln x - \int x/x \, dx$$

$$\int \ln x \, dx = x \ln x - x + c$$

### 16.3.2 Exercises

Evaluate the following:

(1)  $\int x e^{-x} \, dx$         (2)  $\int x \cos x \, dx$

(3)  $\int x \sin x \, dx$         (4)  $\int x \ln x \, dx$

(5)  $\int x^2 \ln x \, dx$        (6)  $\int x^n \ln x \, dx$

(7)  $\int \sin^{-1} x \, dx$      (Use the fact that $d(\sin^{-1} x)/dx = 1/\sqrt{(1 - x^2)}$)

(8)  $\int \tan^{-1} x \, dx$      (Use the fact that $d(\tan^{-1} x)/dx = 1/(1 + x^2)$)

(9)  $\int x^2 e^x \, dx$          (10)  $\int x^2 e^{ax} \, dx$

(11)  $\int x^2 \cos 3x \, dx$     (12)  $\int e^x (x - 3) \, dx$

(13)  $\int x^2 \sin ax \, dx$     (14)  $\int (\ln x)/x^2 \, dx$

## 16.4 Examination Questions

(1)

a.  Integrate with respect to $x$
     (i)  $\sin 4x$,  (ii)  $\frac{1}{2} \cos(\frac{1}{2}x + \frac{1}{2})$.

b.  Evaluate $\int_0^1 (1 + 9x)^{-1} \, dx$.

[AEB add 1986]

(2) Draw a sketch to show the finite region bounded by the curve $y = e^{x/2}$ and the lines $x = 2, x = 4$ and $y = 0$.
Leaving your answer in terms of $e$, calculate the area of this region.

[L add]

(3) Express $\dfrac{2}{(1 + 2x)(1 + 4x^2)}$ in partial fractions, and hence evaluate

$$\int_0^{1/2} \frac{2}{(1 + 2x)(1 + 4x^2)} dx$$

giving your answer correct to 3 significant figures.

[O&C]

(4)

i. Find $\int (3x + 4)e^{2x} dx$.

ii. By using the substitution $x = 2 \tan \theta$, evaluate

$$\int_0^2 \frac{1}{(4 + x^2)^2} dx$$

[L]

(5) Using the substitution $x = 3 + \sin \theta$, show that

$$\int_2^4 \sqrt{(4 - x)(x - 2)} dx = \int_{-\pi/2}^{\pi/2} \cos^2 \theta d\theta.$$

Hence evaluate the integral.

[W]

(6) Sketch the graph of $y = \sin^{-1}(x/a)$, where $a > 0$, stating the domain and the range of the function.

Using the fact that the derivative of $\sin x$ is $\cos x$, show that

$$\frac{dy}{dx} = +\frac{1}{\sqrt{(a^2 - x^2)}}$$

Hence, or otherwise, show that

$$\int_0^1 \frac{dx}{\sqrt{(4 - (x + 1)^2)}} = \frac{\pi}{3}$$

[SMP]

## COMMON ERRORS

### (1) Substitution

a.  When substituting $u$ for $x$, do not forget to change the $dx$ to a $du$ by means of $du/dx$. You cannot integrate a function of $u$ with respect to $x$.

b.  When finding an indefinite integral by substituting $u$ for $x$, you must re-substitute back at the end to get the answer in terms of $x$. Do not give the answer in terms of $u$.

c.  When finding a definite integral by substitution, remember that the limits refer to values of $x$. Do not apply these values to $u$ when working out the final answer.

### (2) Integration by Parts

When integrating something like $xe^x$, integrate the $e^x$ term first. If you integrate the $x$ term first, you will obtain $\frac{1}{2}x^2e^x$, which is harder to integrate than the function you started with.

# EXTRA PURE TOPICS

# 17 Numerical Methods

If a value cannot be found exactly, then an approximate value can often be obtained by *Numerical Methods.*

## 17.1 Solution of Equations

A. *Linear Interpolation* estimates the root of the equation $f(x) = 0$ by drawing a straight line between two known values of the function, and calculating where that straight line crosses the $x$-axis.

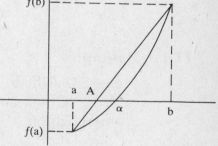

If $a$ and $b$ are near the root $\alpha$, then draw the straight line between $(a, f(a))$ and $(b, f(b))$. If this line crosses the $x$-axis at $A$, then by similar triangles:

$$\frac{A - a}{-f(a)} = \frac{b - A}{f(b)}$$

$$A = \frac{af(b) - bf(a)}{f(b) - f(a)}$$

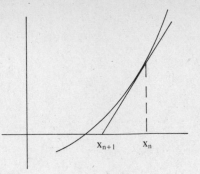

B. The *Newton-Raphson* method obtains approximations to the root of $f(x) = 0$ by drawing a tangent to the curve of $y = f(x)$, and calculating where that tangent crosses the $x$-axis.

Pick a first approximation $x_0$, and successive approximations are given by:

$$x_{n+1} = x_n - \frac{f(x_n)}{f'(x_n)}$$

C. *Picard's* method obtains approximations to the root of $f(x) = x$ by means of the following procedure:

Pick a first approximation $x_0$, and successive approximations are given by:

$$x_{n+1} = f(x_n).$$

Picard's method will work if $|f'(x)| < 1$ near the solution $\alpha$. If this is not the case, then invert the function and apply the iteration:

$$x_{n+1} = f^{-1}(x_n).$$

## 17.1.1 Examples

(1)        Show that there is a root of $x^3 + 3x - 1 = 0$ between 0 and 1. Obtain an approximation for this root by linear interpolation.

Solution     Let $f(x) = x^3 + 3x - 1$. Then $f(0) = -1$, and $f(1) = 3$. Hence the graph of $y = x^3 + 3x - 1$ must cross the $x$-axis at some point $\alpha$ between 0 and 1.

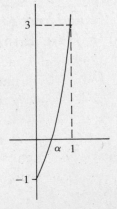

To find an approximation for $\alpha$, apply the formula above, using $a = 0$ and $b = 1$.

$$\alpha \simeq (0 \times 3 - 1 \times -1)/(3 - (-1)) = \frac{1}{4}$$

(2) Use the Newton-Raphson formula to find a solution to $x^3 + 3x - 1 = 0$, accurate to 6 decimal places.

Solution Take $x_0 = \frac{1}{4}$ as the starting point. The iteration is:

$$x_{n+1} = x_n - \frac{x_n^3 + 3x_n - 1}{3x_n^2 + 3}$$

$$x_1 = 0.3235294$$

$$x_2 = 0.3221859$$

$$x_3 = 0.3221854$$

$$x_4 = 0.3221854$$

The last 2 values agree to 6 decimal places.

**The solution is $\alpha = 0.322185$**

(3) Use Picard's Method to solve the equation $x^3 + 3x - 1 = 0$, to 3 decimal places.

Solution Re-write the equation as $x = \frac{1}{3}(1 - x^3)$ and apply the formula, using $x_0 = \frac{1}{4}$ and $f(x) = \frac{1}{3}(1 - x^3)$

$$x_1 = 0.328125, x_2 = 0.321557, x_3 = 0.322250$$

**The solution is $\alpha = 0.322$**

## 17.1.2 Exercises

(1) Show that there is a root of $x^4 + 6x + 1 = 0$ between -1 and 0, and use linear interpolation to find an approximation to that root.

(2) Use Newton-Raphson's iteration to find the solution to the equation in Question 1, accurate to 6 decimal places.

(3) **Find a pair of integers between which there is a root of** $x^3 - 2x^2 - 3 = 0$.
Use linear interpolation to find an approximation to that root.

(4) Find the solution to the equation of Question 3, accurate to 5 decimal places, by means of Newton-Raphson's iteration.

(5) Find the solution to the equation $e^x = 2 - x$, accurate to 6 decimal places.

(6) Solve to 6 decimal places the equation $\sin \theta + \theta = 1$. ($\theta$ is measured in radians).

(7) Solve the equation $\tan\theta = \theta + 1$, accurate to 6 decimal places.

(8) Use Picard's iteration to solve the equation $\cos x = x$, to 3 decimal places.

(9) Show that the equation $x^3 + x - 1 = 0$ can be written either as (a) $x = 1 - x^3$ or as (b)$x = \sqrt[3]{(1-x)}$. Apply Picard's iteration to the equation, using both of the forms (a) and (b). Which one works? Find the solution of the equation, given to 3 decimal places.

## 17.2 Numerical Integration

In many cases a function cannot be exactly integrated. There are two methods for finding the definite integral of $f(x)$ from $x = a$ to $x = b$.

A. Divide the interval $[a, b]$ into $n$ equal intervals of length $h$. ($h = (b-a)/n$)

$$a = x_0 < x_1 < ... < x_n = b.$$

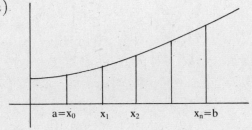

The Trapezium Rule approximates the integral by dividing the area into $n$ trapezia. The formula is:

$$\int_a^b f(x)dx \simeq \frac{1}{2}h(f(a) + f(b) + 2(f(x_1) + f(x_2) + ... + f(x_{n-1})))$$

B. For *Simpson's Rule* there must be an even number of subintervals. So $n$ must be even. The formula is

$$\int_a^b f(x)dx \simeq \tfrac{1}{3}h(f(a) + f(b) + 4(f(x_1) + f(x_3) + ..) + 2(f(x_2) + f(x_4) + ..))$$

### 17.2.1 Examples

(1)  Evaluate $\int_1^2 \sin\sqrt{x}dx$, using (i) the Trapezium Rule with 4 intervals (b) Simpson's Rule with 8 intervals.

Solution  (i) Here $a = 1, b = 2, h = \frac{1}{4}$. Apply the formula:

$$\int_1^2 \sin\sqrt{x}dx \simeq \frac{1}{8}(\sin\sqrt{1} + \sin\sqrt{2} + 2(\sin\sqrt{1\tfrac{1}{4}} + \sin\sqrt{1\tfrac{1}{2}} + \sin\sqrt{1\tfrac{3}{4}}))$$

$$\int_1^2 \sin\sqrt{x}dx \simeq \mathbf{0.931}$$

(ii) Here $h = \frac{1}{8}$. Apply the formula to obtain the approximation:

$(\frac{1}{8}/3)(\sin \sqrt{1} + \sin \sqrt{2} + 4(\sin \sqrt{1\frac{1}{8}} + \sin \sqrt{1\frac{3}{8}} + \sin \sqrt{1\frac{5}{8}} + \sin \sqrt{1\frac{7}{8}}) + 2(\sin \sqrt{1\frac{1}{4}} + \sin \sqrt{1\frac{1}{2}} + \sin \sqrt{1\frac{3}{4}}))$.

$$\int_1^2 \sin \sqrt{x} \, dx \simeq 0.9321$$

(2)    $y$ is a function of $x$: the table below gives 6 values for $x$ and $y$:

| $x$ | 0 | 10 | 20 | 30 | 40 | 50 |
|---|---|---|---|---|---|---|
| $y$ | 1.3 | 1.7 | 2.6 | 2.9 | 3.5 | 4.4 |

Use the trapezium rule to find an approximation for $\int_0^{50} y \, dx$.

Solution    Apply the Trapezium Rule with $a = 0, b = 50, h = 10$.

$$\int_0^{50} y \, dx \simeq \frac{1}{2} \times 10 \times (1.3 + 4.4 + 2(1.7 + 2.6 + 2.9 + 3.5))$$

$$\int_0^{50} y \, dx \simeq 135.5$$

## 17.2.2 Exercises

(1) Evaluate $\int_1^2 \sqrt{(x^3 + 1)} \, dx$, using the Trapezium Rule with 4 intervals.

(2) Evaluate $\int_0^1 \sqrt{(\sin x)} \, dx$, using the Trapezium Rule with 6 intervals.

(3) Evaluate $\int_1^3 (x^2 + 1) \, dx$, using the Trapezium Rule with 8 intervals.

(4), (5), (6) Evaluate the functions above, using Simpson's Rule with the same number of intervals.

(7) Evaluate $\int_0^{\frac{1}{2}\pi} \cos x \, dx$, (a) by exact integration, (b) by the Trapezium rule with 4 intervals, (c) by Simpson's Rule with 4 intervals. What conclusion do you make about the accuracy of the two rules?

(8) Evaluate $\int_0^1 e^{-x^2} \, dx$ by Simpson's Rule, using 4 intervals. Repeat, using 8 intervals. Continue, until you have the value of the integral correct to 5 decimal places.

(9) $y$ is a function of $x$, with values given by the following table:

| $x$ | 2 | 3 | 4 | 5 | 6 | 7 |
|---|---|---|---|---|---|---|
| $y$ | 85 | 74 | 66 | 59 | 51 | 47 |

Use the Trapezium Rule to approximate $\int_2^7 y \, dx$.

(10) $y$ is given in terms of $x$ by the following table:

| $x$ | 0 | 0.2 | 0.4 | 0.6 | 0.8 | 1.0 | 1.2 |
|-----|------|------|------|------|------|------|------|
| $y$ | 0.35 | 0.47 | 0.57 | 0.65 | 0.79 | 0.86 | 1.03 |

Approximate $\int_0^{1.2} y\,dx$, using the Trapezium Rule.

(11) Find $\int y\,dx$ for the table in Question 10, using Simpson's Rule.

(12) $y$ is given in terms of $x$ by the table:

| $x$ | 10 | 13 | 16 | 19 | 22 | 25 |
|-----|-----|-----|-----|-----|-----|-----|
| $y$ | 0.3 | 0.8 | 1.4 | 2.1 | 3.0 | 4.2 |

Find an approximation for $\int y\,dx$ using the Trapezium Rule.

Write out an extra row for the values of $y^2$, and hence find an approximation for $\int y^2\,dx$, using the Trapezium Rule.

(13) $y$ is given in terms of $x$ by the following table:

| $x$ | -0.5 | -0.25 | 0 | 0.25 | 0.5 | 0.75 | 1 |
|-----|------|-------|------|------|------|------|------|
| $y$ | 2.8 | 2.45 | 2.26 | 3.33 | 4.28 | 5.73 | 6.96 |

Use Simpson's Rule to find an approximation for the area between the curve of $y$ and the $x$-axis, from $x = -0.5$ to $x = 1$.

This area is rotated through $360°$ about the $x$-axis. Use Simpson's Rule to find an approximation for the volume of revolution.

(14) If $y$ is given in terms of $x$ by the table of Question 13, use Simpson's Rule to find an approximation for $\int 1/y\,dx$.

## 17.3 Examination Questions

(1) The equation of a curve is $y = x^2 - 3x + 5$. A region is bounded by the curve, the axes and the ordinate at $x = 4$.

i. By using the trapezium rule with four strips of equal width, find an approximate value of the area of the region.

ii. Use a sketch to show why the approximate value of the area of the region is greater than the actual value.

[JMB add]

(2) Sketch the curve $y = \sqrt{(1 + x^3)}$ for values of $x$ from $x = 0$ to $x = 6$, giving a table of values for $x = 0, 1, 2, 3, 4, 5$ and $6$ to 2 decimal places. Use Simpson's rule with six strips, or another suitable method, to calculate the area between the curve and the $x$-axis bounded by $x = 0$ and $x = 6$.

[O&C add]

(3) Show that the cubic equation $x^3 + 2x - 11 = 0$ has only one real root and further that the root lies between $x = 1$ and $x = 2$.

Two possible iterative schemes for finding the root are

(i)   $x_{n+1} = (11 - x_n^3)/2$ and   (ii)   $x_{n+1} = (11 - 2x_n)^{\frac{1}{3}}$

Show that only one of these schemes converges from an initial estimate of $x = 2$ and hence find the root correct to 3 d.p., justifying the accuracy of your answer.

[MEI]

(4) Draw a diagram to show why, if $x_0$ is an approximate solution of the equation $f(x) = 0$, then $x_0 - f(x_0)/f'(x_0)$ is, in general, a better one.

Prove that the cubic equation $x^3 + 6x - 2 = 0$ has a root lying between $0$ and $1$, and find it correct to two decimal places.

[O&C]

(5) Show that $\int_0^1 x^2 e^x dx = e - 2$.

Show that use of the trapezium rule with 5 strips (6 ordinates) gives an estimate that is about 3.8% too high.

Explain why approximate evaluation of this integral using the trapezium rule will always result in an overestimate, however many strips are used.

[MEI]

(6) A function $y = f(x)$ is tabulated for various values of $x$ as shown below:

| $x$ | 1.0 | 1.2 | 1.4 | 1.6 | 1.8 |
|---|---|---|---|---|---|
| $y$ | 3.70 | 3.82 | 4.15 | 4.51 | 5.07 |

Estimate

i.   the value of $y$ at $x = 1.15$;

ii.  the value of $x$ for which $y = 4.40$,

iii. $\int_1^{1.8} y\,dx$, using Simpson's Rule.

[O&C]

149

## COMMON ERRORS

### (1) Index Notation

Do not be confused by the notation $x_n$. For example, do not confuse $x_2$ with $x^2$. $x_2$ is the second approximation in the sequence which started with $x_0$.

### (2) Solution of Equations

In all the methods be very careful with arithmetic. It is very easy to make mistakes, especially with the negative signs in the linear interpolation and Newton-Raphson formulae.

When doing several successive approximations, it is a good idea to keep $x_n$ in the memory of your calculator, and then replace it with $x_{n+1}$ after each approximation is completed.

### (3) Numerical Integration

a.  Make sure that your intervals are correct. They must be equal in length, and for Simpson's Rule there must be an even number of them. (Which means that there are an odd number of $x$-values.)

b.  When approximating something like $\int y^2 dx$, make sure that you square the $y$ values before you use the formula. Be careful of the following:

$$\int y^2 dx \neq \left( \int y dx \right)^2$$

# 18 Series and Induction

A *power series* is an expression of the form:

$$a_0 + a_1 x + a_2 x^2 + ... + a_n x^n + ...$$

where $a_0, a_1, ... a_n, ...$ are constants.

Two special power series have been defined, in Chapters 2 and 3.

$$\frac{1}{1-x} \equiv 1 + x + x^2 + ... + x^n + ... \qquad \text{(the geometric series)}$$

$$(1+x)^n \equiv 1 + nx + n(n-1)x^2/2! + n(n-1)(n-2)x^3/3! + ... \text{(the binomial series)}.$$

Both these series are valid for $-1 < x < 1$

## 18.1 Series for Trig and Exponential Functions

Some standard series are as follows:

$\ln(1 + x) = x - x^2/2 + x^3/3 - x^4/4 + \ldots$

This series is valid for $-1 < x \leq 1$.

$e^x \equiv 1 + x + x^2/2! + x^3/3! + \ldots + x^n/n! + \ldots$

$\sin x \equiv x - x^3/3! + x^5/5! - \ldots$

$\cos x \equiv 1 - x^2/2! + x^4/4! - \ldots$

These series are valid for all $x$. In the expansions for $\sin x$ and $\cos x$ the angle $x$ is measured in radians.

### 18.1.1 Examples

(1)      Find the series for $e^{2x} \cos x$, up to the term in $x^3$.

Solution      Expand both the series, up to the $x^3$ term.

$$e^{2x} \simeq 1 + 2x + (2x)^2/2! + (2x)^3/3! \qquad \cos x \simeq 1 - x^2/2!$$

$$e^{2x} \cos x \simeq (1 + 2x + 2x^2 + 1\tfrac{1}{3}x^3)(1 - \tfrac{1}{2}x^2)$$

$$\mathbf{e^{2x} \cos x \simeq 1 + 2x + 1\tfrac{1}{2}x^2 + \tfrac{1}{3}x^3}$$

(2)      Find the series for $(1 + x^2)^{-1}$, and use it to find the series for $\tan^{-1} x$. Hence find the approximate value of $\tan^{-1} 0.1$.

Solution      To find the series for $(1+x^2)^{-1}$ use the geometric series, replacing $x$ by $-x^2$.

$$\mathbf{(1 + x^2)^{-1} \equiv 1 - x^2 + x^4 - \ldots}$$

Integrate this series to find $\tan^{-1} x$. The constant of integration is zero, as $\tan^{-1} 0 = 0$.

$$\mathbf{\tan^{-1} x \equiv x - x^3/3 + x^5/5 - \ldots}$$

Put in $x = 0.1$ and evaluate:

$$\mathbf{\tan^{-1} 0.1 \simeq 0.0996687}$$

## 18.1.2 Exercises

(1) Find the first three non-zero terms in the series for the following:

(a)  $\cos 2x$     (b)  $\sin 3x$

(c)  $e^{3x}$     (d)  $e^{-2x}$

(e)  $e^x \sin x$     (f)  $e^{-x} \cos x$

(g)  $\ln(1 + 2x)$   (h)  $\ln(1 - x^2)$

(2) Use the series expansions to find approximations for the following:

(a)  $e^{\frac{1}{2}}$     (b)  $\cos \frac{1}{4}$

(c)  $\sin 0.1$   (d)  $1/e$

(e)  $\ln(1.1)$   (f)  $\ln(0.8)$

(3) Multiply together the series for $\cos x$ and $\sin x$, and write the result as a power series up to the $x^3$ term. Verify that your answer is the same as the expansion of $\frac{1}{2} \sin 2x$.

(4) Find the expansion for $\cos^2 x$ up to the $x^4$ term, (a) by squaring the series of $\cos x$ (b) by writing $\cos^2 x = \frac{1}{2} \cos 2x + \frac{1}{2}$, and expanding $\cos 2x$. Verify that the results are the same.

(5) Integrate the series for $1/(1 + x)$, and verify that the result is the series for $\ln(1 + x)$.

(6) By writing $(2 + x)$ as $2(1 + \frac{1}{2}x)$, find the series for $\ln(2 + x)$.

(7) By expanding the terms concerned, find the limit as $x$ tends to zero of

$$\frac{e^x - e^{-x}}{e^{2x} - e^{-2x}}$$

(8) Use the method of Question 7 to find the limit as $x$ tends to zero of:

(a)  $\dfrac{1 - \cos x}{x^2}$     (b)  $\dfrac{x^2 - x \sin x}{1 - \cos x}$

(c)  $\dfrac{\ln(1 + x)}{x}$     (d)  $\dfrac{e^x - e^{-x}}{\sin x}$

(9) By writing $2^x$ as $e^{x \ln 2}$ find the expansion of $2^x$.

(10) Find the limit as $x$ tends to zero of $(2^x - 2^{-x})/(3^x - 3^{-x})$.

(11) Expand $e^{-x}$ up to the term in $x^2$. Hence find an approximate solution for the equation $e^{-x} = x$.

(12) By the method of Question 11 find approximate solutions for:

(a)  $\cos x = 3x$   (b)  $\sin x = \ln(1 + x)$

## 18.2 Maclaurin Series

The *Maclaurin series* for a function $f(x)$ is:

$$f(x) \equiv f(0) + xf'(0) + x^2 f''(0)/2! + \ldots + x^n f^n(0)/n! + \ldots$$

Here $f^n(0)$ represents the $n$'th derivative of $f(x)$, evaluated at $x = 0$.

### 18.2.1 Example

Find the Maclaurin series for $\tan x$, up to the term in $x^3$. Hence find the approximate value of $\tan 0.2$.

Solution　Let $f(x) = \tan x$. Differentiate three times:

$$f'(x) = \sec^2 x \qquad f''(x) = 2 \sec^2 x \tan x$$

$$f^3(x) = 4 \sec^2 x \tan^2 x + 2 \sec^4 x.$$

Put $x = 0$ in each of these derivatives and in $f(x)$ itself.

$$f(0) = 0 : f'(0) = 1 : f''(0) = 0 : f^3(0) = 2.$$

Put these values into the Maclaurin series.

$$\tan x \simeq x + \frac{1}{3}x^3$$

Put $x = 0.2$:

$$\tan 0.2 \simeq 0.2027$$

### 18.2.2 Exercises

(1) Use the fact that the derivative of $e^x$ is $e^x$ to verify that the Maclaurin series for $e^x$ is the series given in 18.1.

(2) Find the first four derivatives of $\cos x$ and of $\sin x$. Hence verify that their Maclaurin series are the same as the series in 18.1.

(3) Find the Maclaurin series for the following functions, up to the term in $x^3$.

(a)　$\sin^{-1} x$　(b)　$\cos^{-1} x$

(c)　$\sec x$　(d)　$e^{\tan x}$

(4) By writing $f(x) = \sin(\pi/6 + x)$, prove that

$$\sin(\pi/6 + x) \simeq \frac{1}{2} + \frac{1}{2}\sqrt{3}x - \frac{1}{4}x^2$$

(5) Find the expansion of $\cos(\frac{1}{3}\pi + x)$ up to the term in $x^2$.

## 18.3 Mathematical Induction

The principle of *Mathematical Induction* provides proofs of theorems about positive whole numbers. It is as follows:

Suppose $\varphi$ is a statement about positive whole numbers. If it can be shown that:

I $\qquad\qquad \varphi$ is true for $n = 1$,

II  if $\varphi$ is true for $n = k$ then $\varphi$ is true for $n = k + 1$,

then it follows by mathematical induction that $\varphi$ is true for all $n$.

### 18.3.1 Examples

(1) Prove by induction that $1 + 3 + 5 + 7 + ... + (2n - 1) = n^2$.

Solution The above is the statement $\varphi$. Checking for $n = 1$:
Left hand side $= 1$. Right hand side $= 1^2 = 1$.
$\varphi$ is true for $n = 1$
Assume that $\varphi$ is true for $n = k$. i.e. assume that:

$$1 + 3 + 5 + ... + (2k - 1) = k^2$$

Add $2k + 1$ to both sides.

$$1 + 3 + 5 + ... + (2k - 1) + (2k + 1) = k^2 + 2k + 1 = (k + 1)^2$$

Hence $\varphi$ is true for $n = k + 1$. Putting these results together, $\varphi$ is true for all $n$.

**By induction $1 + 3 + 5 + ... + (2n - 1) = n^2$**

(2) Let the sequence $u_n$ be defined by:

$$u_1 = 5. \quad u_{n+1} = 2u_n + 1$$

Prove that $u_n = 3(2^n) - 1$.

Solution Call the above statement $\varphi$. Verify that $\varphi$ holds for $n = 1$.

$$3(2^1) - 1 = 5. \text{ Hence } \varphi \text{ is true for } n = 1.$$

Assume that $\varphi$ is true for $n = k$. i.e. assume that:

$$u_k = 3(2^k) - 1.$$

$$u_{k+1} = 2 \times (3(2^k) - 1) + 1 = 3(2^{k+1}) - 2 + 1 = 3(2^{k+1}) - 1$$

Hence $\varphi$ holds for $n = k + 1$. By induction $\varphi$ holds for all $n$.

$$\text{For all n}, u_n = 3(2_n) - 1$$

## 18.3.2 Exercises

Prove the following results by induction.

(1) $1 + 2 + 3 + \ldots + n = \frac{1}{2}n(n+1)$

(2) $1 + 4 + 7 + \ldots + (3n - 2) = \frac{1}{2}n(3n - 1)$

(3) $1^2 + 2^2 + \ldots + n^2 = n(n+1)(2n+1)/6$

(4) $1^3 + 2^3 + \ldots + n^3 = \frac{1}{4}n^2(n+1)^2$

(5) $1 + \frac{1}{2} + \frac{1}{4} + \frac{1}{8} + \ldots + \frac{1}{2}^{n-1} = 2 - \frac{1}{2}^{n-1}$

(6) $1 + 3 + 9 + 27 + \ldots + 3^{n-1} = \frac{1}{2}(3^n - 1)$

(7) $1 \times 2 + 2 \times 3 + 3 \times 4 + \ldots + n(n+1) = n(n+1)(n+2)/3$

(8) $1 \times 3 + 2 \times 4 + 3 \times 5 + \ldots + n(n+2) = n(n+1)(2n+7)/6$

(9) $\dfrac{1}{1 \times 2} + \dfrac{1}{2 \times 3} + \dfrac{1}{3 \times 4} + \ldots + \dfrac{1}{n(n+1)} = 1 - \dfrac{1}{n+1}$

(10) $\dfrac{1}{1 \times 3} + \dfrac{1}{2 \times 4} + \ldots + \dfrac{1}{n(n+2)} = \dfrac{3}{4} - \dfrac{2n+3}{2(n+1)(n+2)}$

(11) $1 \times 1! + 2 \times 2! + 3 \times 3! + \ldots + n \times n! = (n+1)! - 1$

(12) If $u_1 = 4$ and $u_{n+1} = 2u_n$, show that $u_n = 2^{n+1}$.

(13) If $u_1 = 6$ and $u_{n+1} = 2u_n$, show that $u_n = 3 \times 2^n$.

(14) If $u_1 = 7$ and $u_{n+1} = 3u_n - 2$, show that $u_n = 1 + 2 \times 3^n$.

(15) If $y = xe^x$, show that $d^n y/dx^n = xe^x + ne^x$.

$$(d^n y/dx^n \text{ is the } n\text{'th derivative of } y.)$$

(16) If $y = xe^{2x}$, show that $d^n y/dx^n = 2^n xe^{2x} + n2^{n-1}e^{2x}$.

(17) If $y = \cos x$, show that $d^n y/dx^n = \cos(x + n\pi/2)$.

(18) If $y = \sin 3x$, show that $d^n y/dx^n = 3^n \sin(3x + n\pi/2)$.

(19) If $M$ is the matrix $\begin{pmatrix} 1 & 1 \\ 0 & 1 \end{pmatrix}$, show that $M^n = \begin{pmatrix} 1 & n \\ 0 & 1 \end{pmatrix}$

(20) If $M$ is the matrix $\begin{pmatrix} 1 & 1 & 1 \\ 0 & 1 & 1 \\ 0 & 0 & 1 \end{pmatrix}$, show that $M^n = \begin{pmatrix} 1 & n & \frac{1}{2}n(n+1) \\ 0 & 1 & n \\ 0 & 0 & 1 \end{pmatrix}$

(21) Prove that $15^n - 1$ is divisible by 14 for all $n$.

(22) Prove that $n(n^2 - 1)$ is divisible by 6 for all $n$.

(23) Prove that $(3n + 1)7^n - 1$ is divisible by 9 for all $n$.

(24) $n$ lines are in a plane: no two are parallel and no three go through the same point. Prove by induction that the number of regions of the plane separated by the lines is $\frac{1}{2}(n^2 + n + 2)$.

## 18.4 Examination Questions

(1) Find the expansions, in ascending powers of $x$ as far as the term in $x^5$, for

    (i)   $\sin^3 x$    (ii)   $x(1 - \cos x)$.

Find the limit, as $x \to 0$, of the function $(\sin^3 x)/(x(1 - \cos x))$.

[O&C]

(2) When $x$ is so small that $x^3$ and higher powers of $x$ can be neglected, find non-zero constants $a$ and $b$ such that

$$e^{-x} = (1 + ax)/(1 + bx)$$

[L]

(3) *Use Maclaurin's expansion* to obtain the first five non-zero terms of the series for $\log_e(1 + x)$. Hence show that

$$\log_e \left( \frac{1 + x}{1 - x} \right) = 2x + \frac{2x^3}{3} + \frac{2x^5}{5} + \dots$$

and state the range of values of $x$ for which the expansion is valid.

By using a suitable substitution for $x$, an infinite series for $\log_e(n/(n-1))$ may be obtained. Determine this substitution and hence write down the series. Find the range of positive values of $n$ for which this expansion is valid.

Find $k$ such that $\log_e(^9/_8) + k\log_e(^6/_5) = \log_e 1.62$.

Hence *use your series* for $\log_e(^9/_8)$ and $k\log_e(^6/_5)$ to evaluate $\log_e 1.62$ to 5 decimal places.

[AEB 1985]

(4) Given that $y = e^{\tan^{-1} x}$, where $\tan^{-1} x$ denotes the principal value, show that $(1 + x^2)dy/dx = y$

By repeated differentiation of this result, show also that

$$(1 + x^2)\frac{d^4y}{dx^4} + 6x\frac{d^3y}{dx^3} + 6\frac{d^2y}{dx^2} = \frac{d^3y}{dx^3}$$

Hence, or other wise, obtain the expansion of $e^{\tan^{-1}x}$ in ascending powers of $x$ up to and including the term in $x^4$, and show that, when $x$ is small enough for powers above the fourth to be neglected

$$e^{\tan^{-1}x} = e^x - \frac{1}{3}(x^3 + x^4).$$

[C]

(5) By using mathematical induction, or otherwise, prove the following results:

a. $2(1!) + 5(2!) + 10(3!) + ... + (n^2 + 1)(n!) = n[(n + 1)!]$,

b. $\sum_{r=1}^{n} \sin rx = \dfrac{\cos \frac{1}{2}x - \cos(n + \frac{1}{2})x}{2\sin \frac{1}{2}x}$, where $0 < x < 2\pi$

c. $10^n - 13$ is an integer multiple of 3 for all positive integers $n$.

[O&C]

(6) If $n$ great circles are drawn on a spherical surface, no three of them passing through the same point, the number of regions into which the surface is divided is denoted by $u_n$. Write down the values of $u_1, u_2$ and $u_3$. [Great circles are formed as the intersection of the sphere with planes passing through its centre.]

It can be proved that, for every positive integer $n$,

$u_{n+1} = u_n + \alpha n$, where $\alpha$ is a constant.

Use the values of $u_n$ already found, or use a geometrical argument, to find the value of $\alpha$.

Then use the method of mathematical induction, or otherwise, to prove that $u_n$ is equal to $n^2 - n + 2$.

[SMP]

## COMMON ERRORS
### (1) Series

a. The series for $\ln(1 + x)$ is only valid if $|x| < 1$. Do not try to use it if $|x| > 1$. And do not omit the 1; there is no series for $\ln x$.

b. $x$ must be in radians for the series of $\sin x$ and $\cos x$. Do not use the series if $x$ is in degrees.

### (2) Maclaurin series
Do not forget the $n!$ factor when using a Maclaurin series.

## (3) Induction

a.  Do not forget to prove $\varphi$ for $n = 1$. An induction proof must contain this.

b.  Do not "assume the answer" in the induction step. For example, when going from the sum of $k$ terms to the sum of $k+1$ terms, the $k+1'th$ term is added to both sides. You then have to manipulate the right hand side to the appropriate form. Do not immediately assume that the right hand side is in the correct form.

# 19 Complex Numbers

The *square root of minus one*, written $i$ or $j$, is defined by:

$$i^2 = -1$$

A *complex number* is an expression of the form $a + bi$, where $a$ and $b$ are real (ordinary) numbers. The *real part* of $a + ib$ is $a$, and the *imaginary part* is $b$.

$$Re(a + ib) = a : Im(a + ib) = b$$

If two complex numbers are equal, then their real parts are equal and their imaginary parts are equal.

If $a + ib = c + id$, then $a = c$ and $b = d$.

If $z$ is a complex number, the *conjugate*, $z^*$ or $\overline{z}$, is found by multiplying the imaginary part by $-1$.

$$(a + ib)^* = a - ib.$$

## 19.1 Arithmetic of Complex Numbers

Complex numbers are added by adding the real and imaginary parts.

$$(a + ib) + (c + id) = (a + c) + i(b + d)$$

Complex numbers are multiplied by expanding the brackets and simplifying, using the fact that $i^2 = -1$.

$$(a + ib)(c + id) = ac + aid + ibc + i^2bd = (ac - bd) + i(ad + bc)$$

When one complex number is divided by another, the fraction can be simplified by multiplying top and bottom by the conjugate of the bottom.

$$\frac{a + ib}{c + id} = \frac{(a + ib)(c - id)}{(c + id)(c - id)} = \frac{ac + bd + i(bc - ad)}{c^2 + d^2}$$

### 19.1.1 Examples

(1)     For $z = 2 + 3i$ and $w = 3 - i$ find (a) $z + w$ (b) $zw$
(c) $z/w$, in the form $a + ib$.

Solution     (a) Add the real parts and the complex parts.

$$\mathbf{z + w = 5 + 2i}$$

(b) Multiply out the brackets of $(2 + 3i)(3 - i)$.

$$\mathbf{zw = 9 + 7i}$$

(c) Multiply top and bottom of $(2+3i)/(3-i)$ by $(3+i)$.

$$\frac{z}{w} = \frac{(2 + 3i)(3 + i)}{3^2 + 1^2}$$

$$\mathbf{\frac{z}{w} = \frac{3 + 11i}{10} = 0.3 + i1.1}$$

(2)     Solve the equation $z^2 - 2z + 5 = 0$.

Solution    Use the formula for a quadratic:

$$z = \frac{1}{2}(2 \pm \sqrt{(2^2 - 4 \times 1 \times 5)}) = \frac{1}{2}(2 \pm \sqrt{(-16)})$$

Use the fact that $\sqrt{(-16)} = \sqrt{(16 \times -1)} = \sqrt{16} \times \sqrt{-1} = 4i$

$$z = \frac{1}{2}(2 \pm 4i)$$

$$z = 1 + 2i \text{ or } z = 1 - 2i$$

## 19.1.2 Exercises

(1) Write down the real and imaginary parts of the following:

(a). $2 + 5i$        (b)   $-3 + 7i$

(c)   $0.3 - 0.7i$    (d)   $-2 - i/10$

(2) Write down the conjugates of the complex numbers in Question 1.

(3) For $z = 2 + 3i$ and $w = 1 - 5i$ find the following in the form $a + ib$:

(a)   $z + w$   (b)   $z - w$

(c)   $zw$      (d)   $z/w$

(e)   $w/z$     (f)   $z^2$

(4) Repeat Question 4, for $z = -3 - 2i$ and $w = 5 + 3i$.

(5) Solve the following equations, giving your answers in the form $a + ib$:

(a)   $z^2 + 2z + 10 = 0$   (b)   $z^2 - 4z + 20 = 0$

(c)   $z^2 + z + 1 = 0$      (d)   $2z^2 - z + 3 = 0$

(e)   $z^3 - 1 = 0$          (f)   $z^4 - 1 = 0$

(6) Let $w = -\frac{1}{2} + i\frac{1}{2}\sqrt{3}$. Find $w^2$ and $w^3$. What is $w^{51}$?

(7) Let $\alpha = \frac{1}{2} + \frac{1}{2}i$. Find $\alpha^2, \alpha^3, \alpha^4$. What is $\alpha^8$?

(8) Let $z = 3 + 4i$. Find the square roots of $z$. (Hint: let the square root be $x + iy$, and use the equation $(x + iy)^2 = 3 + 4i$ to obtain two simultaneous equations in $x$ and $y$.)

(9) By the method of Question 8 find the square roots of $5 - 12i$.

(10) Solve the following equations, giving your answer in the form $a + ib$.

(a)   $3z + 2i = 8$          (b)   $iz - 4 = 3i$

(c)   $(2 + 3i)z = 4 - 7i$   (d)   $2z + 3i = iz - 4$

(11) $2 + i$ is a root of the equation $z^2 + az + b = 0$. Find $a$ and $b$, given that they are real. What is the other root of the equation?

(12) $3 + 4i$ is a root of the equation $z^3 + az^2 + bz - 75 = 0$. Find $a$ and $b$, given that they are real, and find the other roots.

## 19.2 The Argand Diagram. Modulus and Argument

Complex numbers can be represented on
the plane, with the real part being the
$x$-coordinate and the imaginary part the
$y$-coordinate. So $x + iy$ is placed at $(x, y)$.

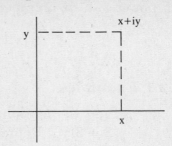

The diagram which represents complex numbers in this way is called the
*Argand Diagram.*

When a complex number $x + iy$ is represented on the Argand Diagram, its
distance from the origin is its *modulus*
$|x + iy|$.

The angle between the line from the origin to the number and the $x$-axis is its
*argument* $arg(x + iy)$.

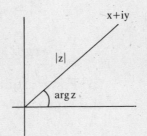

$$|x + iy| = \surd(x^2 + y^2)$$

$$Arg(x + iy) = \tan^{-1} y/x$$

Some common graphs in the Argand Diagram are as follows:

$|z| = k$ is the circle with centre the origin and radius $k$.

$|z - a| = k$ is the circle with centre at $a$ and radius $k$.

$arg(z) = \theta$ is the ray from the origin making $\theta$ with the $x$-axis.

$|z - a| = |z - b|$ is the perpendicular bisector of the line from $a$ to $b$.

If a complex number $x + iy$ has modulus $r$ and argument $\theta$, then $x$ and
$y$ can be found by the formulae:

$$x = r \cos \theta : y = r \sin \theta$$

When complex numbers are multiplied, their moduli are multiplied and their
arguments are added.

$$|zw| = |z||w|; arg(zw) = arg(z) + arg(w)$$

When complex numbers are divided, their moduli are divided and their arguments are subtracted.

$$|z/w| = |z|/|w|; arg(z/w) = arg(z) - arg(w)$$

If a complex number is raised to the $n$'th power, its modulus is raised to the $n$'th power and its argument is multiplied by $n$.

$$|z^n| = |z|^n; arg(z^n) = n \, arg(z)$$

### 19.2.1 Examples

(1)    Find the modulus and argument of (a) $z = 2 + 3i$ (b) $(2 + 3i)^2$. Represent both these points on the Argand Diagram.

Solution    (a) Use the formulae above.

$$\mathbf{|z| = \sqrt{(2^2 + 3^2)} = \sqrt{13}.}$$

$$\mathbf{arg(z) = \tan^{-1}\frac{3}{2} = 56.3°}$$

(b) For $z^2$, square the modulus and double the argument.

$$\mathbf{|z^2| = 13 : arg(z^2) = 112.6°}$$

The Argand Diagram shows the two points.

(2)    Find a square root of $4 + 3i$, in the form $a + ib$.

Solution    The modulus of $4 + 3i$ is 5, and its argument is 36.9°. The square root will have modulus $\sqrt{5}$, and argument $\frac{1}{2} \times 36.9°$. Use the formulae for obtaining the real and imaginary parts in terms of the modulus and argument.

$$a = \sqrt{5}\cos(\frac{1}{2} \times 36.9) : b = \sqrt{5}\sin(\frac{1}{2} \times 36.9)$$

**A square root is $2.12 + i0.71$**

### 19.2.2 Exercises

(1) Find the modulus and argument of the following:

(a)  $4 + 5i$        (b)  $1 + 8i$

(c)  $2 - 3i$        (d)  $-3 - 5i$

(e)  $0.4 + 0.3i$    (f)  $-\frac{1}{2} + \frac{3}{4}i$

(2) Let $z = 1 + 2i$ and $w = 2 + 3i$. Find the modulus and argument of the following, and illustrate them on the same Argand Diagram.

    (a)  $z$    (b)  $w$

    (c)  $zw$    (d)  $z + w$

    (e)  $z^2$    (f)  $z/w$

(3) Repeat Question 2, with $z = 2 - i$ and $w = 2 + i$.

(4) Each of the following exercises gives the modulus $r$ and the argument $\theta$ of a complex number. Express the complex number in the form $x + iy$.

    (a)  $r = 1, \theta = 60°$    (b)  $r = \sqrt{2}, \theta = 45°$

    (c)  $r = 4, \theta = 120°$    (d)  $r = \sqrt{10}, \theta = 250°$

    (e)  $r = 0.3, \theta = 345°$    (f)  $r = 5, \theta = -33°$

(5) Find a square root of the following complex numbers:

    (a)  $1 + i$    (b)  $i$

    (c)  $3 + 5i$    (d)  $-4 + 7i$

(6) Solve the following equations, giving your answers in the form $a + ib$.

    (a)  $z^2 + 2z - i + 1 = 0$   (b)  $z^2 + iz - 3 = 0$

(7) Sketch the following graphs in the Argand diagram:

    (a)  $|z| = 2$         (b)  $|z - i| = 1$

    (c)  $|z - i + 2| = 2$   (d)  $|2z + 3 - 2i| = 4$

    (e)  $arg(z) = 45°$     (f)  $arg(z) = 210°$

    (g)  $|z - 1| = |z - 3|$  (h)  $|z - i| = |z + 2|$

(8) Sketch the region in the Argand Diagram corresponding to $|z| \leq 4$.

(9) Sketch the region in the Argand Diagram corresponding to $|z - 3 - 4i| \leq 1$. Find the greatest and least value of $|z|$ in this region.

## 19.3 De Moivre's Theorem

The complex number with modulus 1 and argument $\theta$ can be written as $\cos\theta + i\sin\theta$. By expanding the functions as series, this can be shown to be equal to $e^{i\theta}$. Note: $\theta$ must be measured in radians.

$$\cos\theta + i\sin\theta = e^{i\theta}.$$

*De Moivre's Theorem* states:

$$(\cos\theta + i\sin\theta)^n = \cos n\theta + i\sin n\theta.$$

### 19.3.1 Examples

(1)      Find the cube roots of $1 + i$, in the form $re^{i\theta}$.

Solution     Let $z$ be such a root. Then $z^3 = 1 + i$. Write $1 + i$ in modulus and argument form:

$$1 + i = \sqrt{2}e^{i\frac{1}{4}\pi}.$$

But the argument of $1 + i$ could be written also as $2\frac{1}{4}\pi$ or as $4\frac{1}{4}\pi$. The three possible arguments give the three roots.

$$z^3 = \sqrt{2}e^{i\frac{1}{4}\pi} \; or \sqrt{2}e^{i2\frac{1}{4}\pi} \; or \sqrt{2}e^{i4\frac{1}{4}\pi}$$

Cube root the modulus, and divide the argument by 3.

**The cube roots are $^6\sqrt{2}e^{i\theta}$, where $\theta = \pi/12, 3\pi/4$ or $17\pi/12$**

(2)      Use De Moivre's theorem to express $\cos 3\theta$ in terms of powers of $\cos\theta$.

Solution     Apply De Moivre for $n = 3$.

$$(\cos\theta + i\sin\theta)^3 = \cos 3\theta + i\sin 3\theta$$

Expand the left hand side:

$$\cos^3\theta + 3i\cos^2\theta\sin\theta - 3\cos\theta\sin^2\theta - i\sin^3\theta = \cos 3\theta + i\sin 3\theta$$

Equate the real parts, and use the identity $\sin^2\theta \equiv 1 - \cos^2\theta$

$$\cos 3\theta = \cos^3\theta - 3\cos\theta(1 - \cos^2\theta)$$

$$\cos 3\theta = 4\cos^3\theta - 3\cos\theta$$

### 19.3.2 Exercises

(1) Express the following in the form $re^{i\theta}$:

    (a)   $1 + 2i$     (b)   $-3 + 4i$

    (c)   $\sqrt{2} - i\sqrt{2}$   (d)   $-3 - 5i$

(2) Express the following in the form $a + ib$:

(a) $2e^{i\pi}$  (b) $3e^{i\frac{3}{4}\pi}$

(c) $4e^{i3\pi}$  (d) $e^i$

(3) Simplify the following:

(a) $(\cos\frac{1}{4}\pi + i\sin\frac{1}{4}\pi)^8$        (b)        $(\cos\frac{1}{3}\pi - i\sin\frac{1}{3}\pi)^6$

(c) $(2 + i2)^{10}$        (d)        $(\frac{1}{2} - i\frac{1}{2}\sqrt{3})^{15}$

(e) $\dfrac{\cos 2\theta + i\sin 2\theta}{\cos\theta - i\sin\theta}$    (f) $\dfrac{(\cos 3\theta - i\sin 3\theta)^2}{(\cos 5\theta + i\sin 5\theta)}$

(4) Use De Moivre's theorem for $n = 3$ to express $\sin 3\theta$ as a polynomial in $\sin\theta$.

(5) Express $\cos 5\theta$ and $\sin 5\theta$ as polynomials in $\cos\theta$ and $\sin\theta$ respectively.

(6) Find the cube roots of the following, leaving your answer in the form $re^{i\theta}$:

$$(a) \quad i \quad (b) \quad 8 - 8i$$

(7) Show that $\cos\theta = \frac{1}{2}(e^{-i\theta} + e^{i\theta})$. Express $\cos^5\theta$ in terms of powers of $e^{i\theta}$ and $e^{-i\theta}$. Hence show that $\cos^5\theta = \frac{1}{16}(\cos 5\theta + 5\cos 3\theta + 10\cos\theta)$.

(8) By the method of question 7 obtain an expression for $\cos^6\theta$ in terms of $\cos 6\theta, \cos 4\theta$ and $\cos 2\theta$.

## 19.4 Polar Coordinates

The position of a point is determined by its distance $r$ from the origin and the angle $\theta$ which the line from the origin makes with the $x$-axis.

If the point is described as $(r, \theta)$, then it is in *polar coordinates*. The modulus and argument of a complex number are its polar coordinates.

The Cartesian coordinates of a point can be found from the polar coordinates by $x = r\cos\theta$ and $y = r\sin\theta$.

The polar coordinates of a point can be found from its Cartesian coordinates by $r^2 = x^2 + y^2$ and $\tan\theta = y/x$.

The area bounded by a polar curve between $\theta = \psi$ and $\theta = \varphi$ is given by:

$$A = \int_{\varphi}^{\psi} \frac{1}{2}r^2 d\theta$$

### 19.4.1 Example

Sketch the curve $r = a(1+\cos\theta)$. Find the area enclosed by the curve.

Solution  Find values of $r$ for $\theta = 0, \frac{1}{4}\pi, \frac{1}{2}\pi, \frac{3}{4}\pi, \pi, 1\frac{1}{4}\pi, 1\frac{1}{2}\pi, 1\frac{3}{4}\pi$. Plot the points on a graph as shown.
Use the formula for area.

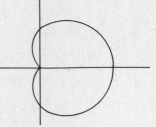

$$A = \int_0^{2\pi} \frac{1}{2}r^2\,d\theta = \int_0^{2\pi} \frac{1}{2}a^2(1 + 2\cos\theta + \cos^2\theta)\,d\theta$$

$$\int_0^{2\pi} \frac{1}{2}a^2(1 + 2\cos\theta + \frac{1}{2} + \frac{1}{2}\cos 2\theta)\,d\theta = \frac{1}{2}a^2[1\frac{1}{2}\theta + 2\sin\theta + \frac{1}{4}\sin 2\theta]_0^{2\pi}$$

$$\text{The area is } \frac{3}{2}\pi a^2$$

### 19.4.2 Examples

(1) Express the following points in polar coordinates:

 (a) (2,2)  (b) (0,5)

 (c) $(1,\sqrt{3})$ (d) $(-\sqrt{6}, \sqrt{2})$

(2) Transform the following polar coordinates to Cartesian coordinates:

 (a) $(4, 45°)$ (b) $(3, 150°)$

 (c) $(3, \pi)$  (d) $(2, 1\frac{3}{4}\pi)$

(3) Translate the following Cartesian equations to polar form:

 (a) $x^2 + y^2 = 36$ (b) $y = x$

 (c) $xy = 3$    (d) $x^2 - y^2 = 1$

(4) Translate the following polar coordinates to Cartesian form:

 (a) $r = 2$   (b) $\theta = \frac{1}{3}\pi$

 (c) $r\cos\theta = 1$ (d) $r = 2\sin\theta$

(5) Show that $r = 4\cos\theta$ is a circle, and find its centre and radius.
(6) Sketch the graph of $r = \theta$.
(7) Sketch the graph of $r^2 = 3\sin\theta$, and find the area it encloses.
(8) Sketch the graph of $r = 2 - \cos\theta$, and find the area it encloses.

### 19.5 Examination Questions

(1) Show by substitution that $1 + 2i$ is a solution of the equation $x^3 + x + 10 = 0$. **Write down** the other complex solution. Hence, or

otherwise, express the left-hand side of the equation as the product of a quadratic factor and a linear factor, both with real coefficients.

[SMP]

(2) The complex number $z$ satisfies the equation $2zz* - 4z = 3 - 6i$, where $z*$ is the complex conjugate of $z$. Find, in the form $x + iy$, the two possible values of $z$.

[JMB]

(3)

a.  Determine (real) numbers $x, y, r$ and $\theta$ such that

$$\frac{8 + 4i}{(1 - i)(1 - 2i)} = x + iy = re^{i\theta}$$

b.  Depict, in an Argand diagram, the set of complex numbers $z = x + iy$ satisfying $|2z + 1| \leq 2$.

[NI]

(4)

a.  Given that $z + 5 + 3i = k(iz + 1 + i)$, where $z = x + iy$ and $k$ is real, prove that $x + 5 = k(1 - y)$ and obtain a second independent relationship between $x, y$ and $k$.
    Hence show that, as $k$ varies, the point with coordinates $(x, y)$ in the Argand diagram lies on a fixed circle. Find the centre and radius of this circle.

b.  Draw two separate Argand diagrams showing the set of points $z$, such that: (i) $|z - 3| = 5$; (ii) $|z - 3| = |z - 1 - 2i|$.

[SUJB]

(5) Expand $(c + is)^5$ by the binomial theorem, where $i^2 = -1$. Hence, by using De Moivre's theorem, show that

$$\frac{\sin 5\theta}{\cos 5\theta} = \frac{s^5 - 10s^3c^2 + 5sc^4}{5s^4c - 10s^2c^3 + c^5},$$

where $c = \cos \theta$ and $s = \sin \theta$.

By substituting $t = s/c = \tan \theta$, deduce an expression for $\tan 5\theta$ in terms of $t$ only. Hence show that $\tan 5\theta = 0$ when $t^5 - 10t^3 + 5t = 0$.

Write down the values of $\theta$ in the range $-\frac{1}{2}\pi < \theta < \frac{1}{2}\pi$ for which $\tan 5\theta = 0$ and deduce that $\tan \pi/5 = \sqrt{(5 - 2\sqrt{5})}$.

[MEI]

(6) In separate diagrams, sketch the curves whose equations are $r \cos \theta = 1$ and $r = \cos 2\theta$, where $r$ and $\theta$ are plane polar coordinates with $r \geq 0$.

[MEI]

(7)

a. Sketch the curve whose equation in polar coordinates is $r = a$ $(3 + 2 \sin \theta)$, for $0 \leq \theta < 2\pi$, where $a$ is a positive constant. Find, by integration, the area of the region enclosed by the curve.

b. Obtain the cartesian equation of the curve whose equation in polar coordinates is $r^2(1 + 24 \sin^2 \theta) = 25a^2$, for $0 \leq \theta < 2\pi$, where $a$ is a positive constant. Sketch the curve.

[C]

## COMMON ERRORS

### (1) Notation

The imaginary part of a complex number must be real. The imaginary part of $3 + 4i$ is 4, not $4i$.

### (2) Arithmetic

Be careful when multiplying or dividing complex numbers. Note the following:

$$(x + iy)(x - iy) = x^2 + y^2. (\text{ Not } x^2 - y^2)$$

$$1/i = -i. (\text{ Not } +i).$$

### (3) Modulus and Argument

a. The modulus of a complex number must be a positive real number. The modulus of $-3$ is $+3$, not $-3$.

b. $\tan^{-1}$ is an ambiguous function, so be very careful when finding arguments. For both $1-i$ and $-1+i$ you will find that $\tan \theta = -1$. But $1 - i$ lies in the fourth quadrant, and hence its argument is $345°$. $-1 + i$ lies in the second quadrant, and hence its argument is $135°$. Similarly the argument of $-1 - i$ is $225°$, not $45°$.

If in doubt place the point on the Argand Diagram, so that you know roughly what its argument should be.

### (4) De Moivre's Theorem

The argument must be measured in radians, when applying De Moivre's Theorem. Do not use degrees.

# 20  Differential Equations

Suppose that $y$ is a function of $x$. An equation which expresses derivatives of $y$ in terms of $y$ and $x$ is a *differential equation*

To *solve* the equation means to obtain $y$ as a function of $x$.

If the solution contains constants of integration then it is a *general solution*.

If the constants can be found from given values of $x$ and $y$, these values are called *initial conditions*.

The solution so found without constants of integration is a *particular solution*.

## 20.1 Equations with Separable Variables

If a differential equation can be re-arranged so that all the $y$ terms are on one side and all the $x$ terms on the other, then the equation has *separable variables*.

### 20.1.1 Examples

(1)　　Find the general solution of the equation $dy/dx = 2xy$. Find the particular solution with the initial conditions of $y = 2$ for $x = 0$.

Solution　Here the $y$ terms can be collected on the left, and the $x$ terms on the right.

$$\int dy/y = \int 2x dx.$$

Integrate both sides:

$$\ln y = x^2 + c.$$

$$y = e^{x^2 + c} = Ae^{x^2}$$

Put $y = 2$ and $x = 0$. $2 = Ae^0$. $A = 2$.

$$\mathbf{y = 2e^{x^2}}$$

(2)　　The weight $W$ of a certain radioactive material decays at a rate proportional to the weight. The half-life, (when half of it has decayed), is 3,000 seconds. If the original weight is 20 grams find the weight after $t$ seconds.

Solution　The rate of change of $W$ is $dW/dt$. $W$ is decreasing, so this is equal to $-\lambda W$, where $\lambda$ is the constant of proportionality.

$$dW/dt = -\lambda W$$

The variables can be separated.

$$\int dW/W = -\lambda \int dt$$

Integrate to obtain:

$$\ln W = -\lambda t + c : W = e^c e^{-\lambda t}$$

$W = 20$ when $t = 0$, so $e^c = 20$.

$$W = 20e^{-\lambda t}$$

When $t = 3,000, W = 10$.
$$10 = 20e^{-3000\lambda} : \lambda = -ln\tfrac{1}{2}/3000 = ln2/3000$$

$$\mathbf{W = 20e^{-t(ln2/3000)} = 20 \times 2^{-t/3000}}$$

### 20.1.2 Exercises

(1) Find the general solutions of the following differential equations:

(a) $dy/dx = 2xy$      (b) $dy/dx = x/y$

(c) $dy/dx = x(1+y)$   (d) $dy/dx = \cos x / \sin y$

(e) $xdy/dx = y(y+1)$  (f) $xdy/dx = e^y$

(2) Find the particular solutions of the following equations with the initial conditions shown:

(a) $dy/dx = xy : x = 1$ when $y = 1$  (b) $dy/dx = y/x : x = 3$ when $y = 4$

(c) $(1+x)dy/dx = y^2 : x = 0$ for $y = -1$

(d) $dy/dx = y \sin x : x = \pi/2$ when $y = 1$  (e) $xdy/dx = e^y : x = 1$ for $y = 0$

(3) The rate of increase of a plant is proportional to the size of the plant, and it takes 12 hours for it to double. Find the height $h$ in terms of time $t$, given that it starts from 6 cm.

(4) The rate of decrease of a radioactive material is proportional to the amount of material, with constant of proportionality $1/1000$. Find the amount $M$ in terms of time $t$, and hence find the half-life of the material.

(5) If $z = y + x$, show that $dz/dx = dy/dx + 1$. Use the substitution $z = x + y$ to solve the equation $dy/dx = x + y$.

(6) By the same substitution as in Question 5 solve the following equations:

(a) $dy/dx = (x + y)^2$  (b) $dy/dx = \tfrac{1}{2}(x + y) - 1$

(7) Solve the following differential equations, using the substitution suggested:

(a) $dy/dx = x - y.\ (z = x - y)$  (b) $dy/dx = 3x + 2y.\ (z = 3x + 2y)$

(8) If $y = xz$, find an expression for $dy/dx$ in terms of $x, z$ and $dz/dx$. Use this substition to solve the following differential equations:

(a) $dy/dx = (y + x)/x$         (b) $x^2 dy/dx = x^2 + xy + y^2$

(c) $x\,dy/dx = y + \sqrt{(x^2 - y^2)}$

## 20.2 Integrating Factors

An expression of the form $f(x)dy/dx + f'(x)y$ is called *exact*. It is the derivative of $f(x)y$ with respect to $x$.

$$f(x)(dy/dx) + f'(x)y = d(f(x)y)/dx$$

The equation $dy/dx + p(x)y = q(x)$ can be multiplied through by a certain factor so that the left hand side is exact. The factor is called the *integrating factor*, and is equal to $e^{\int p(x)dx}$.

### 20.2.1 Example

Find the general solution of $dy/dx + 2y/x = x$. Find the particular solution for which $y = 3$ when $x = 2$.

Solution      Here $p(x) = 2/x$. The integrating factor is:

$$e^{\int 2/x\,dx} = e^{2\,\ln x} = x^2.$$

$x^2 dy/dx + 2xy = x^3$
The left hand side is now exact. It is the derivative of $x^2 y$.
Integrate to obtain $x^2 y = \frac{1}{4}x^4 + c$

$$y = \frac{1}{4}x^2 + c/x^2$$

Put $x = 2$ and $y = 3$.

$$3 = 1 + \frac{1}{4}c. \; c = 8.$$

$$y = \frac{1}{4}x^2 + 8/x^2$$

## 20.2.2 Exercises

(1) Which of the following are exact?

(a) $x^3 dy/dx + 3x^2 y$      (b) $dy/dx - xy$

(c) $e^x dy/dx - e^x y$      (d) $\sin x\, dy/dx + (\cos x)y$

(e) $\cos x\, dy/dx + (\sin x)y$    (f) $e^{-x} dy/dx - e^{-x} y$

(2) Find the general solutions of the following equations:

(a) $dy/dx + y/x = 3x^2$    (b) $dy/dx + 3y/x = 1$

(c) $dy/dx - 3y/x = 2$     (d) $dy/dx - y\tan x = 2$

(e) $e^x dy/dx + e^x y = 2x$   (f) $dy/dx + y/(1+x) = 3$

(g) $dy/dx = x + y$       (h) $dy/dx + 2xy = e^{-x^2}$

(3) Find the particular solutions of the following equations with the initial conditions given.

(a) $dy/dx + y/x = x : x = 3, y = 1$     (b) $dy/dx - 3y/x = 2 : x = 1, y = 4$

(c) $dy/dx = x + y : x = 0, y = 1$       (d) $dy/dx = x + y : x = 0, y = 2$

(e) $dy/dx + (\cot x)y = 1 : y = 1, x = \pi/4$   (f) $dy/dx + ay = 1 : x = 0, y = 1$

## 20.3 Second Order Equations

To save space $dy/dx$ is often written as $y'$, and $d^2y/dx^2$ as $y''$.

An equation of the form $ay'' + by' + cy = f(x)$, where $a, b, c$ are constant, is *linear with constant coefficients.*

If $f(x) \equiv 0$, then the equation is *homogenous.*

The equation $ay'' + by' + cy = f(x)$ is solved in two stages.

A. First find the general solution, called the *Complementary Function,* of the homogenous equation $ay'' + by' + cy = 0$. This is done as follows.

Consider the *associated quadratic* $am^2 + bm + c = 0$. Suppose it has roots $\alpha$ and $\beta$.

Case 1. $\alpha$ and $\beta$ are different and real.

The general solution of $ay'' + by' + cy = 0$ is $y = Ae^{\alpha x} + Be^{\beta x}$

Case 2. $\alpha = \beta$.

The general solution of $ay'' + by' + cy = 0$ is $(Ax + B)e^{\alpha x}$

Case 3. $\alpha$ and $\beta$ are complex, equal to $u + iv$ and $u - iv$

The general solution of $ay'' + by' + cy = 0$ is $e^{ux}(A\cos vx + B\sin vx)$

B. Then find a *particular solution* of $ay'' + by' + cy = f(x)$ as follows.

If $f(x)$ is a quadratic, try $y = Cx^2 + Dx + E$.

If $f(x)$ is trigonometric, say $f(x) = \sin x$, try $y = C\sin x + D\cos x$.

If $f(x)$ is exponential, say $f(x) = e^{2x}$, try $y = Ce^{2x}$

The general solution of $ay'' + by' + cy = f(x)$ is the sum of the general solution of $ay'' + by' + cy = 0$ and a particular solution of $ay'' + by' + cy = f(x)$.

General Solution = Particular Solution + Complementary Function.

## 20.3.1 Examples

(1)    Find the general solution of $y'' - 3y' + 4y = 16x$. Find the solution for which $y = 0$ and $y' = 1$ when $x = 0$.

Solution    The associated quadratic is $m^2 - 3m + 4 = 0$. This has roots 1 and 4. Case 1 of the above applies.

$$\text{Complementary Function} = Ae^x + Be^{4x}$$

For a particular solution, try $y = Cx + D$.

$$0 - 3C + 4(Cx + D) \equiv 16x.$$

Equating coefficients, $C = 4$ and $D = 3$.
The Particular solution is $4x + 3$
**The general solution is $Ae^x + Be^{4x} + 4x + 3$**
$y' = Ae^x + 4Be^{4x} + 4$.
Put $x = 0, y = 0$ and $y' = 1$.
$0 = A + B + 3$ and $1 = A + 4B + 4$. $B = 0$ and $A = -3$.

$$\textbf{The solution is } \mathbf{-3e^x + 4x + 3}$$

(2)    Find the solution of $y'' + 2y' + 5y = 2\cos x - 6\sin x$, for which $y = 2$ when $x = 0$ and $y = 0$ when $x = \pi/4$.

Solution    The associated quadratic is $m^2 + 2m + 5 = 0$. This has the complex roots $-1 + 2i$ and $-1 - 2i$.

$$\text{Complementary Function} = e^{-x}(A\cos 2x + B\sin 2x)$$

For particular solution try $y = C\cos x + D\sin x$.
$-C\cos x - D\sin x + 2(-C\sin x + D\cos x) + 5(C\cos x + D\sin x) = 2\cos x - 6\sin x$.

Equate coefficients of $\cos x$ and $\sin x$.

$$-C + 2D + 5C = 2 \text{ and } -D - 2C + 5D = -6.$$

$$C = 1 \text{ and } D = -1$$

Particular solution $= \cos x - \sin x$

General Solution $= e^{-x}(A\cos 2x + B\sin 2x) + \cos x - \sin x$

Put in the initial conditions.

$2 = A + 1$ and $0 = e^{-\pi/4}B + 1/\sqrt{2} - 1/\sqrt{2}$

$A = 1$ and $B = 0$

$$\mathbf{y = e^{-x}\cos 2x + \cos x - \sin x}$$

## 20.3.2 Exercises

(1) Find the general solutions of the following homogenous equations:

(a) $y'' + 5y' + 6y = 0$    (b) $y'' - 6y' + 8y = 0$

(c) $y'' + y' - 12y = 0$    (d) $y'' - 2y' - 15y = 0$

(e) $y'' + 4y' + 13y = 0$    (f) $y'' - 2y' + 2y = 0$

(g) $y'' + 9y = 0$           (h) $9y'' - 4y = 0$

(2) Find the general solutions of the following equations:

(a) $y'' + 5y' + 6y = 3$           (b) $y'' - 6y' + 8y = 16x - 4$

(c) $y'' + y' - 12y = 16 - 22x - 12x^2$    (d) $y'' - 2y' - 15y = 45e^{2x}$

(e) $y'' + 4y' + 13y = 12\cos x - 4\sin x$    (f) $y'' - 2y' + 2y = 10e^{-x}$

(g) $y'' + 9y = 2x - 1$           (h) $9y'' - 4y = 3e^{-\frac{1}{3}x}$

(3) Find the solutions of the following equations, with the initial conditions given:

(a) $y'' + 5y' + 6y = 3$ : When $x = 0$ $y = 0$ and $y' = 1$

(b) $y'' - 6y' + 8y = 16x - 4$ : When $x = 0$ $y = 3$ and $y' = 8$

(c) $y'' + y' - 12y = 16 - 22x - 12x^2$ : When $x = 0$ $y = -1$ and $y' = -5$

(d) $y'' - 2y' - 15y = 45e^{2x}$ : When $x = 0$ $y = -3$ and when $x = 2$ $y = 0$

(e) $y'' + 4y' + 13y = 12\cos x - 4\sin x$ : When $x = 0$ $y = 1$ and $y' = 6$

(f) $y'' - 2y' + 2y = 10e^{-x}$ : When $x = 0$ $y = 2$ and when $x = \pi/2$ $y = 0$

(g) $y'' + 9y = 2x - 1$ : When $x = 0$ $y = 1$, when $x = \pi/6$ $y = 3$

(h) $9y'' - 4y = 3e^{-\frac{1}{3}x}$ : When $x = 0$ $y = 0$. When $x$ tends to infinity $y$ tends to zero.

## 20.4 Examination Questions

(1) Find the particular solution of the differential equation

$(y + 1)(x^2 + 1)dy/dx = 1 \quad (y \neq -1)$
for which $y = 0$ when $x = 1$, in the form $x = g(y)$.

[W]

(2)

i.  Find $y$ in terms of $x$ given that

$$(1 + x)dy/dx = (1 - x)y$$

and that $y = 1$ when $x = 0$.

ii. A curve passes through (2,2) and has gradient at $(x, y)$ given by the differential equation

$$ye^{y^2} dy/dx = e^{2x}.$$

Find the equation of the curve. Show that the curve also passes through the point $(1, \sqrt{2})$ and sketch the curve.

[L]

(3)

a.  Find the general solution of the differential equation

$$e^x dy/dx + y^{\frac{1}{2}} = 0,$$

expressing $y$ in terms of $x$ and an arbitrary constant.

b.  Find the solution of the differential equation

$$d^2y/dx^2 + 9y = 0$$

in the form $y = f(x)$, where $f(0) = f(\frac{1}{2}\pi)$ and $f'(\frac{1}{2}\pi) = 2$.

[O]

(4)

a.  Find the general solution of the differential equation

$$dy/dx - 2y/x = 0.$$

Sketch the two solution curves passing respectively through the points (2,2) and (−1, −1).

b. Solve the differential equation

$$d^2y/dx^2 + 5dy/dx + 6y = 6x - 1,$$

given that $y = 4$ and $dy/dx = -11$ when $x = 0$.

[C]

(5) The gradient of a curve at any point $(x, y)$ on the curve is directly proportional to the product of $x$ and $y$. The curve passes through the point (1,1) and at this point the gradient of the curve is 4. Form a differential equation in $x$ and $y$ and solve this equation to express $y$ in terms of $x$.

[L]

## COMMON ERRORS

### (1) Separable Variables

a. Make sure that you have separated the variables before you integrate. It is not possible to evaluate $\int x^2 dy$, for example.
b. Do not forget the constant of integration. It often provides the most important part of the solution.
c. When making $y$ the subject of the formula be very careful with logs. Watch out for the following:

From $\ln y = \ln x + c$ do not go to $y = x + \ln c$.

(It should be $y = x \times \ln c$.)

### (2) Second Order Equations

a. When the associated quadratic has complex roots $c \pm id$, then your solution begins: $y = e^{cx}( \dots )$. Do not put $y = e^c( \dots )$
b. If there is no $y'$ term, i.e. your equation is $ay'' + cy = f(x)$, then the associated quadratic is $am^2 + c = 0$. It is not $am + c = 0$.
c. If $f(x)$ is of the form $kx$, then for the particular solution try $Cx + D$. Do not forget the $D$.
d. If $f(x)$ is of the form $\sin x$, then for the particular solution try $C \cos x + D \sin x$. Do not forget the $\cos x$ term.

# 21 Geometry of Lines and Planes

**i, j** and **k** represent unit vectors in the $x$, $y$ and $z$ directions respectively. Vectors can be written either as column matrices or in terms of these unit vectors.

$$\begin{pmatrix} x \\ y \\ z \end{pmatrix} = x\mathbf{i} + y\mathbf{j} + z\mathbf{k}$$

## 21.1 Lines and Planes in Three Dimensions

Suppose a line goes through a point with position vector **a** and is parallel to the vector **v**. Then a general point on the line is:

$$\mathbf{r} = \mathbf{a} + \lambda\mathbf{v}, \text{ where } \lambda \text{ is a scalar.}$$

If $\mathbf{a} = a\mathbf{i} + b\mathbf{j} + c\mathbf{k}$ and $\mathbf{v} = v\mathbf{i} + u\mathbf{j} + w\mathbf{k}$, then the *Cartesian* equations of the line are:

$$\frac{x-a}{v} = \frac{y-b}{u} + \frac{z-c}{w}$$

Suppose a plane goes through a point with position vector **a** and is parallel to vectors **u** and **v**. Then a general point on the plane is:

$$\mathbf{r} = \mathbf{a} + \lambda\mathbf{u} + \mu\mathbf{v}, \text{ where } \lambda \text{ and } \mu \text{ are scalars.}$$

If **n** is a vector perpendicular to the plane, then its equation can be written as:

$$\mathbf{r}.\mathbf{n} = \mathbf{a}.\mathbf{n}$$

If $\mathbf{n} = l\mathbf{i} + m\mathbf{j} + n\mathbf{k}$, then the *Cartesian* equation of the plane is:

$$lx + my + nz = d, \text{ where } d = \mathbf{a}.\mathbf{n} \text{ is a constant.}$$

The shortest, i.e. perpendicular distance from the point $(a, b, c)$ to the plane $lx + my + nz = d$ is:

$$\frac{|la + mb + nc - d|}{\sqrt{(l^2 + m^2 + n^2)}}$$

The angle between two lines is the angle between their direction vectors. This can be found from the scalar product, defined in 12.2.

To find the angle between a line and a plane, find the angle between the direction of the line and the perpendicular to the plane, and subtract that angle from 90°.

The angle between two planes is the angle between their perpendiculars.

### 21.1.1 Examples

(1)     Two lines are given by $\mathbf{r} = \mathbf{i} + 2\mathbf{j} - 3\mathbf{k} + \lambda(2\mathbf{i} - \mathbf{j})$ and $\mathbf{r} = t\mathbf{i} + \mathbf{j} - 4\mathbf{k} + \mu(\mathbf{i} - \mathbf{j} + \mathbf{k})$. Find the value of $t$ so that the lines intersect. Find the angle between the lines.

Solution     Equate the values of **r**.
$\mathbf{i} + 2\mathbf{j} - 3\mathbf{k} + \lambda(2\mathbf{i} - \mathbf{j}) = t\mathbf{i} + \mathbf{j} - 4\mathbf{k} + \mu(\mathbf{i} - \mathbf{j} + \mathbf{k})$.
This gives the following three equations:
$1 + 2\lambda = t + \mu : 2 - \lambda = 1 - \mu : -3 = -4 + \mu$.
From the last two equations $\mu = 1$ and $\lambda = 2$. Substitute these values into the first equation to find $t$.

$$t = 4$$

The angle between the lines is the angle between the two direction vectors. Find this by the scalar product.

$$(\sqrt{5})(\sqrt{3})cos\theta = 3.$$

**The angle is 39°**

(2)    Find the equation of the plane which contains the two lines of example 1.

Solution    Let a perpendicular to the plane be $li + mj + nk$. This vector is at right angles to the direction vectors of the lines.

$$2l - m = 0 \text{ and } l - m + n = 0.$$

These equations are satisfied by $l = 1, m = 2, n = 1$. Hence a perpendicular vector is $i + 2j + k$. The equation of the plane is $x + 2y + z = (i + 2j + k).(i + 2j - 3k)$

**The equation is x + 2y + z = 2**

## 21.1.2 Exercises

(1) Find vector equations for the following lines:
(a) Through (1,1,2), parallel to $2i + j + 7k$
(b) Through (1,0,3), parallel to $4i + 2j$

 (c)  Through (1,3,1) and (2,5,2)   (d)  Through (1,2,−1) and (1,−2,1).

(2) Find the Cartesian equations of the lines in Question 1.

(3) Find the values of $t$ so that the following pairs of lines intersect:

(a) $r = (1,3,2) + \lambda(ti + j)$ and $r = (1,-4,-1) + \mu(2i + 3j + k)$
(b) $\frac{x-1}{t} = \frac{y-4}{1} = \frac{z-5}{2}$ and $\frac{x-1}{2} = \frac{y}{1} = \frac{z+1}{1}$

(4) Find the angles between the pairs of lines in Question 3.

(5) Find in the form $\mathbf{r} = \mathbf{a} + \lambda\mathbf{u} + \mu\mathbf{v}$ the equations of the following planes:
(a) Through (1,2,3) parallel to $(i + j + k)$ and $(i + k)$.
(b) Through (1,2,1), (2,1,3) and (1,−1,1).

(6) Find in the form $\mathbf{r}.\mathbf{n} = k$ the equations of the following planes:
(a) Through (1,2,1), perpendicular to $(2i + j - k)$.
(b) Through (2,1,4), perpendicular to the $z$-axis.
(c) Through (1,1,2), parallel to $(i + j)$ and to $k$.
(d) Through (2,1,2), (2,3,0) and (0,4,1).

(7) Find the angles between the following:

(a) The line $(0,1,2) + \lambda(\mathbf{i} + \mathbf{j})$ and the plane $\mathbf{r}.(-\mathbf{i} + 3\mathbf{j} - \mathbf{k}) = 1$.

(b) The line $\dfrac{x-4}{3} = \dfrac{y+3}{-1} = \dfrac{z-2}{1}$ and the plane $x + 2y + z = 0$

(c) The line $(0,1,1) + \lambda(2\mathbf{i} + \mathbf{j} + \mathbf{k})$ and the plane $(1,1,1) + \mu(\mathbf{i}+\mathbf{j}) + \nu\mathbf{k}$.

(8) Find the angles between the following pairs of planes:

(a) $x + y + 2z = 3$ and $2x - y + z = 1$

(b) $\mathbf{r}.(\mathbf{i} + 2\mathbf{j} + 3\mathbf{k}) = 0$ and
$\mathbf{r}.(-2\mathbf{i} + \mathbf{j} - 3\mathbf{k}) = 3$.

(c) $\mathbf{r} = (1,1,0) + \lambda(\mathbf{i}+\mathbf{k}) + \mu\mathbf{j}$ and $\mathbf{r} = (2,1,7) + \alpha(\mathbf{i}-\mathbf{j}) + \beta\mathbf{k}$

(9) Find the perpendicular distance between the following:

(a) The point $(1,1,1)$ and the plane $x + 2y - z = 4$

(b) The point $(2,0,-3)$ and the plane $2x - 3y + 4z = 1$

(10) Find the point where the line $\mathbf{r} = (5,7,3) + \lambda(\mathbf{i} + 3\mathbf{j} + 2\mathbf{k})$ meets the plane $x + 2y + z = 4$. Find the angle between the line and the plane.

(11) Find the point where the line $\mathbf{r} = (1,0,-1) + \lambda(\mathbf{i} - 2\mathbf{j})$ meets the plane $2x - y - z = 1$. Find the angle between the line and the plane.

## 21.2 Matrix Transformations

A matrix can represent a transformation in a plane or in three dimensions.

The identity matrix leaves each point unchanged. The identity matrix is given by:

$$I = \begin{pmatrix} 1 & 0 \\ 0 & 1 \end{pmatrix} \text{ or } I = \begin{pmatrix} 1 & 0 & 0 \\ 0 & 1 & 0 \\ 0 & 0 & 1 \end{pmatrix} \text{ in 2 and 3 dimensions respectively.}$$

The *inverse* $A^{-1}$ of a matrix $A$ is such that $AA^{-1} = A^{-1}A = I$. In two dimensions it is given by:

$$\text{If } A = \begin{pmatrix} a & b \\ c & d \end{pmatrix} \text{ then } A^{-1} = \frac{1}{ad - bc} \begin{pmatrix} d & -b \\ -c & a \end{pmatrix}$$

The expression $ad - bc$ is the *determinant* of the matrix.

An *invariant point* of a matrix transformation is a point whose position vector $v$ is such that $Av = v$.

An invariant line of a matrix transformation is a line which is mapped onto itself by the transformation. An invariant line may or may not consist of invariant points.

## 21.2.1 Example

For the matrix $A$ below, find (i) its inverse (ii) its invariant points (iii) its invariant lines.

$$A = \begin{pmatrix} 2 & 1 \\ 1 & 2 \end{pmatrix}$$

Solution

i.      Apply the formula above.

$$A^{-1} = \frac{1}{2 \times 2 - 1 \times 1} \begin{pmatrix} 2 & -1 \\ -1 & 2 \end{pmatrix} = \begin{pmatrix} \frac{2}{3} & -\frac{1}{3} \\ -\frac{1}{3} & \frac{2}{3} \end{pmatrix}$$

ii.      Suppose that $(x, y)$ is an invariant point. Then it is unaltered by the matrix transformation.

$$\begin{pmatrix} 2 & 1 \\ 1 & 2 \end{pmatrix} \begin{pmatrix} x \\ y \end{pmatrix} = \begin{pmatrix} x \\ y \end{pmatrix}$$

This gives two equations:

$$2x + y = x \text{ and } x + 2y = y.$$

Both these equations reduce to $y = -x$.
**All points of the form $(x, -x)$ are invariant.**

iii.      Suppose that $y = \lambda x$ is an invariant line. Then $(x, \lambda x)$ lies on this line. Apply the matrix transformation.

$$\begin{pmatrix} 2 & 1 \\ 1 & 2 \end{pmatrix} \begin{pmatrix} x \\ \lambda x \end{pmatrix} = \begin{pmatrix} 2x + \lambda x \\ x + 2\lambda x \end{pmatrix}$$

This vector also lies on the line $y = \lambda x$.

$$x + 2\lambda x = \lambda(2x + \lambda x)$$

$$\lambda^2 = 1$$

**The lines are y = x and y = −x**

## 21.2.2 Exercises

(1) Find, where possible, the inverses of the following matrices:

$$A = \begin{pmatrix} 1 & 1 \\ 0 & 2 \end{pmatrix} \quad B = \begin{pmatrix} 1 & 4 \\ 1 & 2 \end{pmatrix} \quad C = \begin{pmatrix} 3 & -1 \\ 1 & 3 \end{pmatrix} \quad D = \begin{pmatrix} -1 & 4 \\ 2 & -8 \end{pmatrix}$$

(2) For the matrices defined in Question 1, evaluate the following:

(a) $AB$ (b) $BA$ (c) $CD$

(d) $A^2$ (e) $A^3$ (f) $D^2$.

(3) Find, where possible, the invariant points of the matrices defined in Question 1.

(4) Find, where possible, the invariant lines of the matrices defined in Question 1.

(5) Show that every point on the plane is mapped by $D$ onto a certain line, and find that line.

(6) Show that there is a whole line of points which is mapped by $D$ onto the origin (0,0). Find the line.

(7) Repeat Questions 5 and 6 for the matrix defined by $E = \begin{pmatrix} 1 & 2 \\ 2 & 4 \end{pmatrix}$.

(8) Show that the matrix $P = \begin{pmatrix} 1 & 3 \\ 0 & 1 \end{pmatrix}$ represents a shear parallel to the $x$-axis. Find its invariant points and lines.

(9) Show that the matrix $\begin{pmatrix} a & b \\ c & d \end{pmatrix}$ takes $\mathbf{i}$ to $a\mathbf{i} + c\mathbf{j}$. Find where it takes $\mathbf{j}$.

(10) Write down the matrix which takes $\mathbf{i}$ to $2\mathbf{i} + \mathbf{j}$ and takes $\mathbf{j}$ to $2\mathbf{i} - \mathbf{j}$. Find its invariant points and lines.

(11) Write down the matrix which takes $\mathbf{i}$ to $\mathbf{i} - 2\mathbf{j}$ and takes $\mathbf{j}$ to $-\mathbf{i} + 2\mathbf{j}$. Show that all points of the plane are mapped onto a certain line, which is to be found. Show that there is a certain line which the matrix maps onto the origin. Find this line.

(12) Let $M$ be defined by $M = \begin{pmatrix} \cos\theta & -\sin\theta \\ \sin\theta & \cos\theta \end{pmatrix}$. By consideration of its action on the vectors $\mathbf{i}$ and $\mathbf{j}$, show that $M$ represents an anti-clockwise rotation of $\theta$ about the origin. Show that the only invariant point of $M$ is the origin, and that $M$ has no invariant lines.

(13) Let $N$ be defined by $N = \begin{pmatrix} \cos 2\alpha & \sin 2\alpha \\ \sin 2\alpha & -\cos 2\alpha \end{pmatrix}$. By consideration of its action on the vectors $\mathbf{i}$ and $\mathbf{j}$, show that $N$ represents reflection in the line $y = x \tan\alpha$. Verify that $N^2 = I$. Show that $N$ has two invariant lines, one of which consists of invariant points.

## 21.3 Examination Questions

(1) The lines $L$ and $M$ have the equations

$$\mathbf{r} = \begin{pmatrix} 3 \\ 2 \\ 4 \end{pmatrix} + s \begin{pmatrix} 1 \\ 3 \\ -5 \end{pmatrix} \text{ and } \mathbf{r} = \begin{pmatrix} -3 \\ 4 \\ 6 \end{pmatrix} + t \begin{pmatrix} 1 \\ -2 \\ 2 \end{pmatrix}, \text{ respectively. The}$$

plane $\pi$ has the equation $\mathbf{r}.\begin{pmatrix} 2 \\ 0 \\ -1 \end{pmatrix} = 16$.

  i.  Verify that the point $A$ with coordinates $(1, -4, 14)$ lies on $L$ and on $M$ but not on $\pi$.

  ii.  Find the position vector of the point of intersection $B$ of $L$ and $\pi$.

 iii.  Show that $M$ and $\pi$ have no common point.

 iv.  Find the cosine of the angle between the vectors $\begin{pmatrix} 1 \\ 3 \\ -5 \end{pmatrix}$ and

$\begin{pmatrix} 2 \\ 0 \\ -1 \end{pmatrix}$

Hence find, to the nearest degree, the angle between $L$ and $\pi$.

[JMB]

(2) With respect to the origin $O$ the points $A$, $B$, $C$ have position vectors $a(5\mathbf{i} - \mathbf{j} - 3\mathbf{k})$, $a(-4\mathbf{i} + 4\mathbf{j} - \mathbf{k})$, $a(5\mathbf{i} - 2\mathbf{j} + 11\mathbf{k})$ respectively, where $a$ is a non-zero constant. Find

a.   a vector equation for the line $BC$,

b.   a vector equation for the plane $OAB$,

c.   the cosine of the acute angle between the lines $OA$ and $OB$.

Obtain, in the form $\mathbf{r}.\mathbf{n} = p$, a vector equation for $\Pi$, the plane which passes through $A$ and is perpendicular to $BC$.

Find cartesian equations for (d) the plane $\Pi$, (e) the line $BC$.

[L]

(3) The line $L$ passes through $A(0, -1, 1)$ and is parallel to $\begin{pmatrix} 1 \\ 0 \\ 1 \end{pmatrix}$, and

the line $M$ passes through $B(2,1,3)$ and is parallel to $\begin{pmatrix} 1 \\ -1 \\ 2 \end{pmatrix}$. Show that $L$

and $M$ do not intersect.

$M'$ is the line through $A$ parallel to $M$. The lines $M'$ and $L$ lie in the plane $\pi$.

i.   Find the direction of the normal to $\pi$.

ii.   Find the angle between $AB$ and $\pi$.

iii.   Write the equation to $\pi$ in standard Cartesian form.

iv.   Use the formula for the distance of a point from a plane to show that the shortest distance from $B$ to $\pi$ is $\frac{1}{3}AB$. Explain how you could have deduced this result from your answer to (ii).

[SMP]

(4) Given that $A = \begin{pmatrix} 3 & 1 \\ 3 & 1 \end{pmatrix}$ and $B = \begin{pmatrix} 1 & 1 \\ -3 & -3 \end{pmatrix}$, calculate

(a) $AB$, (b) $BA$.

Given also that $C = \begin{pmatrix} 1 & 3 \\ 0 & 1 \end{pmatrix}$ and $D = \begin{pmatrix} 1 & -1 \\ -1 & 2 \end{pmatrix}$, calculate

(c) $(2C + D)(C - D)$, (d) $A(CD)$.

Using your answers to (c) and (d), write down the 2 × 2 matrix which is equal to (e) $2C^2 - 2CD + DC - D^2$, (f) $(AC)D$.
State clearly any properties of matrix multiplication which you assume.
Describe in words the geometrical transformation from $R^2$ to $R^2$ represented by (i) the matrix $A$, (ii) the matrix $C$.

[L add]

(5) Write down the inverse of the matrix $M_1 = \begin{pmatrix} 4 & -5 \\ -1 & 2 \end{pmatrix}$.

Using this result, or otherwise, find the matrices $M_2$ and $M_3$ such that

(i) $\quad M_1 M_2 = \begin{pmatrix} 3 & 6 \\ 9 & -12 \end{pmatrix}$ (ii) $\quad M_3 M_1 = \begin{pmatrix} 3 & 6 \\ 9 & -12 \end{pmatrix}$.

The rectangle whose vertices are (0,0), (5,0), (5,4) (0,4) is transformed by $M_1$ into a new figure $R$. Calculate the area of $R$.

[O&C add]

(6) The matrix $\begin{pmatrix} 3 & a \\ 6 & 2a \end{pmatrix}$, where $a \, \epsilon R$ and $a \neq 0$, is denoted by $A$. When position vectors of points in a plane are premultiplied by $A$, a transformation of the plane results. Show that

  i.  all points in the plane are mapped by $A$ to points of a certain line $L_1$, and state the equation of $L_1$;

  ii.  all points which are mapped by $A$ to the origin lie on a certain line $L_2$, and state the equation of $L_2$;

  iii.  if $L_1$ and $L_2$ coincide, then $A^2 = O$, where $O$ is the null matrix;

  iv.  all points on any given line parallel to $L_2$ are mapped by $A$ to a single point of $L_1$.

[C]

## COMMON ERRORS

### (1) Lines and Planes

a. Do not confuse the position vector of a point on a line and the direction vector of that line.

b. In three dimensions, two Cartesian equations are needed to define a line. If you have only one equation then that will describe a plane.

c. Do not confuse vectors *perpendicular* to a plane with vectors *parallel* to the plane.

### (2) Matrices

a. Be careful of negative signs when working out the determinant of a matrix.

b. A line of invariant points is an invariant line, but the converse is not true. An invariant line may have no invariant points on it, apart from the origin itself.

# MECHANICS.

# 22 Displacement, Velocity, Acceleration

Time, displacement, velocity and acceleration are often symbolised by the letters $t, s, v$ and $a$ respectively. Velocity is the rate of change of displacement, acceleration is the rate of change of velocity.

$$v = ds/dt, a = dv/dt$$

Conversely, velocity is the integral of acceleration, displacement is the integral of velocity.

$$v = \int a\,dt, s = \int v\,dt$$

The constants of integration in these equations are found from the *initial* velocity and the *initial* displacement.

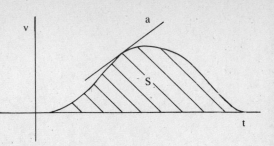

If the velocity is plotted on a graph against time, then the gradient of the graph is the acceleration and the area under the graph is the displacement.

## 22.1 Constant Acceleration

If the acceleration $a$ is constant, then the following hold:

$$v = u + at \text{ (where } u \text{ is the initial velocity)}$$

$$s = \frac{1}{2}(u + v)t$$

$$s = ut + \frac{1}{2}at^2$$

$$v^2 = u^2 + 2as$$

If a body is falling freely under gravity, then its acceleration (neglecting air resistance) is constant with the value $g = 9.8 \text{ m/sec}^2$.

### 22.1.1 Examples

(1)    A car accelerates uniformly for 10 seconds at $1.5 \text{ m/sec}^2$, then travels at a constant speed for 30 seconds, then brakes uniformly to a halt within a space of 25 m. Find the total distance covered and the total time taken.

Solution    The speed it reaches is $10 \times 1.5 = 15 \text{ m/sec}$. The distance it covers while accelerating is:

$$s = 0 \times 10 + \frac{1}{2} \times 1.5 \times 10^2 = 75 \text{ m}.$$

The distance it covers at a constant speed is $30 \times 15 = 450 \text{ m}$.

**Total distance $= 75 + 450 + 25 = 550\text{m}$.**

The deceleration is found from the formula $v^2 = u^2 + 2as$.

$$\text{Deceleration} = 15^2/(2 \times 25) = 4.5 \text{ m/sec}^2$$

The time for deceleration is $15/4.5 = 3\frac{1}{3}$ sec.

$$\textbf{Total time} = 10 + 30 + 3\frac{1}{3} = 43\frac{1}{3} \textbf{ seconds}$$

(2)   A cliff is 45 m high. A stone is thrown down from the top at 10 m/sec, and at the same time a stone is thrown up from the bottom at 80 m/sec. Find how high the stones are when they collide.

Solution   Measure distance $s$ up from the bottom of the cliff. For the first stone:

$$s_1 = 45 - 10t - \frac{1}{2}gt^2$$

For the second stone:

$$s_2 = 80t - \frac{1}{2}gt^2$$

The stones collide when these are equal.
$45 - 10t - \frac{1}{2}gt^2 = 80t - \frac{1}{2}gt^2$. It follows that $t = \frac{1}{2}$ sec.
Put this value into either of the distance formulae.

$$\textbf{The height is } 80 \times \frac{1}{2} - \frac{1}{2} \times 9.8 \times \frac{1}{2}^2 = \textbf{38.775m}$$

(3)   A vehicle accelerates uniformly for 2 seconds, travels at a constant speed for 10 seconds, then decelerates uniformly to rest in 4 seconds. If the total distance travelled is 520 m, find the maximum speed.

Solution   Draw a velocity-time graph as shown. The height of the trapezium is the maximum velocity $v$. The area in the trapezium is the distance, 520 m.

$$520 = \frac{1}{2}v(10 + 16).$$

**The maximum velocity is 40m/sec.**

## 22.1.2 Exercises

(1) A car accelerates at $0.8$ m/sec$^2$ for 5 seconds. Find its speed and the distance it has covered.

(2) A particle is accelerated uniformly from rest, so that after 10 seconds it has achieved the speed of 15 m/sec. Find its acceleration and the distance it has covered.

(3) A car accelerates uniformly from rest, achieving a speed of 20 m/sec after covering 100 m. How long did it take?

(4) The buffers at the end of a railway line can stop a train travelling at 10 m/sec, by being compressed through 10 cm. How long does the deceleration take, assuming that it is uniform?

(5) A car accelerates uniformly from rest, and after 12 seconds it has covered 40 m. What is its acceleration and its final velocity?

(6) A train slows down from 20 m/sec to 15 m/sec, covering 200 m. How long did it take?

(7) A car accelerates uniformly from 5 m/sec to 15 m/sec, taking 7.5 seconds. How far did it travel during this period?

(8) A body starts from rest with constant acceleration $1.5$ m/sec$^2$. How long does it take to cover 12 m?

(9) A particle is accelerated from 1 m/sec to 5 m/sec over a distance of 15m. Find the acceleration and the time taken.

(10) A body falls from the top of a 50 m cliff. Find the time taken and the speed at the bottom.

(11) A body is thrown down from a 50 m cliff at 10 m/sec. Find the time it takes to reach the bottom and its speed at the bottom.

(12) From the top of a 60 m cliff a body is thrown up at 15 m/sec, so that it then falls over the edge of the cliff. Find the greatest height reached and the time it takes to reach the bottom of the cliff. Find its speed at the bottom of the cliff.

(13) A sprinter during a 100 m race accelerates uniformly during the first 50m to his maximum speed of 10 m/sec, and then continues the rest of the race at that speed. Find the time taken and his average speed.

(14) A body is thrown up in the air at 30 m/sec, and 2 seconds later a second body is thrown up at 60 m/sec. Find how high the bodies are when they collide.

(15) A car accelerates at 2 m/sec$^2$ for 4 seconds, then travels at a constant speed for 20 seconds, then decelerates uniformly to rest. The total distance travelled is 200 m. Draw a velocity-time graph and hence find the deceleration.

(16) A car is travelling at 40 m/sec, then it decelerates uniformly to 25 m/sec over 30 seconds, then travels at the slower speed for 500 m. Draw a velocity-time graph, and calculate how much longer the journey took it than if it had continued at a constant speed of 40 m/sec.

(17) A cyclist starts from rest, and accelerates uniformly to a maximum speed of 10 m/sec. This speed is maintained for 20 seconds, and then the cyclist decelerates uniformly to rest. The total distance covered is 250 m. Sketch a velocity-time graph. Sketch a velocity time graph. Find the total time taken and the acceleration.

## 22.2 Non-Constant Acceleration

If the acceleration is not constant, then the formulae of 22.1 can no longer be used. The quantities must be derived from each other by differentiation or integration.

### 22.2.1 Examples

(1)      A particle travels so that its distance $s$ from the origin after time $t$ is given by $s = 8t - \frac{2}{3}t^3$. Find its greatest distance from the origin, and the time when it returns to the origin.

Solution      The velocity $v$ is given by:

$$v = ds/dt = 8 - 2t^2$$

The distance is greatest when the velocity is zero, i.e when $t = 2$.

**The greatest distance is** $8 \times 2 - \frac{2}{3}2^3 = 10\frac{2}{3}\text{m}.$

It returns to the origin when $s = 0$.

$$8t - \frac{2}{3}t^3 = 0. \text{ Hence } t = 0 \text{ or } \pm\sqrt{12}$$

**It returns to the origin after 3.46 seconds.**

(2)      The velocity $v$ of a particle at time $t$ is given by $v = t^2 + 1$. Find its acceleration after 3 seconds, and the distance it has travelled during that time.

Solution      The acceleration is given by:

$$a = dv/dt = 2t.$$

**The acceleration after 3 seconds is** $2\times3 = 6 \text{ m/sec}^2$

The distance travelled is found by integrating the velocity between $t = 0$ and $t = 3$.

$$s = \int_0^3 (t^2 + 1)dt = [\frac{1}{3}t^3 + t]_0^3$$

**The distance is 12 m**

## 22.2.2 Exercises

(1) The displacement of a body is given by $s = 6t - 7t^3$. Find the initial velocity and the acceleration after 3 seconds.

(2) A particle moves so that its displacement after $t$ seconds is given by $s = 4t - 8t^3$. When it returns to the origin it stops. Find:

(a) The initial velocity　(b) The maximum velocity

(c) The time it takes to return to the origin (d) The maximum displacement

(3) The displacement of a body is given by $s = \frac{1}{2}t^4 - 3t^3 + 6t^2 + 4$. Find the greatest and least values of the velocity, and the distance it travels between reaching these values.

(4) The velocity of a particle is given by $v = 3t + t^2$. Find its initial acceleration, and the distance gone after 3 seconds.

(5) The velocity of a body $t$ seconds after it starts is $4t - t^2$. Find the greatest velocity, and the distance it has travelled when it achieves its greatest velocity. Find the time taken for it to return to its starting point, and the total distance it has moved through during this time.

(6) The acceleration of a body is given by $a = 1 + 3t$. Find its velocity after 10 seconds, given that it starts at 4 m/sec. Find the distance travelled after 5 seconds.

(7) A particle starts at 21 m/sec, and accelerates at a rate given by $a = 20 - 2t$. Find:

(a) The maximum velocity　(b) The maximum distance

(c) The time it takes to return to its starting point, and its speed at this time.

(8) Two bodies start from the same position: the first has initial velocity 3 m/sec and acceleration $4 - t$, and the second has initial velocity 1 m/sec and acceleration $2 + t$. Find:

a. When the two bodies are first moving with the same velocity, and their distance apart at this time.

b. When the two bodies are at the same position, and the difference in speeds at this time.

(9) A body $A$ is projected from the origin with speed 5 m/ sec and acceleration $2 + t$. At the same time a second body $B$ starts from a point 90 m away in the direction of motion of the first body, with initial speed 4 m/ sec towards $A$ and acceleration $t$ away from $A$. Find when the two bodies collide, and the relative speed with which they do so.

## 22.3 Vector Quantities

The *displacement* **s** of a body is the vector from its starting position to its present position.

Displacement, velocity and acceleration are all *vectors*. Sometimes these vectors are expressed as $a\mathbf{i} + b\mathbf{j} + c\mathbf{k}$, where $\mathbf{i}, \mathbf{j}$ and $\mathbf{k}$ are unit vectors in the $x, y, z$ directions respectively.

· If the vectors are given in terms of components, then the components can be differentiated or integrated individually. For example:

$$\text{If } \mathbf{v} = f(t)\mathbf{i} + g(t)\mathbf{j}, \text{ then } \mathbf{a} = f'(t)\mathbf{i} + g'(t)\mathbf{j}.$$

*Speed* is the modulus of the vector velocity.

### 22.3.1 Example

The position of a vector is given by $\mathbf{r} = 5t\mathbf{i} + 3t^2\mathbf{j} - \mathbf{k}$. Find:

i. The acceleration.

ii. The time when the speed is 20 m/s.

Solution    i.    Obtain the velocity by differentiating the distance.

$$\mathbf{v} = 5\mathbf{i} + 6t\mathbf{j}.$$

Obtain the acceleration by differentiating the velocity.

$$\mathbf{a} = 6\mathbf{j}.$$

**The acceleration is 6j**

ii.    The speed is the modulus of the velocity.

$$\sqrt{(5^2 + (6t)^2)} = 20$$

$$36t^2 = 375.$$

**The speed is 20m/s after 3.23secs.**

### 22.3.2 Exercises

(1) Find the (vector) velocity when the displacement is given by the following:

(a)  $\mathbf{r} = 3t\mathbf{i} + 7t^2\mathbf{j}$    (b)  $\mathbf{r} = t^3\mathbf{i} - 2t^2\mathbf{j} + 4\mathbf{k}$

(c)  $\mathbf{r} = \cos t\mathbf{i} + \sin t\mathbf{j}$   (d)  $\mathbf{r} = \sin 2t\mathbf{i} + 3\cos 2t\mathbf{j} + t\mathbf{k}$

(2) Find the speed for each of the parts of Question 1.

(3) Find the (vector) acceleration for each of the parts of Question 1.

(4) In each of the following, a particle starts from the origin, and moves with velocity vector given by the expressions below. Find the displacements at time t.

(a)  $\mathbf{v} = 3\mathbf{i} + 5\mathbf{j}$        (b)  $\mathbf{v} = t\mathbf{i} + 3t\mathbf{j} - 5t\mathbf{k}$

(c)  $\mathbf{v} = \cos 2t\mathbf{i} - \sin 3t\mathbf{j}$   (d)  $\mathbf{v} = e^t\mathbf{i} - 3e^{2t}\mathbf{j}$

(5) A particle moves so that at time t its position vector is given by $\mathbf{r} = \cos t\mathbf{i} + \sin t\mathbf{j} + 10\mathbf{k}$. Show that its speed is constant.

(6) A particle moves with displacement vector $\mathbf{r} = (3t^2 + 1)\mathbf{i} + (t - t^2)\mathbf{j}$. Find when the particle is moving (a) parallel to the $x$-axis (b) parallel to the vector $4\mathbf{i} - \mathbf{j}$.

(7) A particle moves so that its displacement is given by $\mathbf{r} = (6 - t)\mathbf{i} + t\mathbf{j}$. Find its velocity vector $\mathbf{v}$. When is its velocity perpendicular to its displacement?

(8) A particle moves so that its displacement is given by $\mathbf{r} = (t - 1)\mathbf{i} + (t^2 - t)\mathbf{j}$. Find its velocity vector $\mathbf{v}$. When is its velocity parallel to its displacement?

### 22.4 Examination Questions

(1) A vehicle starts from rest, accelerates at 3.2 m/s² for 12 s and decelerates at 1.8 m/s² until its speed is 10 m/s.

Calculate the following, giving your answers corrected to two significant figures: (a) the greatest speed: (b) the time taken to decelerate; (c) the distance covered while accelerating; (d) the distance covered while decelerating.

[SMP add]

(2) A particle $P$ moves in a straight line so that its velocity $v$ m/s at time $t$ seconds, where $t \geq 0$, is given by $v = 12t - 5t^2$. Calculate

a.  the value of $t$ when the acceleration of $P$ is zero,
b.  the distance covered by $P$ between the instants when $t = 0$ and $t = 2$.

[L add]

(3) At a certain instant a mass at O has a velocity $\mathbf{u}$ ms⁻¹ given by $\mathbf{u} = 18\mathbf{i} - 24\mathbf{j}$, where $\mathbf{i}$ and $\mathbf{j}$ are unit vectors in the direction of the $x$-axis

and $y$-axis respectively. What is the magnitude of the velocity at this instant? The mass subsequently has an acceleration **a** ms$^{-2}$ given by **a** $= -3\mathbf{i} + 2\mathbf{j}$. In terms of **i** and **j** what is the velocity of the mass 5 seconds later? After what further period of time will the mass be instantaneously moving in a direction parallel to the $y$-axis, and at that time what will its position vector be relative to O?

[MEI add]

(4)

a. A particle moves on the $x$-axis. It starts from rest at the origin O and moves in the positive direction with constant acceleration of 2 ms$^{-2}$ until its velocity reaches 10 ms$^{-1}$. It then continues with constant velocity 10 ms$^{-1}$ for some time, before decelerating uniformly and coming to rest after a total time of 20 s. The total distance travelled is 160 m. Sketch the velocity-time graph for the motion, and find the magnitude of the deceleration.

b. Two particles $P$ and $Q$ move in the positive direction on the $x$-axis, $P$ with constant acceleration 2 ms$^{-2}$ and $Q$ with constant acceleration of 1 ms$^{-2}$. At time $t = 0, P$ is projected from the **origin with speed 1ms$^{-1}$, and at time** $t = 4$ $Q$ **is protected from** O with speed 16 ms$^{-1}$. Find the times between which $Q$ is ahead of $P$. Find also the distance from O at which $Q$ overtakes $P$, and the distance from O at which $P$ overtakes $Q$.

[C]

(5)

i. Two points move in a plane, both starting from the origin, in such a way that, after time $t$ seconds, their position vectors are

$$3(\cos t - 1)\mathbf{i} + (4 \sin t)\mathbf{j}$$

and

$$(3 \sin t)\mathbf{i} + 4(\cos t - 1)\mathbf{j}.$$

Find the value of $t$ when the points are first moving in (a) opposite directions, (b) the same direction.

ii. A particle moves in a straight line with acceleration

$$[(t - 1)e^{-t} + 2 \cos t] \text{ ms}^{-2},$$

starting from rest at the origin at time $t = 0$. Obtain the distance $x$ m travelled from rest in time $t$ seconds.

[L]

(6) The position vector of a particle at time $t$ is given by

$$\mathbf{r} = (a\cos\omega t)\mathbf{i} + (a\sin\omega t)\mathbf{j} + bt\mathbf{k},$$

where $a, b$ and $\omega$ are constants. Find the velocity and acceleration vectors. Show that the speed of the particle is constant and that the magnitude of the particle's acceleration is always non-zero.

Comment briefly on these results.

[W]

## COMMON ERRORS

### (1) Notation

a.  Read a question carefully to make sure that you know which of the quantities distance, speed, acceleration you are dealing with.

b.  To go from displacement to velocity, or from velocity to acceleration, you must *differentiate*. To go the other way you *integrate*. Do not perform the wrong operation.

c.  If a body moves with two different velocities $u$ and $v$, then the *average velocity* is not necessarily $\frac{1}{2}(u + v)$. You must find the total distance and divide it by the total time.

### (2) Constant Acceleration

a.  Make sure that you are consistent with the *signs* of your quantities. Decide that one direction shall be positive, and then displacement, velocity and acceleration in the opposite direction must be negative. Do not have the velocity one way and the acceleration the other.

b.  Suppose a body is moving backwards and forwards. To find the displacement after a period of time you do not need to split up the motion into its positive period and its negative period. The equations cover both the positive period and the negative period.

c.  The *displacement* of a body is the directed distance from the starting point. The *total distance travelled* is the amount of distance covered, in both directions. So if a body returns to its starting point then its displacement is zero, but the total distance travelled is not zero.

### (3) Non-Constant Acceleration

a.  Do not use formulae such as $s = ut + \frac{1}{2}at^2$ for situations in which the acceleration is not constant. You must use calculus to find, for example, the distance from the velocity.

b. Do not ignore negative signs. A negative velocity, for example, means that the particle is moving towards the origin instead of away from it.

c. The maximum distance occurs when the *velocity* is 0. Similarly the greatest velocity occurs when the *acceleration* is 0. Make sure that you put the correct expression equal to zero.

# 23 Force and Acceleration

### 23.1 Newton's First and Second Laws

*Newton's First Law* states that:

Unless acted upon by an external force, a body will remain at rest or move with a constant speed in a straight line.

*Newton's Second Law* states that:

The acceleration experienced by a body is proportional to the external force acting upon it, and is in the same straight line as the force.

These laws can be summarized by the formula:

$$\mathbf{F} = m\mathbf{a}$$

Here $\mathbf{F}$ is the force, $m$ is the mass and $\mathbf{a}$ is the acceleration. Note that $\mathbf{F}$ and $\mathbf{a}$ are vectors.

The unit of force is the *Newton*. 1 Newton applied to 1 kilogram imparts an acceleration of 1 m/sec$^2$.

## 23.1.1 Examples

(1)      A stone of mass 0.3 kg is skimmed across the ice at 10 m/sec, and comes to rest in 100 m. Find the force acting upon it, assuming that it is constant.

Solution   Use the formula for constant acceleration.

$$0^2 = 10^2 + 2 \times a \times 100.$$

$$a = -\frac{1}{2} \text{ m/sec}^2$$

Use the second law:

$$\textbf{Force} = 0.3 \times \frac{1}{2} = \textbf{0.15N}$$

(2)      A man weighs out diamonds in a lift which is accelerating upwards at 1 m/sec$^2$. The balance registers 27 grams. What is the true weight of the diamonds? (Take $g$ to be 9.8 m/sec$^2$)

Solution   If the balance registers 27 grams, then the force it applies is $0.027 \times 9.8$ Newtons.

If the mass of the diamonds is $m$ grams, then the second law gives:

$$0.027 \times 9.8 - m \times 9.8 = m \times 1$$

$$m = 0.0245$$

## The diamonds weigh 24.5 grams

(3)      A body of mass 4 kg moves so that its displacement is given by $\mathbf{r} = (t^2 + 1)\mathbf{i} + t^3\mathbf{j}$. Find in vector form the force acting on the body at time t.

Solution   Differentiate the displacement twice to obtain the acceleration.

$$\mathbf{a} = 2\mathbf{i} + 6t\mathbf{j}$$

Multiply the acceleration by the mass to obtain the force.

**The force is** $8\mathbf{i} + 24t\mathbf{j}$

## 23.1.2 Exercises

Throughout these exercises take $g$ to be 9.8 m/sec$^2$.

(1) A mass of 5 kg is suspended from a string. Find the tension in the string.

(2) A body of mass 70 kg is dragged across the floor at a constant speed of $\frac{1}{2}$ m/sec. If the force dragging it is 30 $N$, find the resistance force.

(3) A body of mass 2 kg is accelerated at 12 m/sec$^2$. Find the force applied to it.

(4) A body experiences a force of 20 $N$, and accelerates at 60 m/sec$^2$. Find the mass of the body.

(5) A mass of 4 kg receives a force of 12 kg. Find its acceleration.

(6) A train of mass 60,000 kg comes to rest from 2 m/sec in 30 seconds. Find the braking force, assuming that it is constant.

(7) A car of mass 1,500 kg accelerates from 1 m/sec to 20 m/sec in 30 seconds. Find the tractive force, assuming that it is constant.

(8) A sprinter of mass 70 kg accelerates constantly over 50 metres, reaching a speed of 12 m/sec at the end. Find the force that he exerts.

(9) A train of mass 100,000 kg accelerates from rest until it reaches 10 m/sec, over a distance of 500 m. Find the tractive force of the train.

(10) A train of mass 80,000 kg is brought to rest from a speed of $\frac{1}{2}$ m/sec by buffers which contract through 20 cm. Find the force, assumed constant, exerted by the buffers.

(11) A parachutist of mass 100 kg falls at a steady speed of $1\frac{1}{2}$ m/sec. What is the force of air resistance?

(12) A particle of mass $\frac{1}{4}$ kg is raised on a string at an acceleration of 2 m/sec$^2$. Find the tension in the string.

(13) A lift cage weighs 1,000 kg. The tension in the supporting cable is 9,500$N$. Find the deceleration of the lift.

(14) A mass supported by a string is accelerated up at $2\frac{1}{2}$ m/sec$^2$. The tension in the string is 12 $N$. Find the mass.

(15) A parachutist has mass 100 kg, and is falling at 1 m/sec. Air resistance is equal to 500 $N$ at this speed. Find his acceleration at this speed.

(16) The air resistance experienced by a 100 kg parachutist is proportional to his velocity, and his maximum speed is $1\frac{1}{2}$ m/sec. Find the air resistance when he is falling at 1 m/sec, and his acceleration at that speed.

(17) A 70 kg man weighs himself on a weighing machine which is in a lift accelerating up at $1\frac{1}{4}$ m/sec². What does he seem to weigh?

(18) A 50 kg woman weighs herself in a lift, and the dial registers 47 kg. What is the deceleration of the lift?

(19) When a man weighs himself in a lift accelerating up at 1 m/sec², the dial registers 77 kg. What is his true weight?

(20) A man weighs an object in a lift with a spring balance. When it is accelerating up at $k$ m/sec², it appears to weigh 1.4 kg. When it is accelerating down at $k$ m/sec², it appears to weigh 1.1 kg. Find the true weight of the object.

(21) A balloon of total mass 500 kg is floating horizontally. If 100 kg of ballast is thrown out, find the acceleration with which the balloon rises.

(22) A balloon of total mass 700 kg is accelerating down at $\frac{1}{8}$ m/sec². How much ballast must be ejected to stop the balloon's descent?

(23) A body of mass 2 kg experiences a force of $3\mathbf{i} + 2\mathbf{j}$. Find its acceleration in vector form.

(24) A body of mass 4 kg experiences an acceleration of $(1 + t)\mathbf{i} + 12\mathbf{j}$. Find in vector form the force acting upon it at time $t$.

(25) A body of mass 6 kg experiences a force of $24t\mathbf{i} + 60t^2\mathbf{j}$. Find its acceleration. If it starts at rest from the origin find its velocity and its displacement.

(26) **The force experienced by a body of mass 0.4 kg is $(\cos t)\mathbf{i} + (\sin t)\mathbf{j}$.** Find its acceleration in vector form. If it starts at rest from the point $\mathbf{i}$ find its velocity and displacement.

## 23.2 Action and Reaction

*Newton's Third Law* states that:

Action and reaction are equal and opposite.

Hence if two bodies $A$ and $B$ are in contact, the force exerted by $A$ on $B$ is equal and opposite to the force exerted by $B$ on $A$.

### 23.2.1 Examples

(1)     A locomotive of mass 50 tonnes drags two coaches of 20 tonnes each, against resistances of 2,000 $N$ for the locomotive and 700 $N$ for each coach. If the acceleration is $\frac{1}{4}$ m/sec², find the force produced by the engine and the tensions in the couplings.

Solution    Considering the train as a whole, and using Newton's first law:
$$F - 3400 = 90,000 \times \tfrac{1}{4}$$

**Force = 25,900N**

Considering the carriages as a whole, and letting $T_1$ be the tension in the first coupling:

$$T_1 - 1400 = 40,000 \times \frac{1}{4}$$

Considering the final carriage on its own, and letting $T_2$ be the tension in the second coupling:

$$T_2 - 700 = 20,000 \times \frac{1}{4}$$

**The tensions are 11,400 and 5,700 Newtons**

(2)    Two masses of 4 and 3 kg are at the ends of a light inextensible string, which is slung over a smooth peg. Find the acceleration of the system, and the force exerted by the peg.

Solution    Letting $a$ be the acceleration and $T$ the tension in the string, obtain the two equations:

$$T - 3g = 3a$$

$$4g - T = 4a$$

Add these two equations:

$$g = 7a$$

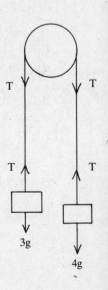

**The acceleration is $g/7 = 1.4$ m/sec$^2$**
The tension in the string is $3a + 3g = 33.6$ N.
**The force exerted by the peg is $2T = 67.2$N**

## 23.2.2 Exercises

Throughout these exercises take $g$ to be 9.8 m/sec$^2$

(1) A car of mass 800 kg tows a caravan of 500 kg, against resistances of 900$N$ for the car and 400$N$ for the caravan. If the acceleration produced is $1\frac{1}{2}$ m/sec$^2$, find the force exerted by the car and the tension in the tow-bar.

(2) A tug tows two barges of mass 100 tonnes each, at an acceleration of 0.1 m/sec$^2$, through water which exerts a drag of 2,000$N$ on each barge. Find the tensions in the ropes between the tug and the first barge and between the two barges.

(3) A train consists of three carriages, each of mass 50 tonnes and each experiencing a resistance of 5000$N$. The train is travelling at 10 m/sec, then brakes are applied to the front carriage which bring the train to a halt in 100 m. Find the thrust in the couplings.

(4) Two masses of 3 kg and 5 kg are connected by a light inextensible string which is slung over a smooth peg. Find the acceleration of the system and the tension in the string. Find the reaction at the peg.

(5) Repeat Question 4, for masses of 10 kg and 5 kg.

(6) Two masses of $m$ and $M$ kg, where $m > M$, are connected by a light inextensible string which is slung over a smooth peg. Show that the acceleration of the system is $(m - M)g/(m + M)$.

(7) A mass of 5 kg lies on a smooth horizontal table, and is connected by a light horizontal string to a mass of 3 kg which hangs over the edge. Find the acceleration of the system and the tension in the string.

(8) Repeat Question 7, with masses of 10 kg and 5 kg.

(9) A mass of $m$ kg lies on a smooth horizontal table, and is connected by a light inextensible string to a mass of $M$ kg which hangs over the edge. Show that the acceleration of the system is $Mg/(m + M)$.

(10) Three masses are as shown in the figure. The table is smooth and horizontal, and the strings are light and inextensible. Find the acceleration of the system and the tensions in the strings.

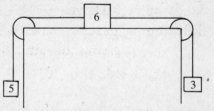

(11) A mass of 4 kg lies on a horizontal table, and is connected by a light inextensible string to a mass of 5 kg which hangs freely. If the system moves with acceleration 2 m/sec$^2$ find the frictional force acting on the 4 kg mass.

(12) Three masses are as shown in the figure. The table is horizontal, and the strings are light and inextensible. If the system moves with acceleration 1 m/sec$^2$, find the frictional force acting on the central mass.

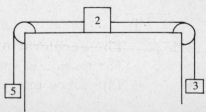

## 23.3 Examination Question

(1) A lift of mass 500 kg accelerates at 2.2 ms$^{-2}$ from rest to its maximum speed and also decelerates at 2.2 ms$^{-2}$ from this maximum speed to rest. What are the maximum and minimum values of the tension in the supporting cable when the lift is not carrying any passengers?

In fact the lift is designed to carry at most five passengers whose average mass can be taken as 75 kg each. What is the maximum tension that the cable must be able to withstand, and what will be the maximum force on the floor of the lift?

[MEI add]

(2) Forces measured in newtons are represented by the vectors

$$\begin{pmatrix} 3 \\ 4 \end{pmatrix}, \quad \begin{pmatrix} 2 \\ 4 \end{pmatrix}, \quad \begin{pmatrix} -2 \\ 1 \end{pmatrix} \quad \text{and} \quad \begin{pmatrix} p \\ 2p \end{pmatrix}$$

They act on a particle to accelerate it in the direction $\begin{pmatrix} -1 \\ -1 \end{pmatrix}$. Find $p$.

If the mass of the particle is 0.1 kg, show that the magnitude of the acceleration is approximately 42.4 ms$^{-2}$.

If the particle is initially at the point $(0,0)$ and moving with velocity $\begin{pmatrix} 1 \\ 4 \end{pmatrix}$ ms$^{-1}$ **find its position vector after 2 seconds.**

[O&C add]

(3) Two particles $A$ and $B$ of masses 0.4 kg and 0.3 kg respectively, are connected by a light inextensible string which passes over a smooth, light, fixed pulley. The particles are released from rest with the string taut and the hanging parts vertical. Calculate

a.  the acceleration, in ms$^{-2}$, of $A$,
b.  the tension, in $N$, in the string.

[L add]

(4) A tug is towing two barges along a canal and slowing down at 0.015 ms$^{-2}$. The mass of each barge is 12 tonnes, and of the tug 8 tonnes.

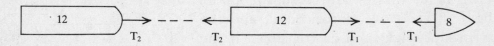

Each of the barges and the tug experiences the same resistance from the water, $R$, and the engines give a forward force of $120N$ on the tug.

Show that the tension $T_1$ in the first cable is double the tension $T_2$ in the second cable.

Calculate the values of $T_1$ and $R$.

[SMP add]

(5) (In this question take $g$ to be $10$ m/sec$^2$)

A balloon of total mass $M$ kg, including the balloonist, his equipment and ballast, is at a height of 2.2 km above the ground, ascending vertically at a steady speed of $10$ ms$^{-1}$. Write down the force of upthrust by the air on the balloon.

The balloonist wishes to land, and he adjusts the balloon so that the upthrust is suddenly reduced to $\frac{9}{10}$ of its previous value, without altering $M$, and remains constant thereafter. Show that, 1 minute later, his height is 1 km and his velocity is $50$ ms$^{-1}$ downwards.

At this moment the balloonist drops overboard $pM$ kg of ballast, where $\frac{1}{10} < p < 1$. Show that the balloon's acceleration changes to

$$\frac{10p - 1}{1 - p} \text{ ms}^{-2} \text{ upwards.}$$

Given that the balloon reaches the ground with zero velocity, find

a.  the value of $p$,
b.  the time between the ballast hitting the ground and the balloon reaching the ground.

[AEB 1986]

(6) In the interval $0 \leq t \leq 6$, where t denotes time in seconds, a particle of mass 2 kg is acted upon by two forces. The first force acts in the direction of the vector $8\mathbf{i} - \mathbf{j} + 4\mathbf{k}$ and has a constant magnitude of $18N$. The second force acts in the direction of the vector $-2\mathbf{i} + 2\mathbf{j} - \mathbf{k}$ and its magnitude decreases uniformly with time from $18N$ when $t = 0$ to zero when $t = 6$. Show that the acceleration of the particle during the interval $0 \leq t \leq 6$ is

$$(2 + t)\mathbf{i} + (5 - t)\mathbf{j} + (1 + \frac{1}{2}t)\mathbf{k} \text{ ms}^{-2}.$$

Given that the particle has velocity $2\mathbf{i}ms^{-1}$ when $t = 0$, find its velocity when $t = 6$.

[JMB]

# COMMON ERRORS

## (1) Force and Acceleration

a. Forces on a system only balance if the system is in equilibrium. If the system is accelerating then you cannot equate the forces to zero.

b. When drawing a diagram of the forces acting on a body, do not put in a force corresponding to the acceleration. The acceleration is a consequence of the forces, not an extra force itself.

## (2) Action and Reaction

When dealing with problems involving weights hanging from strings, do not assume that the tension in the string is equal to the weight. That will only be true if the system is in equilibrium. If the system is accelerating then the tension will be different from the weight.

# 24 Resolving Forces

## 24.1 Forces at an Angle

If a force $F$ makes an angle $\theta$ with a direction, the *resolved part* or component of the force in that direction is $F\cos\theta$.

If two or more forces are equivalent to a single force, that force is the *resultant*.

The resultant can be found by components, or by use of a vector triangle, as shown.

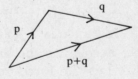

If three forces $P, Q, R$ are in equilibrium, then they form a *triangle of forces* as shown.

Suppose a body is acted on by certain forces. Newton's Laws I and II can be generalized as follows:

**I** If a body is not accelerating in a particular direction, then the sum of the resolved parts of the forces in that direction is zero.

II The acceleration of a body in a particular direction is proportional to the net resolved parts of the forces in that direction.

The process of finding the resolved parts along a certain direction is called *resolving* in that direction.

### 24.1.1 Examples

(1)      Forces of 12N and 15N act through the same point, along bearings of 030° and 345°. Find the magnitude and direction of the force needed to counterbalance them.

Solution      Let the counterbalancing force have South component $S$ and West component $W$.
Resolving North-South:

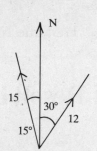

$$S = 12\cos 30° + 15\cos 15° = 24.88N$$

Resolving East-West:

$$W = 12\cos 60° - 15\cos 75° = 2.12N$$

The magnitude $F$ of the force is found by Pythagoras, and its direction $\theta$ by trigonometry.

$$F = \sqrt{(S^2 + W^2)} = 24.97N : \theta = \tan^{-1}\frac{W}{S} = 4.9°$$

**The balancing force is 25.0N, at a bearing of 184.9°**

(2) A barge of mass 50 tonnes is pulled by a rope which makes 10° with the keel of the boat. If the water resistance is $2,000N$, find the force in the rope needed to accelerate the barge at 0.1 m/sec$^2$.

Solution      Let the force be $F$. Resolving along the keel:

$$F\cos 10° - 2,000 = 50,000 \times 0.1$$

**The force needed is** $7108N$

### 24.1.2 Exercises

(1) Find the North component of a force of 24N at a bearing of 075°. Find its East component.

(2) Find the East components of the following forces:

  (a)  25$N$ at 023°    (b)  7$N$ at 180°

  (c)  0.02$N$ at 113°  (d)  65$N$ at 337°

(3) Find the magnitude and direction of the force needed to counterbalance 5$N$ at 066° and 3$N$ at 015°.

(4) Find the magnitudes and directions of the forces needed to counterbalance the following sets of forces:

a.  17$N$ due North and 18$N$ due West

b.  4$N$ at 120° and 3$N$ at 210°

c.  12$N$ due North, 25$N$ at 012° and 33$N$ at 354°

d.  5$N$ at 254°, 7$N$ at 119°, 10$N$ at 331°, 14$N$ at 23°.

(5) Find the resultant of 12$N$ North East and 27$N$ South West.

(6) Find the resultants of the following sets of forces:

  (a)  14$N$ at 25°, 22$N$ at 348°  (b) 2$N$ at 47° and 3$N$ at 183°

  (c)  48$N$ at 63°, 34$N$ at 190° and 41$N$ at 213°.

(7) A body of mass 12 kg is acted upon by two forces, one of which is 6$N$ due north, the other being 7$N$ North East. Find the magnitude and direction of the acceleration of the body.

(8) Find the magnitude and direction of the acceleration of a body of mass 5 kg when it experiences the following set of forces:

$$3N \text{ at } 012°, 3.5N \text{ at } 348° \text{ and } 4.1N \text{ at } 327°.$$

(9) A water skier of mass 80 kg is pulled by a rope which makes 15° with the horizontal. If the water resistance is 20 N, find the force in the rope need to pull him along at a steady speed.

(10) If the skier of Question 9 accelerates at $1\frac{1}{2}$ m/sec², find the tension in the rope.

(11) A body of mass 30 kg lies on a smooth floor, and is pulled by a rope which makes 30° with the horizontal. If the tension in the rope is 12$N$ find the acceleration of the body.

(12) A body of mass 70 kg lies on a rough floor, where the resistance to motion is 43$N$. A rope is attached to the body at 20° to the horizontal. Find the force in the rope necessary to accelerate the body at 2 m/sec².

(13) If in Question 12 the force in the rope is 60$N$, find the acceleration of the body.

(14) Three forces $P, Q$ and $R$ act at a point, and are in equilibrium. Let $\hat{p}$ be the angle between $Q$ and $R$, with $\hat{q}$ and $\hat{r}$ defined similarly. Prove that:

$$(\sin \hat{p})/P = (\sin \hat{q})/Q = (\sin \hat{r})/R.$$

## 24.2 Problems Involving Weight

*Weight* always acts vertically downwards. It is sometimes necessary to resolve the weight of a body.

Throughout this section take $g$ to be 9.8 m/sec$^2$

### 24.2.1. Examples

(1)         A body of mass 3 kg lies on a smooth slope of angle 20°.
            Find the acceleration of the body down the slope.
Solution    The forces are as shown in the diagram.
            Resolving down the slope:

$$3g \cos 70° = 3a$$

**The acceleration is g $\cos 70° = 3.35$ m/sec$^2$**

(2)         A body of mass 12 kg hangs from a string, and is pulled
            aside by a horizontal force of $30N$. Find the tension in
            the string and the angle it makes with the vertical.
Solution    Resolving vertically:

$$T \cos \theta = 12g$$

Resolving horizontally:

$$T \sin \theta = 30$$

Divide the second equation by the first:

$$\tan \theta = 30/12g : \theta = 14.3°$$

Substitute into either equation to find T.

**The tension is $121N$ and the angle is $14.3°$**

(3)         Three particles $A, B, C$ of masses 4 kg, 5 kg, 6 kg re-
            spectively, are tied in that order on a light inextensible
            string. The string is slung over two smooth pegs $X$ and
            $Y$, with $X$ between $A$ and $B$ and $Y$ between $B$ and $C$.
            Find the angle made by $XB$ with the vertical.

Solution    The situation is as shown. The three forces acting at $B$ are 4g, 5g, 6g. Rearrange the three forces into a triangle of forces.

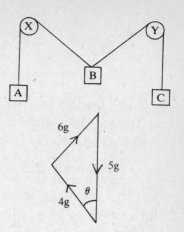

Use the cosine rule to find $\theta$.

$$\cos\theta = 0.125$$

**$XB$ makes 83° with the vertical.**

## 24.2.2 Exercises

(1) A body of mass 30 kg lies on a smooth slope of angle 35°. Find the acceleration down the slope.

(2) A body lies on a smooth slope of angle $\alpha$. Show that the acceleration down the slope is $g \sin\alpha$.

(3) A body of mass 10 kg lies on a smooth slope of angle 20°. Find the normal reaction.

(4) A body mass 20 kg lies on a smooth slope of angle 25°. Find the force acting up the slope which will keep it in equilibrium.

(5) A body mass 12 kg lies on a smooth slope of angle 10°. A horizontal force of $3N$ acts on it up the slope. Find the acceleration down the slope.

(6) A body of mass 14 kg lies on a slope of angle 27°, experiencing a frictional force of $57N$. Find its acceleration down the slope.

(7) A body of mass 5 kg lies on a smooth slope of angle 30°. It is attached to a light inextensible string, which passes over a smooth peg at the top and is attached to a weight of 4 kg which hangs freely. Find the acceleration of the system and the tension in the string.

(8) The 5 kg mass of Question 7 is replaced by a heavier mass so that the system is now in equilibrium. Find the new mass.

(9) The 4 kg mass of Question 7 is replaced by a lighter mass so that the system accelerates at $\frac{1}{2}$ m/sec$^2$. Find the new mass.

(10) The 4 kg mass of Question 7 is replaced by a lighter mass so that the system accelerates in the other direction at $\frac{1}{2}$ m/sec$^2$. Find the new mass.

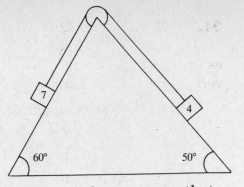

(11) Bodies of mass 4 kg and 7 kg lie on the sides of smooth slopes of angle 50° and 60° respectively, connected by a light inextensible string as shown. Find the acceleration of the system.

(12) The 7 kg mass of Question 11 is replaced by a lighter mass so that the system is in equilibrium. Find the new mass.

(13) The 7 kg mass of Question 11 is replaced by a heavier mass so that the system accelerates at 5 m/sec². Find the new mass.

(14) A mass of 6 kg hangs at the end of a string and is pulled aside by a horizontal force of 23N. Find the tension in the string and the angle it makes with the vertical.

(15) The mass of Question 14 is pulled aside by a horizontal force, so that the string makes 12° with the vertical. Find the force.

(16) The mass of Question 14 is pulled aside by a horizontal force, so that the tension in the string is 65N. Find the force.

(17) The mass of Question 14 is pulled aside by a force of 36N which is at right angles to the string. Find the tension in the string and the angle which it makes with the vertical.

(18) The mass of Question 14 is pulled aside by a force which is at right angles to the string. The string now makes 33° with the vertical. Find the force and the tension in the string.

(19) A mass of 7 kg is supported by two strings, which make 30° and 40° with the vertical. Find the tensions in the strings.

(20) A mass of 8 kg is supported by two strings, each of which exerts a tension of 45N. Find the angles that the strings make with the vertical.

(21) A mass of 10 kg is supported by two strings. One string exerts 60N and is at 20° to the vertical. Find the tension in the other string and the angle it makes with the vertical.

(22) A mass of 10 kg is supported by two strings. If the tensions in the strings are 60N and 70N find the angles which they make with the vertical.

## 24.3 Examination Questions

(1) Particles of masses 500g at $B$ and 250g at $C$ are supported by 3 strings as shown in the figure. The string $AB$ is inclined at an angle of 30° to the vertical and $BC$ is horizontal.

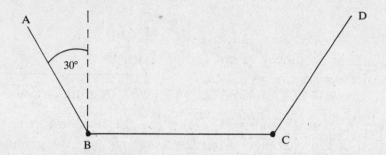

a. Draw accurately a triangle of forces for the particle at $B$ and hence find the tension in $AB$ and in $BC$.

b. Find by drawing or by calculation the angle which $CD$ makes with the vertical.

[AEB add 1986]

(2) A particle of mass 0.3 kg is suspended in equilibrium by two light strings inclined to the horizontal at 30° and 60° respectively. Calculate the tensions in the strings.

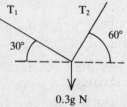

A horizontal force of $x$ newton, acting in the plane of the two strings, as shown in the diagram below, is now applied to the particle and the system is held in equilibrium with the tensions in the two original strings now being equal. By resolving in the direction $AB$ shown in the diagram, or otherwise, find the value of $x$.

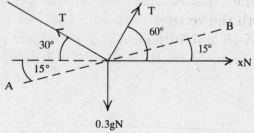

[O&C add]

(3) A particle $A$ of mass 2 kg is placed on a long smooth plane inclined at an angle $\theta$ where $\sin\theta = \frac{3}{50}$. It is attached by a light inelastic string to a particle $B$ of mass 2 kg. The string passes over a smooth peg $P$ with the particle $B$ hanging vertically below the peg.

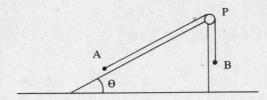

The system is released from rest. Calculate the tension in the string and the acceleration of the particles. After 2 seconds $B$ hits the ground without rebounding, and the string becomes slack. Calculate the total distance which $A$ moves before it comes instantaneously to rest.

[O add]

(4)

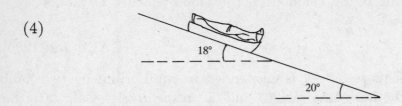

A sledge with rider, of total mass 100 kg, slides down an 18° slope at constant speed. Calculate the force of resistance to its motion. [Take $g$ to be 10 m s$^{-2}$, and give your answer to 2 significant figures.]

The angle of the slope increases to 20°. Assuming that the resistance stays the same, and that the sledge remains in contact with the surface, find the rate at which it accelerates.

[SMP]

(5) Two particles, masses $2M$ and $3M$, fastened to the ends of a light inelastic string which passes over two smooth pegs $A$ and $B$ are kept in equilibrium by a third particle, mass $aM$. fastened to point $C$ of the string, $C$ lying between $A$ and $B$. If the line $AB$ is horizontal and if, in equilibrium, the string is such that the angle $A\hat{C}B = 120°$, find $a$.

[NI]

# COMMON ERRORS
## Resolving Forces

a. Do not forget to multiply forces by the factor of $\cos\theta$. The resultant of two forces of $5N$ and $6N$ is not $11N$, unless they happen to be in the same direction.

b. Do not assume that the sum of forces is zero, unless the body is in equilibrium.

# 25 Friction

### 25.1

Suppose two bodies are in contact. If they are sliding or about to slide then friction is said to be *limiting*.

The maximum frictional force between them, achieved when friction is limiting, is proportional to the normal force between them.

The constant of proportionality is the *coefficient of friction $\mu$*.

Suppose two bodies are in contact, and $R$ is the resultant of the normal and frictional forces. The greatest possible angle between $R$ and the normal is the *angle of friction*.

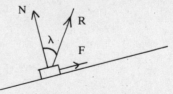

The angle of friction $\lambda$ is given in terms of the coefficient of friction $\mu$ by the equation $\mu = \tan \lambda$.

### 25.1.1 Examples

(1)        A stone of mass 0.1 kg is skimmed across ice. It starts at 5 m/sec and comes to rest after 50 m. Find the coefficient of friction $\mu$.

Solution The deceleration is found from the formula $v^2 = u^2 + 2as$
The deceleration is 0.25 m/sec$^2$.
The normal force is 0.1g. As the stone is sliding friction is limiting.

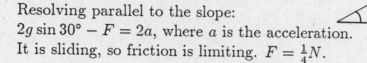

$$\mu \times 0.1g = 0.1 \times 0.25$$

**The coefficient of friction is 0.026**

(2) A body of mass 2 kg lies on a slope of angle 30°, where $\mu = \frac{1}{4}$. Find the acceleration of the body down the slope.

Solution Resolving perpendicular to the slope:

$$N = 2g\cos 30°$$

Resolving parallel to the slope:
$2g \sin 30° - F = 2a$, where $a$ is the acceleration.
It is sliding, so friction is limiting. $F = \frac{1}{4}N$.

$$2a = 2g \sin 30° - \frac{1}{2}g \cos 30°$$

**The acceleration is 2.78m/sec$^2$**

## 25.1.2 Exercises

(1) A mass of 6 kg lies on a rough table where the coefficient of friction $\mu$ is 0.5. Find the least horizontal force needed to move it.

(2) A mass of 8 kg on a rough floor can just be moved by a horizontal force of $45N$. Find the coefficient of friction.

(3) A body of mass 3 kg slides on a rough horizontal table where the coefficient of friction is $\frac{1}{2}$. If it starts with a speed of 5 m/sec find how far it skids.

(4) A body of mass 12 kg lies on a rough horizontal table, and a horizontal force of $24N$ is applied. If the body does not move find the frictional force.

(5) A body of mass 9 kg slides along a rough horizontal table, coming to rest from 3 m/sec in 1 m. Find the coefficient of friction.

(6) A body lies on a slope of angle 23°, where the coefficient of friction is $\frac{1}{4}$. Find its acceleration down the slope.

(7) A body of mass 12 kg lies on a rough slope of angle 17°. If it does not slip find the frictional force.

(8) A body lies on a slope of angle 43°, and accelerates at 5 m/sec². Find the coefficient of friction.

(9) A body can just rest on a slope where the coefficient of friction is $\frac{1}{2}$. Find the angle of the slope.

(10) A body can just rest on a slope of angle $\alpha$. Show that the angle of friction is $\alpha$.

(11) A body lies on a slope of angle $\alpha$, where the angle of friction is $\lambda$. ($\lambda < \alpha$). Show that its acceleration down the slope is $g\sin(\alpha - \lambda)/\cos\lambda$.

(12) A body of mass 3 kg lies on a slope of angle 30°, where the coefficient of friction is $\frac{1}{4}$. Find the least force parallel to the slope which will prevent it from sliding down. Find the least force parallel to the slope which will push it up the slope.

(13) A car of mass 700 kg is travelling at 25 m/sec when the engine seizes, causing the wheels to lock. The coefficient of friction between tyre and ground is $1\frac{1}{2}$. Find how long it takes to come to a halt (a) along level ground (b) down a slope of angle 10° (c) up a slope of angle 5°.

(14) A body of mass 23 kg lies on a floor where the coefficient of friction is $\frac{1}{2}$. A rope is attached to it at an angle $\theta$ to the horizontal. Find the least tension in the rope which will pull the body along in the cases when $\theta$ is (a) 0° (b) 25° (c) 40°.

(15) A body of mass 75 kg lies on a floor where the coefficient of friction is $\frac{1}{4}$. It is pushed by a rod making $\theta$ with the horizontal. Find the least force in the rod which will move the body in the cases when $\theta$ is (a) 0° (b) 12° (c) 20°.

(16) A body of mass 3 kg lies on a slope of angle 20°, where the coefficient of friction is $\frac{1}{8}$. A rope is attached to it, making 10° with the slope. Find the least tension in the rope which will prevent the body from sliding down. Find the least tension which will pull the body up.

(17) A mass of 3 kg lies on a horizontal table where the coefficient of friction is $\frac{1}{2}$. It is attached to a light inextensible string, which passes over the table and supports a mass of 7 kg which hangs freely. Find the acceleration of the system.

(18) A mass of 5 kg lies on a rough horizontal table, and is attached by a light inextensible string to an equal mass which hangs freely. The system moves with an acceleration of 4 m/sec². Find the coefficient of friction.

(19) A mass of 4 kg lies on a slope of an-
gle 20° and coefficient of friction $\frac{1}{8}$, and is
attached by a light horizontal string to a
mass of 6 kg which hangs freely. Find the
acceleration of the system.

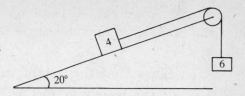

## 25.2 Examination Questions

(1)

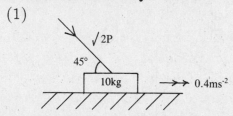 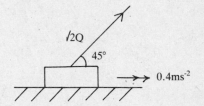

A block of wood is made to slide along a rough horizontal plane by a
force $\sqrt{2}P$ newtons applied at an angle of 45° as in the Fig 1. Copy this
figure and mark in clearly all the forces acting on the block.

If the coefficient of friction is $\frac{1}{3}$ and if the force $\sqrt{2}P$ newtons causes the
block to accelerate along the plane at 0.4 m s$^{-2}$, calculate the value of $P$.

If a new force $\sqrt{2}Q$ newtons is applied to the block instead of the original
force, as in Fig 2, and if the acceleration is unaltered, prove that $Q = \frac{1}{2}P$.

[O&C add]

(2)

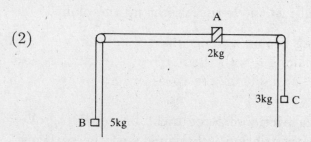

The diagram shows a particle A of mass 2 kg resting on a horizontal
table. It is attached to particles $B$ of mass 5 kg and $C$ of mass 3 kg by
light inextensible strings hanging over light smooth pulleys. Initially the
plane $ABC$ is vertical, the strings are taut and pass over the pulleys at right
angles to the edges of the table. In the ensuing motion from rest find the
common acceleration of the particles and the tension in each string before $A$
reaches an edge

a. when the table is smooth,
b. when the table is rough and the coefficient of friction between
   the particle $A$ and the table is $\frac{1}{2}$. (Take $g$ as 10m/s$^2$.)

[L]

(3) A weight $W$ is placed on a rough plane inclined at an angle $\alpha$ to the horizontal and the angle of friction between the weight and the plane is $\lambda(<\alpha)$.

 i.   Show that the weight will slide down the plane.

 ii.   If the weight is just prevented from sliding down by a force $P$ inclined to the upward vertical at an acute angle $\beta$ show that

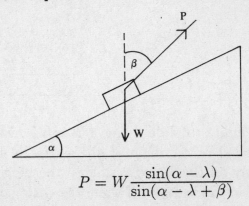

$$P = W\frac{\sin(\alpha - \lambda)}{\sin(\alpha - \lambda + \beta)}$$

Obtain the least value of $P$ as $\beta$ varies and the corresponding value of $\beta$.

iii.   If $\alpha + \lambda < \pi/2$, what is the direction and magnitude of the smallest force which will just move the weight up the plane?

                  [SUJB]

## COMMON ERRORS

 a.   Do not assume that the frictional force must be equal to $\mu N$. This is only the case when friction is limiting, i.e. the surfaces are sliding or about to slide. In general, $F \leq \mu N$.

 b.   When a body lies on a surface, do not assume that $N = mg$. If the surface is not horizontal, or if there are extra forces involved, then you must find $N$ by resolving along the normal.

# 26 Moments

If a force acts on a large body, then the *moment* of the force about a point is the turning effect of the force about that point.

If the body does not turn about a point, then the sum of the clockwise moments about that point is equal to the sum of the anti-clockwise moments.

The operation of equating the clockwise and anti-clockwise moments about a point is called *taking moments* about that point.

## 26.1 Perpendicular Forces

Suppose a lever is pivoted at $A$, and the force $F$ acts at $d$ from the pivot and is at right angles to the lever.

The moment of the force about $A$ is $Fd$.

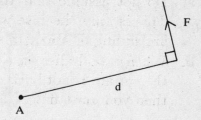

### 26.1.1 Example

A see-saw is balanced at its centre. Zoe, who weighs 45 kg, sits 2 m from the centre. Where should Yvonne, who weighs 50 kg, sit in order for the see-saw to balance?

Solution    Suppose that Yvonne sits $y$ m from the centre. Her (clockwise) moment about the centre is $50y$. This must exactly balance Zoe's (anti-clockwise) moment.

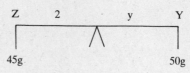

$$50y = 2 \times 45. \ y = 1.8$$

**Yvonne should sit 1.8 m from the centre**

### 26.1.2 Exercises

(1) In each of the diagrams below the system is in equilibrium. Find the unknown forces.

(a)      (b)      (c)

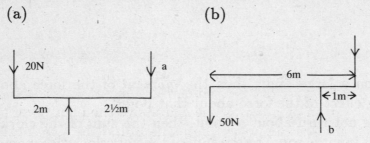

(2) In each of the diagrams below the system is in equilibrium. Find the unknown distances.

(a)      (b)      (c)

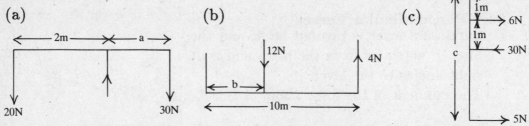

(3) A see-saw of length 5 metres is pivoted at its centre. Naomi, weighing 40 kg, sits at one end. Where should Osric, weighing 75 kg, sit to balance the see-saw?

(4) Osric gets off the see-saw of Question 3, and Peregrine sits on it 2 m from the centre. If it is in balance how much does he weigh?

(5) A light rod of length 2 m has weights of 7 kg and 13 kg at each end. Where should it be pivoted if it is to balance?

(6) A light rod of length 1.4 m is pivoted 0.5 m from one end. 4.5 kg is placed at the shorter end: how much weight should be put at the longer end to balance it?

(7) A uniform beam of length 2 m and mass 50 kg is pivoted 0.8 m from one end. What weight should be put at the shorter end in order to balance it?

(8) A non-uniform rod of length 2 m and mass 40 kg is such that its weight acts through a point 20 cm from the centre. If it is pivoted at its centre, what weight should be put at an end in order to balance it?

(9) A uniform rod of mass 12 kg and length 1.6 m is smoothly hinged at one end. It is held horizontal by a force acting vertically at its free end. What is the force?

(10) A uniform rod of mass 20 kg and length 2.4 m is smoothly hinged at one end. It is held horizontal by a force of $15g$ acting vertically. Where does the force act?

(11) A uniform beam of mass 50 kg and length 2 m is held by two supports which act at 0.2 m from one end and 0.1 m from the other. Find the forces exerted by the supports.

(12) A non-uniform beam of length 3 m is supported at both ends. The upthrusts from the supports are $30g$ and $50g$. Where does the weight of the beam act?

(13) A diving-board of mass 70 kg is a uniform plank of length 2 m. It is held in a horizontal position by a bar at one end above the plank, and a bar 0.25 m from the same end acting below the plank. Find the forces exerted by the bars.

(14) A pipe of mass 50 g. is such that its weight acts through a point 8 cm from the mouthpiece. It is held horizontal by the upper and lower teeth of the smoker, which act 1 cm and 2 cm respectively from the mouthpiece. Find the forces exerted by the teeth.

## 26.2 Forces Acting at an Angle

Suppose a lever is pivoted at $A$, and the force $F$ acts at $d$ from the pivot and makes an angle $\theta$ with the lever.

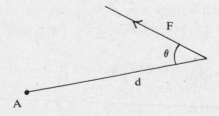

The moment of the force about the pivot is $Fd\sin\theta$. This can be though of as either of the following:

I. Taking the component of the force which is perpendicular to the lever.

II. Taking the perpendicular distance from the pivot to the line of action of the force.

### 26.2.1 Examples

(1)     A uniform plank of mass 80 kg and length 2 m is freely hinged at one end. It is held horizontal by a rope at the other end which is tied to a point 1 m above the hinge. Find the force in the rope.

Solution     The angle $\theta$ between the rope and the plank is $\tan^{-1}\frac{1}{2}$. Taking moments about the hinge:

$$80g \times 1 = T \times 2 \times \sin\theta$$

**The force in the rope is 876.5 N**

(2)     A uniform ladder of mass 20 kg and length 2 m leans on a rough floor against a smooth wall. If it makes 60° with the horizontal find the least possible coefficient of friction.

Solution     The forces are as shown in the diagram. Resolving vertically:

$$N = 20g$$

Resolving horizontally:

$$F = P$$

Taking moments about the base of the ladder:

$$20g \times 1 \times \cos 60° = P \times 2 \times \sin 60°$$

If friction is limiting, $F = \mu N$.

$$\mu = F/N = P/N = \cos 60° / (2 \sin 60°)$$

## The least coefficient of friction is 0.29

### 26.2.2 Exercises

(1) In each of the diagrams below the system is in equilibrium. Find the unknown forces. H denotes a hinge.

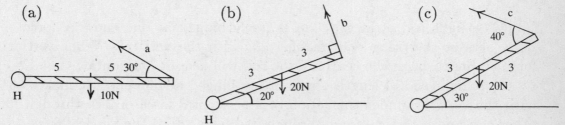

(a)   (b)   (c)

(2) In each of the diagrams below the system is in equilibrium. Find the unknown distances. H denotes a hinge.

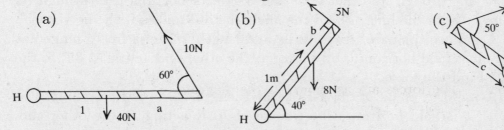

(a)   (b)   (c)

(3) In each of the diagrams below the system is in equilibrium. Find the unknown angles. H denotes a hinge.

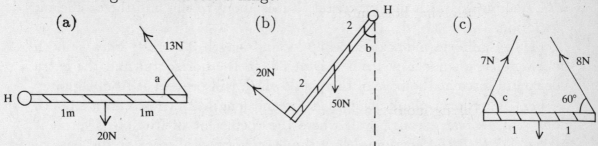

(a)   (b)   (c)

(4) A light rod of length 1 m is freely hinged at one end. A vertical force of 2 N acts at the other end, and a horizontal force acts in the middle. If the rod makes 30° with the vertical find the horizontal force.

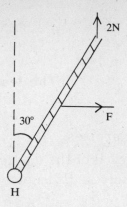

(5) A light rod of length 1 m is freely hinged at one end. A force of 12 N acts at the other end, making 20° with the vertical. What vertical force acting through the centre of the rod will keep it horizontal?

(6) A light rod of length 1 m is freely hinged at one end. It makes 50° with the vertical, under the action of a horizontal force of 3 N through its other end and a vertical force through its centre. Find the vertical force.

(7) A light rod of length 1 m is freely hinged at one end. 5 N acts vertically up through its other end, and 3 N acts horizontally through its centre away from the hinge. Find the angle the rod makes with the vertical.

(8) A uniform plank of mass 10 kg and length 1.2 m is freely hinged at one end. It is held horizontal by a force at the other end acting at 35° to the vertical. Find the force.

(9) A uniform plank of mass 10 kg and length 1.2 m is freely hinged at one end. It is held horizontal by a force of 70 N acting at the other end. Find the angle this force makes with the vertical.

(10) A uniform plank of length 3 m rests on a rough floor against a smooth wall, making 70° with the horizontal. If it is about to slip find the coefficient of friction.

(11) A uniform plank of mass 60 kg and length 3 m rests on a smooth floor against a smooth wall. If it is at 60° to the horizontal find the extra horizontal force at the base of the plank which will prevent it from slipping.

(12) A uniform plank of mass 20 kg and length 2 m rests on a smooth floor and against a rough wall where the coefficient of friction is $\frac{1}{2}$. If it makes 60° with the horizontal find the least horizontal force at the base of the ladder which will prevent it from slipping.

(13) A uniform ladder rests against a smooth wall and on a rough floor where the coefficient of friction is $\frac{1}{4}$. Find the greatest angle it can make with the vertical before it slips.

(14) A uniform bar of length 1.2 m and mass 5 kg rests on a rough floor, its other end being held by a horizontal string. If the bar makes 50° with the vertical find the force in the string and the least possible coefficient of friction.

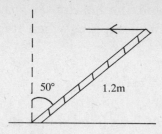

## 26.3 Examination Questions

(1) A uniform straight plank $AB$, of mass 12 kg and length 2 m, rests horizontally on two supports, one at $C$ and the other at $D$, where $AC = CD = 0.6$ m. A particle $P$ of mass $X$ kg is hung from $B$ and the plank is on the point of tilting.

a. Find the value of $X$.
   The particle $P$ is removed from $B$ and hung from $A$.
b. Find, in N, the magnitude of the force exerted on the plank at each support.

[L add]

(2) A uniform ladder of length 6 m and mass 25 kg rests with one end in contact with a smooth vertical wall, and the other end on rough horizontal ground. The ladder is in a vertical plane perpendicular to the wall.

The lower end of the ladder is 1.5 m from the base of the wall, and the coefficient of friction between the ladder and the ground is 0.15.

A man of mass 110 kg ascends the ladder.

Draw a neat diagram showing clearly all of the forces acting on the ladder when the man is 1 m up the ladder.

Find how far along the ladder the man can ascend before the ladder starts to slip.

[NI add]

(3) A uniform ladder of weight $W$ is inclined at an angle $\alpha$ to the horizontal. Its foot rests on rough horizontal ground (coefficient of friction $\mu_1$) and its top against a smooth vertical wall. Show that slipping will not occur provided

$$\tan \alpha \geq (2\mu_1)^{-1}.$$

(Note that the appearance of $\geq$ in this relation must be justified.)

The same ladder is now moved to lean against a rough vertical wall (coefficient of friction $\mu_2$), with the coefficient of friction between the foot of the ladder and the horizontal ground still being $\mu_1$. Show that the ladder is on the point of slipping when its angle of inclination to the horizontal is

$$\text{arc } \tan((1 - \mu_1\mu_2)/2\mu_1).$$

[MEI]

(4) $AC$ is a fixed rough straight horizontal wire of length greater than $4a$. A straight uniform rod $AP$ of mass $4M$ and length $2a$ is smoothly jointed to the wire at $A$. The end $P$ of the rod is attached by means of a light inelastic thread $PB$ of length $2a$ to a bead $B$ of mass $M$ which can slide on the wire.

a. The system is in equilibrium with $P\hat{A}B$ equal to $\theta$. By taking moments about $A$ for the rod $AP$, or otherwise, show that the tension in the string is $Mg/\sin\theta$. Find the frictional force at $B$ and show that $\mu \geq \frac{1}{2}\cot\theta$, where $\theta$ is the coefficient of friction between the bead and the wire.

b. With $P\hat{A}B = \theta$, suppose $\mu = \frac{1}{4}\cot\theta$ and that a horizontal force $S$ applied at $P$ in the plane $APB$ keeps the system in equilibrium. If $B$ is on the point of slipping towards $A$, show that the tension in the string is $Mg/(3\sin\theta)$ and find the value of $S$.

c. When $P\hat{A}B = \theta, \mu = \frac{1}{4}\cot\theta$ and no horizontal force is applied at $P$, what is the minimum value of the mass of $B$ required to ensure equilibrium?

[W]

(5) The diagram shows a uniform rod $AB$, of length $4a$ and weight $2W$, freely jointed at $A$ to a vertical wall. A light inextensible string of length $4a$ joins $B$ to the point $C$ of the wall distant $4a$ vertically above $A$. A uniform disc of weight $W$ and radius $a/\sqrt{3}$ rests in equilibrium touching the rod and wall. The points of contact are frictionless. Find

i. the magnitudes of the reactions of the wall and the rod on the disc;
ii. the tension in the string;
iii. the magnitude and direction of the reaction of the joint at *A* on the rod.

[SUJB]

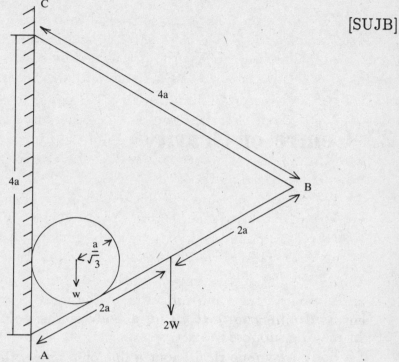

## COMMON ERRORS
### Taking Moments

a. State clearly the point about which you are taking moments. In general, the moment will depend on the point.
b. The point about which you take moments does not have to be a fulcrum or pivot. If a body is in equilibrium then the sum of moments about any point is zero.
c. If the force and the lever are not at right-angles to each other, then do not forget the factor of $\sin\theta$ when you are taking moments.
d. The moment of a force about a point is the product of the force and the distance to the *line of action* of the force. It is not the product of the force and the distance to the *point of action* of the force.

# 27 Centre of Gravity

The *centre of gravity (c.g.)* of a body is the point through which its weight may be supposed to act.

If a body is symmetrical about a line or a plane, then the c.g. must lie on that line or plane.

The centre of gravity of a body may be found by taking moments.

## 27.1 One Dimensional Problems

### 27.1.1 Examples

(1)     Masses of 1 kg, 3 kg and 5 kg lie at points (2,0), (4,0), (8,0) along the $x$-axis. Find the co-ordinates of the centre of gravity.

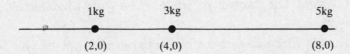

Solution    Let the *c.g.* be at $(\overline{x},0)$. Take moments
            about the origin:

$$\overline{x} \times (1 + 3 + 5) = 2 \times 1 + 4 \times 3 + 8 \times 5$$

### The c.g. is at (6, 0)

(2)         A hammer consists of a head which is of mass 0.5 kg
            and height 3 cm, attached to a shaft which is of mass
            0.1 kg and length 20 cm. The top of the shaft is flush
            with the top of the head. Find the position of the centre
            of gravity.

Solution    Let the *c.g.* be $x$ cm from the top of the
            head. Taking moments about the top of
            the head:

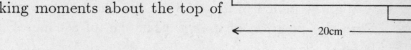

$$x \times (0.5 + 0.1) = 1.5 \times 0.5 + 10 \times 0.1$$

### The c.g. is $2\dfrac{11}{12}$ cm from the top of the head

### 27.1.2 Exercises

(1) Find the *c.g.* of masses of 2 kg, 3 kg, 7 kg at $x = 3, x = 4, x = 6$
respectively.

(2) Find the *c.g.* of masses of 1 kg, $1\frac{1}{2}$ kg, 2 kg at $(-1,0)$, $(0,0)$, $(2,0)$.

(3) A mass of 2 kg lies at $(1,0)$. Another mass is at $(-1,0)$, and their *c.g.*
is at $(\frac{1}{2},0)$. Find the size of the second mass.

(4) A mass of 3 kg lies at $x = 4$. A second mass of 2 kg is such that their
centre of gravity is at $(-1,0)$. Find the position of the second mass.

(5) A car aerial consist of 4 sections, each a uniform cylinder of length
10 cm, and masses 50 g, 45 g, 40 g, 35 g. Find the position of its centre of
gravity when fully extended.

(6) A fishing rod consists of 3 sections, each a uniform cylinder. The first is 1.2 m and 0.1 kg, the second 0.8 m and 0.06 kg, the third 0.5 m and 0.04 kg. Find the position of its *c.g.*

(7) A lollipop consists of a disc of radius 3 cm and mass 50 g, on top of a stick which is 10 cm long and weighs 10 g. Find the position of the *c.g.*

(8) A uniform plank is 2 m. long and weighs 20 kg. Edward, who weighs 50 kg sits at one end and Fiona, who weighs 40 kg sits at the other. Where is the centre of gravity?

(9) In Question 8, where should Gordon (55 kg) sit, if the centre of gravity is to be at the centre of the plank?

(10) Two cubes are made out of the same material: one has side 20 cm and the other side 10 cm. If the smaller is placed symmetrically on top of the larger where is their centre of gravity?

(11) A pencil of length 8 cm has the last two cm sharpened into a cone. Find the position of its *c.g.* (The *c.g.* of a cone of height $h$ is $\frac{1}{4}h$ from its base.)

(12) A solid hemisphere of radius 5 cm is placed on top of a solid cylinder of radius 5 cm and height 12 cm. If they are made out of the same material find the position of the c.g. (The *c.g.* of a solid hemisphere of radius $a$ is $\frac{3}{8}a$ from the centre.)

(13) A jar is made out of thin uniform metal, in the form of a cylinder with bottom but no top. Its radius is 3 cm and its height 8 cm. Find the position of its *c.g.*

(14) A uniform disc of radius 10 cm has a disc of radius 1 cm cut out. The centres of the two discs are 3 cm apart. Find the *c.g.* of the remaining part.

(15) A uniform solid sphere has radius 10 cm. A sphere of radius 1 cm is removed from the inside. The centres of the two spheres are 3 cm apart. Find the *c.g.* of the remaining solid.

## 27.2 Two and Three Dimensional Problems

### 27.2.1 Example

(1)        The shape shown is made out of a uniform sheet of cardboard. Find the position of its centre of gravity.

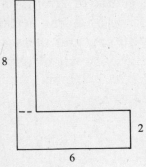

Solution     Divide the shape into two rectangles, one 6 by 2 and the other 6 by 1. The total area is 18 cm². Let the $x$-axis be along the base, and the $y$-axis up its side. Let the c.g. be at $(\overline{x}, \overline{y})$. Taking moments about the $x$-axis:

238

$$18 \times \overline{y} = 12 \times 1 + 6 \times 5$$

$$\overline{y} = 2\frac{1}{3}$$

Similarly, taking moments about the $y$-axis:

$$18 \times \overline{x} = 12 \times 3 + 6 \times \frac{1}{2}$$

**The c.g. is at $(2\frac{1}{6}, 2\frac{1}{3})$**

### 27.2.2 Exercises

(1) Masses of 1 kg, 3 kg, 6 kg are at $(1,1)$, $(2,3)$, $(1,-1)$. Find the position of their *c.g.*

(2) Masses of 3 kg, 2 kg, $x$ kg are at $(1,1)$, $(3,1)$, $(2,2)$. If their *c.g.* is at $(1.9, 1.5)$ find $x$.

(3) Masses of 4 kg and 5 kg are at $(1,0)$ and $(0,5)$. Where should a mass of 8 kg be placed to ensure that the *c.g.* is at $(4,7)$?

(4) Find the *c.g.s* of the following shapes:

(a)

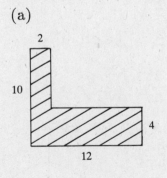

(b)

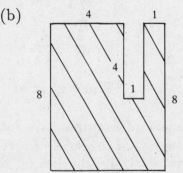

(c)

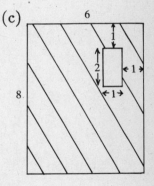

(5) A uniform wire of length 10 cm is bent in half into an $L$ shape. Find the position of the *c.g.*

(6) A uniform wire of length 12 cm is bent so that the two parts are of length 5 cm and 7 cm and are at right angles to each other. Find the position of the *c.g.*

(7) A uniform wire of length 20 cm is bent so that the two parts are of length 8 cm and 12 cm, and are at 45° to each other. Find the position of the c.g.

(8) Masses of 4 kg, 3 kg and 5 kg are at $(1,0,1)$, $(2,3,2)$, $(4,0,5)$. Find the position of the *c.g.*

(9) Masses of 3 kg and 8 kg are at $(1,1,1)$ and $(2,-1,-2)$. Where should a mass of 1 kg be placed to ensure that the *c.g.* is at $(4,5,6)$?

## 27.3 Problems Involving Calculus

### 27.3.1 Examples

(1)    A uniform lamina occupies the region enclosed by the positive axes and the curve $y = 1 - x^2$. Find the position of the c.g.

Solution    Say the c.g. is at $(\overline{x}, \overline{y})$. Divide the area into vertical strips as shown. To find $\overline{x}$, the sum of the moments of the strips about the y-axis is equal to the total area multiplied by $\overline{x}$.

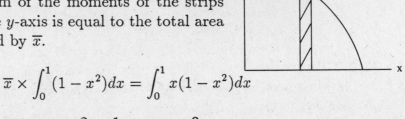

$$\overline{x} \times \int_0^1 (1 - x^2)dx = \int_0^1 x(1 - x^2)dx$$

$$\overline{x} \times \frac{2}{3} = \frac{1}{4}. \qquad \overline{x} = \frac{3}{8}.$$

Taking moments about the x-axis:

$$\overline{y} \times \frac{2}{3} = \int_0^1 \frac{1}{2}y(1 - x^2)dx = \int_0^1 \frac{1}{2}(1 - x^2)^2 dx$$

$$\overline{y} \times \frac{2}{3} = \frac{4}{15}. \qquad \overline{y} = \frac{2}{5}.$$

**The c.g. is at $\left(\dfrac{3}{8}, \dfrac{2}{5}\right)$**

(2)    The region of example 1 is rotated about the y-axis. Find the c.g. of the solid of revolution.

Solution    By symmetry the c.g. lies on the y-axis. Say it is at $(0, \overline{y})$. Divide the solid into thin discs as shown. Taking moments about the x-axis:

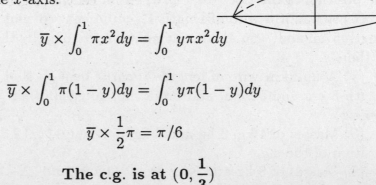

$$\overline{y} \times \int_0^1 \pi x^2 dy = \int_0^1 y\pi x^2 dy$$

$$\overline{y} \times \int_0^1 \pi(1 - y)dy = \int_0^1 y\pi(1 - y)dy$$

$$\overline{y} \times \frac{1}{2}\pi = \pi/6$$

**The c.g. is at $\left(0, \dfrac{1}{3}\right)$**

## 27.3.2 Exercises

(1) A uniform lamina consists of the region enclosed by the $x$-axis, the line $x = 1$ and the curve $y = x^2$. Find the coordinates of its centre of gravity.

(2) The shape of Question 1 is rotated about the $x$-axis. Find the centre of gravity of the solid of revolution.

(3) A uniform lamina occupies the region enclosed by the positive axes and the curve $y = 1 - x^3$. Find its centre of gravity.

(4) A uniform lamina occupies the region enclosed by the $x$-axis, the lines $x = 1$ and $x = 2$ and the curve $y = 1/x^2$. Find its centre of gravity.

(5) The area of Question 4 is rotated about the $x$-axis. Find the centre of gravity of the solid of revolution.

(6) A uniform lamina occupies the region enclosed by the positive axes and the curve $y = 9 - x^2$. Find its centre of gravity.

(7) The area of Question 6 is rotated about the $y$-axis. Find the centre of gravity of the solid of revolution.

(8) The area of Question 6 is rotated about the $x$-axis. Find the centre of gravity of the solid of revolution.

(9) A triangle of height $h$ and base $2a$ is enclosed by the region between the lines $y = xa/h$, $y = -xa/h$, $x = h$. Show that its centre of gravity is at $(\frac{2}{3}h, 0)$.

(10) A cone of height $h$ and base radius $a$ is formed by rotating the triangle of Question 9 about the $x$-axis. Show that the centre of gravity of the cone is at $(\frac{3}{4}h, 0)$.

(11) A semicircular disc of radius $a$ is contained by the $x$-axis and the circle $y = \sqrt{(a^2 - x^2)}$. Find its centre of gravity.

(12) A hemisphere of radius $a$ is obtained by rotating the disc of Question 11 about the $y$-axis. Find its centre of gravity.

## 27.4 Statics Problems

When a body is suspended, its centre of gravity is directly below the point of suspension.

A body is about to topple when its centre of gravity is above the edge about which it will topple.

## 27.4.1 Examples

(1)    A uniform semi-circular disc is hung from one end of the
bounding diameter. Find the angle the diameter makes
with the vertical. (The *c.g.* of such a disc of radius $a$ is
$4a/3\pi$ from the centre.)

Solution    The *c.g.* of the disc must be below the
point of suspension.

$$\tan\theta = (4a/3\pi)/a = 4/3\pi$$

### The angle is 23°

(2)    A cone of height 8 and base radius 3 rests with its base
on a rough plane. The plane is gradually tilted: what
angle will the plane make when the cone topples? (The
*c.g.* of a cone is $\frac{1}{4}h$ from its base.)

Solution    The angle $\theta$ is found from
$\tan\theta = (\frac{1}{4} \times 8)/3$.

$$\theta = 33.7°$$

The cone topples when the *c.g.* is above the edge $A$. For
this to be true:

$$\alpha + \theta = 90°.$$

### The angle of tilt is 56.3°

## 27.4.2 Exercises

(1) A uniform lamina consists of a rectangle of sides 6 cm and 8 cm. It
is hung from one corner: find the angle made by the longer side with the
vertical.

(2) A uniform lamina consists of a rectangle, one of whose sides is 10
cm. When the lamina is hung from one corner this side makes 23° with the
vertical. Find the other side of the rectangle.

(3) A uniform lamina is a square $ABCD$ of mass $5m$. Masses of $m$, $2m$,
$3m$, $4m$ are placed at $A, B, C, D$ respectively. If it is hung from $A$ find the
angle which $AB$ makes with the vertical.

(4) A lamina is in the shape of an isosceles triangle with sides 8, 8, 3. It is
suspended from one of the base angles. Find the angle between the base side
and the vertical. (The *c.g.* of a triangle of height $h$ is $h/3$ from the base.)

(5) A wire $ABC$ of length 10 cm is bent into an $L$ shape, where $AB = 6, BC = 4$ and $A\hat{B}C = 90°$. If it is suspended from $A$ find the angle $AB$ makes with the vertical.

(6) A uniform cube is placed on a rough plane, which is gradually tilted. Find the angle of the plane when the cube starts to topple.

(7) A uniform cuboid with square base of side 4 cm is placed on a rough plane. The plane is gradually tilted, and the cuboid topples when the plane is at 20°. Find the height of the cuboid.

(8) A uniform cylinder of height 10 cm is placed with its base on a rough plane. The plane is gradually tilted, and when it is at 40° the cylinder topples. Find the base radius of the cylinder.

## 27.5 Examination Questions

(1) A thin uniform wire, of length 40 cm, is bent to form the sides of a right-angled triangle $ABC$ in which $AB = 8$ cm, $BC = 15$ cm and $CA = 17$ cm.

a.  Show that the centre of mass of the triangular wire is at a distance 6 cm from $AB$ and at a distance 2.5 cm from $BC$.
    The vertex $B$ is smoothly hinged to a fixed point so that the triangular wire can rotate freely in a vertical plane about $B$.
b.  Find, to the nearest degree, the acute angle made by $BC$ with the vertical when the wire rests in equilibrium.

[L add]

(2) A uniform solid right circular cone has height $h$ and base of radius $r$ and centre $O$. From this cone, there is removed a solid right circular cone with the same base but having vertex $V$, where $OV = kh$ ($0 < k < 1$). Find the distance of $G$, the centre of gravity of the remaining body, from $O$.
For what value of $k$ will $G$ coincide with $V$?

[O&C]

(3) Three uniform triangular laminas, $AOB.BOC, COD$, each in the form of an equilateral triangle of side $a$, have masses $m, 2m, 3m$ respectively. A composite lamina is formed by joining the triangles together along the edges $OB, OC$ (see diagram) so that $AOD$ is a straight line. Using the axes $Ox, Oy$, shown on the diagram, find the coordinates of the centre of mass of the composite lamina.

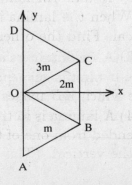

243

The composite lamina is free to move in a vertical plane about a smooth horizontal axis at $C$ and is maintained in equilibrium with $D$ vertically above $C$ by a vertical force acting at $A$. Find, in terms of $m$ and $g$, the magnitude of this force.

[C]

(4) Prove that the centroid of a uniform hemispherical shell of radius $a$ is at a distance $a/2$ from $O$, the centre of the circular rim of the shell.

A toy tower is constructed of thin uniform sheet metal and consists of a right circular cylinder, with open ends, of height $h$ and radius $r$, where $h > r$, covered by a hemispherical cap of radius $r$. Show that for such a tower the centre of gravity is at a distance $\bar{x}$ from the ground, where

$$\bar{x} = \frac{1}{2}(h + r).$$

The tower is suspended from a string which is attached to a point on the rim of the hemispherical cap. Show that, when the tower hangs in equilibrium, the axis of symmetry of the tower is inclined at an angle $\alpha$ to the horizontal, where

$$\tan \alpha = (h - r)/2r.$$

[L]

(5) Show that the area $A$ of the region in the first quadrant bounded by the axes and the curve whose equation is $(x^2/a^2) + (y^2/b^2) = 1$ satisfies

$$A = \left(\frac{b}{a}\right) \int_0^a \sqrt{(a^2 - x^2)}dx.$$

By means of the substitution $x = a\sin\theta$, or otherwise, show that $A = \frac{1}{4}\pi ab$

The centre of mass of a uniform lamina in the shape of this region is the point with coordinates $(\bar{x}, \bar{y})$. Show by integration that

$$\bar{x} = 4a/3\pi.$$

Deduce, or obtain otherwise, the value of $\bar{y}$.

This lamina is suspended freely from the origin and hangs at rest under gravity. Find the tangent of the angle between the vertical and the edge of the lamina of length $a$.

[MEI]

## COMMON ERRORS

(1) Make full use of symmetry. The *c.g.* must lie on a line of symmetry: do not waste time by ignoring this.

(2) When using calculus to find centres of gravity, make sure that you do not try to integrate a function of $x$ with respect to $y$. That is, do not try to evaluate $\int f(x)dy$. Write $f(x)$ in terms of $y$ and then integrate.

# 28 Miscellaneous Statics

## 28.1 Couples

If a system of forces has zero resultant, but does have a turning effect, then it is called a *couple*.

The simplest couple consists of two equal and opposite forces.

The moment of a couple about a point is the same for all points.

The sense of a couple is either clockwise or anti-clockwise, depending on the way in which it tends to turn the system.

### 28.1.1 Examples

(1)     A table $ABCD$ is a square of side 1.4 m. Forces of 2 N, 3 N, 2 N, 3 N act along $AB, BC, CD, DA$ respectively. Show that the forces form a couple, and find its moment.

Solution    The force along $AB$ balances that along $CD$. The force along $BC$ balances that along $DA$. Hence the system has zero resultant.

Taking moments about $A$:

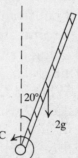

$$\text{Moment} = 3 \times 1.4 + 2 \times 1.4$$

**The moment of the couple is 7 Nm.**

(2)    A trapdoor is a uniform square of side 0.8 m. and mass 2 kg. It is hinged along one side, and it can just stay open at 20° to the vertical. Find the couple exerted by the hinge.

Solution    The forces are as shown. The door is about to fall clockwise, so the couple $C$ is anti-clockwise. Taking moments about the hinge:

$$C = 2g \times 0.4 \times \sin 20°$$

**The couple of the hinge is 2.68 Nm.**

### 28.1.2 Exercises

(1) In each of the diagrams below show that the forces form a couple and find its moment.

(a)                         (b)                         (c)

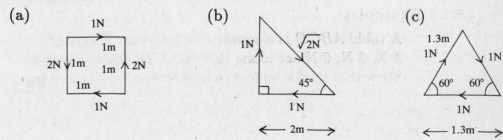

(2) The forces in each of the diagrams below form a couple. Find the unknown forces, and find the moments of the couples.

(a)                          (b)                          (c)

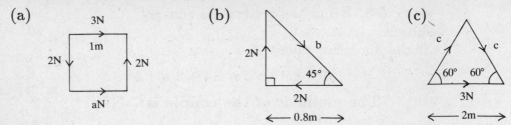

(3) $ABCD$ is a square of side 2 m. Forces of 2 N, 3 N and 5 N act along $AB, AC, AD$ respectively. Find the forces along $CD$ and $CB$ which will ensure that the system is a couple, and find its moment.

(4) A spanner of length 10 cm can just turn a nut when a force of 150 N is applied to its end. Find the couple exerted by the nut.

(5) A stiff tap can just be turned when forces of 20 N are applied at two points 3 cm from its axis. Find the couple that these forces exert.

(6) An inn-sign is a uniform square of side 0.6 m and mass 3 kg. It is hinged along its top, and will just rest at 25° to the vertical. Find the couple at the hinges.

(7) What is the least horizontal force applied to the base of the inn-sign of Question 6 which will hold it at 40° to the vertical?

(8) What is the least horizontal force applied to the base of the inn-sign of Question 6 which will raise it when it is 35° to the vertical?

## 28.2 Equivalent Systems

A system of forces acting in a plane is equivalent either to a single force or to a single couple.

### 28.2.1 Example

ABCD is a square of side 1 m, and forces of 3 N, 2 N, 2 N act along $AB, DC, AC$ respectively. Show that these forces are equivalent to a single force, and find where the line of action of this force crosses $BC$.
Show also that the system is equivalent to a force through $A$ and a couple $G$, which is to be found.

Solution    The force is the resultant of the three forces. Letting $F_1$ and $F_2$ be the components of the resultant parallel to $AB$ and $BC$ respectively:

$$F_1 = 3 + 2 + 2\cos 45° : F_2 = 2\sin 45°.$$

Use Pythagoras and trigonometry to find the resultant.

### The force is 6.57N at 12° to AB

Suppose the resultant cuts $BC$ at $x$ m from $C$. Take moments about $C$. (Only the component of the resultant parallel to $AB$ need be considered.)

$$6.414 \times x = 3 \times 1$$

### The resultant cuts $BC$ at 0.47 m from $C$

Suppose instead that the resultant acts through $A$. Then the extra couple required is found by taking moments about $A$.

$$G = 2 \times 1$$

### The couple is 2 Nm

## 28.2.2 Exercises

(1) Each of the following are squares of side 1 m. Find the equivalent force, and the point at which it crosses $AB$.

(a)                                        (b)

(2) $ABCD$ is a square of side 2 m. Forces of 3 N, 4 N and 5 N act along $AB, BC$ and $AC$ respectively. Find the equivalent force and where it crosses $AB$.

(3) Forces of $2\mathbf{i}, 3\mathbf{i}, 4\mathbf{j}$ act at the points $A(1,0)$, $B(2,0)$ and $C(3,0)$ respectively. Find the equivalent force and where it crosses the $x$-axis.

(4) $ABC$ is a triangle, with $AB = AC = 5$ cm, $BC = 4$ cm. Forces of 3 N, 4 N, 7 N act along $AB, AC, BC$ respectively. Find the equivalent force and where it crosses $BC$.

(5) $ABCD$ is a rectangle, $AB = 6$ cm and $AD = 8$ cm. Forces of 2 N, 4 N and 5 N act along $AB, AD, BD$ respectively. Find the equivalent single force, and where it crosses $AB$. Show that the system is equivalent to a force through $A$ and a couple, which is to be found.

(6) Forces of $\mathbf{i}, 4\mathbf{j}, 2\mathbf{i} - 3\mathbf{j}$ act through the points $A(0,1)$, $B(3,0)$, $C(1,0)$ respectively. Find the single equivalent force, and where it crosses the $y$-axis. Show that the system is equivalent to a force through the origin and a couple, which is to be found.

## 28.3 Three Forces in Equilibrium

If there are exactly three forces acting on a body, then either they are all parallel or else they all go through the same point.

This can sometimes be used to solve problems in statics. The method is particularly powerful when combined with the use of the angle of friction.

### 28.3.1 Example

A uniform ladder rests against a smooth wall and on a rough floor. It is about to slip when it makes 30° with the vertical. Find the coefficient of friction.

Solution    The forces are as shown in the diagram. Combine the normal reaction and the friction into a single resultant making $\lambda$ with the normal.

The three forces must meet, at the point above the centre of the ladder.

$$\tan \lambda = AB/AE = \frac{1}{2}AC/AE = \frac{1}{2}\tan 30°.$$

**The coefficient of friction is** $\tan \lambda = 1/(2\sqrt{3}) = 0.289$

### 28.3.2 Exercises

All these questions are to be solved by the method of this section.

(1) A non-uniform rod of length 2 m hangs horizontally from two strings, one at each end, which make 40° and 50° with the horizontal. Find the position of the centre of gravity of the rod.

(2) A uniform rod of length 2 m hangs from two strings, one at each end, which make 30° and 60° with the rod. Show that the point of suspension must be 1 m above the midpoint of the rod. Hence find the angle to the horizontal of the rod.

(3) A uniform bar $AB$ is jointed at $A$ to a wall. It is held horizontal by a string attached to $B$, which is fixed to a point of the wall above $A$ so that the string makes 70° with the vertical. Find the direction of the reaction at the hinge.

(4) A uniform bar $AB$ of length 1 m is held horizontal with A against a rough wall, and with a string $B$ of length 2 m fixed to a point on the wall vertically above $A$. Find the least possible coefficient of friction between $A$ and the wall.

(5) A uniform bar $AB$ is hinged at A to a wall. A string is attached to $B$ and makes 90° with the rod. If the bar is raised to 20° above the horizontal find the direction of the reaction at A.

(6) A uniform bar $AB$ is hinged at $A$ to a wall, and $B$ is attached to a string which is perpendicular to the bar. If the bar is at 45° below the horizontal find the direction of the reaction between $A$ and the wall.

(7) A uniform bar $AB$ rests with $A$ on a smooth slope of angle 30°. It is held horizontal by a string attached to $B$. Find the angle that the string makes with the vertical.

(8) A uniform bar $AB$ rests with $A$ on rough ground, and $B$ is attached to a string which is perpendicular to the bar. If the bar makes 10° with the ground find the least coefficient of friction between $A$ and the ground.

(9) Two smooth planes of angles 40° and 50° meet in a horizontal line. A non-uniform bar of length 2 m lies horizontally on the planes. Find the position of the centre of gravity of the bar.

(10) Two rough planes of angles 30° and 60° meet in a horizontal line. A uniform bar rests horizontally on the planes. If it is on the point of slipping find the angle of friction between the bar and the planes.

(11) A uniform ladder rests on rough ground against a smooth wall. If it is about to slip when it makes 50° with the horizontal find the coefficient of friction.

(12) A uniform ladder rests on rough ground against a smooth wall. The coefficient of friction is $\frac{1}{2}$. Find the greatest angle the ladder can make with the vertical.

(13) A uniform ladder of mass 50 kg rests on rough ground against a smooth wall. The coefficient of friction is $\frac{1}{2}$. If it is at 40° to the vertical find how far up the ladder a 50 kg man can safely ascend.

## 28.4 Light Frameworks

A system of light rods smoothly jointed together is a *light framework*.

For each rod, the reactions at each end are equal and opposite and act along the line of the rod.

If the rod is being compressed, it is under *thrust*. If it is being stretched it is under *tension*.

### 28.4.1 Example

The light framework shown supports a load of $W$. All the angles concerned are 90°, 60° or 30°. Find the force in each rod, indicating whether it is tension or thrust.

Solution     Let the forces in $BC, CD, BD$ and $AB$ be $T_1, T_2, T_3$ and $T_4$ respectively.

Resolving vertically at $C$, $T_1 \sin 60° = W$.

Resolving horizontally at $C$, $T_2 = T_1 \cos 60°$.

Taking moments about $D$, $Wa = T_4 a \cos 30°$.

Resolving vertically at $B$, $T_3 \cos 30° = T_1 \cos 30°$.

The results are:

$$\mathbf{T_1} = \mathbf{2W/\sqrt{3}}, \quad \textbf{tension.}$$
$$\mathbf{T_2} = \mathbf{W/\sqrt{3}}, \quad \textbf{thrust.}$$
$$\mathbf{T_3} = \mathbf{2W/\sqrt{3}}, \quad \textbf{thrust.}$$
$$\mathbf{T_4} = \mathbf{2W/\sqrt{3}}, \quad \textbf{tension.}$$

### 28.4.2 Exercises

For each of the following light frameworks, find the forces in the rods, indicating which are thrusts and which tensions.

(1)

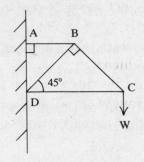

(2)

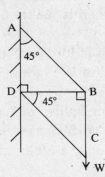

In the following questions A and B are resting on smooth supports.

(3)

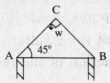

(4)

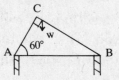

(5)

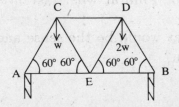

## 28.5 Examination Questions

(1) A uniform rod $AB$, of mass 0.5 kg and length 0.4 m, is held at an angle of 30° to the upward vertical by means of a frictional couple applied to the lower end $A$. Calculate, in $Nm$, the magnitude of this couple.

[L add]

(2) *In this question the unit of distance is the metre.*

A rectangle $OABC$ has vertices at (0,0), (4,0), (4,3) and (0,3) respectively. Forces of magnitudes 2, 4, 5, 3 and 6 N act along $OA, BA, BC, OC$ and $AC$ respectively, the directions being indicated by the order of the letters. The system is equivalent to a force $\mathbf{R}$, acting through O together with a couple $G$. Calculate

a. the magnitude and direction of $\mathbf{R}$,
b. the equation of the line of action of $\mathbf{R}$,
c. the magnitude and sense of $G$, stating the units in which your answer is measured.

[AEB add 1986]

(3) Forces of magnitude 2 N, 4 N, and 4 N act in the sense indicated by the letters along the sides $AB, BC, CA$ respectively of an equilateral triangle $ABC$ of side 2 m. Find the magnitude and direction of their resultant and the point where its line of action cuts $AC$ produced.

This system is to be reduced to equilibrium by the addition of a couple in the plane $ABC$ and a force which acts through $A$. Find the magnitude and direction of the force and the magnitude and sense of the couple.

[L]

(4) A rectangle $ABCD$ with $AB = 2a$ and $BC = a$ has forces 6, 3, 2 and $P$ newtons acting along $AB, BC, CD$ and $AD$ in directions indicated by the letters. If the resultant passes through the midpoint of $AB$ find

(i) the value of $P$; (ii) the magnitude of the resultant;
(iii) the distance from $C$ where the line of action of the resultant meets $CD$.

The force in $AD$ is reduced to zero. Find at what distance from $A$ the line of action of the new resultant force meets $AB$. If the rectangle were free to move in its own plane about $A$ what would be the sense and moment of the couple necessary to prevent motion?

[SUJB]

## COMMON ERRORS

### (1) Equivalent Systems

a. If a force is said to act along $AB$, then it acts from $A$ to $BA$. Do not get this the wrong way round.

b. A system of forces in a plane can be reduced to either a force *or* a couple. (Not both). If, however, the resultant force must go through a fixed point, then the system is equivalent to that force *and* a couple.

### (2) Three Forces

The rule about forces meeting at a point applies if there are only 3 forces acting. If there are four or more forces then they may not go through the same point.

# 29 Work, Energy, Power

If the point of action of a force $F$ moves a distance $d$ in the direction of the force, then the work done is $Fd$. A force of 1 Newton acting over 1 metre does 1 Joule ($J$) of work.

A $kJ$ (kilojoule) is a thousand Joules.

If the force $\mathbf{F}$ and the distance $\mathbf{d}$ are vectors which are not parallel then the work done is the scalar product of the force and the distance.

$$\text{Work done is } \mathbf{F}.\mathbf{d}.$$

*Energy* is the capacity for doing work.

If a body of mass $m$ is raised through a height of $h$, it gains *potential energy* (*P.E.*) of $mgh$.

If a body of mass $m$ is moving with speed $v$, it has *kinetic energy* (*K.E.*) of $\frac{1}{2}mv^2$.

The work done by forces on a body is equal to the increase in its kinetic and potential energies.

## 29.1 Work and Energy

### 29.1.1 Examples

(1)   A car of mass 500 kg brakes to a halt from 20 m/sec over a horizontal distance of 40 m. Assuming that the braking force is constant, how far would it take to brake to rest from 30 m/sec?

Solution   If the braking force is $F$, then the loss of kinetic energy is equal to the work done by the brakes.

$$F \times 40 = \frac{1}{2} \times 500 \times 20^2$$

$$F = 2,500N$$

If it travels $d$ m to brake from 30 m/sec:

$$2,500 \times d = \frac{1}{2} \times 500 \times 30^2$$

**The braking distance is 90 m**

(2)   A roller-coaster starts from rest at it highest point. If resistances are ignored, how fast is it going at its lowest point 20 m below?

Solution   Suppose it moves at $v$ m/sec at the lowest point. The loss of potential energy is equal to the gain in kinetic energy.

$$\frac{1}{2}mv^2 = m \times 9.8 \times 20$$

**It is travelling at 19.8 m/sec**

### 29.1.2 Exercises

(1) A force of 12 N moves through a distance of 5 m. Find the work done.

(2) A force of 8 N performs work of 80 J. Find the distance through which it has moved.

(3) A force performs 0.3 J by moving through 0.1 m. Find the force.

(4) Find the potential energy gained by:

(a)   A mass of 2 kg raised through 10 m   (b)   2.5 kg raised through 1 m

(c)   3 grams raised through 12 cm   (d)   5 kg falling through 2 m

(5) Find the kinetic energy of the following:

  (a)  2 kg moving at 3 m/sec  (b)  500 kg moving at 30 m/sec

(6) A constant force acts for 2 m, and accelerates a mass of 3 kg to $1\frac{1}{2}$ m/sec. What is the force?

(7) A force of 12 N acts on a body of mass 3 kg. How far will it have to act to accelerate it to 7 m/sec?

(8) What force is needed to stop in 4 m a mass of 25 kg moving at 10 m/sec?

(9) A car of mass 600 kg slows down from 20 to 10 m/sec over a distance of 60 m. What force has achieved this?

(10) A car of mass 400 kg travelling at 15 m/sec experiences a force in its direction of motion of 2,000 N. How fast is it travelling after 40 m?

(11) A body falls freely. How fast is it going after falling 10 m from rest?

(12) A body slides down a smooth slope of angle 20°. How fast is it going after 2 m?

(13) A body is thrown up at 12 m/sec. How high is it when it is moving at 4 m/sec?

(14) A body is thrown downwards at 5 m/sec. What is its speed when it has travelled 6 m?

(15) A body is projected up a smooth slope of angle 30° at 2 m/sec. How far does it go before it comes to rest?

(16) A body of mass 2 kg is projected at 10 m/sec up a slope of angle 30°, where the resistance to motion is 4 N. How far does it go before it comes to rest?

(17) A body of mass 6 kg is projected at 12 m/sec down a slope of angle 20° against a resistance of 3 N. What is its speed after it has travelled 20 m?

(18) A particle of mass 1.5 kg hangs from a light string of length 2 m, the other end of which is fixed. The string is held horizontal and released. Find the speed of the particle at the bottom of the swing.

(19) A particle of mass 0.6 kg hangs from a light string of length 1.2 m. The string is held at 20° to the vertical. Find the speed of the particle at the bottom of the swing.

(20) A particle of mass 0.5 kg hangs at the end of a light string of length 1 m. It is given a horizontal velocity of 0.5 m/sec. Find the height it reaches, and hence the greatest angle which the string makes with the vertical.

(21) A force of $2\mathbf{i} + 3\mathbf{j}$ moves from the point (2,7) to (4,12). Find the work done.

(22) A force of $\mathbf{i} - 3\mathbf{j} + 2\mathbf{k}$ moves from (1,2,3) to (4,0,5). Find the work done.

(23) A body of mass 2 is constrained to move along the line $y = x + 3$. It is acted upon by a force of $3\mathbf{i} + 4\mathbf{j}$. Ignoring the effect of gravity, find its speed after it has moved from $(0,3)$ to $(2,5)$.

## 29.2 Power

*Power* is the rate of doing work. A power of 1 Joule per second is 1 Watt. ($W$).

A thousand Watts is a kilowatt. ($kW$).

If the point of action of a force $F$ is moving at speed $v$ then the power is $Fv$.

### 29.2.1 Examples

(1)        A car of mass 500 kg drives up a slope of 5° against a resistance of 300 N at a constant speed of 15 m/sec. Find the power developed by the car.

Solution    The car has to work against the resistance and the component of its weight down the slope.

$$\text{Total Force } = 300 + 500g\sin 5°$$

Using the equation Power = Force × Velocity:

$$P = (300 + 500g\sin 5°) \times 15$$

**The power is 10,900W**

(2)        A pump raises water through 10 m and expels it at 5 m/sec. If the power of the pump is 2,000 W find the volume of water it ejects each second.

Solution    Let the volume ejected per second be $V$ litres. Every second V kg is raised through 10 m and given a velocity of 5 m/sec. The work done per second is therefore:

$$\frac{1}{2}V5^2 + V \times 10 \times 9.8 = 2,000$$

**The volume per second is 18 litres**

### 29.2.2 Exercises

(1) A body is dragged at 2 m/sec against a resistance of 200 N. Find the power.

(2) Find the velocity with which a power of 100 W can overcome a resistance of 50 N.

(3) A mass of 12 kg is raised at 0.5 m/sec. Find the power needed.

(4) A 70 kg man climbs up a rope at 0.5 m/sec. What power is he exerting?

(5) A pump raises 20 kg of water per second through 5 m. Find its power.

(6) A hose emits 10 kg of water each second at 7 m/sec. Find its power.

(7) A hose which exerts 1,000 W of power emits 10 kg of water per second. Find the velocity of the water.

(8) A 70 kg man runs up a 10° slope at 5 m/sec. Find his power.

(9) A 60 kg man can exert 300 W of power. How fast can he run up a 5° slope?

(10) A car of mass 400 kg can exert 4,000 W. If resistances are 250 N what is its maximum speed? What is its acceleration at half the maximum speed?

(11) What is the maximum speed at which the car of Question 10 can ascend a slope of 4°? (The resistance is the same.)

(12) What is the steepest hill which the car of Question 10 can ascend at 6 m/sec?

(13) A car of mass 400 kg experiences resistance which is 20$v$, where $v$ is its velocity. If its maximum speed on level ground is 20 m/sec find its power.

(14) Find the maximum speed of the car of Question 13 up a slope of 5°.

(15) Find the maximum speed of the car of Question 13 down a slope of 7°.

(16) Find the acceleration of the car of Question 13 when it is travelling at 10 m/sec along level ground.

(17) Find the acceleration of the car of Question 13 when it is travelling up a slope of 4° at 5 m/sec.

(18) A force of $2\mathbf{i} + 5\mathbf{j}$ moves from (2,5) to (4,7) in 3 seconds. Find the power of the force.

(19) A body of mass 3 is constrained to move along the line $y = 2x - 3$. A force of $3\mathbf{i} + 2\mathbf{j}$ acts upon it, and it moves with constant speed 2. Ignoring the effect of gravity find the power of the force.

## 29.3 Examination Questions

(1) The total mass of a cyclist and his machine is 140 kg. The cyclist rides along a horizontal road against a constant total resistance of magnitude 50 N. Find, in $J$, the total work done in increasing his speed from 6 m/s to 9 m/s whilst travelling a distance of 30 m.

[L add]

(2)

a. A pump forces water through a nozzle so as to produce a vertical jet. The mass of water emitted per second is 0.24 kg and the power output of the pump is 7.68 W. Find the height of the jet and the speed with which the water leaves the nozzle.

b. A goods vehicle works at a constant power output of 200 kW. Its maximum speed on a horizontal road is 20 m s$^{-1}$. Calculate the total resistance to motion.

The vehicle now travels up a slope whose inclination to the horizontal is $\alpha$, where $\sin \alpha = \frac{4}{15}$. Given that the mass of the vehicle is $2.5 \times 10^3$ kg, and that the resistance to motion is unchanged, calculate

i. the acceleration of the vehicle when its speed is 8 m s$^{-1}$,

ii. the greatest possible speed of the vehicle.

[C add]

(3) In this question take $g = 10$ m/s$^2$.

The resistance to motion of a motor car is a constant force of $R$ newtons. The engine of the car can work at rates up to 40 kW.

i. If the maximum speed that the car can maintain on a straight, level road is 144 km/hour, calculate the value of $R$.

ii. The car accelerates from rest up a hill of inclination $\theta$ to the horizontal where $\sin \theta = \frac{1}{15}$. The mass of the car is 1200 kg and the total mass of the driver and passengers is 400 kg. If the engine is working at maximum power, calculate the acceleration when the speed of the car is 36 km/hour.

iii. Calculate the total mass of driver and passengers which would just cause the car to freewheel from rest down this hill.

[NI add]

(4) [In this question the effect of gravity may be neglected.]

A small ring, of unit mass, is threaded on a fixed smooth straight wire which passes through the points $A(1, -2, 3)$ and $B(4, 0, -3)$. The ring moves under the action of a force **F**, where $\mathbf{F} = 2\mathbf{i} - 8\mathbf{j} - 18\mathbf{k}$, and starts from rest at $A$. Show that the work done by **F** in moving the ring from $A$ to $B$ is 98 units, and find the speed of the ring at $B$.

The force **F** has two components, $\mathbf{F_1}$ in the direction of $AB$ and $\mathbf{F_2}$ perpendicular to $AB$. Find

(i)  $\mathbf{F_1}$ and $\mathbf{F_2}$   (ii)  the reaction, **R**, of the wire on the ring.

[JMB]

(5) The frictional resistance to the motion of a train is $k$ times the combined weight of the engine and its coach. An engine of mass $M$ works at a constant power $P$ and attains a maximum speed $U$ when pulling a coach of mass $M$ up a hill of inclination $\alpha$ to the horizontal. Down the same hill with a coach of mass $\frac{1}{2}M$, the engine can attain a maximum speed $2U$. Show that $P$ is $12kgUM/5$.

The engine pulls a coach of mass $1\frac{1}{2}M$ on level ground. Find the acceleration of the train when the speed is $\frac{1}{5}U$ and show that the maximum speed is $\frac{24}{25}U$.

[C]

(6) *Take the acceleration due to gravity to be* 10 m/s$^2$.

A small curtain ring of mass 0.5 kg is moving with constant velocity along a rough horizontal rail, and the coefficient of friction between the ring and the rail is 0.3. The motion is caused by a girl pulling on a light inextensible cord which is attached to the ring and which lies in the same vertical plane as the rail. Given that the cord makes an acute angle $\theta$ with the downward vertical and that the girl pulls the cord with tension $T$ N, show that

(a) $T = \dfrac{1.5}{\sin\theta - 0.3\cos\theta}$, (b) $\tan\theta > 0.3$.

The girl suddenly doubles her pull to 2T N without changing $\theta$. Show that the ring then moves with acceleration 3 m s$^{-2}$.

Given that the ring's initial velocity was 1 m s$^{-1}$ and assuming that it continues to slide along the rail with acceleration 3 m s$^{-2}$ with the tension unaltered at 2T N, find, in terms of $\theta$, the work W J done by the girl during the first second of accelerated motion, and show that $W > 7.5$.

[AEB 1986]

## COMMON ERRORS

(1) Work done is the product of force and *distance*. It is not the product of force and *time*.

(2) Force and distance can only be multiplied together directly if they are in the same direction. If they are not parallel there is an extra factor of $\cos\theta$, where $\theta$ is the angle between them. In particular, if the force is perpendicular to the distance moved, then no work at all is done.

# 30 Relative Velocity

The velocity of $A$ as seen by $B$ is the *relative velocity* of $A$ to $B$. It is written as $_A\mathbf{v}_B$. Relative velocities are combined by the rule:

$$_A\mathbf{v}_B =_A \mathbf{v}_C -_B \mathbf{v}_C$$

These vectors may be added either by a vector triangle or by components.

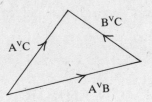

## 30.1 Calculation of Relative Velocity

### 30.1.1 Examples

(1)    A moves with velocity $3\mathbf{i} + 2\mathbf{j}$. $B$ moves with velocity $\mathbf{i} - 4\mathbf{j}$. Find the magnitude of the relative velocity of $A$ to $B$.

Solution    Use the formula above.

$$_A\mathbf{v}_B = (3\mathbf{i} + 2\mathbf{j}) - (\mathbf{i} - 4\mathbf{j}) = 2\mathbf{i} + 6\mathbf{j}$$

Use Pythagoras to find the magnitude of this vector.

**The relative velocity has magnitude $\sqrt{(2^2+6^2)} = \sqrt{40} = 6.32$**

(2)    A man can row at 5 km h$^{-1}$ in still water. A river is
flowing at 3 km h$^{-1}$. Where should he steer in order to
reach a point which is directly opposite?

Solution    He wants to travel along $PQ$. He must
row so that his velocity relative to the
bank is along the line $PQ$. Use the formula:

$$_M\mathbf{v}_B = {_M}\mathbf{v}_R + {_R}\mathbf{v}_B$$

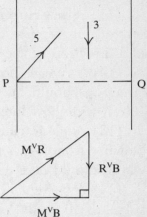

Construct a vector triangle of velocities as
shown.

$$\sin\theta = \frac{3}{5}$$

**He should row at 37° to the line directly across the river**

## 30.1.2 Exercises

(1) $A$ moves at $\mathbf{i} + 3\mathbf{j}$, and $B$ moves at $3\mathbf{i} + 2\mathbf{j}$. Find the magnitude of the
relative velocity of $A$ to $B$, and the angle it makes with the $x$-axis.

(2) $A$ moves at $3\mathbf{i} - 4\mathbf{j}$ and $B$ moves at $2\mathbf{i} + \mathbf{j}$. Find the magnitude of the
relative velocity of $A$ to $B$, and the angle it makes with the $x$-axis.

(3) $A$ moves at $2\mathbf{i} - 7\mathbf{j}$, and the relative velocity of $A$ to $B$ is $3\mathbf{i} + 2\mathbf{j}$. find
the velocity of $B$ in vector form. Find its magnitude and direction.

(4) Ship $A$ sails at 12 km h$^{-1}$ on a bearing of 030°, and ship $B$ sails at
15 km h$^{-1}$ on a bearing of 355°. Find the relative velocity of $A$ to $B$.

(5) A fighter plane flies at 1,000 km h$^{-1}$ on a bearing of 170°, and a
bomber flies at 800 km h$^{-1}$ on a bearing of 220°. Find the velocity of the
fighter relative to the bomber.

(6) A galleon sails at 2 km h$^{-1}$ on a bearing of 080°, and a pirate ship sails
at 3 km h$^{-1}$ on a bearing of 130°. Find the velocity of the galleon relative
to the pirate.

(7) A ship is sailing due north at 14 km/hr. The wind appears to come
from 045° with speed 20 km h$^{-1}$. Find the true direction and speed of the
wind.

(8) A bomber flies at 900 km h$^{-1}$ on a bearing of 030°. A fighter appears
to come from 070° at 2,000 km h$^{-1}$. Find the true velocity of the fighter.

(9) A river 100 m wide is flowing at 3 km h$^{-1}$. A man can row at 5 km
h$^{-1}$. If he rows directly across the river how far downstream will he land?

(10) A wind is blowing at 20 km h$^{-1}$ from a bearing of 070°. A sparrow, that can fly at 15 km h$^{-1}$ in still air, flies due north. Find its actual speed and direction.

(11) A sea-current is flowing at 2 km h$^{-1}$ on a bearing of 220°. A ship sets off on a course of 340° at 12 km h$^{-1}$ relative to the sea. Find the speed and direction of the ship.

(12) A river is flowing at 1 m/sec. A man can row at $1\frac{1}{2}$ m/sec. In which direction should he row if he is to cross the river directly? If the river is 100 m wide how long will it take him?

(13) A plane can fly at 200 km h$^{-1}$ in still air. A wind of 50 km h$^{-1}$ is blowing from 045°. If the pilot wishes to reach a place 300 km due north where should he steer? How long will it take him?

(14) A current flows at 2 km h$^{-1}$ on a bearing of 140°. A boat which can travel at 10 km h$^{-1}$ is to sail 40 km due east. In what direction should it be steered, and how long will the journey take?

## 30.2 Interception

If one object $A$ is to intercept another object $B$, then the relative velocity of $A$ to $B$ is along the straight line joining them.

### 30.2.1 Example

A cat, which can run at 15 m/sec, spies a mouse 4 m away due north. The mouse is running due east at 5 m/sec. Find the direction the cat should take in order to catch the mouse, and how long it is before interception takes place.

Solution    The cat $C$ should run so that its velocity relative to the mouse $M$ is due north. Letting $G$ represent the ground:

$$_C\mathbf{v}_M = {}_C\mathbf{v}_G - {}_M\mathbf{v}_G$$

Draw a vector diagram as shown. The angle of attack is given by $\sin\theta = \frac{1}{3}$.

**The cat should run on a bearing of 19°**

The magnitude of the relative velocity is given by Pythagoras.

$$|_C\mathbf{v}_M| = \sqrt{200}$$

**Interception takes place after $4/\sqrt{200} = 0.28$ secs.**

## 30.2.2 Exercises

(1) A bomber is flying due west at 800 km h$^{-1}$. A fighter is 20 km due north of the bomber, and it sets off in pursuit at 1200 km h$^{-1}$. What course should the fighter pilot set, and how long will interception take?

(2) A ship sails due north at 10 km h$^{-1}$. A submarine is 12 km away on a bearing of 045°. If the submarine can travel at 8 km h$^{-1}$, what course should be set to intercept the ship? How long will it be before interception?

(3) Object $A$ is at the origin and moves with velocity vector $\mathbf{i}+2\mathbf{j}$. Object $B$ has vector position $10\mathbf{i}$, and can travel with speed 3. What direction should $B$ move in in order to intercept $A$? What is the vector position of their point of collision?

(4) $A$ starts from the origin with vector velocity $3\mathbf{i} + 4\mathbf{j}$. $B$ is at $-3\mathbf{j}$ and can move with a speed of 6. Find the direction $B$ should take in order to intercept $A$, and the vector position of the point of interception.

(5) Ship $A$ is 50 km west of ship $B$. $A$ sets off at 15 km h$^{-1}$ on a course of 048°. If ship $B$ can travel at 20 km h$^{-1}$ find the course it should take to intercept $A$.

(6) In a game of football a forward is running along the touchline at 9 m/sec. A defender, who can run at 8 m/sec, is 20 m from the touchline and 30 m nearer the goal than the forward. What direction should the defender run in in order to intercept the forward? How long will it take?

(7) A batsman strikes the ball at 10 m/sec so that its direction makes 70° with the line of wickets. A fielder, who can run at 7 m/sec, is standing 20 m from the batsman, so that the line between the players makes 30° with the line of wickets. Where should the fielder run in order to intercept the ball?

## 30.3 Shortest Distance

If two objects are moving closer to each other, but not necessarily on a collision course, then there is a *shortest distance* between them.

## 30.3.1 Example

Ship $A$ is 100 km due west of Ship $B$. $A$ sets off at 12 km h$^{-1}$ on a course of 045°, and $B$ sets off at 15 km h$^{-1}$ on a bearing of 330°. Find the shortest distance between them, and the time when this shortest distance is achieved.

Solution    First the relative velocity of $A$ to $B$, $_A\mathbf{v}_B$, must be found, by the methods of 30.1.

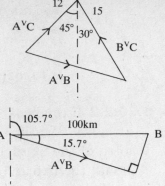

$_A\mathbf{v}_B$ is 16.6 km h$^{-1}$, at 105.7°.

From the point of view of $B$, $A$ is moving with velocity $_A\mathbf{v}_B$. The shortest distance is the perpendicular distance from $B$ to the line of $_A\mathbf{v}_B$

**Shortest distance** $= 100 \times \sin 15.7° = 27$ **km**

To find the time taken, divide the relative distance travelled by $A$ by the relative velocity.

**Time taken** $= (100 \times \cos 15.7)/16.6 = 5.8$ **hours**

### 30.3.2 Exercises

(1) Alfred is 100 m due south of a crossroads, and is walking towards it at $1\frac{1}{2}$ m/sec. Beatrice is 100 m due east of the crossroads, and is walking towards it at $1\frac{1}{4}$ m/sec. Find the shortest distance between them, and when this least distance is reached.

(2) Clarice is 80 m south of a crossroads, and is walking north at $1\frac{1}{2}$ m/sec. Dorothy is 60 m due east, and is walking west at 1 m/sec. Find the least distance between them, and how far Dorothy is from the crossroads when they are at this least distance.

(3) $A$ starts from the origin with velocity vector $\mathbf{i} + \mathbf{j}$, and at the same time $B$ starts from the point with position vector $5\mathbf{i}$ and moves with velocity vector $-2\mathbf{i} + 3\mathbf{j}$. Find the least distance between them.

(4) $A$ starts from the origin with velocity vector $2\mathbf{i} + 3\mathbf{j}$, and at the same time $B$ starts from $-\mathbf{i} + \mathbf{j}$ with velocity $2\mathbf{i}$. Find the shortest distance between them, and $B$'s position when this least distance is reached.

(5) Airplane $A$ is 300 km due north of airplane $B$. $A$ flies at 600 km h$^{-1}$ on a bearing of 097°, and $B$ flies at 400 km h$^{-1}$ at 023°. Find the closest distance apart of the two planes, and the time when they are at this distance.

(6) A vessel is sailing due east at 14 km h$^{-1}$. A second vessel, initially 35 km due north of the first, sails at 9 km h$^{-1}$ on a bearing of 235°. Find the shortest distance between the two ships.

## 30.4 Examination Questions

(1)

a. An aircraft flies in a straight line from a point $A$ to a point $B$ 200 km East of $A$. There is a wind blowing at 40 km h$^{-1}$ from the direction 240° and the aircraft travels at 300 km h$^{-1}$ in still air. Find

   i. the direction in which the pilot must steer the aircraft,

   ii. the time, to the nearest minute, for the journey from $A$ to $B$.

b. To an observer in a ship sailing due North at 10 km h$^{-1}$, a second ship appears to be sailing due East at 24 km h$^{-1}$. Find the magnitude and direction of the actual velocity of the second ship.

[C add]

(2) An aircraft $A$ is 1000 m due north of a second aircraft $B$. $A$ is flying with constant velocity 170 m/s due west and $B$ is flying with constant velocity 200 m/s in a direction 330° (N 30° W). Both aircraft are flying at the same height. Draw a clear velocity diagram and find by drawing or calculation the velocity of $A$ relative to $B$. How long does it take the two aircraft to reach the closest point to each other, and how far apart are they at that time?

[O add]

(3) At noon two boats, $A$ and $B$, are at sea with B 40 km due East of $A$. $A$ moves with constant velocity 50 km h$^{-1}$ in a direction $N20°E$ and $B$ with constant velocity 25 km h$^{-1}$ in a direction $N40°W$.

Find, each correct to 2 significant figures,

   i. the magnitude and direction of the velocity of $A$ relative to $B$;

  ii. the shortest distance between $A$ and $B$ and the time interval (in minutes) during which $A$ is within 30 km of $B$.

When $A$ is due North of $B$ it changes course without changing speed in order to intercept $B$. Calculate $A$'s new course correct to 2 significant figures.

[SUJB]

(4) The vectors $\mathbf{i}$ and $\mathbf{j}$ are unit vectors in the directions East and North respectively. A man walks with constant speed 6 km h$^{-1}$ due North and to him the wind appears to have a velocity $u_1(\sqrt{3}\mathbf{i} - 3\mathbf{j})$ km h$^{-1}$. Without changing speed the man alters his course so that he is walking in the direction

of the vector $(-\sqrt{3}/2\mathbf{i} + \frac{1}{2}\mathbf{j})$ and the velocity of the wind now appears to him to be $u_2\mathbf{i}$ km h$^{-1}$. Find $u_1$ and $u_2$. Find also the actual velocity of the wind.

[L]

(5) The wind velocity is $W(\cos\alpha\mathbf{i} + \sin\alpha\mathbf{j})$, where $\mathbf{i}$ and $\mathbf{j}$ are unit vectors due North and due West respectively. An aeroplane makes a journey from a place $O$ to a place $A$, where $A$ is due North of $O$, and then it returns to $O$. The aeroplane works at constant power so that, if there were no wind, its constant speed on both parts of the journey would be $V$, where $V > W$.

On the outward journey, the aeroplane is steered parallel to the unit vector $(\cos\beta\mathbf{i} - \sin\beta\mathbf{j})$, so that the resultant velocity relative to the ground is $U_1\mathbf{i}$. Find $\sin\beta$ in terms of $V, W$ and $\alpha$, and deduce that

$$U_1 = W\cos\alpha + \sqrt{(V^2 - W^2\sin^2\alpha)}.$$

Obtain a similar expression for $U_2$, where $-U_2\mathbf{i}$ is the velocity of the aeroplane relative to the ground for the return journey. Given that $OA = a$, deduce that the difference between the times of flight for the two parts of the journey is $(2aW\cos\alpha)/(V^2 - W^2)$.

[MEI]

(6) In this question the units of distance, time and speed are $km, h$ and $kmh^{-1}$ respectively.

$A, B$ and $C$ are three small spheres. At time $t = 0$, $A$ is at the origin $O$, and $B$ and $C$ have position vectors $6\mathbf{i} + 8\mathbf{j}$ and $16\mathbf{i} + 8\mathbf{j}$ respectively where $\mathbf{i}$ and $\mathbf{j}$ are unit vectors due $E$ and $N$ respectively. They move with constant velocities given by

$$\mathbf{v}_A = 3\mathbf{i} + 4\mathbf{j}, \mathbf{v}_B = \lambda\mathbf{i} + \mu\mathbf{j} \text{ and } \mathbf{v}_C = -\mathbf{i} + 2\mathbf{j}.$$

i. Show that $A$ and $C$ collide and find the time when this happens. Find the distance of the point of collision from $O$.
ii. To an observer on $A, B$ appears to be moving due $N$ and to an observer on $C, B$ appears to be moving due $NE$. Find the values of $\lambda$ and $\mu$ and the shortest distance between $B$ and $C$.

[SUJB]

## COMMON ERRORS
### (1) Relative Velocity
When adding or subtracting velocities, remember that you must treat them as *vectors*. Do not just add the magnitudes.

## (2) Shortest Distance

a. When solving a "shortest distance" problem, do not confuse your distance diagram and your velocity diagram. The velocity diagram is used to find the relative velocity, and the distance diagram is used to find the shortest distance.

b. Once you have found $_A\mathbf{v}_B$, then the shortest distance is the line from $B$ perpendicular to the relative velocity line of $A$. It is not perpendicular to the line $AB$.

# 31 Projectiles

Throughout this chapter the effect of air resistance is ignored.

When a body is projected, its *horizontal* motion has constant velocity. Its *vertical* motion is subject to a constant acceleration $g$.

Throughout this chapter take $g$ to be 9.8 m/sec$^2$.

If the initial horizontal and vertical velocities are $u_h$ and $u_v$ respectively, then the equations of motion for horizontal and vertical motion are:

$$dx/dt = u_h \quad dy/dt = u_v - gt$$
$$x = u_h t \qquad y = u_v t - \tfrac{1}{2}gt^2$$

## 31.1 Horizontal Projection

If a body is projected horizontally with speed $u$, then $u_h = u$ and $u_v = 0$.

### 31.1.1 Example

A body is projected horizontally with speed 10 m/sec from the top of a cliff of height 50 m. Find (a) the time it takes to reach the bottom (b) its speed at the bottom (c) its distance from the base of the cliff (d) the angle at which it is travelling when it lands.

Solution

(a) Suppose it lands at the bottom after $t$ secs.

$$-50 = -\frac{1}{2} \times 9.8 \times t^2$$

**It lands after 3.19 secs**

(b) The horizontal speed is constant at 10 m/sec. The vertical speed can be found by $v = gt = 31.3$ m/sec. Combine these velocities by Pythagoras:

**The speed at the bottom is 32.9 m/sec**

(c) The horizontal distance it has travelled is found by multiplying the horizontal speed by the time.

**It lands 31.9 m from the base of the cliff**

(d) The tan of the angle at which it is travelling is given by the ratio of the vertical velocity to the horizontal velocity.

$$\tan \theta = 31.3/10$$

**It travels at 72° to the horizontal**

### 31.1.2 Exercises

(1) A body is projected at 20 m/sec from the top of a cliff. It hits the bottom after 3 seconds. Find how high the cliff is, and how far from the base of the cliff the body lands.

(2) A body is projected at 15 m/sec from the top of a 70 m cliff. Find the time it takes to reach the bottom, and its distance from the foot of the cliff.

(3) A marble rolls off the top of a 1.5 m table at 1 m/sec. Find how long it takes to reach the floor, and how far from the table it lands.

(4) A dart is thrown horizontally at 20 m/sec at a board 3 m away. Find how far it has fallen when it hits the board.

(5) A gun is fired horizontally at 1000 m/sec. If the target is 500 m distant find how far the bullet has fallen below the level of the gun.

(6) A gun is fired horizontally at a target 200 m distant. When it strikes it has fallen 5 cm. Find the muzzle velocity of the bullet.

(7) A tennis ball is struck horizontally at 5 m/sec. When it reaches the net it has fallen 30 cm. How far away is the net?

(8) A car is driven off the top of a 50 m cliff at 25 m/sec. Find the speed with which it hits the sea. Find the angle to the horizontal at which it is travelling when it lands.

(9) A cricket ball is struck horizontally from a height of 1 m at a speed of 13 m/sec. Find its velocity when it lands, and the angle to the horizontal with which it is travelling.

(10) A bomber flies horizontally at 300 m/sec at a height of 3,000 m when it drops its bomb to hit a certain target on the ground. Find the distance from the target. Find the speed with which the bomb hits the target, and the angle with which it does so.

## 31.2 Projection at an Angle

If a body is projected at $\theta$ to the horizontal, its initial horizontal velocity $u_h$ is $u\cos\theta$, and its initial vertical velocity $u_v$ is $u\sin\theta$. The equations of motion are:

$$dx/dt = u(\cos\theta) \quad dy/dt = u(\sin\theta) - gt$$

$$x = u(\cos\theta)t \qquad y = u(\sin\theta)t - \tfrac{1}{2}gt^2$$

The horizontal range of a projectile is $u^2(\sin 2\theta)/g$. The greatest horizontal range is $u^2/g$, achieved when $\theta = 45°$.

### 31.2.1 Example

A body is projected at 20 m/sec at 30° to the horizontal. Find its range, its time of flight and the greatest height reached.

Solution    Put $u = 20$ and $\theta = 30°$ into the formula above.

$$\textbf{Horizontal range} \ = 20^2 \sin 60°/9.8 = \textbf{35m}.$$

It will hit the ground when its vertical displacement is 0.

$$20 \times \sin 30°t - \frac{1}{2} \times 9.8t^2 = 0. \ t = 0 \ \text{ or } 2.04 \ \text{ secs}.$$

**Its time of flight is 2.04 secs**

The greatest height is reached halfway through the flight, i.e. when $t = 1.02$ secs. Put this value into the expression for the vertical displacement.

$$\textbf{Greatest height} \ = 20 \times \sin 30° \times 1.02 - \frac{1}{2} \times 9.8 \times 1.02^2 = \textbf{5.1m}.$$

## 31.2.2 Exercises

(1) A particle is projected at 40 m/sec at 40° to the horizontal. Find its range, the time it is in flight and the greatest height it reaches.

(2) A particle is projected at 30 m/sec at 60° to the horizontal. Find the greatest height it reaches, and the time it takes to reach this height.

(3) A gun fires a bullet at 1,000 m/sec, at an elevation of 5°. Find the horizontal range of the gun.

(4) A particle is projected at 50 m/sec at 35° to the horizontal. Find how high it has risen after 1 second. Find the angle at which it is moving at that time.

(5) A particle is thrown at 15 m/sec at an elevation of 25°. Find its range, and the greatest height it reaches.

(6) A particle is thrown at 20 m/sec at an elevation of 30°. Find its speed after $\frac{1}{2}$ second. At what angle is it travelling at this time? When is the particle moving at 20° to the horizontal?

(7) A cricket ball is hit at 15 m/sec at an elevation of 50°. Find the angle of its direction after $\frac{1}{4}$ sec. When is it descending at an angle of 30° to the horizontal?

(8) A stone is thrown at 20 m/sec at an elevation of 40°, from the top of a 60 m cliff. Find how long it takes to reach the bottom, and its distance from the foot of the cliff. At what angle does it enter the sea?

(9) A particle is projected at 30 m/sec at 50° to the horizontal. A vertical wall is 10 m distant from the point of projection: how high up the wall does the particle strike? At what angle does it strike?

(10) An arrow is fired at a speed of 30 m/sec at an angle of 20°, from the top of a 30 m castle tower. How far from the base of the tower does it land?

(11) An aircraft is diving at 200 m/sec at an angle of 20° to the horizontal. It releases a bomb when it is 1,000 m above a certain point on the ground. How far from the point does the bomb land?

## 31.3 Trajectory

The path along which a projectile travels is its *trajectory*.

If the particle is projected at speed $u$ with an elevation of $\theta$, its trajectory is:

$$y = x \tan \theta \ - \ \frac{\frac{1}{2}gx^2}{u^2 \cos^2 \theta}$$

If the angle of elevation $\theta$ is to be found, the equation is written as:

$$y = xT - \frac{\frac{1}{2}gx^2(1 + T^2)}{u^2}, \text{ where } T = \tan \theta$$

## 31.3.1 Example

A boy can throw a stone at 14 m/sec. At what angle should he throw in order to hit a window which is 10 m away horizontally and 5 m higher than him?

Solution    In the equation above, put $u = 14$, $x = 10$ and $y = 5$.

$$5 = 10T - \frac{\frac{1}{2}g10^2(1 + T^2)}{14^2}$$

Re-arrange this into a quadratic equation.

$$T^2 - 4T + 3 = 0$$

$T = 1$ or $3$. Recall that $T = \tan\theta$.

### He should throw at an elevation of 45° or of 72°

## 31.3.2 Exercises

(1) The muzzle velocity of a gun is 400 m/sec. What are the possible angles of elevation to achieve a horizontal range of 10,000 m?

(2) A boy can throw a stone at 20 m/sec. What angle should he throw at to achieve a range of 30 m?

(3) A particle can be projected at 21 m/sec. What should be the angle of projection if it is to hit a target 2 m high and 15 m distant?

(4) A gun can be fired at 200 m/sec. What should be the angle of elevation to hit a target 1 m high and 2,000 m distant?

(5) An arrow can be fired at 42 m/sec. What should be the angle of elevation to strike a target 10 m high and 25 m distant?

(6) An archer stands on the top of a 30 m tower. He can shoot an arrow at 49 m/sec. What is the lower angle at which the arrow should aimed to hit a target which is 250 m from the base of the tower? At what angle does it enter the target?

(7) From a window 25 m above the street a boy throws stones at a target 40 m away from the foot of the house. If he can throw at 21 m/sec find the angle at which he should throw.

## 31.4 Examination Questions

(1) A particle is projected from a point O on horizontal ground with velocity 40 m s$^{-1}$ at an angle of 30° to the horizontal.

Given that, 0.7 seconds after projection, the particle is at a point $P$, calculate

274

  i.   the height of $P$ above the ground,

  ii.  the magnitude and direction of the velocity of the particle at $P$.

   The particle reaches the ground again at a point $Q$. Calculate

   (iii)  the time of flight,   (iv) the greatest height reached,

  (v) the distance $OQ$.

[C add]

(2) The height in metres of a stone above ground level $t$ seconds after being thrown until it hits the ground, is given by

$$h = 80 + 15t - 5t^2.$$

a.  State the height from which it was thrown.

b.  Calculate, to the nearest tenth of a second, when it hits the ground.

c.  Rewrite $h$ in the form $5[B - (A - t)^2]$, stating the values of the positive numbers $A$ and $B$.

d.  Hence, or otherwise, state when the stone is highest and give this height.

e.  Find the height after 0.8 second and calculate for how long it is above this.

[SMP add]

(3) A boy threw a ball directly at the vertical wall of a building which was 42 m in front of him. 2 s later the ball struck a window in that wall at a point which was 2.8 m above the point from which the ball was thrown.

  i.   Show that the ball was thrown at an angle $\theta$ to the horizontal where $\tan\theta = \frac{8}{15}$.

  ii.  Calculate the maximum height reached by the ball above the point from which it was thrown.

 iii.  Calculate the distance from the building at which the boy would have needed to stand in order that the ball, thrown in exactly the same manner, would have hit the wall at a point which was at the same level as the point from which the ball was thrown.

[JMB add]

(4) A particle is projected vertically upwards with speed $V$ from a point $O$. Find $H$, the maximum height of the particle above $O$.

When the particle is projected from $O$ with the same speed $V$, but at an

275

angle of elevation $\theta$ to the horizontal, the maximum height of the particle above the horizontal plane through $O$ is $h$ and the range on the horizontal plane is $R$.

    a.  When $R = H$, show that there are two possible values of $\theta$, and find the two corresponding values of $h$.

    b.  When $h = \frac{1}{2}H$, show that there is only one possible value of $\theta$, and find the corresponding value of $R$.

        [L]

(5) A boy throws a small ball towards a wall so that the flight of the ball is in a vertical plane perpendicular to the wall. The boy and the wall stand on horizontal ground 9 m apart.

    a.  The ball leaves the boy's hand in a horizontal direction with a speed of 20 m s$^{-1}$ at a height of 1.1 m above the ground. Calculate, to the nearest cm, the height above the ground of the point at which the ball strikes the wall.

    b.  A can stands on the wall, directly opposite the boy, at a height of 2 m above the ground. In order to knock the can off the wall it is necessary for the ball to strike the can with a velocity whose horizontal component is at least 16 m s$^{-1}$. Determine the speed, in m s$^{-1}$ to 1 decimal place, with which the ball must be thrown just to knock the can off the wall.

In this case determine, in degrees to 1 decimal place, the angle which the ball's trajectory makes with the horizontal

    (i)  as the ball leaves the boy's hand,  (ii)  at the moment of impact.

        [AEB 1985]

(6)

    a.  A particle is projected under gravity from a point $O$ with speed $u$ at an angle $\alpha$ to the horizontal. Write down expressions for the horizontal and vertical displacements $x$ and $y$ of the particles from $O$ at time $t$.

    b.  A boy throws a ball from the foot of a plane inclined at an angle $\beta$ to the horizontal and later the ball falls on to the plane. The motion of the ball takes place in the vertical plane containing the line of greatest slope of the plane. The initial velocity of the ball has magnitude $u$ and is inclined at an angle $\alpha(\alpha > \beta)$ to the horizontal.

i.  By using the results given in (a), show that the ball meets the inclined plane after a time $(2u \sin(\alpha - \beta))/(g \cos \beta)$.

    [Hint: the equation of the line of greatest slope of the plane is $y = x \tan \beta$.]

ii. Find the range on the inclined plane.

iii. Given that the ball strikes the plane at right-angles, show that $\tan \alpha = \cot \beta + 2 \tan \beta$.

[W]

## COMMON ERRORS
### Equations of Motion

a.  Be very careful of signs. The positive direction for $y$ is upwards. So $g$ is negative. If a body is thrown down 50 m then put $y = -50$.

b.  Do not confuse the various quantities. When a body strikes the ground, then $y = 0$. When it is at its greatest height, then $dy/dt = 0$. Do not get these the wrong way round.

c.  When finding the angle at which a projectile is moving, you must take the ratio of the vertical and horizontal *velocities*. Do not take the ratio of the *distances*.

# 32 Momentum

If a body of mass $m$ is moving with velocity $v$, then its *momentum* is $mv$.

The *Principle of Conservation of Momentum* states that:

If there are no external forces acting on a system, its total momentum is constant.

## 32.1 Impulse

If a force $F$ acts on a body for a time $t$, then the *impulse* it gives to the body is $Ft$. The impulse is equal to the change of momentum of the body.

A *light inextensible string* is one whose weight is negligible and whose length is constant. When such a string becomes taut then the bodies at each end of the string receive equal and opposite impulses along the direction of the string.

Impulse and momentum are vectors. If the motion does not take place in a straight line then impulses must be found from a vector triangle.

### 32.1.1 Examples

(1)   A sphere of mass 1 kg travelling north at 3 m/sec strikes a stationary sphere of mass 2 kg. After the collision the second sphere travels North East with speed $\frac{1}{2}$ m/sec. Find the velocity of the first sphere, and the impulse received by the second sphere.

Solution   Let the first sphere be travelling at $v$ m/sec north and $u$ m/sec west. By conservation of momentum in the north-south direction:

$$1 \times 3 = 1 \times v + 2 \times \frac{1}{2} \cos 45°$$

$$v = 2.293 \text{ m/sec}$$

By conservation of momentum in the east-west direction:

$$0 = 1 \times u - 2 \times \frac{1}{2} \sin 45°$$

$$u = 0.707 \text{ m/sec}$$

Combine these velocities:
**The velocity of the first sphere is 2.4 m/sec at 343°**
The impulse given to the second sphere is its change of momentum.

**The impulse is 1N − sec at 045°**

(2)   A shell of mass 5 kg is travelling horizontally at 100 m/sec when it explodes into two parts. One part of mass 2 kg travels in the original direction at 200 m/sec. Find the speed of the other part, and find the gain in energy due to the explosion.

Solution   Suppose the 3 kg part moves at $v$ in the original direction. By conservation of momentum:

$$5 \times 100 = 2 \times 200 + 3 \times v$$

**The 3 kg part travels at $33\frac{1}{3}$ m/sec in the original direction**

The energy gained is the difference between the kinetic energies before and after the explosion.

Energy gained $= \frac{1}{2} \times 2 \times 200^2 + \frac{1}{2} \times 3 \times 33\frac{1}{3}^2 - \frac{1}{2} \times 5 \times 100^2$

**The energy gained is 16,667 Joules**

(3)     Two bodies $A$ and $B$, of masses 1 kg and 3 kg respectively, are connected by a light inextensible string of length $h$. They lie a distance $\frac{1}{2}h$ apart on a smooth horizontal table, with $A$ on the edge. $A$ is tipped over the edge. Find the speed of $B$ immediately after the string becomes taut.

Solution     $A$ falls freely under gravity for a distance of $\frac{1}{2}h$. Its speed is then found from the formula $v^2 = u^2 + 2as$:

$$\text{Speed is } \sqrt{(gh)}.$$

After the string becomes taut, the two bodies move as one with speed $w$. By conservation of momentum,

$$4w = \sqrt{(gh)}.$$

**$B$ starts to move with speed $\frac{1}{4}\sqrt{(gh)}$**

(4)     A body of mass 3 kg is travelling with velocity $3\mathbf{i} + 2\mathbf{j}$. It receives a blow, and then travels with velocity $2\mathbf{i} - 4\mathbf{j}$. Find the magnitude of the impulse it has received.

Solution     The change of velocity is obtained by subtracting the two vectors. The change of momentum is the mass times the change of velocity.

$$\text{Change of momentum } = 3(-\mathbf{i} - 6\mathbf{j}) = -3\mathbf{i} - 18\mathbf{j}.$$

Use Pythagoras to find the magnitude of this vector.

**The magnitude of the impulse is 18.25Ns**

## 32.1.2 Exercises

(1) Find the momentum of the following:

a. A car of mass 500 kg moving at 20 m/sec.

b. A ball of mass 0.1 kg moving at 5 m/sec.

(2) An impulse of 12 N-sec is applied to a stationary mass of 3 kg. Find its velocity afterwards.

(3) An impulse of 20 N-sec is applied to a mass of 4 kg moving at 3 m/sec in the direction of the impulse. Find the new velocity of the mass.

(4) A stationary ball of mass 0.2 kg is struck so that it moves at 12 m/sec. Find the impulse it has been given.

(5) A body of mass 3 kg moving at 6 m/sec is struck by an impulse acting in the same direction as the motion. If it now moves at 9 m/sec find the impulse.

(6) A cricket ball of mass 0.12 kg is bowled at 20 m/sec. The batsman hits it back to the bowler at 25 m/sec. Find the impulse he has given to the ball.

(7) A car of mass 500 kg moves at 10 m/sec and collides with a stationary car of mass 400 kg. If they move on together find their common speed. Find the loss of energy in the collision.

(8) A car of mass 500 kg moving at 20 m/sec bumps into a car of mass 600 kg which is moving in the same direction at 15 m/sec. If they stay fixed together find their speed.

(9) A car of mass 500 kg travelling at 20 m/sec has a head-on collision with another car travelling in the opposite direction at 25 m/sec. If they are both brought to a halt find the mass of the second car.

(10) An arrow of mass 50 g flying horizontally at 40 m/sec strikes a hanging target of mass 4 kg. Find the velocity with which they move. Find the loss of energy. If the arrow penetrates to a depth of 3 cm find the average force of resistance of the target.

(11) An arrow of mass 50 g travelling horizontally at 30 m/sec strikes an apple of mass 100 g and embeds itself in it. Find the speed with which they begin to move. If the arrow penetrates to a depth of 10 cm find the force of resistance of the apple.

(12) A stake of mass 10 kg is to be driven vertically into the ground. It is struck by a sledgehammer of mass 20 kg moving at 15 m/sec. The hammer and stake stay together after collision. Find their velocity after collision. If the stake penetrates 20 cm find the force of resistance of the ground.

(13) Two particles of masses 2 kg and 4 kg are connected by a light inextensible string. The lighter particle is projected away from the heavier with speed 3 m/s. Find their common speed after the string becomes taut. Find the loss of energy caused by the tightening of the string.

(14) *A* and *B*, of masses 2 kg and 6 kg respectively, are connected by a light inextensible string. They are projected away from each other with speeds 4 m/s and 3 m/s respectively. Find their speeds after the string becomes taut. Find the impulse in the string.

(15) A particle of mass 4 kg moves with velocity $5\mathbf{i} - 3\mathbf{j}$. After a blow it moves with velocity $7\mathbf{i} + 4\mathbf{j}$. Find the magnitude of the impulse it has received.

(16) A particle of mass 2 kg and velocity $2\mathbf{i} + 3\mathbf{j}$ receives an impulse of $4\mathbf{i} + 7\mathbf{j}$. Find its new velocity, and the energy it has gained.

(17) Two particles, of masses 5 kg and 2 kg and velocities $\mathbf{i} + 2\mathbf{j}$ and $-2\mathbf{i} - 3\mathbf{j}$, collide and coalesce. Find their new velocity, and the impulse each has received.

(18) A ball of mass 3 kg travelling at 2 m/sec strikes a stationary ball of mass 1 kg. The smaller ball then travels at $1\frac{1}{2}$ m/sec at 30° to the original line of motion of the larger. Find the new velocity of the larger ball.

(19) A ball of mass 0.3 kg strikes a stationary ball of mass 0.8 kg at 2 m/sec, and is deflected through 90° and its velocity is reduced to 1 m/sec. Find the velocity of the larger ball.

(20) A rifle of mass 4 kg fires a bullet of mass 10 g at 800 m/sec. Find the initial speed of recoil of the rifle. Find the energy of the explosion.

(21) A shell of mass 20 kg travelling horizontally at 200 m/sec explodes into two equal halves, one of which is brought to a halt. Find the speed of the other. Find the energy of the explosion.

(22) A cricket ball of mass 0.12 kg, bowled at 20 m/sec, is struck so that it travels at right-angles to its original direction at 30 m/sec. Find the impulse given to the ball.

(23) A cricket ball of mass 0.12 kg, bowled at 25 m/sec, is deflected through 20° and its speed is reduced to 15 m/sec. Find the impulse given to the ball.

(24) A cricket ball of mass 0.12 kg, bowled at 17 m/sec, is struck back to the bowler so that it travels at 35 m/sec and makes 20° with its original direction. Find the magnitude of the impulse given.

(25) If the cricket ball of Question 22 is struck by an impulse of 3 N-sec at right angles to its original direction find its new velocity.

(26) The cricket ball of Question 24 is struck back to the bowler by an impulse of 5 N-sec in a direction which makes 10° with its original direction. Find its new speed.

## 32.2 Elastic Collisions

When two bodies collide, their relative velocity is reversed and multiplied by a constant factor $e$. This factor is the *coefficient of restitution*.

$$e = (\text{relative speed after})/(\text{relative speed before})$$

$e$ lies between 0 and 1. Bodies for which $e = 1$ are called *perfectly elastic*. Bodies for which $e = 0$ are *perfectly inelastic*.

## 32.2.1 Examples

(1)   A body is dropped from a height of 10 m onto a horizontal surface for which the coefficient of restitution is
$\frac{3}{4}$. Find the height it rises to after the first bounce.

Solution   The velocity with which it strikes the floor is found from
the formula $v^2 = 2as$. The speed is
$\sqrt{(2g \times 10)} = 14$ m/sec. This is then multiplied by $e$.

Speed after bounce = 10.5 m/sec

The height can be found from the same formula.

**The height is $10.5^2/2g = 5.625$ m.**

(2)   Three spheres $A, B, C$ of masses 2, 2, 1 respectively lie
in that order on a horizontal table. The coefficient of
restitution is $\frac{1}{2}$. A is given a speed of 4 m/sec towards
$B$. Find the speed with which $C$ begins to move.

Solution   The three diagrams below show the situations (a) before
the first collision (b) after the first collision but before
the second (c) after the second collision.

(a)   $A \quad \rightarrow 4 \quad B \qquad\qquad C$

(b)   $A \quad \rightarrow u \quad B \quad \rightarrow v \quad C$

(c)   $A \quad \rightarrow u \quad B \quad \rightarrow p \quad C \quad \rightarrow q$

By conservation of momentum in the first collision:

$$2 \times 4 = 2 \times u + 2 \times v$$

By restitution in the first collision:

$$v - u = \frac{1}{2} \times 4$$

Solve these to find that $u = 1$ and $v = 3$.
Repeat the process for the second collision.

$$2v = 2p + q \text{ (Conservation of momentum)}$$

$$q - p = \frac{1}{2}v \text{ (Restitution)}$$

Solve these equations to find $q$, using $v = 3$.

## The velocity of C is 3 m/sec.

(3)        A body strikes a wall at an angle of 40° to the wall. If
the coefficient of restitution is $\frac{1}{2}$ find the angle it makes
with the wall after striking it.

Solution        Let the speed of the ball be $u$. The velocity parallel to the wall is $u \cos 40°$. This
is unchanged. The velocity perpendicular
to the wall is $u \sin 40°$. This is multiplied
by $\frac{1}{2}$. Find the angle $\theta$ which the ball now
makes with the wall, by considering the
ratio of the velocities.

$$\tan \theta = \frac{1}{2} u \sin 40° / u \cos 40° = \frac{1}{2} \tan 40°$$

## It now makes 23° with the wall

### 32.2.2 Exercises

(1) A ball falls from a height of $2\frac{1}{2}$ m, onto a floor where the coefficient
of restitution is $\frac{7}{8}$. Find the height it reaches after the first bounce.

(2) A ball falls from a height of 8 m, and after the first bounce it reaches
a height of 2 m. Find the coefficient of restitution.

(3) A ball of mass 3 kg moving at 4 m/sec strikes a stationary ball of mass
2 kg. If the coefficient of restitution is $\frac{1}{4}$ find their velocities after collision.

(4) Two balls collide, the first being of mass 2 kg and travelling at
2 m/sec and the second of mass 3 kg and travelling at 1 m/sec in the opposite direction. If the coefficient of restitution is $\frac{1}{3}$ find their velocities after
impact.

(5) A ball of mass 1 kg moving at 5 m/sec strikes a stationary ball of mass
2 kg. If the larger ball moves off at 2 m/sec find the coefficient of restitution.

(6) A ball of mass 3 kg travelling at 2 m/sec strikes a ball of mass 2 kg
travelling in the same direction at $1\frac{1}{2}$ m/sec. If the first ball now moves at
$1\frac{3}{4}$ m/sec find the coefficient of restitution.

In Questions 7 to 10 two balls $A$ and $B$
lie as shown. $A$ is projected towards $B$
with speed 2 m/sec. $B$ bounces off the
wall, and returns to strike $A$. The coefficients of restitutions between $A$ and $B$

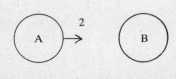

and between $B$ and the wall are $e$ and $e'$ respectively. Find the final velocity of $A$ in each of the following cases.

(7) $e = e' = \frac{1}{2}$. $A$ and $B$ have equal mass.

(8) $e = e' = \frac{1}{2}$. $A$ has twice the mass of $B$.

(9) $e = e' = \frac{1}{2}$. $A$ has half the mass of $B$.

(10) $e = \frac{1}{2}$, $e' = \frac{1}{3}$. $A$ and $B$ have equal mass.

In Questions 11 to 14 three balls $A, B, C$ lie in a straight line as shown. $A$ is projected towards $B$ at 2 m/sec. The coefficient of restitution is $\frac{3}{4}$. In each case find the velocity of $C$ after it has been struck.

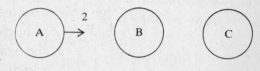

(11) $A, B, C$ have equal mass.

(12) The mass of $A$ is twice that of $B$ or $C$.

(13) The masses of $A, B$ and $C$ are in the ratio 3:2:1.

(14) The masses of $A, B, C$ are in the ratio 1:2:3.

(15) A ball strikes a wall at 60° to the wall. If the coefficient of restitution is 0.7 find the angle it makes with the wall after collision.

(16) A ball strikes a wall at 40° to the wall. After collision it makes 35° with the wall. Find the coefficient of restitution.

(17) In Questions 15 and 16 find the impulses experienced by the ball, if it is initially travelling at 12 m/sec and has mass 0.5 kg.

## 32.3 Examination Questions

(1) In a traffic pile up on a smooth icy road a car, of mass 800 kg travelling at 14 m s$^{-1}$, hits a stationary car of mass 1100 kg and the two move on together. Calculate their common velocity in m s$^{-1}$ after impact, and the loss of energy on impact, giving your answer in joules.

Without losing any further velocity the two cars slide until they come to rest on hitting a stationary lorry, of mass 10,000 kg, which is just in front. Calculate the velocity of the lorry, in m s$^{-1}$, immediately after the impact.

If the lorry is brought to rest by a uniform frictional force after moving 10 m, calculate the retarding force in newtons.

[O&C add]

(2) In using a pile driver, a mass of 3000 kg is released from rest to fall freely through 2.5 m to strike a pile of mass 500 kg. What is the velocity of the 3000 kg mass immediately before it hits the pile? What is the common

velocity of the total mass of 3500 kg immediately after impact, assuming that there is no rebound?

If the constant resistance of the ground is R N, write down the net force acting on the mass of 3500 kg (allowing for the weight), and hence calculate the value of R if the mass penetrates 0.5 m into the ground before coming to rest.

[MEI add]

(3) A shot of mass 8 kg is fired horizontally from a stationary gun of mass 0.5 tonne. The gun is free to recoil. The impulse given by the gun to the shot is 2000 N s.

a.  Calculate the speed of the shot and the speed of the gun immediately after firing.
    The gun is subsequently brought to rest by a constant horizontal force $F$ in 2 seconds. Calculate

(b)  the magnitude of $F$,  (c)  the distance the gun moves.

[AEB add 1986]

(4) A Thark of mass $5.7 \times 10^{-7}$ kg, initially travelling at $3.4 \times 10^6$ m/s, receives an impulse which deflects it through 90° and doubles its speed.

(a) Calculate the magnitude and direction of this impulse.

Shortly afterwards the Thark disintegrates into two. One third of the mass deflects through 40° and moves at $7.9 \times 10^6$ m/s at 50° to the direction in which it was initially travelling.

(b), Find, by drawing or calculation, the speed and direction of the other two-thirds.

[SMP add]

(5) (*Take the acceleration due to gravity to be* 10 m s$^{-2}$)

An archer shoots an arrow of mass 0.2 kg at a wooden target of mass 5 kg which he has hung from a fixed point by a cord of length 2 m. The target is free to move in the direction of the arrow's motion, and it is hanging at rest when the arrow strikes it horizontally with a speed of 39 m s$^{-1}$, and sticks into it. Find the velocity with which the target begins to move.

The maximum angle which the cord makes with the vertical in the subsequent swinging motion is $\theta$. Regarding the target and arrow as a particle, and using conservation of energy, find the value of $\theta$ to the nearest degree.

The archer recovers his arrow by tugging it horizontally out of the target as it is passing through the lowest point of its swing, moving away from him This action leaves the target at rest and the arrow moving away from it at a speed of 2 m s$^{-1}$. Draw a diagram to show the impulse acting on the arrow and on the target, and find the magnitude of the impulse which the archer exerts on the arrow.

[AEB 1987]

(6) A ball is thrown vertically downwards from a height $d$ above a level floor with speed $\sqrt{(3gd)}$. Find the time taken to reach the floor, and show that the ball rebounds with speed $e\sqrt{(5gd)}$, where $e$ is the coefficient of restitution between the ball and the floor.

The height of the ceiling above the floor is $2d$. Find the minimum value of $e$ that ensures that the ball reaches the ceiling.

Find the maximum height of the ball above the floor for the case when $e^2 = \frac{3}{5}$ and determine its speed when it returns to the point of projection after striking the floor once.

[MEI]

(7) Three perfectly elastic smooth spheres $A, B, C$ of equal radii but of masses $3m$, $2m$ and $1m$ respectively, lie at rest on a horizontal plane with their centres in a straight line. Sphere $A$ is projected with speed $u$ to collide directly with sphere $B$ which then collides directly with sphere $C$. Find the speed of each sphere after each of these collisions. Explain why there are only two collisions between the spheres.

[L]

(8) A particle $A$ of mass $m$ is attached to a particle $B$ of mass $2m$ by a light inextensible string of length $a$. The particles lie at rest on a frictionless horizontal plane and $A$ is projected towards $B$ with speed $u$. If the coefficient of restitution between the particles is $\frac{3}{4}$ show that the direction of motion of $A$ is reversed after impact with $B$. Find

i.   the speeds of $A$ and $B$ immediately after the string tightens;
ii.  the magnitude of the impulsive tension in the string;
iii. the time that elapses between the impact and the tightening of the string;
iv.  the total loss of energy due to the impact and tightening of the string.

[SUJB]

(9)

a. Two particles $A$ and $B$ of masses $3m$ and $5m$ respectively are placed on a smooth horizontal table. The particle $A$ is projected along the table with speed $u$ directly towards $B$, which is at rest. After impact $A$ continues to move in the same direction with speed $u/6$. Find

    i. the speed of $B$ after impact,

    ii. the coefficient of restitution between $A$ and $B$,

    iii. the loss in kinetic energy due to the collision.

b. The same particles $A$ and $B$ are now connected by a light inextensible string and are placed side by side on the smooth horizontal table. The particle $A$ is projected horizontally, directly away from $B$, with a speed $v$. Calculate

    i. the resulting common speed of the two particles after the string has tightened,

    ii. the magnitude of the impulse in the string when the string tightens,

    iii. the loss in kinetic energy due to the tightening of the string.

[AEB 1986]

## COMMON ERRORS

### 1) Momentum

Momentum and impulse are both vectors. So if a body changes direction as well as speed, the change in velocity is not just the difference between its speeds before and after. Find the change of velocity by components or by a vector triangle.

### 2) Impact Problems

a. Do not forget that energy is usually lost in collisions. Do not try to solve problems by claiming that energy is conserved before and after a collision has taken place.

b. When working with problems which involve penetration, do not ignore gravity. Note the difference between:

    i. An arrow enters a target horizontally. The energy lost will be kinetic energy.

    ii. A stake enters the ground vertically. The energy lost will be kinetic energy plus potential energy.

## 3) Coefficient of Restitution

Be careful with signs. It is probably wise to take all the velocities in the same direction. Then if a body is travelling in the opposite direction its velocity is negative.

# 33 Variable Acceleration

The equations of motion such as $s = ut + \frac{1}{2}at^2$ apply only to situations in which the acceleration is constant. If the acceleration is not constant then calculus must be used.

Acceleration can be a function of time, or of velocity, or of distance.

Situations in which the acceleration was a function of time were dealt with in Chapter 22.

Frequently the identity $dv/dt = v\,dv/ds$ is applied.

## 33.1 Force as a Function of Velocity

The *terminal* velocity of an object is its final velocity. The acceleration is zero when the terminal velocity is reached.

## 33.1.1 Examples

(1)      A body of mass 2 kg falls under gravity, experiencing air resistance which is proportional to the square of its velocity. The terminal velocity is 14 m/sec. Find the constant of proportionality.

Solution      Let the force of resistance be $kv^2$. The equation of motion is:

$$2 \times dv/dt = 2g - kv^2.$$

When $v = 14, dv/dt = 0$. This gives $k = 0.1$.

**The constant of proportionality is 0.1**

(2)      A body with unit mass moves under a force of $3\sqrt{v}$ directed towards the origin, where $v$ is the velocity. It is projected at 9 m/sec away from the origin. Find the distance $X$ it travels before coming to rest.

Solution      The equation of motion is:

$$dv/dt = -3\sqrt{v}$$

Use the identity $dv/dt = vdv/ds$, to obtain:

$$vdv/ds = -3\sqrt{v}$$

Separate the variables and integrate. $v$ goes from 9 to 0. $s$ goes from 0 to $X$.

$$\int_9^0 \sqrt{v}dv = -3\int_0^X ds$$

$$-3X = [\frac{2}{3}v^{1\frac{1}{2}}]_9^0 = -18$$

**It travels 6 m before coming to rest.**

## 33.1.2 Exercises

(1) A body of mass 5 kg falls under gravity against a resistance equal to a quarter of its velocity. Find the terminal velocity.

(2) A body of mass 3 kg falls under gravity against a force equal to half its velocity squared. Find its terminal velocity.

(3) A car drives along horizontal ground, with constant power equal to 10,000 W, and against a constant resistance of 400 N. Find its terminal velocity.

(4) A car of mass 500 kg rolls down a slope of angle 10°, against a resistance equal to twenty times its velocity. Find the terminal velocity.

(5) A body of mass 10 kg falls under gravity against a resistance proportional to its velocity. If its terminal velocity is 50 m/sec, find the constant of proportionality.

(6) A body of mass $2\frac{1}{2}$ kg falls under gravity against a resistance proportional to the velocity squared. If the terminal velocity is 8 m/sec find the constant of proportionality.

(7) A car of mass 800 kg rolls down a slope of 5°, against a resistance proportional to its velocity. If the terminal velocity is 4 m/sec find the constant of proportionality.

(8) A unit mass experiences a force of $2v^{1\frac{1}{2}}$ away from the origin. It starts at the origin with speed 16. Find the time it takes to reach a speed of 25.

(9) Find the distance covered by the mass of Question 8.

(10) A body starts from the origin with speed 10. It experiences an acceleration towards the origin of $(1 + v)$. Find the time it takes to come to a halt.

(11) A body starts from rest at the origin and experiences an acceleration away from the origin of $(2 - v)$. Find the terminal velocity, and the time it has taken to reach half the terminal velocity.

(12) A body starts from the origin with speed 20, and experiences an acceleration of $(1 + v^2)$ directed towards the origin. Find the time it takes to come to rest.

(13) Find the distance covered by the body of Question 12.

(14) The resistance experienced by a body of unit mass is $v + v^2$. It starts from the origin with speed 12. Find the distance it has covered when it is brought to rest.

## 33.2 Force as a Function of Distance

### 33.2.1 Example

> A body of mass 2 starts at rest from $x = 3$, under a force of $2x/9$ directed towards the origin. Find its speed when it reaches the origin, and the time it has taken.

Solution    Write down the equation of motion:

$$2v\,dv/dx = -2x/9$$

Separate the variables and integrate:

$$v^2 = k - x^2/9$$

When $x = 3, v = 0$. This gives $k = 1$.
$v = \sqrt{(1 - x^2/9)}$. Put $x = 0$:

### At the origin the velocity is 1.

Write $v = dx/dt$ and separate the variables again.

$$\int dt = \int_3^0 \frac{1}{\sqrt{(1 - x^2/9)}} dx = \int_3^0 \frac{3dx}{\sqrt{9 - x^2}}$$

### The time taken is $3 \sin^{-1} 3/3 = 3\pi/2$

## 33.2.2 Exercises

(1) The equation of motion of a body is $dv/dt = 3s$. It is at rest at the origin, and is displaced slightly. Find its speed after travelling 10 m.

(2) A body starts from the origin with an initial speed of 1 m/sec, and its equation of motion is $2dv/dt = 1/(1 + s)$. Find its speed after travelling 2 m.

(3) A body moves from rest at the origin so that its equation of motion is $dv/dt = 2/(1+s)$. Find how far it has travelled when its speed is 1 m/sec.

(4) A body moves from the origin with an initial speed of 2 m/sec, and its equation of motion is $3dv/dt = s$. Find how far it has travelled when its speed is 10 m/sec.

(5) A body of mass 3 kg experiences a force equal to $2s$, where $s$ is its distance from the origin. It is at rest at the origin, and is displaced slightly. Find its velocity when it has moved 2 m.

(6) A body of mass 1 kg experiences a force of $1/s^2$, directed towards the origin, where $s$ is its distance from the origin. It starts 2 m away from the origin with a speed of 1 m/sec towards the origin. Find (a) its velocity when it is $\frac{1}{2}$ m from the origin (b) the time it takes to reach this position.

(7) A planet has radius $R$. When a particle is $r$ from the centre the acceleration due to gravity towards the centre is $gR^2/r^2$. A body is projected from the surface of the planet with speed $u$. Show that when it has come to rest its distance $r$ from the centre of the planet is given by $r = 2gR^2/(2gR - u^2)$.

(8) A particle is projected from the surface of the earth at 3,000 m/sec. Use Question 7 to find the greatest height it reaches. (Ignore air resistance: take $R$ to be $6.4 \times 10^6$ m.)

(9) Use Question 7 to find the "escape velocity" from the earth, i.e. the velocity a particle must have to escape completely from the earth's gravitational field.

## 33.3 Examination Questions

(1) A particle moves in a straight line so that its speed is inversely proportional to $(t+1)$, where $t$ is the time in seconds for which it has been moving. After 2 seconds, the particle has a retardation of $10/9$ m/s$^2$. Calculate the distance moved in the first second of the motion.

[L]

(2) A particle moves in a straight line with variable velocity. When its displacement from a fixed point O on the line is $x$ its velocity is $v$. Show that the acceleration is then $v\,dv/dx$

The particle is projected from O with velocity $u$ (where $u > 0$) and moves under the action of a force directed towards O and proportional to $v^{3/2}$. When $x = a$ the velocity of the particle is $u/4$. Find its velocity when $x = 4a/3$.

[JMB]

(3) Given that $v = \dfrac{dx}{dt}$, show that $\dfrac{dv}{dt} = \dfrac{d(\frac{1}{2}v^2)}{dx}$.

A particle of mass 0.1 kg moves in a straight path under the action of a variable force $F$, such that when the particle is at distance $x$ metres from a fixed point O on the path, the force $F$ has magnitude $0.4/x^3$ newtons, and acts towards O. If $v$ m s$^{-1}$ is the speed at time $t$ seconds, and the particle starts (at $t = 0$) from position $x = 1$ with initial speed $v = 2$ (in the direction of $x$ increasing), show that

(i)   $v = 2/x$   (ii)   after 2 seconds $x$ has increased to 3.

Find the loss of kinetic energy as the particle moves from $x = 1$ to $x = 3$, and *verify* that this is the work done by $F$ in retarding the particle over this interval.

[SMP]

(4) A train of mass $2.4 \times 10^5$ kg travelling at a speed $v$ m s$^{-1}$ on a horizontal track experiences a resistance of $40(100 + bv)$ N. The engine exerts a constant force of $F$ newtons. When the train is travelling at a constant speed of

20 m s$^{-1}$ the power output of the engine is $1.6 \times 10^5$ watts. Find $F$ and $b$. If the train starts from rest,

  i.   how long does it take to reach speed 10 m s$^{-1}$?

 ii.   how far has it travelled when its speed reaches 10 m s$^{-1}$?

[NI]

(5)

a. A particle $P$ moves along the $x$-axis with acceleration $6e^{-3t}$ at time $t$. Its velocity at time $t$ is denoted by $v$. When $t = 0, v = 1$. Find the value of $t$ when $v = 2$. Find also the limiting value of the speed as $t$ becomes very large.

b. At time $t$ the displacement from the origin O of a particle $Q$ of mass $m$ moving on the $x$-axis is $x$ and its velocity is $v$. The particle moves under the action of a force directed towards O and of magnitude $F$ given by

$$F = \begin{cases} mn^2x & \text{when } x \geq a, \\ mn^2x^3/a^2 & \text{when } x \leq a, \end{cases}$$

where $n$ is a positive constant. At time $t = 0$, the particle is released from rest at the point where $x = 2a$. Show that when it reaches the point where $x = a$ its speed $V$ satisfies the equation

$$V^2 = 3a^2n^2.$$

Find the speed of the particle when it reaches O.

[C]

(6) A particle moves along the $x$-axis, with an acceleration in the positive $x$ direction of $k[3a^2/x^2 - 1]$, where $k$ and $a$ are positive constants. When $x = 2a$ the particle has a speed $(ka)^{\frac{1}{2}}$ in the positive $x$ direction. Find the speed of the particle in terms of $x$, $a$ and $k$ and determine the maximum and minimum values of $x$.

The table shows, for particular values of $a$ and $k$, approximate values of the speed $v$ m s$^{-1}$ of the particle and the corresponding values of $x$, measured in metres.

| x | 12.5 | 15 | 17.5 | 20 | 22.5 |
|---|------|-----|------|-----|------|
| v | 1/54 | 1/45 | 1/43 | 1/45 | 1/49 |

Show that the time taken for $x$ to increase from 12.5 to 22.5 is given by $t = \int_{12.5}^{22.5} \frac{dx}{v}$ and use Simpson's rule to estimate this time.

[AEB 1986]

## COMMON ERRORS

a. Do not forget the constant of integration. It is often the most important part of the solution. In a numerical example the constant can be found from the initial conditions.

b. Do not try to integrate a function of $s$ with respect to $t$. That is, do not attempt to evaluate $\int f(s)\,dt$. Usually writing $v\,dv/ds$ in place of $dv/dt$ will help you to avoid this.

c. Be careful with signs. If a body experiences a force *towards* the origin, then its acceleration *away* from the origin is negative.

# 34 Circular Motion

If a body is moving round a circle, the angle (in radians) through which the radius passes per second is the *angular velocity*.

If the circle has radius $r$ and the angular velocity is $\omega$ then the speed $v$ of the body is $\omega r$.

A body moving in a circle of radius $r$, with angular velocity $\omega$ or speed $v$ accelerates towards the centre of the circle at $\omega^2 r$ or $v^2/r$. This is the *centripetal acceleration*.

The force which produces the centripetal acceleration is the *centripetal force*.

## 34.1 Two-dimensional Problems

### 34.1.1 Examples

(1)     A body of mass 2 kg is on a smooth horizontal table, and moves in a circle at the end of a light string of length $1\frac{1}{2}$ m. The body makes 70 revolutions per minute. Find the tension in the string.

Solution  Convert 70 r.p.m. to angular velocity.

$$\omega = 70 \times 2\pi \div 60 \text{ rads/sec.}$$

The body accelerates at $r\omega^2$ m/sec$^2$.

**The tension in the string is mr$\omega^2$ = 161.2 N**

(2)  A turn-table rotates at 4 rads/sec. A body lies on the table, and the coefficient of friction between it and the table is $\frac{1}{4}$. Find the greatest distance it can be from the centre of the table.

Solution  Let the mass of the body be $m$, and let the body be on the point of slipping when the radius is $r$. The normal force is $mg$, and hence the frictional force is $\frac{1}{4}mg$. This force provides the centripetal acceleration.

$$\frac{1}{4}mg = mr4^2$$

**The greatest radius is $\frac{1}{4}$g/16 = 0.153 m.**

### 34.1.2 Exercises

(1) Convert the following to angular velocities:

(a)  24 revolutions per second  (b)  77 revolutions per minute

(c)  15° per second  (d)  1,000° per hour.

(2) Find the angular velocities of the following:

(a)  The hour hand of a clock  (b)  The minute hand of a clock

(c)  The earth about its axis  (d)  The earth about the sun.

(3) A turntable rotates at 40 rads/sec. Find the speed of a point 0.2 m from the centre.

(4) A roundabout rotates at 8 revolutions per minute. Find the speed of a child 2 m from the centre.

(5) A roundabout rotates so that it takes 12 seconds to make a full circle. Find the speed of a child 1 m from the centre.

(6) A body of mass 3 kg moves in a horizontal circle of radius $2\frac{1}{2}$ m with angular speed 12. Find its acceleration. Find the horizontal force experienced by the body.

(7) A body of mass 0.3 kg moves in a horizontal circle with angular speed 3 under a horizontal force of 12 N. Find the radius of the circle.

(8) A body of mass 1.5 kg moves in a horizontal circle of radius $1\frac{1}{4}$ m under a horizontal force of 13 N. Find its angular velocity.

(9) A turntable rotates at 2 rads/sec. The coefficient of friction between it and a body on it is $\frac{1}{2}$. Find the greatest possible distance of the body from the centre.

(10) A turntable rotates at 40 r.p.m. A body can just stay on the table at a distance of 12 cm from the centre. Find the coefficient of friction.

(11) The coefficient of friction between a body and a turntable is $\frac{3}{8}$. It is on the point of slipping when it is 5 cm from the centre. Find the angular speed of the turntable.

(12) The coefficient of friction between the tyres of a car and the ground is 0.9. It travels in a horizontal circle.

  a.  Find the greatest speed with which it can go round a circle of radius 50 m.

  b.  What is the least radius of a circle which it can go round at a speed of 20 m/sec?

(13) A car can just go round a circle of radius 45 m at 25 m/sec. Find the coefficient of friction between the tyres and the ground.

(14) Bodies $A$ and $B$ of masses 3 kg and 4 kg are connected by a light string. $A$ lies on a smooth horizontal table. The string passes through a hole in the table and supports $B$. If $A$ moves in a horizontal circle of radius $1\frac{1}{2}$ m find its speed.

(15) The "Rotor" at a funfair consists of a vertical cylinder of radius $2\frac{1}{2}$ m, which rotates at 2 rad/sec. Customers stand against the inside wall of the cylinder, and the floor gradually sinks away. Find the least coefficient of friction between the customers and the wall if they are to remain fixed on it.

## 34.2 Three-dimensional Problems

### 34.2.1 Examples

(1)    A conical pendulum consists of a mass $m$ suspended by a string of length $h$ from a fixed point. The mass performs horizontal circles at $\omega$ rads/sec. Find the angle the string makes with the vertical.

Solution    The mass does not move vertically. Hence, resolving vertically:

$$T \cos \theta = mg.$$

Resolving horizontally:

$$T \sin \theta = mh \sin \theta \omega^2.$$

Eliminate $T$ by dividing the first equation by the second.

$$\cos \theta = g/h\omega^2$$

**The angle is $\cos^{-1} g/h\omega^2$**

(2)　　　A race track of radius 50 m is banked at 20° to the horizontal. If the coefficient of friction between a car's tyres and the track is 0.9, find the greatest speed at which it can go round the track without slipping.

Solution　　Resolving vertically:

$$R \cos 20° - F \sin 20° = mg$$

Resolving horizontally:

$$R \sin 20° + F \cos 20° = mv^2/50$$

If it is about to slip, $F = 0.9R$. Eliminate $R$ by dividing the second equation by the first:

$$\frac{v^2}{50g} = \frac{\sin 20° + 0.9 \cos 20°}{\cos 20° - 0.9 \sin 20°}$$

**The maximum speed is 30.3 m/sec**

## 34.2.2 Exercises

(1) A conical pendulum consists of a mass 0.5 kg at the end of a string of length 1.2 m. It performs horizontal circles at 3 rads/sec. Find the angle the string makes with the vertical.

(2) If the conical pendulum of Question 1 rotates so that the string is at 30° to the vertical, find its angular velocity.

(3) A conical pendulum makes an angle of 20° to the vertical, and rotates at an angular velocity of 0.8 rads/sec. Find the length of the string.

(4) Two strings each of length 1.5 m are attached to a mass of 1 kg. Their free ends are attached to points $A$ and $B$, where $A$ is 2.4 m vertically above $B$. Find the least angular speed with which the mass can rotate if the lower string is not to become slack.

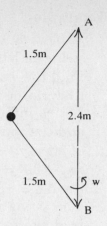

(5) If, in Question 4, the mass rotates at 4 rads/sec, find the tension in the lower string.

(6) In Question 4 the mass rotates so that the tension in the upper string is twice that in the lower string. Find the angular velocity.

(7) Point $A$ is 1.2 m above $B$. A string of length 1.8 m is attached to $A$ and $B$, and a mass of 2 kg is smoothly threaded on it. The mass rotates around $AB$ at the same level as $B$. Find its angular speed.

(8) A circular race track of radius 50 m is banked at 30°. Find the speed at which a car travelling round the track has no tendency to side-slip.

(9) If, in Question 8, the coefficient between tyres and track is 0.8, find the greatest speed with which a car can go round the track.

(10) If, in Question 8, a car can just go round the track at 40 m/sec, find the coefficient of friction between its tyres and the track.

(11) A race-track is banked at 25°, and the coefficient of friction between tyre and track is $\frac{1}{2}$. If the greatest safe speed is 35 m/sec find the radius of the track.

(12) A race track is of radius 60 m. The coefficient of friction is $\frac{3}{4}$. At what angle should the track be banked if the fastest speed is 30 m/sec?

(13) A particle performs horizontal circles on the smooth inner surface of a sphere of radius 10 cm. If the particle is 5 cm below the centre of the sphere find its speed.

(14) A particle moves in horizontal circles round the inner surface of a smooth vertical cone of angle 30°, which is held with its axis vertical and its point downwards. If the body moves at 3 m/sec find its height above the point.

## 34.3 Motion in a Vertical Circle

If a particle moves freely in a vertical circle then its velocity will vary. The velocity is best found by considerations of energy.

## 34.3.1 Example

(1)    A particle of mass $m$ kg hangs at the end of a light string of length 1.4 m, the other end of which is fixed. Find the least velocity the particle must be given if it is to perform vertical circles.

Solution    Let $v_b$ and $v_t$ be the speeds at the bottom and the top respectively. By conservation of energy:

$$mg \times 2.8 = \tfrac{1}{2}mv_b^2 - \tfrac{1}{2}mv_t^2$$
$$g \times 5.6 = v_b^2 - v_t^2$$

The string is most likely to collapse when the particle is at the top. Resolving vertically:

$$mg + T = mv_t^2/1.4$$

Vertical circles will be performed provided that $T \geq 0$.

$$mv_t^2/1.4 \geq mg$$

$$v_t^2 \geq 9.8 \times 1.4$$

$$v_b^2 \geq 9.8 \times 1.4 + 9.8 \times 5.6$$

**The least velocity is 8.28 m/sec**

## 34.3.2 Exercises

(1) A particle hangs at the end of a light string of length 0.6 m. Find the least velocity it must be given to perform vertical circles.

(2) A particle hangs at the end of a light string, and when it is given an initial speed of 6 m/sec it just performs vertical circles. Find the length of the string.

(3) A hollow cylinder with inside radius 20 cm is held with its axis horizontal. A smooth stone makes vertical circles inside it: find the least speed that the stone has at its lowest point.

(4) A roller-coaster contains a vertical circle of radius 10 m. Find the least speed that the cars must have at the bottom of the circle if they are not to fall off the track at the top of the circle.

(5) A body of mass 2 kg is at the end of a string of length 2 m. It is given a speed of 20 m/sec. Find (a) the speed at the top of the swing (b) the tension in the string at the top of the swing.

(6) Find the speed of the body of Question 5 when the string is horizontal. Find also the tension in the string at this time.

(7) A body of mass 1 kg is tied to the end of a string of length 1.4 m. It is given a velocity of 1 m/sec. Find (a) the greatest angle $\theta$ the string makes with the vertical (b) the tension in the string when the string makes $\frac{1}{2}\theta$ with the vertical.

(8) A smooth wire is bent into a vertical circle of radius 0.5 m. A bead of mass 0.05 kg is threaded on it. At the lowest point of the wire the bead is given a speed of 5 m/sec. Find its speed at the top of the circle and the reaction of the wire.

(9) The bead of Question 9 is instead given a velocity of 2 m/sec. Find the greatest height the bead rises to. Find the reaction of the wire when it has reached half this height.

## 34.4 Examination Questions

(1) A particle $B$ of mass 200 g is attached to two light inextensible strings $AB$ and $BC$, where $AB = BC = 0.5$ m. The ends $A$ and $C$ are held fixed so that $A$ is vertically above $C$ and $AC = 0.6$ m. The particle is made to rotate in a horizontal circle.

a. Calculate the tensions in both strings if the angular speed is $3\sqrt{10}$ rad/s.

b. Calculate the minimum angular speed if both strings are to remain taut.

[AEB add 1986]

(2) Write down the magnitude and indicate the direction of the acceleration of a particle travelling in a fixed circular path of radius $r$ at a constant speed $v$.

A satellite is in steady circular orbit at height $h$ above the surface of the earth. At this height the gravitational pull on the satellite has magnitude $GmM/(R + h)^2$, where $m$ is the mass of the satellite, $M$ is the mass of the earth, $R$ is the radius of the earth, and $G$ is constant. Find the speed of the satellite, and show that it will take a time

$$2\pi(R + h)^{3/2}(GM)^{-\frac{1}{2}}$$

to travel once round the orbit.

[SMP]

(3) 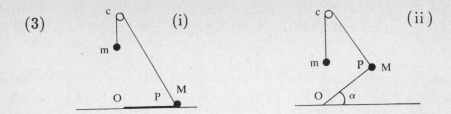 (i) (ii)

A light inextensible string has one end fastened to a fixed point at $O$. A particle of mass $m$ is attached to the other end of the string. The string passes through a small smooth ring at the fixed point $C$, vertically above $O$, and carries a smooth bead $P$ of mass $M$, which is free to move on the string. The system rotates about $OC$ with constant angular velocity $\omega$.

a. Given that the bead moves on a smooth horizontal plane, in a circle of radius $r$ and centre $O$(see Fig. (i)), with $O\hat{P}C = 60°$, show that $m/M \leq 2/\sqrt{3}$ and that $m/M = 2r\omega^2/3g$.

b. Given that the bead moves, in a horizontal circle of radius $R$, above the plane (see Fig. (ii)), with $O\hat{P}C$ a right-angle and with $OP$ inclined to the horizontal at an angle $\alpha$, where $\cos \alpha = \frac{4}{5}$, show that $m = 5M$ and that $R\omega^2 = 7g$.

[C]

(4) A small bead $P$ of mass $m$ is threaded on a smooth thin wire, in the form of a circle of radius $a$ and centre $O$, which is fixed in a vertical plane. The bead is initially at the lowest point $A$ of the circle and is projected along the wire with a velocity which is just sufficient to carry it to the highest point. Denoting the angle $POA$ by $\theta$, find, in terms of $m, g$ and $\theta$, the magnitude of the reaction of the wire on the bead.

Express $d\theta/dt$, where $t$ denotes time, in the form $C\cos(\theta/2)$, where $C$ is a constant. Show that the time taken for the bead to reach the horizontal diameter is $(a/g)^{\frac{1}{2}}\ln(\sqrt{2}+1)$

[JMB]

(5) One end of a light inextensible string of length $a$ is fastened to a fixed point O. The other end of the string is fastened to a particle $P$ of mass $m$. The particle is projected vertically upwards with speed $u$ from the position in which the particle is at the same level as O, the string being taut. When $OP$ makes an acute angle $\theta$ with the upward vertical through O, speed of the particle is $v$ and the tension in the string is $T$. Find expressions for $v^2$ and $T$ in terms of $m, a, u, \theta$ and $g$, assuming that the string is still taut.

If $u^2 = \frac{1}{2}(3\sqrt{3})ag$, show that the string becomes slack when $\theta = 30°$ and verify that in the subsequent motion the string again becomes taut when $OP$ is horizontal.

[O&C]

## COMMON ERRORS

### (1) Angular Velocity

Do not measure angular velocity in degrees. It must be measured in radians.

### (2) Centripetal Force

a. A body moving in a circle is accelerating towards the centre. This must be provided by the *centripetal* force. It is incorrect to put in a *centrifugal* force.

b. When working out the forces acting on a body moving in a circle, do not forget that the body is accelerating towards the centre.

### (3) Motion in a Vertical Circle

For a body on the end of a string to reach the top of a circle, it is not sufficient for it to have enough energy to get there. It must also have sufficient speed for the tension in the string to be non-zero at the top.

# 35 Elasticity and Oscillations

## 35.1 Elasticity

A material which changes its shape under tension is said to be *elastic*.

If an elastic string under tension $T$ extends by a length $x$, then *Hooke's Law* states:

The tension is proportional to the extension. $T \propto x$.

The constant $k$ of proportionality is the *spring rate*.

For different lengths of the same string, $k$ is inversely proportional to the length. The constant $\lambda$ of proportionality is the *modulus of elasticity*.

$T = \lambda x/L$, where $L$ is the unstretched length of the string.

Energy is stored in the string in the form of *elastic potential energy*. If a string of length $L$ and modulus $\lambda$ is stretched by $x$, the energy stored is:

$$\frac{1}{2}\frac{\lambda}{L}x^2.$$

## 35.1.1 Examples

(1)    An elastic string of natural length 20 cm stretches to 25 cm under a load of 1 kg. Find the modulus of elasticity. What will its length be under a load of $2\frac{1}{2}$ kg?

Solution    Here the extension is 5 cm. Using Hooke's Law:

$$1 \times g = \lambda \times 0.05/0.2.$$

**The modulus of elasticity is 4g = 39.2 N**

If the load is $2\frac{1}{2}$, then the extension $x$ is given by:

$$2\frac{1}{2}g = 4gx/0.2. \text{ Hence } x = 0.125 \text{ m.}$$

**The new length will be 32.5 cm.**

(2)    A man of mass 80 kg jumps off a bridge, tied to the bridge by an elastic rope of natural length 20 m and modulus 1568 N. Find the greatest depth that he reaches, and his depth below the bridge when he stops bouncing.

Solution    Suppose that his greatest depth occurs when the string is stretched by $x$ m. The loss of gravitational potential energy must equal the gain of elastic potential energy.

$$80 \times g \times (x + 20) = \frac{1}{2} \times 1568/20x^2$$

$$x^2 - 20x - 400 = 0$$

$$x = 32.4\text{m or } -12.4\text{m.}$$

**His greatest depth is 52.4 m below the bridge**
When he stops bouncing his weight must equal the tension in the rope. Let $y$ be the extension when this occurs:

$$80g = 1568/20y. \text{ Hence } y = 10 \text{ m.}$$

**When he stops bouncing he will be 30 m below the bridge**

## 35.1.2 Exercises

(1) An elastic string of natural length 2 m and modulus 40 N supports a mass of 3 kg. Find the extension of the string.

(2) An elastic string of unstretched length 0.4 m and modulus 49 N supports a load. If the extension is 5 cm find the load.

(3) An elastic string of natural length 0.6 m extends 9 cm under a load of 0.5 kg. Find its modulus of elasticity.

(4) An elastic string of modulus of elasticity 49 N extends by 30 cm under a load of 2 kg. Find its natural length.

(5) When a mass of 2 kg hangs from the end of an elastic string its length doubles. Find its modulus of elasticity.

(6) A spring of natural length 10 cm is compressed 0.1 cm when it supports a mass of 5 kg. Find the modulus of elasticity.

(7) The length of a string is 1.2 m under a load of 4 kg, and 1.4 m under a load of 6 kg. Find its natural length and its modulus of elasticity.

(8) A string, of natural length 1.5 m and modulus 19.6 N, is tied to a similar string, and a mass of 1.3 kg is suspended from the free end of the second string. Find the total extension of the strings.

(9) The two strings of Question 8 are joined together at both ends. A mass of 1.3 kg is hung from the combined string. Find the extension.

(10) Point A is 3 m above point B. Two elastic strings, of natural length 1 m and moduli 19.6 N, are tied at $A$ and $B$. The free ends of the strings are tied to a mass of 0.5 kg. Find the height of the mass above $B$.

(11) Find the energy stored in an elastic string of length 50 cm and modulus 9.8 N when it is extended by 10 cm.

(12) Find the energy stored in an elastic string of length 2 m and modulus 49 N when it supports a mass of 3 kg.

(13) A spring of length 20 cm and modulus 98 N is compressed by 5 cm. It fires a mass of 10 grams. Assuming that all the energy is imparted to the mass, find its velocity after it is fired.

(14) A catapult consists of two parallel elastic strings, each of natural length 15 cm and modulus 49 N. A 10 gram stone is placed between the strings and they are pulled back 20 cm and released. Assuming that all the energy is imparted to the stone, find its initial velocity.

(15) A body of mass 0.1 kg travelling horizontally at 25 m/sec is brought to rest by a spring of natural length 40 cm and modulus 490 N. Find the compression of the spring.

(16) A mass of 4 kg is tied to the end of an elastic string of length 2 m and modulus 98 N. The mass is thrown horizontally at 12 m/sec on a smooth surface. Find the extension of the string when it is brought to rest by the string.

(17) A mass of 40 kg hangs at the end of an elastic rope of natural length 10 m and modulus 4900 N. Find the extension of the string. It is then given a downward velocity of 1 m/sec. Find the greatest depth to which it falls.

(18) A mass of 60 kg is tied to the end of an elastic string of natural length 15 m and modulus 2450 N. The other end is tied to the top of a building, and the mass is dropped. Find (a) the greatest depth it sinks to (b) the speed with which it is moving when it has fallen 20 m (c) its depth when it stops bouncing.

(19) A mass of 20 kg rests on top of a spring of natural length 0.2 m and modulus 490 N. Find the compression of the spring. The mass is then pushed down a further 2 cm and released. Find the speed of the mass when it passes through its original position.

## 35.2 Simple Harmonic Motion

If a body moves to and from about a fixed point, it is *oscillating* about that point.

Oscillations in which the motion of a body is given by $x = a \sin(\omega t + \varphi)$ is called *simple harmonic motion. (S.H.M.).*

The motion can also be written as $x = A \cos \omega t + B \sin \omega t$, where $a^2 = A^2 + B^2$ and $\tan \varphi = A/B$.

The *amplitude* of the motion is $a$.

The *period* of the motion is $2\pi/\omega$.

The *frequency* of the motion is $\omega/2\pi$.

The *phase angle* of the motion is $\varphi$.

### 35.2.1 Example

A body executes simple harmonic motion, with amplitude 3 cm and period $2\pi/5$ seconds. When $t = 0$ the displacement is zero. Find (a) the value of the displacement at time $t$ (b) the maximum velocity (c) the time for it to reach 1 cm.

Solution

a. Let $x$ be the displacement. Then $a = 3$ and $\omega = 5$. When $t = 0$ $x = 0$, and hence $\varphi = 0$. Write down the equation for $x$:

$$x = 3 \sin 5t.$$

b.     Differentiate $x$ to find the velocity.

$$dx/dt = 15\cos 5t$$

**The maximum velocity is 15 cm/sec.**

c.     Put $x = 1$.

$$1 = 3\sin 5t$$

$$\sin 5t = \frac{1}{3}. \; t = \frac{1}{5}\sin^{-1}\frac{1}{3}.$$

**It reaches 1 cm after 0.068 secs.**

### 35.2.2 Exercises

(1) For each of the following equations of simple harmonic motion, write down the amplitude, the period and the phase angle.

(a)   $x = 3\sin(2t + 1)$     (b)   $x = 4\sin(\frac{1}{2}t - 2)$

(c)   $x = 3\cos t + 4\sin t$   (d)   $x = 12\cos 3t - 5\sin 3t$

(e)   $x = 2\cos(3t - \frac{1}{4}\pi)$   (f)   $x = \cos(\frac{1}{2}t + \pi/6) + 2\sin(\frac{1}{2}t + \pi/6)$

(2) A point moves with S.H.M. of period $\pi$, and its maximum velocity is 3. Find its amplitude.

(3) A point starts from the origin and performs S.H.M. with period $\pi/3$ and amplitude 10. Find the displacement in terms of time.

(4) A point moving with S.H.M. has maximum velocity 12 and amplitude 4. Find its period.

(5) A point moving with S.H.M. has frequency 6 and maximum velocity 8. Find its amplitude.

(6) A point moves with S.H.M. of period $\pi$. If its amplitude is 10 cm find the time it takes to travel 5 cm from the origin.

(7) A point moves with S.H.M of period $\frac{1}{4}\pi$. It takes 0.1 secs to go 5 cm from the origin. Find its amplitude.

(8) A point moves with S.H.M. of amplitude 6 cm. It takes 3 secs to travel 3 cm from the origin. Find its period.

(9) A point moves with S.H.M. of period $\pi/3$ and amplitude 10 cm. Find its distance from the origin when its speed is 4 cm/sec.

(10) A point executes S.H.M. with period $4\pi$ and amplitude 20 cm. What is its maximum velocity? How long does it take for its speed to change from zero to 4 cm/sec?

## 35.3 Systems which Perform S.H.M.

Let $x$ measure the displacement of a system. If $d^2x/dt^2 = -\omega^2 x$, then the system performs S.H.M. of period $2\pi/\omega$.

A heavy particle which swings at the end of a light string is a *simple pendulum*.

### 35.3.1 Examples

(1) A simple pendulum consists of a mass of 0.2 kg at the end of a light string of length 1.2 m. Find the period of small oscillations.

Solution  Suppose the mass is pulled aside through a distance $x$. Resolving perpendicular to the string:
$0.2 \, d^2x/dt^2 = -0.2 \times g \sin\theta$.
If $\theta$ is small, then $\sin\theta \simeq x/1.2$.

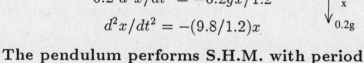

$$0.2 \, d^2x/dt^2 = -0.2gx/1.2$$
$$d^2x/dt^2 = -(9.8/1.2)x$$

**The pendulum performs S.H.M. with period**
**$2\pi\sqrt{(1.2/9.8)} = 2.2$ seconds.**

(2) An elastic string of unstretched length 1.5 m and modulus 21 N supports a mass of 0.1 kg. It is displaced slightly: find the period of the following oscillations.

Solution  When it is hanging in equilibrium, the extension $e$ is given by:

$$0.1 \times 9.8 = 21/1.5 \times e. \text{ Hence } e = 0.07 \text{ m}.$$

If it falls a further distance $x$, the equation of motion is:
$$0.1 \, d^2x/dt^2 = 0.1 \times 9.8 - 21/1.5(e + x)$$

The constant terms on the right hand side cancel out. Divide both sides by 0.1 to obtain:

$$d^2x/dt^2 = -140x$$

**The period of the oscillations is**
**$2\pi/\sqrt{140} = 0.53$ secs.**

## 35.3.2 Exercises

(1) A simple pendulum consists of a mass of 1 kg at the end of a string of length 2 m. Find the period of small oscillations.

(2) A simple pendulum has period 5 seconds. Find its length.

(3) On a certain planet a simple pendulum of length 1.5 m has period 3 secs. Find the acceleration due to gravity on that planet.

(4) Through long use the length of a simple pendulum increases by 1%. Find the percentage increase in its period.

(5) The bob of a simple pendulum of length 1 m has a velocity of $\frac{1}{2}$ cm/sec at its lowest point. Find the amplitude of the displacement of the bob.

(6) A simple pendulum of length 1.4 m swings through a total angle of $2°$. Find the maximum speed of its bob.

(7) A mass of 5 kg hangs from an elastic string of length 0.5 m and modulus 49 N. If it is displaced slightly downward, find the frequency of its oscillations.

(8) A mass of 10 kg lies on a smooth horizontal table, and is attached to a spring of length 0.4 m and modulus 500 N. The mass is given an initial velocity of 0.02 m/sec. Find the period and amplitude of the following oscillations.

(9) A mass of 1 kg lies on a smooth horizontal table, and is attached to a spring of length 0.2 m and modulus 100 N. It is pulled through a distance of 1 cm. Find the period of the following oscillations, and its maximum velocity.

(10) A smooth wire is bent into the shape of a circle of radius $a$, and is fixed in a vertical plane. A small bead is threaded on the wire, and is disturbed slightly from the bottom position. Find the frequency of the following oscillations.

(11) A cube of side $a$ cm has a uniform density of $\rho$. ($\rho < 1$). It floats in a large lake, with two faces horizontal. If it is pushed a small distance $x$ downwards, show that the net upthrust is $a^2xg$. Hence find the period with which it bobs up and down in the water.

## 35.4 Examination Questions

(1) State Hooke's law.

a. A particle of mass 2 kg is attached to one end of a spring of natural length 0.5 m and modulus of elasticity 160 N. The other end is fastened to a point on a smooth horizontal table. If the particle is made to describe circles on the table at $4/\pi$ revolutions per second, find the extension of the spring.

b. A particle of mass 5 kg describes horizontal circles suspended on the end of an extended elastic string whose natural length is 0.16

m and modulus of elasticity is 400 N. The string is extended by 0.04 m beyond its natural length. Find the inclination of the string to the vertical and the speed with which the particle is rotating.

(Assume that the acceleration due to gravity is 10 m s$^{-2}$)

[NI]

(2) A uniform rod $AB$, of length $2a$ and mass $m$, rests in equilibrium with its lower end $A$ on a rough horizontal floor. Equilibrium is maintained by a horizontal elastic string, of natural length $a$ and modulus $\lambda$. One end of the string is attached to $B$ and the other end to a point vertically above $A$. Given that $\theta$, where $\theta < \pi/3$, is the inclination of the rod to the horizontal, show that the magnitude of the tension in the string is $\frac{1}{2}mg \cot \theta$.

Prove also that $2\lambda = (mg \cot \theta)/(2 \cos \theta - 1)$.

Given that the system is in limiting equilibrium and that the coefficient of friction between the floor and the rod is $\frac{2}{3}$, find $\tan \theta$. Hence show that $\lambda = 10mg/9$.

[L]

(3) A uniform rod $AB$ of length $2a$ and weight $W$ has its ends joined by a light elastic string of natural length $a$ and modulus of elasticity $\lambda$. The string passes over a small smooth peg at C and the rod rests in equilibrium at an angle 30° to the horizontal with $A$ in contact with a rough horizontal plane. C is vertically above A and $AC = 2a$. Show that (i) $\lambda = W/6$; (ii) $\mu \geq \sqrt{3}$, where $\mu$ is the coefficient of friction between the rod and the plane. Find the magnitude and direction of the force that the peg exerts on the string.

[SUJB]

(4) A particle of mass 0.02 kg is performing simple harmonic motion with centre O, period 6 s and amplitude 2 m. Find, correct to 2 significant figures in each case,

  i.  the maximum speed $V$ of the particle;

  ii.  the distance of the particle from O when its speed is $0.9V$;

  iii.  the magnitude of the force on the particle when it is 1 m from O.

Show also that the power exerted by the force on the particle is a periodic function of time, and state its period.

(Simple harmonic motion formulae may be quoted without proof.)

[MEI]

(5) A particle $P$ moves along the $x$-axis so that its displacement $x$ from the origin at time $t$ satisfies the differential equation

$$\frac{d^2x}{dt^2} + 9x = 18.$$

At times $t = \pi/6, \pi/3$ the values of $x$ are 6, 5 respectively. Assuming that the solution to the equation is $x = A\cos nt + B\sin nt + c$, find values for $A, B, c$ and $n$.

Prove that the solution may be written in the form

$$x = 5\sin(3t - \alpha) + 2,$$

where $\alpha$ is the angle in the first quadrant such that $\tan\alpha = \frac{3}{4}$.

Assuming that the motion starts at $t = 0$, determine

  i.  the initial displacement and the greatest displacement

 ii.  the initial speed and the greatest speed.

Draw rough sketches of $x$ and of $dx/dt$ against $t$ in the range $0 \le t \le \frac{2}{3}\pi$.

[O&C]

(6) A point $P$ moves along the line $A'OA$, where $A'O = OA = a$ such that when $OP = x$, its acceleration $d^2x/dt^2 = -\omega^2 x$. Without assuming any formulae relating to simple harmonic motion show that

  i.  if the speed $v = 0$ when $x = a$ then
$$v^2 = \omega^2(a^2 - x^2),$$

 ii.  a solution of the differential equation such that $v = 0$ when $t = 0$
is $x = a\cos\omega t$.

At time $t = 0$ $P$ is at $A$ and it moves a distance of 1 m to $B$ where its speed is 6 m s$^{-1}$ and after moving a further 1 m to $C$ its speed is 8 m s$^{-1}$. If $C$ and $B$ are between $O$ and $A$ find the values of $a$ and $\omega$ and the time taken for $P$ to move from $B$ to $C$.

A rough horizontal platform moves horizontally according to the above law with these values of $a$ and $\omega$. When the platform is instantaneously at rest a weight is placed on it. If the coefficient of friction between the weight and the platform is 0.8 and the acceleration due to gravity is 9.8 m s$^{-2}$ determine whether the weight slides or remains at relative rest.

[SUJB]

(7) A light elastic string $AB$ obeying Hooke's law is of natural length 1 m and has the end $A$ fixed. When a particle of mass 2 kg is attached to the string at $B$ and is allowed to hang freely, the string is extended by a length of 0.14 m. Find the modulus of elasticity, stating the units in which it is measured.

The particle is pulled down a further 0.2 m and is then released from rest at time $t = 0$. Show that until the string becomes slack, the motion is simple harmonic. Show also that the particle passes through the equilibrium position after approximately 0.19 seconds and find the speed of the particle at that time.

From energy considerations or otherwise, find how high above the point of release the particle reaches during the subsequent motion.

[W]

## COMMON ERRORS
### (1) Hooke's Law
Do not confuse the spring rate and the modulus of elasticity. If you are given the modulus $\lambda$ then you must divide by the natural length in order to use Hooke's law.
### (2) S H M
When dealing with simple harmonic motion, all angles must be measured in radians. Do not measure them in degrees.

# STATISTICS

# 36 Probability

The *probability* of an event is a measure of our belief that it occurs. The probability of an event $A$ is written $P(A)$.

If $A$ is certain then $P(A) = 1$.

If $A$ is impossible then $P(A) = 0$.

If there are $n$ equally likely outcomes of an experiment, then the probability of each is $^1/n$.

The set of all the possible outcomes of an experiment is the *sample space*.

If two events cannot happen together, then they are *exclusive*. If events are exclusive then the probability that one or the other occurs is the sum of their probabilities.

$P(A$ or $B) = P(A) + P(B)$, provided that $A$ and $B$ are exclusive.

## 36.1 Simple Probability

A *Tree Diagram* shows the probabilities of successive events.

### 36.1.1 Examples

(1)   Two fair dice are rolled. What is the probability that the sum is 5?

Solution   There are $6 \times 6 = 36$ possible pairs of values for the scores on the two dice. The ones which give a total of 5 are:

$$(1,4), (2,3), (3,2), (4,1).$$

**The probability of a total of 5 is $\frac{4}{36} = \frac{1}{9}$**

(2)   A bag contains 5 red and 6 black marbles. Two are drawn without replacement. What is the probability that:

(a)   Both are red   (b)   They are different colours.

Solution   Construct the tree diagram as shown. The top branch corresponds to both marbles being red. Multiply the probabilities along this branch.

a.   **The probability that both are red is** $(\frac{5}{11}) \times (\frac{4}{10}) = \frac{2}{11}$
The two middle branches correspond to the marbles having different colours.
b. **P(Different colours)**
$= (\frac{5}{11}) \times (\frac{6}{10}) + (\frac{6}{11}) \times (\frac{5}{10}) = \frac{6}{11}$

### 36.1.2 Exercises

(1) Two fair dice are rolled. Find the probabilities that:

(a)   Both are sixes        (b)   The total is 2

(c)   The total is 7        (d)   The first is greater than the second

(e)   A "double" is thrown   (f)   At least one of the dice is a six.

(2) Two cards are drawn without replacement from a well-shuffled pack. Find the probabilities that:

(a)   The first is a heart   (b)   Both are hearts

(c) The first is a heart and the second is a spade (d) The first is a King and the second is a Queen.

(3) A bag contains 5 blue and 4 green counters. Two are drawn without replacement. Find the probabilities that:

(a)  Both are blue          (b)  They are the same colour

(c)  There is at least one blue   (d)  The second is green

(4) A sweet box contains 5 toffees, 6 liquorices and 8 chocolates. Two are drawn out. Find the probabilities that:

(a) The first is a toffee and the second is a chocolate.

(b)  At least one is a liquorice   (c)  Neither is a toffee

(5) Two fair dice are rolled. The score is the larger of the numbers showing. Find the probabilities that:

(a)  The score is 1   (b)  The score is 6

(6) Two children $A$ and $B$ each pick at random a single digit from 1 to 9. Find the probabilities that:

(a)  They pick the same number   (b)  $A$'s number is larger than $B$'s

(7) To start a certain board game a die is rolled until a six is obtained. Find the probabilities that:

(a)  A player starts on his first roll   (b)  He starts on his second roll

(c)  He starts on his third roll      (d)  He has not started by his fourth roll

(8) To start at darts a "double" must first be thrown. Albert has probability $\frac{1}{10}$ of throwing a double, and Beatrice has probability $\frac{1}{8}$. Albert throws first. Find the probabilities that:

(a) Both start on their first throw

(b) Beatrice starts on her second throw but Albert has not started by then.

## 36.2 Independent Events and Conditional Probability

Two events are *independent* if the truth of one of them does not alter the probability of the other.

If events $A$ and $B$ are independent then the probability of them both occuring is the product of their probabilities.

$$P(A\&B) = P(A) \times P(B)$$

The *conditional probability* of $A$ given $B$ is the probability of $A$, once it is known that $B$ is true.

The conditional probability of $A$ given $B$ is written $P(A|B)$. It is obtained from the formula:

$$P(A|B) = P(A\&B)/P(B).$$

If $A$ and $B$ are independent then $P(A|B) = P(A)$

### 36.2.1 Examples

(1)    Two cards are drawn without replacement from a pack. Events $A, B, C$ are as follows:

$A$ :    the first is a heart      $B$ :    the second is a heart

$C$ :    the second is a king

Which pairs of these events are independent?

Solution    If $A$ is true, then there is one less heart in the pack. The probability of $B$ is $\frac{12}{51} < \frac{1}{4}$. Hence $A$ and $B$ are not independent.

If $A$ is true then $C$ is neither more likely or less likely than before. Its probability is still $\frac{1}{13}$. Hence $A$ and $C$ are independent. Similarly the truth of $B$ does not alter the probability of $C$.

**The pairs $A$ and $C, B$ and $C$ are independent**

(2)    A woman travels to work by bus, car or on foot with probabilities $\frac{1}{6}, \frac{1}{3}, \frac{1}{2}$ respectively. For each type of transport her probabilities of being late are $\frac{1}{5}, \frac{1}{4}, \frac{1}{20}$ respectively. If she arrives late one morning, find the probability that she came by bus.

Solution    Here let $L$ be the event that she is late, and $B$ the event that she came by bus. Use the formula for conditional probability:

$$P(B|L) \quad = \quad \frac{P(B\&L)}{P(L)}$$

$$P(B|L) \quad = \quad \frac{\frac{1}{6} \times \frac{1}{5}}{\frac{1}{6} \times \frac{1}{5} + \frac{1}{3} \times \frac{1}{4} + \frac{1}{2} \times \frac{1}{20}}$$

**The probability that she came by bus is $\frac{4}{17}$**

### 36.2.2 Exercises

(1) Two cards are drawn from a pack without replacement.  Events $A, B, C, D$ are as follows:

$A$:    the first is an ace    $B$:    the second is an 8

$C$:    the first is red        $D$:    the second is a spade.

Which pairs of events are independent?

(2) Two dice are rolled. Events $A, B, C, D$ are as follows:

  $A$: the first is a 5   $B$: the total is 8

  $C$: the total is 7   $D$: the dice show the same number

Which pairs of events are independent?

(3) Two dice are rolled. Events $A, B, C, D$ are as follows:

  $A$: the total is 7           $B$: the second die is a 2

  $C$: both dice are less than 5  $D$: at least one die is a 6

Which pairs of events are independent?

(4) Three fair coins are spun. Events $A, B, C, D$ are as follows:

  $A$: the first coin is a head   $B$: all the coins are heads

  $C$: there is at least one tail  $D$: the first and last coins show the same.

Which pairs of events are independent?

(5) With events $A, B, C, D$ as defined in Question 1, find the following:

  (a)  $P(B|A)$  (b)  $P(D|C)$

(6) With $A, B, C, D$ defined as in Question 2, find the following:

  (a)  $P(A|B)$  (b)  $P(B|D)$

(7) With events $A, B, C, D$ as defined in Question 3, find the following:

  (a)  $P(A|B)$  (b)  $P(C|D)$

(8) With events $A, B, C, D$ as in Question 4, find the following:

  (a)  $P(B|A)$  (b)  $P(C|A)$

(9) A bag contains 5 red and 6 blue marbles. Two are drawn without replacement. If the second is red find the probability that the first was blue.

(10) In his drawer a man has 7 left shoes and 10 right shoes. He picks two out at random. Find the probabilities that:

a.  He has one left shoe and one right shoe.

b.  He has one left and one right, given that the first was a left.

c.  The second is a left, given that he has one left and one right.

(11) A man travels to work by bus, car and motorcycle with probabilities 0.4, 0.5, 0.1 respectively. With each type of transport his chances of an accident are $\frac{1}{500}, \frac{1}{50}, \frac{1}{10}$ respectively. Find the probabilities that:

a.  He goes by car and has an accident.

b.  He does not have an accident.

c.  He went by motorcycle, given that he had an accident.

(12) 1% of the population has a certain disease. There is a test for the disease, which gives a positive response for $\frac{9}{10}$ of the people with the disease, and for $\frac{1}{50}$ of the people without the disease. A person is selected at random and tested.

   a.  What is the probability that the test gives a negative response?

   b.  If the test is positive, what is the probability that the person has the disease?

   c.  If the test is negative, what is the probability that the person does not have the disease?

(13) An island contains two tribes; $\frac{2}{3}$ of the population are Wache, who tell the truth with probability 0.7, and $\frac{1}{3}$ are Oya, who tell the truth with probability 0.8. I meet a tribesman who tells me that he is a Wache. What is the probability that he is telling the truth?

(14) In a certain town $\frac{3}{4}$ of the voters are over 25, and they vote for the Freedom Party with probability $\frac{1}{3}$. Voters under 25 support the Freedom Party with probability $\frac{4}{5}$. If a supporter of the Freedom Party is picked at random, what is the probability that he or she is under 25?

## 36.3 Examination Questions

(1) A 2p coin and a 10p coin are thrown on a table. Event $A$ is "A head occurs on the 2p coin. Event $B$ is "A head occurs on the 10p coin". Event $C$ is "Two heads or two tails are obtained".

State, giving reasons, which of the following statements is (are) true and which is (are) false.

   a.  $A$ and $B$ are independent events

   b.  $B$ and $C$ are independent events.

   c.  $A$ and $C$ are mutually exclusive events

   d.  $A$ and $B \cap C$ are independent events.

   e.  $P(A \cap B \cap C) = P(A).P(B).P(C)$

[L add]

(2) In a College there are 500 students, of whom 300 study Mathematics, 200 study Physics and 50 study Geology. There are 140 students who study both Mathematics and Physics and, of these, 30 also study Geology. There are 38 students studying Mathematics and Geology and there are also 38 who study both Physics and Geology. Draw a Venn diagram to show this information. Hence find the number of students at this College who study none of these subjects.

A student is selected at random. Find the probability that the student will be studying

a. Mathematics and Physics but not Geology,
b. at least two of the subjects Mathematics, Geology and Physics,
c. at least one of the subjects Physics and Geology, given that he studies Mathematics.

[L add]

(3) Six coloured balls yellow, green, brown, blue, pink and black have values 2, 3, 4, 5, 6, 7 respectively. They are identical in size and are placed in a box. Two balls are selected together from the box at random and the total number of points is recorded.

i. Find the probability that the total score is (a) 7, (b) 9, (c) 10, (d) greater than 9, (e) odd.

ii. A game between two players, $X$ and $Y$, starts with the six balls in a box. Each player in turn selects at random two balls, notes the score and then returns the balls to the box. The game is over when one of the players reaches a total score of 25 or more.

a. If $X$ starts, calculate the probability that $X$ wins on his second turn;

b. if $Y$ starts, calculate the probability that $X$ wins on his second turn.

[O add]

(4)

a. The two electronic systems $C_1$, $C_2$ of a communications satellite operate independently and have probabilities of 0.1 and 0.05 respectively of failing. Find the probability that

  (i) neither circuit fails,   (ii) at least one circuit fails,
  (iii) exactly one circuit fails.

b. In a certain boxing competition all fights are either won or lost; draws are not permitted.

If a boxer wins a fight then the probability that he wins his next fight is $\frac{3}{4}$; if he loses a fight the probability of him losing the next fight is $\frac{2}{3}$.

Assuming that he won his last fight, use a tree diagram, or otherwise, to calculate the probability that of his next three fights

  (i) he wins exactly two fights,   (ii) he wins at most two fights.

State the most likely and least likely sequence of results for these three fights.

[NI add]

(5)

i. The events $A$ and $B$ are such that
$P(A) = 0.4, P(B) = 0.45, P(A \cup B) = 0.68$. Show that the events A and B are neither mutually exclusive nor independent.

ii. A bag contains 12 red balls, 8 blue balls and 4 white balls. Three balls are taken from the bag at random and without replacement. Find the probability that all three balls are of the same colour.

Find also the probability that all three balls are of different colours.

[L]

(6) A box contains 25 apples, of which 20 are red and 5 are green. Of the red apples, 3 contain maggots and of the green apples, 1 contains maggots. Two apples are chosen at random from the box. Find, in any order,

i. the probability that both apples contain maggots,
ii. the probability that both apples are red and at least one contains maggots,
iii. the probability that at least one apple contains maggots, given that both apples are red,
iv. the probability that both apples are red given that at least one apple is red.

[C]

(7)

a. Two digits $X$ and $Y$ are taken from a table of random sampling numbers. Event $R$ is that $X = Y + 1$ and event $S$ is that $X$ and $Y$ are both less than 2. Write down

   (i)   $P(R)$       (ii)   $P(R \cap S)$,

   (iii)   $P(R \cup S)$   (iv)   $P(R|S)$

b. Conveyor belting for use in mines is tested for both strength and safety (the safety test is based on the amount of heat generated if the belt snaps). A testing station receives belting from three different suppliers: 30% of its tests are carried out on samples of belting from supplier $A$, 50% from $B$; 20% from $C$. From past experience the probability of failing the strength test is 0.02 for a sample from $A$, 0.12 from $B$ and 0.04 from $C$.

i.   What is the probability that a particular strength test will result in a failure?

ii.  If a strength test results in a failure, what is the probability that the belting came from supplier A?

iii. What is the probability of a sample failing both strength and safety tests given the following further information:

Supplier *A* - the probability of failing the safety test is 0.05 and is independent of the probability of failing the strength test;

Supplier *B* - 1% of samples fail both strength and safety tests;

Supplier *C* - exactly half the samples which fail the strength test also fail the safety test.

[AEB 1985]

## COMMON ERRORS

### (1) Single Probability

If there are $n$ outcomes to an experiment, then each has probability $\frac{1}{n}$ only if they are *equally likely*. When two dice are rolled, there are 11 possible results for the total score. But a total of 12 is less likely than a total of 7, so neither has probability $\frac{1}{11}$.

### (2) Addition of Probabilities

You can only add probabilities if the events concerned are *exclusive*. In general:

$$P(A \text{ or } B) \le P(A) + P(B)$$

### (3) Multiplication of Probabilities
You can only multiply probabilities if the events concerned are *independent*.

### (4) Conditional Probability

a.   Do not forget to divide by $P(B)$ when working out $P(A|B)$.

b.   In the formula $P(A\&B)|P(B)$ do not assume that $P(A\&B)$ is $P(A) \times P(B)$. This is only true if $A$ and $B$ are independent.

c.   Conditional probability is concerned with belief, not with cause and effect.

If $P(A|B) \ne P(A)$, then it does not follow that $B$ has caused $A$ or prevented $A$. It may even be that $B$ happened after $A$ did.

# 37 Permutations and Combinations

The number of ways in which $n$ objects can be arranged in a definite order is:

$$n(n-1)(n-2)(n-3)...3.2.1$$

This is pronounced "$n$ factorial", and written $n!$. By convention, $0! = 1$.

If $r$ objects are to be *permuted* from $n$ objects, i.e. arranged in a definite order, then the number of ways in which this can be done is:

$$^nP_r = \frac{n!}{(n-r)!} = n(n-1)(n-2)...(n-r+1)$$

If $r$ objects are to be *combined* from $n$ objects, i.e. selected in any order, then the number of ways in which this can be done is:

$$^nC_r = \frac{n!}{r!(n-r)!} = \frac{n(n-1)(n-2)...(n-r+1)}{r!}$$

$^nC_r$ is often written as $\begin{pmatrix} n \\ r \end{pmatrix}$

The expression $^nC_r$ was also defined as the binomial coefficient in Chapter 3.

## 37.1 Simple Arrangement Problems

### 37.1.1 Examples

(1)    Find (a) $^{10}P_3$ (b) $^{100}C_3$

Solution

    a.    Use the definition.

$$^{10}P_3 = 10!/7! = 720$$

    b.    The second form of the definition must be used, as a calculator will not be able to handle 100!.

$$^{100}C_3 = 100 \times 99 \times 98/3! = 161,700$$

(2)    In a game of poker, 5 cards are dealt from a pack of 52. How many possible poker hands are there?

Solution    Here 5 cards are selected from 52, without regard to order. This is a combinations problem.

$$\textbf{Number of hands} =^{52}\textbf{C}_5 = \textbf{2,598,960}$$

(3)    A telephone number contains 6 digits. How many possible telephone numbers are there in which no digit is repeated?

Solution    There are ten digits. For a telephone number the order of digits is important. Hence the total number of possible telephone numbers in which no digit is repeated is:

$$^{10}P_6 = 151,200$$

### 37.1.2 Exercises

  (1) Evaluate the following:

  (a) 6! (b) 10! (c) 11! (d) $^5P_2$ (e) $^{12}P_4$ (f) $^{20}P_5$ (g) $^6C_2$ (h) $^{12}C_5$

  (2) Evaluate the following:

  (a) $^5P_5$ (b) $^{100}P_4$ (c) $^{10}C_{10}$ (d) $^{1001}C_2$ (e) $^{1001}C_{999}$

  (3) Show that $^{20}C_6 =^{20} C_{14}$

(4) Show that $^nC_r = ^nC_{n-r}$. Explain in words why this is true.

(5) Is it true that $^nP_r = ^nP_{n-r}$?

(6) How many ways can you arrange the letters from the word CODES?

(7) At Scrabble$^{TM}$ you have the letters $XZJYPVK$. How many 3 letter arrangements can be made from them?

(8) A travelling salesman must visit 15 towns. In how many different ways can he plan his journey?

(9) How many numbers between 100 and 1000 use only odd digits, no digit being repeated?

(10) In Mastermind$^{TM}$ a code is picked using 4 out of 7 colours. How many codes are possible, if no colour can be used twice?

(11) There are 14 horses in a race. In how many ways can the first 3 places be filled?

(12) A class contains 25 pupils. In how many ways can prizes be awarded in Latin, French and Mathematics, if no pupil can win more than one prize?

(13) In how many ways can eight books be arranged along a shelf?

(14) At Scrabble$^{TM}$ the letters $QWYPKGDZXBM$ are left in the bag. In how many ways can you draw out four of them?

(15) You are given 12 points on a plane, no three of them being in a straight line. How many triangles can be drawn using the points as vertices?

(16) You are given 9 points on a circle. How many chords do they form?

(17) You have 10 blue flowers and 5 red flowers. In how many ways can they be planted in a row, if we do not distinguish between flowers of the same colour?

(18) The travelling salesman of Question 8 decides to visit only 5 towns. In how many ways can his selection be made? How many possible journeys does he have now?

(19) In Bridge each player receives 13 out of the 52 cards. How many possible Bridge hands are there?

(20) A coin is tossed 10 times, and heads comes up 4 times. In how many ways can this have happened?

(21) You win a tennis set 6-4. How many ways can this have happened?

## 37.2 Compound Problems

### 37.2.1 Examples

(1)      How many arrangements are there of the letters of the word SCROOGE? In how many of these are the O's together?

Solution    If the O's were different, there would be 7! arrangements. But the O's can be permuted without changing the arrangement. Hence there are:

$$7!/2! = 2520 \text{ arrangements.}$$

If the O's are kept together, then they can be considered as one single letter. The number of arrangements is therefore:

$$6! = 720.$$

(2)    A squash team is to contain 3 men and 2 women, chosen from 15 men and 9 women. In how many ways can the team be chosen?

Solution    The men can be picked in $^{15}C_3 = 455$ ways. The women can be picked in $^9C_2 = 36$ ways. The total number of possible teams is therefore:

$$455 \times 36 = 16,380$$

(3)    4 six-sided dice are rolled. What is the probability that the numbers they show are all different?

Solution    The number of ways in which 4 different numbers could be selected is $^6P_4 = 360$. The number of ways in which the 4 numbers, not necessarily different, could be selected is $6 \times 6 \times 6 \times 6 = 1296$. The probability is therefore:

$$\frac{360}{1296} = \frac{5}{18}$$

## 37.2.2 Exercises

(1) Find the number of arrangements of the letters of:

(a) DREAD (b) CASSETTE (c) TERROR (d) HORROR (e) INTERDENOMINATIONAL

(2) How many arrangements are there of the letters from ABACUS in which the $A$'s are together?

(3) How many arrangements are there of the letters from ABACUS in which the $A$'s are not together?

(4) How many arrangements are there of the letters from BRAINS in which the vowels are together?

(5) How many arrangements are there of the letters from IDAHO in which the consonants are separated?

(6) A library contains 10 thrillers and 18 science-fiction books. In how many ways can a borrower select 2 of each?

(7) A committee must contain 3 men and 4 women. In how many ways can the committee be chosen from 10 men and 6 women?

(8) In how many ways can 7 men and 8 women sit on a bench, if no 2 women can sit next to each other?

(9) A shelf contains 5 Western books and 4 Romances. In how many ways can they be arranged (a) without any restrictions (b) if all the Westerns are together and all the Romances are together (c) if all the Westerns are together (d) if no two Westerns are together?

(10) How many codes are there in the Mastermind game of Question 10, 37.1.2, without the restriction that colours may not be repeated?

(11) How many numbers are there between 100 and 1000 in which the digit 0 does not appear?

(12) How many numbers between 500 and 1000 are there using only the digits 1, 3, 4, 6, 7?

(13) How many odd digits are there between 5000 and 10000 are there using only the digits 1, 3, 6, 7, 8?

(14) 12 circles are drawn on a piece of paper. What is the greatest possible number of intersection points?

(15) In a certain country car registration numbers consist of 3 letters and 4 numbers. How many registrations are possible if (a) no letter or digit may be repeated (b) without such a restriction?

(16) How many 3 letter arrangements can be taken from the letters of DREAD?

(17) In its sweet-box a child has 3 toffees, 2 chocolates and 1 liquorice. Its mother only allows it to eat 3. In how many ways can this be done?

(18) There are 27 children in a class. Find the probability that:

a.  Their birthdays are all different.

b.  At least two children have the same birthday.

(Ignore leap years; assume that all days of the year are equally likely; leave your answer in factorial form)

(19) In Bridge the 52 cards are dealt to 4 players. How many possible Bridge deals are there?

(20) Find the probability that a Bridge hand of 13 cards contains:

(a)  7 spades   (b)   7 cards all of the same suit.

(21) In a game of Bridge, North and South have 8 hearts between them. What is the probability that the remaining 5 are split 3-2 or 2-3 between East and West?

(22) A railway carriage has 4 seats on each side. In how many ways can 6 men and 2 women sit if (a) the women sit opposite each other (b) the women do not sit next to each other?

(23) A diagonal of a polygon is a line joining two vertices which are not next to each other. How many diagonals are there for a (a) 10 sided polygon (b) $n$ sided polygon.

(24) In how many ways can two taxis, each of which will take at most 4 passengers, take a party of 7 people if 2 of them refuse to be in the same taxi?

## 37.3 Examination Questions

(1) In the small country of Ruritania, car registration plates consist of different arrangements of groups of 4 letters taken from the Ruritanian alphabet which consist of 10 letters. Calculate the number of different registration plates which can be made if

(a) repetitions of letters are not allowed,

(b) the letters can be repeated any number of times.

In case (b), all the different possible arrangements are listed and one arrangement is then to be chosen at random. Calculate the probability of choosing an arrangement which has

(c) two or more letters the same,

(d) different letters at the beginning and the end of the arrangement.

[L add]

(2) Three girls and three boys enter a railway compartment in which there are six seats altogether, three on each side. In how many different ways can the seats be occupied?

If the girls all sit on one side and the boys sit opposite in how many different ways can the seats be occupied?

If the girls enter the compartment first and occupy three of the four corner seats and the boys then follow them and occupy the remaining seats, in how many different ways can the seats be occupied?

[MEI add]

(3) John and Mary are members of a group of eight boys and two girls.

a. In how many ways can they all be seated in a row if John and Mary always sit together? (Leave your answer in factorial form.)

b. In how many ways can a subcommittee of five be chosen from the same group of ten if:

  i. both John and Mary are on it,

  ii. either John or Mary is on it but not both,

  iii. at least one girl is on it?

[O&C add]

(4) A certain game is played with a number of cards, each of which has a single letter printed on it. A player has ten cards, which are lettered $A, C, E, E, E, F, L, L, W, X$ respectively.

  (i) A "word" is any arrangement of these ten letters, for example $LXCELWFEEA$

a. Find the total number of different "words" that the player can make.

b. Find the number of these "words" which begin and end with $E$ and in which the two letters $L$ are consecutive.

  (ii) A second player chooses three of the first player's ten cards at random, and takes them from the first player. Calculate the probability that

a. the three cards will all carry the letter E or L,

b. the first player's remaining seven cards will all carry different letters.

[C]

(5) How many distinguishable arrangements of the 10 letters of the word STATISTICS are possible?

Three letters are selected without replacement from these ten and the number of distinguishable ways of arranging them is calculated. What is the total number of distinguishable arrangements for all possible such selections?

The ten letters are written one on each of ten cards. Two cards are selected at random and from these any card not carrying an $S$ or a $T$ is discarded and another selected in its place from the remaining cards. What is the probability that the cards now chosen are either two $S$'s or two $T$'s?

[O&C]

## COMMON ERRORS

(1) Make sure you do not confuse $^nP_r$ and $^nC_r$. If the order is important then $^nP_r$ is used, if it is not important then $^nC_r$ is used.

(2) $0! = 1$, not 0. In particular, $^nC_0 = 1$. If we select 0 objects out of $n$, then there is 1 way of doing it. (Don't pick any!)

(3) Suppose you are making two different selections, say of 5 from a group of 10 and 6 from another group of 9. The total number of ways is the *product* of $^{10}C_5$ and $^9C_6$. Do not add the expressions.

(4) Suppose $r$ items are are selected out of $n$. If repetition is allowed, then the number of ways is $n^r$. If repetition is not allowed, the number of ways is $^nP_r$. Do not confuse these.

# 38 Representation of Data

## 38.1 Mean, Median, Variance, Standard Deviation

Suppose $x_1, x_2, ..., x_n$ are $n$ numbers. The mean $x$ is their average:

$$\overline{x} = (x_1 + x_2 + ... + x_n)/n.$$

This is sometimes known as the *Arithmetic mean*. The *Geometric mean* is given by:

$$x_G = \sqrt[n]{(x_1 x_2 ... x_n)}$$

If some of the values are thought to be more important than the others, then a *weighted mean* is found. If the weights are $\lambda_1, \lambda_2, ... \lambda_n$, then the weighted mean is:

$$\frac{\lambda_1 x_1 + \lambda_2 x_2 + ... + \lambda_n x_n}{\lambda_1 + \lambda_2 + ... + \lambda_n}$$

The *median* of the figures is the middle figure, in the sense that half of the figures are less than the median and half are greater than it.

The *Variance* $S^2$ of the figures is a measure of their spread. It is found from the formula:

$$S^2 = ((x_1 - \overline{x})^2 + (x_2 - \overline{x})^2 + ... + (x_n - \overline{x})^2)/n$$

It can be shown that this is equivalent to:

$$S^2 = (x_1^2 + x_2^2 + ... + x_n^2)/n - \overline{x}^2.$$

The *Standard Deviation* is the square root of the variance.

Another measure of spread is the *mean deviation from the mean*. It is given by the formula:

$$(|x_1 - \overline{x}| + |x_2 - \overline{x}| + ... + |x_n - \overline{x}|)/n$$

Suppose the $x$ figures are scaled by the function $y = a + bx$, where $a$ and $b$ are constants. Then the mean, variance and standard deviation of the $y$ figures are given by:

$$\overline{y} = a + b\overline{x} : S_y^2 = b^2 S_x^2 : S_y = bS_x$$

### 38.1.1 Examples

(1)    Find the mean, median and standard deviation of the following set of figures.

$$22, 23, 24, 26, 21, 29, 19, 26, 30, 27.$$

Solution    For the mean, add these numbers together and divide by 10.

**The mean is 24.7**

For the median, note that the 5th number is 24 and the 6th is 26. Take half way between these.

**The median is 25**

It is easier to use the second formula to find the variance. $S^2 = (22^2 + 23^2 + ... + 27^2)/10 - 24.7^2 = 11.21$. Square root this to find the standard deviation.

**The standard deviation is 3.35**

(2)   The prices of four commodities $A, B, C, D$ are given weights 3, 4, 1, 2 respectively. Over a year these prices rise by 5%, 10%, 15%, 2% respectively. Calculate the weighted average percentage rise in price.

Solution   Find the weighted mean of the percentages, using the weights given.

Average price rise $= (5 \times 3 + 10 \times 4 + 15 \times 1 + 2 \times 2)/(3 + 4 + 1 + 2)$

**The weighted average is 7.4%**

(3)   The marks for a certain exam have mean 45 and variance 144. In order to harmonize them with previous years they are to be scaled so that their mean is 50 and their variance 64. Find the scaling function, in the form $y = a + bx$.

Solution   Use the formulae above, for the mean and variance of figures after they have been scaled.

$$50 = a + 45b : 64 = b^2 144.$$

$$b = \frac{2}{3} : a = 20.$$

**The scaling function is $y = 20 + \dfrac{2}{3}x$**

(4)   In a test sat by 37 pupils, 15 scored at most 20 and 6 scored more than 40. Estimate the median mark.

Solution   The median mark is the mark of the 19th pupil. 15 scored less than 21, and so we want the 4th mark from the 16 which are between 21 and 40. If these 16 marks are evenly spread, then the 4th mark is a quarter of the way along.

**The median is approximately $21 + \dfrac{1}{4}(20) = 26$**

### 38.1.2 Exercises

(1) Find the means of the following sets of figures:

    (a) 12, 11, 13, 14, 12, 15, 20, 21, 18    (b) 1.3, 1.8, 1.6, 0.9, 1.2

    (c) 67, 65, 58, 59, 71, 62    (d) 103, 132, 122, 134, 112, 108

(2) Find the medians of the sets of figures in Question 1.

(3) Find the geometric means of the figures in Question 1.

(4) Find the variances and standard deviations of the sets of figures in Question 1.

(5) Find the means and variances of the sets of figures in Question 1 after they have been scaled by the function $y = 2 + 10x$.

(6) A set of figures consists of 5 repeated 4 times, and 7 repeated 6 times. Find the mean and the variance of the figures.

(7) The values of a set of figures are given by the following frequency table:

| Value | 2 | 3 | 4 | 5 |
|---|---|---|---|---|
| Frequency | 3 | 10 | 12 | 5 |

Find the mean and standard deviation of the figures.

(8) The values of a set of figures are given by the following table:

| Range | $0 - 10$ | $10 - 20$ | $20 - 30$ | $30 - 40$ |
|---|---|---|---|---|
| Frequency | 12 | 35 | 43 | 17 |

By taking mid-interval values, estimate the mean and standard deviation. Estimate the median of the figures.

(9) Estimate the mean, median and standard deviation from the following table:

| Range | $0 - 0.5$ | $0.5 - 1$ | $1 - 1.5$ | $1.5 - 2$ | $2 - 2.5$ | $2.5 - 3$ |
|---|---|---|---|---|---|---|
| Frequency | 3 | 23 | 33 | 31 | 21 | 9 |

(10) The quantities $A, B, C, D, E$ are given weights 1, 2, 2, 3, 3 respectively. Find the weighted mean if $A, B, C, D, E$ have values 12, 20, 25, 10, 8 respectively.

(11) A set of marks has mean 60 and variance 200. The marks are scaled by the function $y = 10 + \frac{1}{2}x$. (a) What is a mark of 80 scaled to? (b) What mark is scaled to 40? (c) What mark is unaltered by the scaling? (d) What are the mean and variance of the scaled marks?

(12) How should the marks of Question 11 be scaled so that their mean is 50 and their variance 8?

## 38.2 Histograms and Cumulative Frequency

A *histogram* is a bar-chart used to represent numerical data. The area of each rectangle is proportional to the frequency in the range it covers.

The *cumulative frequency* at a value is the running total of all the frequencies up to that value. A *cumulative frequency curve,* or *ogive,* is a graph of the cumulative frequencies.

The median corresponds to a cumulative frequency of $\frac{1}{2}$. The *lower quartile* corresponds to a cumulative frequency of $\frac{1}{4}$, and the *upper quartile* to a cumulative frequency of $\frac{3}{4}$.

The *interquartile range* is the difference between the quartiles. Like the variance or standard deviation, it is a measure of how widely spread the figures are.

### 38.2.1 Example

120 pupils took an exam which was marked out of 100.

Their marks are shown in the table below:

| Mark range | 0 − 30 | 31 − 40 | 41 − 50 | 51 − 55 | 56 − 60 | 61 − 70 | 71 − 100 |
|---|---|---|---|---|---|---|---|
| Frequency | 9 | 15 | 23 | 19 | 17 | 17 | 20 |

Plot a histogram and a cumulative frequency curve. Find the interquartile range.

Solution  The most common width of interval is 10 marks. Let that be the standard. The first and last intervals are three times the standard width, hence their heights must be divided by 3. The two intervals in the 50's are half the standard width, hence their heights must be doubled. Plot the histogram as shown.

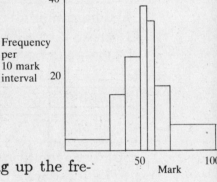

Find the cumulative frequencies by adding up the frequencies. Add an extra row to the table.

| Mark range | 0 − 30 | 31 − 40 | 41 − 50 | 51 − 55 | 56 − 60 | 61 − 70 | 71 − 100 |
|---|---|---|---|---|---|---|---|
| Frequency | 9 | 15 | 23 | 19 | 17 | 17 | 20 |
| Cum. Frequ. | 9 | 24 | 47 | 66 | 83 | 100 | 120 |

Plot these Cumulative Frequencies as shown. The lower quartile corresponds to the mark of the 30'th pupil. This is approximately 43. The upper quartile corresponds to the mark of the 90'th pupil, which is approximately 64.

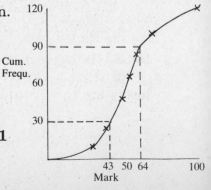

**The interquartile range is 21**

## 38.2.2 Exercises

(1) The sales figures in 100's of a certain text book over a period of 40 weeks were as given by the table below. Plot a histogram to illustrate the figures.

| Week | 0 – 10 | 10 – 15 | 15 – 20 | 20 – 25 | 25 – 30 | 0 – 40 |
|------|--------|---------|---------|---------|---------|--------|
| Sales | 24 | 18 | 24 | 32 | 26 | 28 |

(2) The heights of a collection of 80 plants were as given by the table below. Plot a histogram to illustrate the figures.

| Height in cm | 0 – 10 | 10 – 12 | 12 – 14 | 14 – 15 | 15 – 17 | 17-20 |
|--------------|--------|---------|---------|---------|---------|-------|
| Frequency | 10 | 9 | 18 | 13 | 14 | 16 |

(3) 60 children ran a 100 m race. Their times are given by the table below. Plot a histogram to illustrate the figures.

| Time in s | 11-12 | $12 - 12\frac{1}{2}$ | $12\frac{1}{2} - 13$ | $13 - 13\frac{1}{2}$ | $13\frac{1}{2} - 15$ |
|-----------|-------|------------------------|------------------------|------------------------|------------------------|
| Frequency | 12 | 10 | 16 | 9 | 13 |

(4) The ages of 1000 members of a political party were as shown in the table below. Plot a histogram to illustrate the figures.

| Age | 20-25 | 25-30 | 30-35 | 35-40 | 40-50 | 50-70 |
|-----|-------|-------|-------|-------|-------|-------|
| Frequency | 120 | 230 | 240 | 223 | 112 | 75 |

(5) 80 cats were weighed, and the results are given in the table below. Plot a histogram to illustrate the data.

| Weight in kg | $2 - 2\frac{1}{2}$ | $2\frac{1}{2} - 2\frac{3}{4}$ | $2\frac{3}{4} - 3$ | $3 - 3\frac{1}{4}$ | $3\frac{1}{4} - 3\frac{1}{2}$ | $3\frac{1}{2} - 4$ |
|--------------|---------------------|--------------------------------|---------------------|---------------------|--------------------------------|---------------------|
| Frequency | 7 | 12 | 19 | 21 | 11 | 10 |

(6) Plot a cumulative frequency curve for the data in Question 2. Find the interquartile range. Estimate the proportion of plants which were less than 16 cm.

(7) Plot a cumulative frequency curve for the data in Question 3. Find the interquartile range. What speed did the fastest 10% achieve?

(8) Plot a cumulative frequency curve for the data in Question 4. Find the interquartile range. What proportion of the party is over 60?

(9) Plot a cumulative frequency curve for the data in Question 5. How heavy are the heaviest 20% of the cats?

## 38.3 Examination Questions

(1) During the eight successive hours of a working day at a small television factory, the following numbers of sets were completed.

$$10 \quad 14 \quad 26 \quad 20 \quad 18 \quad 8 \quad 10 \quad 6.$$

Calculate

(i)  the arithmetic mean,          (ii) the median,

(iii)  the mean deviation from the median   (iv) the variance,

(v)  the geometric mean.

[AEB add 1987]

(2) The marks of 20 students in a test are given in the table.

| Mark $x$ | 20 | 22 | 24 | 25 | 26 | 27 | 30 | 33 | 34 | 35 | 36 | 38 | 40 |
|---|---|---|---|---|---|---|---|---|---|---|---|---|---|
| Frequency | 1 | 1 | 1 | 1 | 1 | 1 | 8 | 1 | 1 | 1 | 1 | 1 | 1 |

Show that the mean and standard deviation are 30 and 5 respectively. Show all necessary working.

The marks are to be scaled using a transformation $m = px + q$, where $p$ and $q$ are integers, so that the new mean is 50 and the standard deviation is 15. Calculate $p$ and $q$ and hence the scaled mark corresponding to an original test mark of 26.

[O add]

(3) Mr and Mrs Smith and Mr and Mrs Jones each decided to calculate a personal cost of living index which is the weighted arithmetic mean of index numbers for the following four categories of expenditure: Food, Fuel and Transport, Housing and Clothing. In January 1980 they allocated a base index number of 100 to each of these categories and the associated weights are shown in the table below.

| Category | Weights Smith | Jones | Index January 1980 | Index January 1981 |
|---|---|---|---|---|
| Food | 4 | 3 | 100 | 112 |
| Fuel & Transport | 3 | 4 | 100 | 110 |
| Housing | 2 | 3 | 100 | 115 |
| Clothing | 1 | 2 | 100 | 105 |

Using the index numbers for each category for January 1981 also shown in the table, calculate the cost of living index for each couple at that time.

In January 1982 the index numbers for Fuel and Transport, and for Housing had risen to 130 and 120 respectively. Both couples then found that their cost of living index was 120. Calculate the values of the index numbers for Food and for Clothing at that time.

[MEI add]

(4)

a.  The grouped frequency distribution table gives the lengths, recorded to the nearest mm, of 250 nails produced from a particular machine.

| Length (mm) | $98 - 99$ | $100 - 101$ | $102 - 103$ | $104 - 105$ | $106 - 107$ | $108 - 109$ |
|---|---|---|---|---|---|---|
| Number of Nails | 12 | 36 | 106 | 58 | 30 | 8 |

Draw the cumulative frequency curve and from your graph estimate

    i.  the interquartile range,

    ii.  the percentage of nails having a length below 103 mm.

Given that the top 10% and bottom 10% of this distribution are rejected, estimate from your graph the limits between which the length must lie if it is to be accepted.

b.  The masses of 100 male students were recorded to the nearest kg and are grouped in the following table.

| Mass (kg) | 50-59 | 60-74 | 75-94 |
|---|---|---|---|
| Number of Students | 20 | 50 | 30 |

    i.  Draw a histogram to represent this information.

    ii.  Estimate the median mass of these students.

[C add]

## COMMON ERRORS
### (1) Mean and Median

a. When finding the mean from grouped data, divide by the number of terms, not by the number of groups.

b. When finding a weighted mean, divide by the sum of the weights, not by the number of the weights.

c. The median of 19 numbers is not 10. It is the 10th number.

### (2) Variance and Standard Deviation

a. Be very careful when using the formula for variance. In particular, make sure you do the squaring and subtracting in the correct order.

b. Most scientific calculators will work out for you the mean and variance of a set of data. But do not rely on your calculator - many questions require you to show how the mean and variance are obtained.

### (3) Histograms
If the intervals of a histogram are not uniform, then take account of this by dividing or multiplying the height of the bars. It is the *area* of each bar which represents the frequency, not its height.

### (4) Cumulative Frequency
The points on a cumulative frequency curve must go at the *ends* of the intervals, not at the midpoints.

# 39 Discrete Random Variables

## 39.1 Distribution of Discrete Random Variables

A variable $X$ whose values are determined by chance is a *random variable*.

If the values of $X$ are separated from each other then $X$ is a *discrete* random variable.

Usually, but not always, $X$ takes whole number values.

$X$ may take either finitely many or infinitely many values.

The *distribution* of a random variable $X$ gives the possible values of $X$ with their appropriate probabilities. The distribution may be given by a formula or by a table.

Let $X$ take the values $x_1, x_2, x_3, ..., x_n, ...$ , with associated probabilities $p_1 = P(X = x_1), p_2 = P(X = x_2), ..., p_n = P(X = x_n)$ and so on. Each $p_n$ must be greater or equal to 0, and their sum must be 1.

$$p_n \geq 0 \text{ and } \sum p_n = 1.$$

### 39.1.1 Examples

(1)     $X$ is a discrete random variable with distribution given by the table below. Find the value of $c$.

| $i$ | 1 | 2 | 3 | 4 |
|---|---|---|---|---|
| $P(X=i)$ | 0.1 | 0.3 | c | 0.2 |

Solution     The sum of all the probabilities must be 1.

$$0.1 + 0.3 + c + 0.2 = 1$$

$$c = 0.4$$

(2)     3 fair coins are spun, and $X$ is the number of heads obtained. Write down the distribution of $X$.

Solution     Denoting heads by $H$ and tails by $T$, the 8 possible outcomes are $HHH, HHT, HTH, HTT, THH, THT, TTH, TTT$. In one of these outcomes, $HHH$, there are 3 heads. Hence $P(X = 3) = \frac{1}{8}$. In 3 of the outcomes $X = 1$. Hence $P(X = 1) = \frac{3}{8}$. The other probabilities are found similarly. Fill in the table below:

| $i$ | 0 | 1 | 2 | 3 |
|---|---|---|---|---|
| $P(X = i)$ | $\frac{1}{8}$ | $\frac{3}{8}$ | $\frac{3}{8}$ | $\frac{1}{8}$ |

### 39.1.2 Exercises

(1) The discrete random variable $X$ has the distribution given by the table below. Find the value of $a$.

| $i$ | 0 | 1 | 2 | 3 |
|---|---|---|---|---|
| $P(X = i)$ | $a$ | 0.1 | 0.3 | 0.2 |

(2) The discrete random variable $X$ has the distribution given by the table below. Find the value of $m$.

| $i$ | 2 | 3 | 4 | 5 | 6 |
|---|---|---|---|---|---|
| $P(X = i)$ | $m$ | 0.1 | $\frac{1}{2}$ | $2m$ | 0.05 |

(3) The discrete random variable $X$ takes values $i = 0$, 1, 2, 3 with probabilities $\lambda i + 0.1$. Find $\lambda$.

(4) $X$ takes values $i = 1$, 2, 3, 4, 5 with probabilities $i/20 + \mu$. Find $\mu$.

(5) $X$ takes values $i = 1$, 2, 3, 4, with probabilities $i^2/100 + \beta$. Find $\beta$.

(6) A fair die is rolled, and $X$ is the score. Write down the distribution of $X$.

(7) Two fair dice are rolled, and $X$ is the total score. Write down the distribution of $X$.

(8) Two fair dice are rolled, and $X$ is the larger of the scores showing. (If the dice show the same number, then $X$ is that number.) Write down the distribution of $X$.

(9) 10 cards are numbered 1, 2, 2, 3, 3, 3, 4, 4, 4, 4. They are shuffled and one is drawn at random. Let $X$ be the number on the drawn card. Write down the distribution of $X$.

(10) A bag contains 4 red and 3 blue marbles. Two are drawn without replacement. $X$ is the number of red marbles drawn. Write down the distribution of $X$.

## 39.2 Expectation

The *expectation* or *mean* of a random variable $X$ is the average value that $X$ takes. For a discrete random variable expectation is given by the formula:

$$E(X) = \sum iP(X = i)$$

### 39.2.1 Examples

(1)         $X$ has the distribution given by the table below. Find $E(X)$.

| $i$ | 2 | 3 | 4 | 5 | 6 |
|---|---|---|---|---|---|
| $P(X = i)$ | 0.05 | 0.1 | 0.4 | 0.4 | 0.05 |

Solution    Use the formula for expectation:

$$E(X) = 2 \times 0.05 + 3 \times 0.1 + 4 \times 0.4 + 5 \times 0.4 + 6 \times 0.05$$

$$\mathbf{E(X) = 4.3}$$

(2)    Michelle and Robert play a game as follows: from a bag containing 4 red and 5 blue marbles two are drawn without replacement. If both are red Robert wins 50p, if exactly one is red it is a draw. If both are blue Michelle wins: how much should she gain if the game is to be fair?

Solution    The probabilities of the number of red marbles are as follows:

$$P(2 \text{ red}) = \tfrac{4}{9} \times \tfrac{3}{8} = \tfrac{1}{6} \quad P(1 \text{ red}) = \tfrac{4}{9} \times \tfrac{5}{8} + \tfrac{5}{9} \times \tfrac{1}{2} = \tfrac{5}{9}$$

$$P(0 \text{ red}) = \tfrac{5}{9} \times \tfrac{1}{2} = \tfrac{5}{18}.$$

If Michelle wins $xp$ when two blues are drawn, then Robert's expected gain for the game is:

$$50 \times \left(\frac{1}{6}\right) + 0 \times \left(\frac{5}{9}\right) - x \times \left(\frac{5}{18}\right)$$

For the game to be fair Robert's expected gain is zero.

$$50 \times \left(\frac{1}{6}\right) - x \times \left(\frac{5}{18}\right) = 0. \text{ Hence } x = 30$$

**Michelle should gain 30 $p$ if both marbles are blue**

### 39.2.2 Exercises

(1) If $X$ has the distribution given by the table below, find $E(X)$.

| $i$ | 1 | 2 | 3 | 4 | 5 |
|---|---|---|---|---|---|
| $P(X = i)$ | $\tfrac{1}{8}$ | $\tfrac{1}{4}$ | $\tfrac{3}{8}$ | $\tfrac{1}{8}$ | $\tfrac{1}{8}$ |

(2) $X$ has the distribution given by the table below. Find $E(X)$.

| $i$ | 11 | 12 | 13 | 14 |
|---|---|---|---|---|
| $P(X = i)$ | 0.3 | 0.4 | 0.1 | 0.2 |

(3) & (4) Find the expectations for the distributions given in Examples 1 and 2 of 39.1.1.

(5) to (14) Find the expectations for the distributions given in Exercises 1 to 10 of 39.1.2.

(15) $X$ has the distribution given by the table below. $E(X) = 3$. Find $a$.

| $i$ | 1 | 2 | $a$ | 4 | 5 |
|---|---|---|---|---|---|
| $P(X = i)$ | $\frac{1}{8}$ | $\frac{1}{4}$ | $\frac{3}{8}$ | $\frac{1}{8}$ | $\frac{1}{8}$ |

(16) $X$ has the distribution given by the table below. $E(X) = 2.8$. Find $a$ and $b$.

| $i$ | 1 | 2 | 3 | 4 |
|---|---|---|---|---|
| $P(X = i)$ | 0.2 | 0.1 | $a$ | $b$ |

(17) Cards numbered 1, 1, 2, 2, 2, 3, 3, 3, 4, 4, 4, 4, 4 are shuffled and one is drawn out. Find the expected value of the number on the drawn card.

(18) A bag contains 5 black and 7 white beads. Two are drawn out without replacement. Find the expectation of the number of white beads.

(19) In a dice game the player receives the score on the die in pounds, except when it is 1, in which case he has to pay the banker. If it is a fair game, how much does he pay?

If instead he pays £21, how much will he expect to lose if he plays the game 100 times?

(20) A coin game is follows. A fair coin is tossed either 3 times or until a head has turned up, whichever is the sooner. If a head first appears on the 1st, 2nd, 3rd go then the player receives £1, £3, £7 respectively. If no head appears on all three goes then the player has to pay the bank. If the game is fair, how much should be paid to the bank if no head appears?

## 39.3 Variance

The *variance* of a random variable is a measure of how widely spread the values are.

If $X$ is a random variable with expectation $\mu$, then the variance of $X$ is given by:

$$Var(X) = E((X - \mu)^2)$$

An equivalent formula for the variance is:

$$Var(X) = E(X^2) - \mu^2$$

(The mean of the square minus the square of the mean)
The square root of the variance is the *standard deviation* $\sigma$.

$$\sigma = \sqrt{Var(X)} : \sigma^2 = Var(X)$$

### 39.3.1 Example

$X$ has the distribution given by the table below. Find $Var(X)$.

| $i$ | 0 | 1 | 2 | 3 | 4 |
|---|---|---|---|---|---|
| $P(X = i)$ | $\frac{1}{8}$ | $\frac{1}{4}$ | $\frac{3}{8}$ | $\frac{1}{8}$ | $\frac{1}{8}$ |

Solution    First find the expectation $\mu$.

$$\mu = 0 \times \frac{1}{8} + 1 \times \frac{1}{4} + 2 \times \frac{3}{8} + 3 \times \frac{1}{8} + 4 \times \frac{1}{8} = 1\frac{7}{8}$$

To find $E(X^2)$, average the value of $X^2$.

$$E(X^2) = 0^2 \times \frac{1}{8} + 1^2 \times \frac{1}{4} + 2^2 \times \frac{3}{8} + 3^2 \times \frac{1}{8} + 4^2 \times \frac{1}{8} = 4\frac{7}{8}.$$

Use the second version of the formula for variance:

$$\mathbf{Var(X)} = 4\frac{7}{8} - \mu^2 = 1\frac{23}{64}$$

### 39.3.2 Exercises

(1) $X$ has a distribution given by the following table. Find $Var(X)$.

| $i$ | 1 | 2 | 3 | 4 |
|---|---|---|---|---|
| $P(X = i)$ | $\frac{1}{6}$ | $\frac{1}{6}$ | $\frac{1}{4}$ | $\frac{5}{12}$ |

(2) $X$ has a distribution given by the table below. Find $Var(X)$.

| $i$ | −1 | 0 | 1 | 2 | 3 |
|---|---|---|---|---|---|
| $P(X = i)$ | 0.1 | 0.05 | 0.35 | 0.25 | 0.25 |

(3) & (4) Find the variance for each of the distributions in Examples 1 & 2 of 39.1.1.

(5) $X$ has distribution given by the table below. $E(X) = 3.5$ and $Var(X) = 2.65$. Find $a$ and $b$.

| $i$ | 1 | 2 | $a$ | $b$ |
|---|---|---|---|---|
| $P(X = i)$ | 0.1 | 0.3 | 0.4 | 0.2 |

(6) A bag contains 4 red and 6 blue balls. Two are drawn without replacement. Find the mean and variance of the number of red balls.

(7) A fair die is rolled twice. Let $X$ and $Y$ be the scores on the first and second throw respectively, and let $Z = X + Y$ be the total score. Find $E(X)$ and $Var(X)$. Write out the distribution table for $Z$, and find $E(Z)$ and $Var(Z)$.

(8) With $X$ and $Y$ as defined in Question 7, let $W = X - Y$ be the difference between the scores. Write down the distribution table for $W$. Find the mean and variance of $W$.

## 39.4 Examination Questions

(1) Two dice, each in the shape of a regular tetrahedron, have the numbers 0, 1, 2, 3 respectively on their four faces. When the dice are thrown the score recorded is the product of the numbers on the two faces resting on the ground.

| × | 0 | 1 | 2 | 3 |
|---|---|---|---|---|
| 0 | 0 | . | . | . |
| 1 | . | . | . | . |
| 2 | . | . | . | 6 |
| 3 | . | 3 | . | . |

Copy and complete the table of scores recorded when the dice are thrown, and write down the probability of achieving each possible score. What is the expected score when the two dice are thrown?

In a game played with these two dice, and scores calculated in the same way, a player wins 10p if he makes a maximum score; wins 4p if he scores an odd number other than the maximum; loses 4p if he scores an even number (not zero); and loses 2p if he scores zero. Calculate the expected loss or gain for a player in 100 throws.

[MEI add]

(2) An urn contains 2 black and 3 white balls. Balls are drawn successively from the urn, at random and without replacement, until a black ball is

obtained. Given that $X$ is the random variable representing the number of draws required, copy and complete the following table:

| $n$ | 1 | 2 | 3 | 4 |
|---|---|---|---|---|
| $P(X = n)$ | | | | |

Hence show that $E(X) = 2$.

(ii) A bag contains 4 red and 2 blue counters. Pairs of counters are drawn successively from the bag, at random and without replacement, until a pair of counters with the same colour is obtained. Given that $Y$ is the random variable representing the number of draws required, copy and complete the following table:

| $m$ | 1 | 2 | 3 |
|---|---|---|---|
| $P(Y = m)$ | | | |

Hence find the value of $E(Y)$.

[L add]

(3) In a shooting competition competitors aim at a target which consists of a central circle surrounded by three concentric rings. If a competitor hits the central circle he is awarded 5 points; the points awarded for hitting the rings are 4, 3 and 1 respectively. Each competitor hits the target with every shot. The object of the competition is to score at least 3 points in as few shots as possible.

The probabilities that a certain competitor, A, will score 5, 4, 3 or 1 points with any one shot are given in the table below.

| Points | 5 | 4 | 3 | 1 |
|---|---|---|---|---|
| Probability | $\frac{1}{8}$ | $\frac{3}{16}$ | $\frac{5}{16}$ | $\frac{3}{8}$ |

Find the probability that $A$ will require (i) one shot, (ii) two shots, (iii) three shots, to score at least 3 points.

Given that $X$ denotes the number of shots required by $A$ to score at least 3 points, calculate $E(X), E(X^2)$ and the variance of $X$.

The probabilities that a second competitor, $B$, will score 5, 4, 3 or 1 points with any one shot are all equal. Find the probability that $B$ will require (iv) one shot, (v) two shots, (vi) three shots, to score at least 3 points.

Given that $Y$ denotes the number of shots required by $B$ to score at least 3 points, calculate $E(Y), E(Y^2)$ and the variance of $Y$.

Using these results, explain briefly who, in a series of contests between $A$ and $B$, is the more likely to be (vii) the first to score at least 3 points on most occasions, (viii) the more consistent marksman.

[C add]

(4) Each trial of a random experiment must result in one and only one of the events $A, B$ and $C$ occurring, the probabilities of these events being $\frac{1}{2}, \frac{1}{4}$ and $\frac{1}{4}$, respectively. Independent trials of the experiment are to be conducted until one of the three events occurs for the second time.

  i.  Show that the probability that the trials will stop with $A$ occurring for the second time (a) in the second trial is $\frac{1}{4}$, (b) in the third trial is $\frac{1}{4}$, (c) in the fourth trial is $\frac{3}{32}$.
 ii.  determine the corresponding probabilities that the trials will stop with $B$ occurring for the second time.
iii.  Let $X$ denote the number of trials that will be conducted. Find the distribution of $X$. Hence determine the most probable value of $X$ and the expected value of $X$.

[W]

(5) Two riflemen, $A$ and $B$, shoot independently at a target; a game consists of 10 shots each. Their probabilities of hitting the target with any one shot are $\frac{1}{5}$ and $\frac{1}{10}$ respectively. $N_A$ is the number of shots taken by $A$ before $A$ first hits the target, if at all. $N_B$ is similarly defined for $B$. $A$ wins if $N_A < N_B$, $B$ wins if $N_B < N_A$, and otherwise a game is drawn. Find the probability that $A$ wins a game.

Since $A$ is a better shot than $B$, they play a series of games in which $A$ has to win 2 games before $B$ wins 1 game in order that $A$ should win the series; otherwise $B$ wins the series. Who is most likely to win the series, and with what probability?

[O&C]

## COMMON ERRORS
### (1) Distributions
Do not forget the condition that the sum of all the probabilities must be 1. If this is not the case then you must have made a mistake in your calculations.
### (2) Expectation
Suppose that $X$ takes the values 1, 2, 3, 4 with probabilities $p_1, p_2, p_3, p_4$. The mean is $\sum i \, p_i$. Do not divide this answer by 4.

## (3) **Variance**

a. When working out $E(X^2)$ you must square $X$ first and then average it. If you do this the other way round then you will obtain zero for your variance.

b. When working out $E(X^2)$ it is the values of $x$ that are squared. Do not square the probabilities.

# 40 Binomial and Poisson Distributions

## 40.1 The Binomial Distribution

Suppose there is a trial for which the probability of success is $p$, and the probability of failure is $q = 1 - p$.

This trial is repeated independently $n$ times. Let $X$ be the number of successes. $X$ is said to have a *Binomial Distribution*. This is often written as:

$$X \sim B(n, p)$$

The distribution of $X$ is given by the formula:

$$P(X = r) = {}^n C_r p^r q^{n-r}, \text{ for } r = 0, 1, 2, ..., n.$$

Recall that ${}^n C_r = \dfrac{n!}{r!(n - r)!}$, as defined in Chapters 3 and 37.

If $X \sim B(n, p)$, then the mean and variance of $X$ are given by:

$$E(X) = np : Var(X) = npq$$

### 40.1.1 Examples

(1)     A fair die is rolled 10 times. Find the probability that there are (a) 2 sixes (b) at least 1 six.

Solution     Here the trial consists of rolling the die, and obtaining a six is called a success. Letting $X$ be the number of sixes, $X$ has a binomial distribution, $X \sim B(10, \frac{1}{6})$.

a.     $$P(X = 2) =^{10} C_2(\tfrac{1}{6})^2(\tfrac{5}{6})^8$$

**The probability that there are 2 sixes is 0.291**

b.     There will be at least one six unless there are no sixes.

$$P(X \geq 1) = 1 - P(X = 0) = 1 - (\frac{5}{6})^{10}$$

**The probability that there is at least one six is 0.838**

(2)     7 children are picked at random. Find the mean and standard deviation of the number of girls. (Assume that boys and girls are equally likely.)

Solution     Picking a girl is counted as a success. Letting $X$ be the number of girls, $X \sim B(7, \frac{1}{2})$. Use the formulae for mean and variance:

$$E(X) = 7 \times \frac{1}{2} : Var(X) = 7 \times \frac{1}{2} \times \frac{1}{2}$$

**The mean is $3\frac{1}{2}$ and the standard deviation is $\sqrt{1\frac{3}{4}} = 1.32$**

### 40.1.2 Exercises

(1) A trial with probability $\frac{1}{4}$ of success is repeated 6 times. Let $X$ be the number of successes. Find the probability that:

(a)   $X = 2$   (b)   $X = 5$

(c)   $X > 0$   (d)   $X \leq 4$

(2) $X \sim B(12, \frac{1}{3})$. Evaluate the following:

   (a)  $P(X = 4)$  (b)  $P(X = 5)$

   (c)  $P(X \leq 2)$  (d)  $P(X \geq 2)$

(3) When a dart is thrown at the dartboard, the probability of hitting the bullseye is 0.1. If the dart is thrown 20 times, find the probability of:

   (a)  Exactly 3 bullseyes    (b)  No bullseyes

   (c)  At least one bullseye  (d)  Less than 2 bullseyes

(4) It is estimated that 3 out of 4 tulip bulbs will flower. If I buy 10, find the probability that:

   (a)  All flower          (b)  exactly 8 flower

   (c)  At least 9 will flower.

(5) A multiple choice exam contains 20 questions, with 5 possible answers for each question. A candidate answers the questions at random. Find the probabilities that:

   (a)  He gets none right  (b)  He gets all right

   (c)  He gets 4 right     (d)  He gets at least 2 right

(6) One in ten of a batch of apples is bad. If 6 are bought, find the probabilities that:

   (a)  One is bad  (b)  At least 2 are bad

(7) Find the expectation and variance of the number of bullseyes in Question 3.

(8) Find the mean and variance of the number of flowering bulbs in Question 4.

(9) Find the mean and variance of the number of correct answers obtained by the candidate in Question 5.

(10) Find the mean and variance of the number of bad apples among the six bought, as described in Question 6.

(11) When a fair die is rolled several times, the expected number of sixes is 3. How many times was it rolled?

(12) A fair coin is tossed several times, and the expected number of heads is $4\frac{1}{2}$. How many times was it rolled?

(13) A biased coin is tossed 20 times, and the expected number of heads is 16. What is the probability that a single toss will give heads?

(14) When an arrow is fired at a target 50 times, the expected number of golds is 5. What is the probability that a single arrow will hit the gold?

## 40.2 The Poisson Distribution

$X$ has a *Poisson Distribution* when its distribution is given by the following formula:

$$P(X = r) = e^{-\mu}\mu^r/r!, \text{ where } r = 0, 1, 2, 3, \ldots$$

The mean and variance of $X$ are both equal to $\mu$.

$$E(X) = \mu \text{ and } Var(X) = \mu.$$

A Poisson Distribution is often used as an approximation to the Binomial Distribution $B(n, p)$, when $n$ is very large and $p$ is very small.

If $X \sim B(n, p)$, for large $n$ and small $p$, then $X$ is approximately Poisson with mean $\mu = np$.

### 40.2.1 Examples

(1)     $X$ has a Poisson distribution with mean 3. Find the probability that (a) $X = 2$ (b)$X \geq 2$.

Solution

a.      Use the formula with $\mu = 3$.

$$P(X = 3) = e^{-3}3^2/2!$$

The probability that $X$ is 2 is 0.224

b.      If $X$ is greater or equal to 2, then it cannot be 0 or 1.

$$P(X \geq 2) = 1 - P(X = 0 \text{ or } X = 1) = 1 - (e^{-3}3^0/0! + e^{-3}3^1/1!)$$

**The probability that X is at least 2 is 0.801**

(2)     On average, there are 2 misprints on each page of a newspaper. Assuming a Poisson distribution for the number of misprints, find the probabilities that there are (a) 3 misprints on page 1 (b) 5 misprints on the first two pages.

Solution

a.      For the first page, the distribution of the number of misprints is Poisson with mean 2. Use the formula:

**The probability of 3 misprints is**
$$e^{-2}2^3/3! = 0.180$$

b.     The number of misprints on the first two pages has a Poisson distribution with mean 4. Use the formula:

**The probability of 5 misprints is**
$$e^{-4}4^5/5! = 0.156$$

## 40.2.2 Exercises

(1) $X$ has a Poisson distribution with mean $1\frac{1}{2}$. Find the probabilities that:

(a)  $X = 3$  (b)  $X = 0$

(c)  $X \leq 2$  (d)  $X \geq 2$

(2) The distribution of $X$ is Poisson with mean 5. Find the following probabilities:

(a)  $P(X = 3)$  (b)  $P(X = 2 \text{ or } 4)$

(c)  $P(X < 3)$  (d)  $P(X \geq 2)$

(3) The number of letters a man receives each day has a Poisson distribution with mean 3. Find the probabilities that:

(a)  In one day he receives 4 letters.  (b)  In two days he receives 6 letters.

(4) The number of meteorites which fall on a field in a year has a Poisson distribution with mean $\frac{1}{2}$. Find the probabilities that:

(a) 2 meteorites fall in a year (b) No meteorites fall in 6 months.

(5) The number of customers in an antique shop in an hour follows a Poisson distribution with mean 4. Find the probabilities that:

a.  There will be 6 customers in an hour.

b.  There will be 5 customers in two hours.

c.  There will be at least one customer in half an hour.

(6) The number of goals in a football match follows a Poisson distribution with mean 3. Find the probability that:

(a) There will be 2 goals in the match.

(b) The score will be 0-0 at half-time.

(7) The number of buses which arrive at a bus-stop over a period of an hour follows a Poisson distribution with mean 4. Find the probabilities of:

(a)  3 buses in one hour  (b)  6 buses in 2 hours

(c)  1 bus in 15 minutes  (d)  At least 1 bus in half an hour.

(8) The number of cases of a certain rare disease in a town follows a Poisson distribution. The probability that there are no cases at all in the town is $\frac{1}{2}$.

  a.  Find the expected number $\mu$ of cases.

  b.  Find the probability that there are exactly 2 cases.

(9) The number of telephone calls I receive in a day has a Poisson distribution. The probability that I receive no calls is $\frac{1}{4}$. Find the average number of calls I receive in a day, and find the probability that in 2 days I receive a total of 5 calls.

(10) The number of flaws in a length of cloth follows a Poisson distribution. One in twenty of the lengths has no flaws at all. Find the probability that a length has 4 flaws.

(11) A certain rare disease afflicts 0.000002 of the population. A town has a population of 100,000. Assuming that the number of cases in the town follows a Poisson distribution, find the probability that there are 2 cases in the town.

(12) It is thought that the proportion of bad eggs is 0.002. Find the probability of 1 bad egg in a batch of 1000.

(13) The probability that an answer in the back of a Mathematics textbook is wrong is 0.003. Find the probability that in a hundred answers there will be at least two mistakes.

(14) 2% of the population has a certain disease. 60 people are chosen at random. Find the probability that there are 2 cases of the disease among them:

  a.  By using the binomial distribution.

  b.  By using the Poisson approximation.

## 40.3 Examination Questions

(1) In order to qualify for a quiz contest, at least three students out of a team of four have to pass a test. To pass this test, a student has to answer correctly at least two questions out of five. The probability of a student answering any particular question correctly is $\frac{1}{3}$. Show that the probability of a student passing the test is $\frac{131}{243}$.

Hence calculate, to three significant figures, the probability that the team qualifies for the quiz contest.

[L add]

(2) A golfer has a probability of $\frac{1}{3}$ of holing his first putt. In a round of nine holes he attempts five such putts. What is the probability that he holes

i. exactly three of these putts;

ii. less than three of these putts?

If he fails to hole a putt at the first attempt, the probability that he will hole the putt at the second attempt is $\frac{3}{4}$. In another round of nine holes he fails on four occasions to hole his first putt. What is the probability that at the second attempt he holes more putts than he misses?

[MEI add]

(3) The server at tennis is required to serve the ball into a specified region of the court. If a first attempted serve is out of this region (a fault) then a second serve is allowed. If the second serve is also out of the specified region then this is called a double-fault. Forty per cent of McLendl's first serves are faults as are ten per cent of his second serves. Assuming that the outcome of each of McLendl's attempted serves is independent of all previous outcomes, determine the probability that

i. a sequence of four of his first attempted serves contains precisely one fault,

ii. McLendl serves a double-fault.

After each of McLendl's serves (or pair of serves) either he or his opponent wins a point. If his first serve is not a fault then there is a probability of 0.8 that he wins the point; the corresponding probability for a second serve is 0.3. In the event of his serving a double-fault his opponent wins the point. Show that the overall probability of McLendl winning the point is 0.588.

In competing for four successive points, McLendl has three first serves that are not faults and one second serve that is not a fault. Determine the probability that he wins exactly three of the four points.

[C]

(4) A discrete random variable $X$ has a Poisson distribution given by

$$P(X = r) = e^{-a}a^r/r!, r = 0, 1, 2, \ldots$$

Prove that the mean of $X$ is $a$.

A garage has two cars $A$ and $B$ which it hires out on a daily basis (for a complete day). The number of demands per day follows a Poisson distribution with mean 2.5. Find the most probable number of demands per day.

Calculate, each correct to 3 significant figures,

i. the percentage of days when at least one demand would have to be refused;

ii. the probability that on two successive days a total of two demands will have to be refused;

iii. the probability of car $A$ being idle on a particular day if the cars are used equally.

[SUJB]

(5) A randomly chosen doctor in general practice sees, on average, one case of a broken nose per year and each case is independent of other similar cases.

i. Regarding a month as a twelfth part of a year,
(a) show that the probability that, between them three such doctors see no cases of a broken nose in a period of one month is 0.779, correct to three significant figures,
(b) find the variance of the number of cases seen by three such doctors in a period of six months.

ii. Find the probability that, between them, three such doctors see at least three cases in one year.

iii. Find the probability that, of three such doctors, one sees three cases and the other two see no cases in one year.

[C]

(6) An advertising display contains a large number of light bulbs which are continually being switched on and off. Individual lights fail at random times, and each day the display is inspected and any failed lights are replaced. The number of lights that fail in any one-day period has a Poisson distribution with mean 2.2. Calculate

i. the probability that no light will need to be replaced on a particular day,

ii. the probability that at least four lights will need to be replaced on a particular day,

iii. the least number of consecutive days after which the probability of at least one light having to be replaced exceeds 0.9999.

Calculate also the probability that, in a period of seven days, at least four lights will need to be replaced on at least two days.

[C]

## COMMON ERRORS

### (1) Binomial Distribution

a. You can only use the binomial distribution if the repeated trials are independent. If this is not the case then some other distribution must be used.

b. Do not forget the $^nC_r$ term when working out binomial probabilities.

c. Do not be vague about what you are dealing with. If a problem involves the number of sixes when a die is rolled 20 times, do not write. *The sixes are binomial.* State clearly: "Let $X$ be the number of sixes: $X$ has a binomial distribution, with $n$ equal to 20 and $p$ equal to $\frac{1}{6}$". To save space you may use the abbreviation: $X \sim B(20, \frac{1}{6})$.

### (2) Poisson Distribution

a. Suppose $X$ is Poisson with mean $\mu$, and you are asked for $P(X > 2)$. You cannot calculate this directly: you must calculate this by taking $P(X > 2) = 1 - P(X \leq 2)$.

b. The Poisson approximation to the binomial is only valid for large $n$ and small $p$. As a rough guide, $n$ should be at least 50 and $p$ at most 0.02.

# 41 Continuous Random Variables

## 41.1 Probability Density Function, Expectation and Variance

If $X$ is a random variable which can take any value from a continuous range, then $X$ is a *continuous random variable*.

The *Probability Density Function*, or *p.d.f.*, $f(x)$ of $X$ gives the density of the probability of $X$ at each point. Hence if $\delta x$ is a small number:

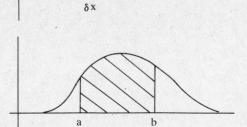

$P(x \leq X \leq x + \delta x) \simeq f(x)\delta x.$

The probability that $X$ lies within a certain range is found by integrating the p.d.f of $X$ along that range.

$$P(a \leq X \leq b) = \int_a^b f(x)dx$$

If $f(x)$ is a p.d.f., then it must be non-negative and the total area under its curve must be 1.

$$f(x) \geq 0 \text{ and } \int_{-\infty}^{\infty} f(x)dx = 1.$$

A random variable whose p.d.f. is constant is called *uniform* or *rectangular*.

The *Expectation* $E(X)$ of $x$ is found by the formula:

$$E(X) = \int_{-\infty}^{\infty} xf(x)dx$$

The *variance* of $X$ is found from the same formula as for a discrete random variable.

$$Var(X) = E(X^2) - (E(X))^2$$

Here $E(X^2)$ is $\int x^2 f(x)dx$

## 41.1.1 Example

(1)  $X$ is a continuous random variable which takes values between 0 and 1, with p.d.f. $f(x) = kx^2$ for $0 \leq x \leq 1$, where $k$ is a constant. Find (a) $k$, (b) the mean of $X$ (c) the variance of $X$, (d) the median of $X$.

Solution

a.  The total amount of probability must be 1.

$$\int_0^1 kx^2 dx = 1$$

$$[kx^3/3]_0^1 = 1$$

$$k = 3$$

b.     Use the formula for expectation.

$$E(X) = \int_0^1 x3x^2 dx = [\frac{3}{4}x^4]_0^1$$

**The mean of X is** $\frac{3}{4}$

c.     First find the expectation of $X^2$.

$$E(X^2) = \int_0^1 x^2 3x^2 dx = [\frac{3}{5}x^5]_0^1 = \frac{3}{5}$$

Now use the formula for variance.

**The variance of X is** $\frac{3}{5} - (\frac{3}{4})^2 = 0.0375$

d.     The median $m$ is such that the probability that $X$ is less than $m$ is $\frac{1}{2}$.

$$P(X \leq m) = \int_0^m 3x^2 dx = \frac{1}{2}$$

$$\frac{1}{2} = [x^3]_0^m = m^3$$

$$m = \sqrt[3]{\frac{1}{2}} = 0.794$$

### 41.1.2 Exercises

(1) $X$ is a continuous random variable with p.d.f given by the function:

$$f(x) = \begin{cases} 0 \text{ for } x < 0 \\ 4x^3 \text{ for } 0 \leq x \leq 1. \\ 0 \text{ for } x > 1 \end{cases}$$

(a)   Check that $f(x)$ is a p.d.f.   (b)   Find $P(X \geq \frac{1}{2})$

(c)   Find $P(\frac{1}{4} \leq X \leq \frac{3}{4})$       (d)   Find $P(X \leq \frac{1}{8})$

(2) $X$ is a continuous random variable with p.d.f. as follows:

$$f(x) = \begin{cases} 0 \text{ for } x < 0 \\ 1 - \frac{1}{2}x \text{ for } 0 \leq x \leq 2 \\ 0 \text{ for } x > 2. \end{cases}$$

(a)   Check that $f(x)$ is a p.d.f.   (b)   Sketch the graph of $f(x)$

(c)   Find $P(X \geq 1\frac{1}{2})$           (d)   Find $P(\frac{1}{2} \leq X \leq 1.8)$

(3) The p.d.f of $X$ is given by the formula:

$$f(x) = \begin{cases} 0 \text{ for } x \leq 1 \\ 2/x^3 \text{ for } x \geq 1 \end{cases}$$

(a)   Check that $f(x)$ is a pdf.   (b)   Sketch the graph of $f(x)$

(c)   Find $P(1 < X < 2)$           (d)   $P(X \geq 3)$

(4) The p.d.f. of $X$ is $f(x) = kx$ for $0 \leq x \leq 1$, and 0 elsewhere. Find the value of $k$.

(5) The p.d.f. of $X$ is $f(x) = 2 - kx$ for $0 \leq x \leq 1$, and 0 elsewhere. Find the value of $k$.

(6) The p.d.f of $X$ is $f(x) = k/x^2$ for $x \geq 2$, and 0 elsewhere. Find the value of $k$.

(7) The p.d.f. of $X$ is $f(x) = x^2$ for $0 \leq x \leq b$. Find the value of $b$.

(8) The p.d.f. of $X$ is $f(x) = \frac{1}{2} + x$ for $1 \leq x \leq c$. Find the value of $c$.

(9) and (10) For each of the distributions in Questions 1 and 2, find (a) the mean (b) the variance (c) the median.

(11) Find the mean and median for the distribution of Question 3. Show that the variance does not exist.

(12) $X$ is uniform between 2 and 5. Find the p.d.f. of $X$.

(13) $X$ is uniform between $a$ and $b$, where $a < b$. Find the p.d.f. of $X$.

(14) $X$ is uniform between $-1$ and $k$, with p.d.f. $f(x) = 0.1$ for $-1 \leq x \leq k$. Find the value of $k$.

(15) $X$ has p.d.f given by the function:

$$f(x) = \begin{cases} 0 \text{ for } x < -1 \\ \frac{1}{2}(x+1) \text{ for } -1 \leq x \leq 0 \\ \frac{1}{2}(1 - \frac{1}{3}x) \text{ for } 0 \leq x \leq 3 \\ 0 \text{ for } x > 3 \end{cases}$$

(a)   Check that $f(x)$ is a p.d.f.   (b)   Find $P(X \geq 1)$

(c)   Find $P(-\frac{1}{2} \leq X \leq 2)$   (d)   Find $E(X)$

(e)   Find $Var(X)$.

## 41.2 Cumulative Frequency

The *Cumulative Frequency* of a random variable $X$ at a point $x$ is the probability that $X$ is less than $x$.

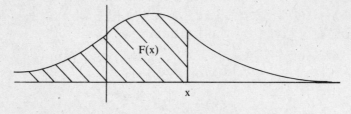

$$P(X < x) = \int_{-\infty}^{x} f(x)dx$$

The function $F(x)$ giving the cumulative frequency is the *cumulative distribution function,* or *c.d.f.* The c.d.f. is the integral of the p.d.f., and the p.d.f is the derivative of the c.d.f.

$$F(x) = \int f(x)dx : f(x) = dF(x)/dx$$

### 41.2.1 Examples

(1)        $X$ is a continuous random variable with p.d.f. given by:

$$f(x) = \begin{cases} 0 \text{ for } x < 0 \\ ke^{-\lambda x} \text{ for } x \geq 0. \end{cases}$$

Find the value of $k$ and the c.d.f. of $X$.

Solution     Use the definition of a p.d.f.

$$1 = \int_{0}^{\infty} ke^{-\lambda x}dx = [-(k/\lambda)e^{-\lambda x}]_{0}^{\infty} = k/\lambda$$

$$\mathbf{k = \lambda}$$

Use the definition of a c.d.f.

$$F(x) = \int_0^x \lambda e^{-\lambda x} dx = [-e^{-\lambda x}]_0^x$$

$$\mathbf{F(x) = 1 - e^{-\lambda x}}$$

(2) The probability that a light-bulb will last more than $x$ years is $e^{-2x}$. Find the p.d.f. of the lifetime of a bulb. Find the probability that a 1 year old bulb will last for a further 2 years.

Solution Let $X$ be the lifetime. $X$ is a continuous random variable. From the information given:

$$P(X > x) = e^{-2x}$$

The c.d.f. of $x$ is given by:

$$F(x) = P(X \le x) = 1 - P(X > x) = 1 - e^{-2x}$$

$$\textbf{The p.d.f. of X is } d\mathbf{F(x)}/dx = 2e^{-2x}$$

If the bulb is a year old then $X$ is at least 1. Use the formula for conditional probability:

$$P(X > 3 | X > 1) = \frac{P(X > 3 \& X > 1)}{P(X > 1)} = \frac{P(X > 3)}{P(X > 1)}$$

$$\textbf{The probability is } e^{-6}/e^{-2} = e^{-4}$$

### 41.2.2 Exercises

(1) Find the c.d.f. for the distributions with p.d.f.s given below.

(a)  $f(x) = 4x^3$ for $0 \le x \le 1$      (b)  $f(x) = 1 - \frac{1}{2}x$ for $0 \le x \le 2$

(c)  $f(x) = \sin x$ for $0 \le x \le \pi/2$   (d)  $f(x) = 1/x^2$ for $x \ge 1$

(2) Find the p.d.f. for the functions with the following c.d.f.s:

(a)  $F(x) = \frac{1}{2}x + \frac{1}{2}x^2$ for $0 \le x \le 1$   (b)  $F(x) = 1 - 4/x^2$ for $x \ge 2$

(c)  $F(x) = \sin 2x$ for $0 \le x \le \frac{1}{4}\pi$   (d)  $F(x) = 1 - e^{-3x}$ for $x \ge 0$

(3) to (5) Find the c.d.f. of each of the distributions given in Questions 1 to 3 of 41.1.2.

(6) The c.d.f. of a continuous random variable is $F(x) = x + \frac{1}{2}x^2$ for $0 \le x \le k$. Find the value of $k$.

(7) The c.d.f of $X$ is $F(x) = kx + \frac{1}{8}x^2$ for $0 \leq x \leq 2$. Find the value of $k$.

(8) The lifetime $X$ of a car tyre is a continuous random variable with p.d.f. $f(x) = 1/(x+1)^2$, where $x$ is measured in thousands of miles. Find the probability that the tyre lasts more than 5,000 miles.

(9) If the tyre of Question 8 has lasted 1,000 miles, what is the probability that it will last for a further 3,000 miles?

(10) When I arrive at a bus stop, the probability that I will have to wait more than $x$ minutes is $e^{-x/15}$.

a.  Find the p.d.f. of the time I have to wait.

b.  Find the mean time that I must wait.

c.  Find the median time that I must wait.

d.  If I have waited for 30 minutes, what is the probability that I will have to wait a further 15 minutes?

(11) $X$ is uniformly distributed between $a$ and $b$. Find the c.d.f. of $X$. Find the mean and the variance of $X$.

## 41.3 Examination Questions

(1) The size, $X$ mm, of a certain component used in the construction of an electrical appliance is found to have a continuous probability density function given by

$$f(x) = \begin{cases} cx(4-x), & 0 \leq x \leq 3, \\ 0, & \text{elsewhere}, \end{cases}$$

where $c$ is a positive constant.

(i)  Show that $c = \frac{1}{9}$  (ii)  Calculate the mean and variance of $X$.

[AEB add 1987]

(2) A random variable $X$ has probability density function

$$f(x) = \begin{cases} k(4-x^2), & 0 \leq x \leq 2, \\ 0 & \text{otherwise}. \end{cases}$$

Prove that $k = \frac{3}{16}$. Find the probability that $X$ has a value greater than $1\frac{1}{2}$. Find also the mean and variance of $X$.

[You may leave your answers as fractions in their lowest terms]

[O&C]

(3) A continuous random variable $X$ has probability density function

$f(x) = k(2 - x) \quad 0 \le x \le 2$

$f(x) = 0 \qquad\qquad$ otherwise

where $k$ is a constant. Obtain an expression for $P(X \le t)$, the probability that $x$ is less than or equal to $t$, in terms of $k$ and $t$, where $t$ is a value such that $0 \le t \le 2$. By substituting $t = 2$, verify that $k = \frac{1}{2}$.

Using the expression for $P(X \le t)$ above, or otherwise, determine the probability $P(\frac{1}{2} \le X \le 1\frac{1}{2})$.

[NI]

(4) The guarantee by a retailer ensures that a faulty television tube is replaced within the first year of purchase. The probability distribution of the life of the tube can be modelled by

$f(x) \quad = \quad A/x^4 \text{ for } 1 \le x \le \infty,$

$f(x) \quad = \quad 0 \text{ for } x < 1,$

where $x$ is the lifetime in years. Find,

  (i)   the value of $A$;   (ii)   the mean and variance of $x$;

(iii) the probability that the tube lasts longer than five years.

Show that, if a tube has lasted for $n$ years, the probability that it will fail during the next year is

$$1 - \left(\frac{n}{n + 1}\right)^3$$

[SUJB]

(5) The random variable $X$ has a rectangular distribution whose probability density function $f(x)$ is given by

$$f(x) = \begin{cases} \frac{1}{6} \text{ for } -2 \le x \le 4, \\ 0 \text{ otherwise.} \end{cases}$$

Sketch the probability density function of $X$ and hence, or otherwise, find the probabilities that

  (i)   $X \le 2,$                    (ii)   $|X| \le 2,$

(iii)   $|X| \le x$ for $0 \le x \le 2,$    (iv)   $|X| \le x$ for $2 < x \le 4,$

(v) $|X| \leq x$ for $x > 4$.

Hence obtain, and sketch, the probability density function of $|X|$. Thus determine the mean of $|X|$.

[MEI]

(6) A continuous random variable $T$ has a negative exponential distribution given by

$$f(t) = Ae^{-t/a}, t \geq 0$$
$$= 0 \text{ elsewhere}$$

Show that $A = 1/a$ and that the mean and variance of $T$ are $a$ and $a^2$ respectively.

(You may assume that $\int_0^\infty t^n e^{-t/a} dt = a^{n+1} n!$ for integral values of $n$.)

The life in hours of a type of electric battery can be modelled by the above distribution and when a sample of 800 is tested the mean life is found to be 92.2 h. What are the values of $A$ and $a$ based on this figure?

i. What is the probability that battery will last for at least 200 h?

ii. If a battery has lasted 200 h what is the probability that it will last for at least a further 100 h?

iii. If two batteries are bought what is the probability that one fails before 200 h and the other after 200 h?

[SUJB]

## COMMON ERRORS

### (1) Continuous variables

a. The p.d.f. $f(x)$ does not give the probability that $X = x$. (For a continuous variable that probability is zero.) Probabilities are only obtained after $f(x)$ has been integrated, as in:

$$P(a \leq x \leq b) = \int_a^b f(x) dx$$

b. Do not worry about whether you have $P(X < a)$ or $P(X \leq a)$. If $X$ is continuous, these are numerically equal.

c. Do not forget the conditions that $f(x) \geq 0$ and $\int f(x) dx = 1$.

d. Mistakes are often made when evaluating the definite integral of the exponential function. That is:

$$\int_0^\infty e^{-x} dx = [-e^{-x}]_0^\infty$$

At the top end, when $x$ tends to $\infty$ then $e^{-x}$ tends to 0. (Not 1, or $\infty$). At the bottom end, when $x = 0$ then $e^{-x} = 1$. (Not 0).

## (2) **Expectation and Variance**

a.  When finding $E(X)$ you must integrate $xf(x)$. You do not integrate $f(x)$ and then multiply by $x$.

b.  When finding $E(X^2)$ you integrate $x^2 f(x)$. You do not integrate $xf(x)$ and then square the result.

## (3) **Cumulative Frequency**

a.  A c.d.f. must be positive and increasing, and it must be 0 at its left hand end and 1 at its right hand end. If it does not obey these conditions then it cannot be a c.d.f.

b.  To go from the p.d.f. to the c.d.f. you integrate. To go from the c.d.f. to the p.d.f. you differentiate. Do not get these the wrong way round.

# 42 Sampling and Estimation

## 42.1 Sums of Random Variables

Suppose $X$ and $Y$ are random variables, and $a$ and $b$ are constant. The means and variances of combinations of $X$ and $Y$ are given by the following:

$$E(X + Y) = E(X) + E(Y) : E(X - Y) = E(X) - E(Y)$$

$$E(aX) = aE(X) : E(aX + bY) = aE(X) + b(E(Y).$$

$$E(X + a) = E(X) + a$$

$$Var(aX) = a^2 Var(X) : Var(X + a) = Var(X).$$

If $X$ and $Y$ are independent, then the following are also true:

$$E(XY) = E(X) \times E(Y).$$

$$Var(X + Y) = Var(X) + Var(Y) : Var(X - Y) = Var(X) + Var(Y).$$

$$Var(aX + bY) = a^2 Var(X) + b^2 Var(Y).$$

### 42.1.2 Example

Suppose $X$ and $Y$ are independent variables with means 2 and 3 respectively and variances 3 and 4 respectively.

i.    Find the mean of $X + 2Y^2 + 1$.

ii.    Find constants $a$ and $b$ so that $aX + bY$ has mean 13 and variance 48.

Solution    i. First use the fact that
$Var(Y) = E(Y^2) - (E(Y))^2$ to show that $E(Y^2) = 13$.
$E(X + 2Y^2 + 1) = E(X) + 2E(Y^2) + 1$

### The mean of $X + 2Y^2 + 1$ is 29

ii. Use the formulae above to find two equations in $a$ and $b$.

$2a + 3b = 13$   :   $3a^2 + 4b^2 = 48$

Solve these equations simultaneously:

### $a = 2$ and $b = 3$

### 42.1.2 Exercises

(1) $X$ is a random variable with mean 3 and variance 5. Find the following:

(a)   $E(2X)$          (b)   $Var(3X)$

(c)   $E(X^2)$          (d)   $E(3X - 13)$

(e)   $Var(2X + 3)$   (f)   $E(2X^2 - 3X + 2)$

(2) $X$ and $Y$ are independent random variables with expectations 5 and 3 respectively, and variances 4 and 1 respectively. Find the following:

(a)   $E(X + Y)$        (b)   $Var(X + Y)$

(c)   $E(3XY)$          (d)   $Var(X - Y)$

(e) $E(X + 3Y^2)$   (f) $Var(2X - 3Y - 1)$

(g) $E((X + Y)^2)$   (h) $E((X - Y)^2)$

(3) $X$ is a variable with expectation 5 and variance 12. Find constants $a$ and $b$ so that $aX + b$ has expectation 10 and variance 48.

(4) $Y$ is a variable with mean 8 and variance 64. Find constants $a$ and $b$ so that $aY + b$ has mean 0 and variance 1.

(5) $Z$ is a variable with mean $\mu$ and variance $\sigma^2$. Find constants $a$ and $b$ so that $aZ + b$ has mean 0 and variance 1.

(6) $X$ and $Y$ are independent variables, each with mean 2 and variance 4. Find constants $a$ and $b$ so that $aX + bY$ has mean 0 and variance 72.

(7) The amount in $cm^3$ of coffee dispensed by a drinks machine is a variable, with mean 200 and variance 12. The amount of milk it adds has mean 10 and variance 6. Find the mean and variance of the total drink.

While taking it back to his table a customer spills an amount which has mean 40 and variance 20. Find the mean and variance of the amount left to be consumed.

## 42.2 Estimation from Samples

A distribution from which values are taken at random is a *parent* or *background* or *population* distribution.

A value taken from this distribution is a *sample* value.

A *sample of size n* consists of $n$ independent sample values $X_1, X_2, ...X_n$.

A function of the sample is an *unbiased* estimate of the mean $\mu$ if the expectation of the function is $\mu$ itself.

The function is *consistent* if its variance tends to zero as the sample size $n$ tends to infinity.

Let a background distribution X have mean $\mu$ and variance $\sigma^2$. Suppose $X_1, X_2, ...X_n$ is a sample from $X$ of size $n$. The *sample mean* is the average of the sample.

$$\overline{X} = (X_1 + X_2 + ... + X_n)/n$$

The expectation and variance of the sample mean are given by:

$$E(\overline{X}) = \mu \text{ and } Var(\overline{X}) = \sigma^2/n$$

It follows that $\overline{X}$ is an unbiased and consistent estimator of $\mu$.

The standard deviation of $\overline{X}$ is the *standard error*. It is given by the formula:

$$SE(\overline{X}) = \sigma/\sqrt{n}$$

Suppose a proportion $\pi$ of a large population has a certain property. A sample of size $n$ is taken from the population, and $m$ of the sample have the property. The *sample proportion* is the proportion of the sample which have the property.

$$\theta = m/n$$

The expectation and variance of the sample proportion are given by:

$$E(\theta) = \pi \text{ and } Var(\theta) = \pi(1-\pi)/n$$

The sample proportion is an unbiased and consistent estimator of the population proportion.

### 42.2.1 Examples

(1)      A machine produces ball-bearings whose diameter has variance 0.001 cm but whose mean $\mu$ is unknown. A sample of 12 ball-bearings had diameters:
1.11, 1.12. 1.12, 1.13, 1.09, 1.08, 1.09, 1.11, 1.10, 1.11, 1.12, 1.11
Estimate the background mean, and give the standard error of your estimation.

Solution      Estimate the background mean $\mu$ by the sample mean $\overline{X}$.

$$\overline{X} = (1.11 + 1.12 + ... + 1.11)/12$$

**The estimate for the true mean is 1.1075**

The standard error is the square root of 0.001/12.

**The standard error is 0.009**

(2)      An opinion poll was taken on two days: on the first day 200 people were questioned, of whom 45% supported the Freedom Party. The next day 42% of a sample of 300 supported it. Estimate the true support for the party.

Solution      In all, 500 people were questioned. The number who supported the Freedom Party was $200 \times 0.45 + 300 \times 0.42 = 216$.

**The proportion is estimated at 216/500 = 43.2%**

### 42.2.2 Exercises

(1) The following figures were taken from a distribution with variance 20. Estimate the mean of the distribution, and state the standard error.

$$23, 25, 16, 30, 29, 17, 17, 24, 26$$

(2) The following figures were taken from a distribution with variance 0.01. Estimate the mean, and find the standard error.

$$3.04, \ 3.21, \ 3.11, \ 3.09, \ 2.99, \ 2.97, \ 3.05$$

(3) The average weight of a group of 100 people was 70 kg, and that of a further group of 200 people was 73 kg. Assuming that the two groups come from the same parent distribution, estimate the mean of that distribution.

(4) Three groups containing 100, 250, 400 tomatoes had average weights 100 g, 90 g, 95 g respectively. Assuming that the tomatoes all came from the same background distribution estimate the mean of that distribution.

(5) A sample of 100 eggs was examined, and 3 were found to be bad. Estimate the probability that an egg picked at random will be bad.

(6) Two samples of apples, of sizes 100 and 250, were tested. The proportion of underweight apples was 0.1 in the first and 0.16 in the second. Assuming that the apples come from the same parent distribution estimate the proportion of underweight apples.

(7) A distribution $X$ is thought to be binomial $B(n, p)$ with $n = 3$. A sample of 100 was tested, with the following results:

| Value of $X$ | 0 | 1 | 2 | 3 |
|---|---|---|---|---|
| Frequency | 40 | 44 | 14 | 2 |

Estimate the mean of $X$. Hence estimate the value of $p$.

(8) A distribution $X$ is thought to be binomial $B(n, p)$ with $n = 4$. A sample of 200 was tested, with the following results:

| Value of $X$ | 0 | 1 | 2 | 3 | 4 |
|---|---|---|---|---|---|
| Frequency | 0 | 5 | 31 | 82 | 82 |

Estimate the value of $p$.

(9) A distribution is thought to be Poisson with unknown mean $\mu$. A sample of 50 gave the following results:

| Value of $X$ | 0 | 1 | 2 | 3+ |
|---|---|---|---|---|
| Frequency | 27 | 16 | 5 | 2 |

Estimate the value of $\mu$.

(10) A distribution is thought to be Poisson with unknown mean $\mu$. A sample of 200 gave the following results:

| Value of $X$ | 0 | 1 | 2 | 3 | 4+ |
|---|---|---|---|---|---|
| Frequency | 60 | 72 | 43 | 18 | 7 |

Estimate the value of $\mu$.

(11) $X$ and $Y$ are independent variables with the same (unknown) mean $\mu$. Constants $a$ and $b$ are found so that $Z = aX + bY$ is an estimator of $\mu$.

i.   Show that if $Z$ is an unbiased estimator, then $a + b = 1$
ii.  Suppose that $Var(X) = 1$ and $Var(Y) = 4$. How should $a$ and $b$ be chosen so that $Z$ has minimal variance?

## 42.3 Estimation of the Sample Variance

Let $X_1, X_2, ... X_n$ be a sample from a distribution with mean $\mu$ and variance $\sigma^2$. The *sample variance* $S^2$ is defined by:

$$S^2 = \frac{\sum(X_i - \overline{X})^2}{n} = \frac{\sum X_i^2 - n\overline{X}^2}{n}$$

$S^2$ is biased, in that $E(S^2) = (n-1)\sigma^2/n$

The *unbiased sample variance* is defined by:

$$\hat{\sigma}^2 = \frac{nS^2}{n-1} = \frac{\sum(X_i - \overline{X})^2}{n-1} = \frac{\sum X_i^2 - n\overline{X}^2}{n-1}$$

### 42.3.1 Example

Find the unbiased sample variance for the following figures:

23, 22, 31, 26, 25, 25, 26, 26, 24, 28, 30

Solution    The mean is found as in 42.2.

$$\overline{X} = 26$$

Use the formula for the unbiased sample variance:

$$\hat{\sigma}^2 = \frac{\sum X_i^2 - n\overline{X}^2}{n-1} = \frac{23^2 + 22^2 + ... + 30^2 - 11 \times 26^2}{10}$$

**The unbiased sample variance is 7.6**

## 42.3.2 Exercises

(1) Find the sample variance and the unbiased sample variance for the following sets of figures:

a.  55, 56, 54, 54, 55, 56, 57, 53, 52
b.  102, 99, 110, 94, 112, 120, 89, 100
c.  0.014, 0.009, 0.017, 0.012, 0.010, 0.011, 0.019
d.  —1.7, —1.2, —2, 0.2, 0.1, —1, —1.5, —1.6, —0.8, —0.4

(2) Find the sample variance and the unbiased sample variance for the samples which have frequency tables as below:

(a)

| Value | 1 | 2 | 3 | 4 | 5 |
|---|---|---|---|---|---|
| Frequency | 14 | 9 | 4 | 2 | 1 |

(b)

| Value | −1 | 0 | 1 | 2 | 3 |
|---|---|---|---|---|---|
| Frequency | 2 | 9 | 18 | 16 | 4 |

(c)

| Value | 98 | 99 | 100 | 101 | 102 |
|---|---|---|---|---|---|
| Frequency | 12 | 23 | 38 | 16 | 3 |

(3) A sample of size 10 was taken from a distribution. The sum of the values was 23, and the sum of the squares of the values was 55. Find the unbiased sample variance.

(4) In the following, $n$ is the sample size, $\sum X$ is the sum of the sample values, $\sum X^2$ is the sum of the squares of the values. Find the unbiased sample variance in each case.

(a)  $n = 8, \sum X = 300, \sum X^2 = 20,000$   (b)  $n = 15, \sum X = 23, \sum X^2 = 60$

## 42.4 Use of Random Numbers

*Random digits* are equally likely to be any of the 10 digits 0, ... 9. They can be found in books of statistical tables, or from computers and calculators.

They can be used to find samples from any distribution. The cumulative probability of the random number found is matched up with the cumulative probability of the distribution concerned.

### 42.4.1 Example

The numbers 3, 8, 7, 5, 4, 5 are obtained from the random number generator of a calculator. Use these numbers to obtain

a.        one observation from the distribution with p.d.f. $e^{-x}$, for $x \geq 0$,

380

b.        two observations from $B(20, 0.1)$.

Solution    Join the random digits together to form the random number 0.387545. This random number comes from a distribution which is rectangular in the interval $0 \leq x \leq 1$. Hence the cumulative probability up to this number is 0.387545.

Match this up to the cumulative probability for the variable with p.d.f. $e^{-x}$.

$$1 - e^{-x} = 0.387545$$

### The observation is 0.49028

(b) Use the random digits to form two random numbers, 0.387 and 0.545. Accumulate probabilities from $B(20, 0.1)$ until these two values are reached. If $X \sim B(20, 0.1)$ :

$$P(X \leq 0) = 0.122 : P(X \leq 1) = 0.392 : P(X \leq 2) = 0.677.$$

Note that the two random numbers occur in the second and third ranges.

### The observations are 1 and 2

### 42.4.2 Exercises

(1) The number 0.236 is found from the random number generator of a calculator. Use the number to find:

  a.  One observation from the rectangular distribution for $0 \leq x \leq 2$

  b.  Three observations from this distribution.

(2) $X$ is a continuous variable with p.d.f $f(x) = e^{-x}$, for $0 \leq x$. Use the random digits 6, 0, 8, 5, 3, 3 to find (a) one observation of $X$ (b) two observations of $X$ (c) three observations of $X$.

(3) The random numbers 5, 2, 7 were found from a table of random numbers. Use them to find one observation from (a) $B(10, 0.2)$ (b) a variable with a Poisson distribution with mean 0.8.

(4) $X$ is a continuous variable with p.d.f. $f(x) = 1 - \frac{1}{2}x$, for $0 \leq x \leq 2$. The random digits 3, 8, 0, 0, 9, 2 are found. Use them to find from $X$ (a) two observations (b) three observations.

(5) The numbers 4, 4, 6, 9, 1, 3 were found from random number tables. Use them to find:

(a) One observation from $B(6, 0.4)$ (b) Two observations from $B(12, 0.1)$

(6) A roulette wheel has slots numbered from 0 to 36, and the ball is equally likely to land in any of them. Use the random number 0.852 to simulate one spin of the wheel.

(7) Use the random digits 7, 3, 7, 3, 7, 6 to simulate (a) one roll of a fair die (b) 2 rolls of the die (c) 6 rolls of the die.

## 42.5 Examination Questions

(1) The continuous random variable $X$ has probability density function $f(x)$. Define the variance $V(X)$ of $x$ in terms of $f(x)$ and deduce from your definition that, for any constants $a$ and $b$,

$$V(aX + b) = a^2 V(X).$$

Explain why $V(X) \geq 0$.

The random variables $X_1$ and $X_2$ are independent and each has probability density function

$$1/\sqrt{x} - 1, \text{ where } 0 < x < 1, 0 \text{ elsewhere.}$$

Find the variance of $Y = 2X_1 - 4X_2 + 2$. What range of values does $Y$ take?

[O&C]

(2) What are the values of the mean and variance of the number of successes in $n$ independent repetitions of a trial in which the probability of success is $p$?

An ordinary shaped die is biased in such a way that the probabilities of throwing a 1 and a 6 are equal but different from $\frac{1}{6}$. Denote this common probability by $\theta$. Two methods are suggested for estimating $\theta$. These are:

Method 1: Toss the die 20 times; record the number $X$ of sixes that occur; take $P_1 = (X/20)$ as the estimate of $\theta$.

Method 2: Toss the die 10 times; record the total number $Y$ of ones and sixes that occur; take $P_2 = (Y/20)$ as the estimate of $\theta$.

Show that $E(P_1) = E(P_2) = \theta$. Calculate the variances of $P_1$ and $P_2$, and hence decide which of the methods is the better one for estimating $\theta$.

[MEI]

(3) (i) At a garden centre, the sales of flower pots are investigated. A sample of 20 flower pot sales is taken and the number of sales, $f$, of each

size, $x$ inches, of flower pot is recorded below.

| $x$ | 4 | 5 | 6 | 8 | 12 |
|-----|---|---|---|---|----|
| $f$ | 2 | 3 | 6 | 4 | 5  |

Calculate, each to 2 decimal places, the mean and the variance of the sizes of the 20 flower posts sold.

Find, to 2 decimal places, unbiased estimates of the mean and the variance of the population of sizes of flower pots sold by this garden centre.

(ii) The discrete random variable $R$ has probability function $p(r)$ defined by

$$p(0) = p(6) = \frac{1}{16}, \ p(1) = p(4) = \frac{1}{4}, \ p(3) = \frac{3}{8}, \ p(r) = 0 \text{ elsewhere.}$$

Find $E(R)$ and $Var(R)$. Find the mean and variance of (a) $2R - 5$, (b) $R_1 - R_2$, where $R_1$ and $R_2$ are independent observations of $R$.

[L]

(4) The discrete random variable $X$ has the distribution $P(X = 1) = 0.4, P(X = 2) = 0.2, P(X = 3) = 0.4$. Calculate the variance of $X$.

Let $X_1$ and $X_2$ denote two independent observations of $X$. Derive the sampling distribution of $T = \frac{1}{2}(X_1 - X_2)^2$, and verify that $T$ is an unbiased estimator of the variance of $x$.

[W]

## COMMON ERRORS
### (1) Sums of Random Variables

a. If $X$ and $Y$ are subtracted, their variances are added. (Not subtracted).

b. Variances can only be added together if the variables concerned are independent.

c. If $X$ is multiplied by $c$, then its variance is multiplied by $c^2$. (Not by $c$).

d. If $c$ is added to $X$, then its variance is unchanged. Do not add $c$ to the variance.

### (2) Samples

Do not confuse the population mean $\mu$ and the sample mean $\overline{X}$. $\mu$ is a fixed number, even though it may be unknown. $\overline{X}$ is a random variable, though as the sample size increases $\overline{X}$ tends to the fixed value $\mu$.

# 43 The Normal Distribution

The probability density function of the *normal distribution* has a graph which is the familiar bell-shaped curve.

The fact that a random variable $X$ is normal with mean $\mu$ and variance $\sigma^2$ is often written as $X \sim N(\mu, \sigma^2)$.

## 43.1 Use of Tables

If $Z$ is normal with mean 0 and variance 1, then Z has the *standard normal distribution*. In symbols, $Z \sim N(0, 1)$.

The cumulative distribution function of $Z$ is called $\Phi(z)$.

$$\Phi(z) = P(Z < z)$$

Values of $\Phi(z)$ can be found from the statistical tables on page 504. The tables give $\Phi(z)$ for $z \geq 0$. For negative values of $z$ use the formula $\Phi(z) = 1 - \Phi(-z)$.

If $X$ is a normal variable, then $X$ can be converted to the standard normal variable as follows:

$$\text{If } \mathbf{X} \sim \mathbf{N}(\mu, \sigma^2), \text{ then } \frac{X - \mu}{\sigma} = \mathbf{Z} \sim \mathbf{N(0, 1)}$$

### 43.1.1 Examples

(1)     Let $X \sim N(3, 25)$. Find the probability that $X$ is less than 5.

Solution     Convert $X$ to the standard form by the formula above.

$$P(X < 5) = P\left( \frac{X - 3}{5} < \frac{5 - 3}{5} \right) = P(Z < 0.4) = \Phi(0.4)$$

Use the tables to find $\Phi$ (0.4)

**The probability that $X$ is less than 5 is 0.655**

(2)     Find the upper quartile of the standard normal distribution.

Solution     The upper quartile is the value $u$ such that
$P(Z < u) = \frac{3}{4}$. Look through the normal tables for the value of $z$ such that $\Phi(z) = \frac{3}{4}$.

**The upper quartile of Z is 0.674**

(3)     The weights of the apples from a certain tree follow a normal distribution. A quarter of the apples weigh less than 70 g, and a third weigh more than 120 g. Find the average weight of the apples.

Solution     Let $X$ be the weight of an apple picked at random. $X \sim N(\mu, \sigma^2)$. From the information given:

$$P(X < 70) = \frac{1}{4} \text{ and } P(X > 120) = \frac{1}{3}.$$

Standardize these values:

$$\Phi((70 - \mu)/\sigma) = \frac{1}{4} \text{ and } \Phi((120 - \mu)/\sigma) = \frac{2}{3}$$

Use the tables to obtain:

$$70 - \mu = -0.674\sigma \text{ and } 120 - \mu = 0.43\sigma$$

Solve to find that $\sigma = 45.3$ and $\mu = 100.5$.

**The average apple weighs 100.5 g.**

## 43.1.2 Exercises

(1) $Z$ has the standard normal distribution $N(0, 1)$. Find the following:

(a) $P(Z < 2\frac{1}{2})$      (b) $P(Z > 1\frac{1}{2})$

(c) $P(Z < -1.4)$      (d) $P(Z > -2.7)$

(e) $P(0.3 < Z < 1.4)$    (f) $P(-0.2 < Z < 1.2)$

(2) $Z \sim N(0, 1)$. Find the values of $a$ satisfying the following:

(a) $P(Z < a) = 0.8$    (b) $P(Z > a) = 0.3$

(c) $P(Z > a) = 0.54$    (d) $P(Z < a) = 0.12$

(3) $X$ has a normal distribution with mean 3 and variance 4. Find the following:

(a) $P(X < 4)$      (b) $P(X > 5.5)$

(c) $P(X > 2\frac{1}{2})$    (d) $P(X < 1\frac{3}{4})$

(4) $X \sim N(2, 9)$. Find the quartiles of $X$.

(5) $X \sim N(5, 1.44)$. Find the value of $a$ such that $P(X < a) = 0.85$.

(6) $X \sim N(75, 100)$. Find the values of $a$ which satisfy the following:

(a) $P(X < a) = 0.9$      (b) $P(X > a) = 0.23$

(c) $P(X > a) = 0.83$    (d) $P(X < a) = 0.02$

(7) $X$ is a normal variable with mean 4, such that $P(X < 5) = 0.6$. Find the variance of $X$.

(8) $X$ is a normal variable with mean 93. $P(X < 90) = 0.48$. Find the standard deviation of $X$.

(9) $X$ is a normal variable with standard deviation 2.5. $P(X < 4) = 0.54$. Find the mean of $X$.

(10) $X$ is a normal variable with variance 121. $P(X > 76) = 0.7$. Find the mean of $X$.

(11) The number of c.c. in cartons of orange juice follows a normal distribution. A tenth of the cartons are below 995 c.c., and a twentieth are above 1010 c.c. Find the mean and variance of the contents.

(12) The width of certain bolts follows a normal distribution. 1% of the bolts are above 2.001 cm, and 5% are below 1.995 cm. Find the mean width.

(13) The distance that a javelin thrower can reach follows a normal distribution. A third of her throws exceed 40 m., and a quarter exceed 45 m. Find the average distance she can throw.

## 43.2 Sums and Differences of Normal Variables

If $X$ and $Y$ are independent normal variables with means $\mu$ and $\lambda$, variances $\sigma^2$ and $\nu^2$ respectively, then their sum and difference are also normal, as follows:

If $X \sim N(\mu, \sigma^2)$ and $Y \sim N(\lambda, \nu^2)$, then:

$$X + Y \sim N(\mu + \lambda, \sigma^2 + \nu^2) \quad X - Y \sim N(\mu - \lambda, \sigma^2 + \nu^2)$$

In general, for $a$ and $b$ constant, $aX + bY \sim N(a\mu + b\lambda, a^2\sigma^2 + b^2\nu^2)$

Suppose $X_1, X_2, X_3, ..., X_n$ are independent normal variables, each with mean $\mu$ and variance $\sigma^2$.

The sum $S = X_1 + X_2 + ... + X_n$ is normal with mean $n\mu$ and variance $n\sigma^2$

The average $S/n$ is normal with mean $\mu$ and variance $\sigma^2/n$.

### 43.2.1 Examples

(1) $X$ and $Y$ are independent variables with $X \sim N(2, 4)$ and $Y \sim N(3, 6.25)$. Find (a) the probability that $X + Y$ is less than 6 (b) the upper quartile of $Y - X$.

Solution

a. $X + Y$ has a distribution given by
$X + Y \sim N(5, 10.25)$.
$P(X + Y < 6) = \Phi((6 - 5)/\sqrt{10.25})$

**The probability that $X + Y$ is less than 6 is 0.62**

b. Similarly, $Y - X \sim N(1, 10.25)$. The upper quartile is obtained by finding the value of $z$ for which $\Phi(z) = \frac{3}{4}$.

$$\Phi(0.674) = \frac{3}{4}$$

**The upper quartile is $1 + 0.674 \times \sqrt{10.25} = 3.16$**

(2) Jason and Daniel run a 100 m race. Jason's time for this distance is normal with mean 12 seconds and variance 1.3, while Daniel's time is normal with mean 12.5 and

variance 4. Their times are independent of each other. Find the probability that Daniel wins the race.

Solution    Letting $X$ be Jason's time and $Y$ Daniel's, Daniel will win if $Y < X$. But $Y - X$ is normal, with mean 0.5 and variance 5.3.

$$P(Y < X) = P(Y - X < 0) = \Phi((0 - 0.5)/\sqrt{5.3})$$

**The probability that Daniel wins is 0.41**

(3)    The contents in c.c. of cartons of orange juice is normal with mean 1,000 and variance 12. Find the probability that the average contents of 20 cartons is less than 998 c.c.

Solution    Let $X_1, X_2, ..., X_{20}$ be the contents of the cartons. The distribution of their average $\overline{X}$ is normal with mean 1,000 and variance $\frac{12}{20}$.

$$P(\overline{X} < 998) = \Phi((998 - 1000)/\sqrt{(\frac{12}{20})})$$

**The probability is 0.005**

## 43.2.2 Exercises

(1) $X$ and $Y$ are independent normal variables with means 4 and 7 and variances 5 and 4. Find the following:

(a)   $P(X + Y < 11)$ 　　　(b)   $P(X + Y > 9.5)$

(c)   $P(X - Y < 1)$ 　　　(d)   $P(2X + 3Y < 30)$

(e)   $P(3X - 2Y > -1\frac{1}{2})$   (f)   $P(X > Y)$

(g)   $P(4X > 3Y)$ 　　　(h)   $P(3Y > 23)$

(2) $X$ and $Y$ are independent normal variables with means 23 and 19, and variances 3 and 2. Find the values of $a$ for which:

(a)   $P(X + Y < a) = 0.8$ 　　(b)   $P(X - Y < a) = 0.75$

(c)   $P(3X + 2Y > a) = 0.2$   (d)   $P(5X - 4Y < a) = 0.35$

(e)   $P(2X < a) = 0.78$ 　　　(f)   $P(5Y > a) = 0.23$

(3) The weight of an empty can is normal with mean 20 g and variance 2, and the weight of its contents is normal with mean 100 g and variance 5. Find the probability that the full can weighs more than 125 g.

(4) When a man goes to work he walks to the bus-stop, waits for a bus, takes the bus to his office. The times for all three stages are normal with means 3 min, 10 min, 20 min and variances 0.5, 8, 5 respectively. Find the probability that he takes more than 35 minutes for the whole journey.

(5) The width of a bolt is normal with mean 1 cm and standard deviation 0.001: the width of the hole of a nut is normal with mean 1.005 and standard deviation 0.002. Find the probability that the bolt will go into the nut.

(6) A bus leaves the bus-stop at 9.00 precisely; the time it takes to reach the station is normal with mean 10 minutes and variance 4. The train arrives at the station at a time after 9.00 which is normal with mean 11 minutes and variance 0.25. Find the probability that a passenger on the bus will be able to catch the train.

(7) $X_1, X_2, ..., X_{16}$ are independent normal variables with mean 3 and variance 0.5. $S$ is their sum and A is their average. Find the following:

(a) $P(S < 50)$          (b) $P(S > 40)$

(c) $P(A < 3.01)$         (d) $P(A < 2.98)$

(e) $P(|A - 3| < 0.05)$    (f) $P(2.97 < A < 3.03)$

(8) With the variables as defined in Question 7, find the values of $a$ for which:

(a) $P(S < a) = 0.7$        (b) $P(S > a) = 0.77$

(c) $P(A < a) = 0.99$       (d) $P(A > a) = 0.95$

(e) $P(|A - 3| < a) = 0.98$   (f) $P(|A - 3| > a) = 0.05$

(9) The weight of a ball-bearing is distributed normally with mean 5 g and variance 0.001. If 100 ball-bearings are chosen, find the probabilities that (a) the total weight is greater than 500.5 g (b) the average weight is less than 4.999 g.

(10) I calculate that my journey to work is normally distributed with mean 25 minutes and variance 12. Over 50 journeys, evaluate the probabilities that (a) my total journey time is more than 1300 mins (b) my average journey time is more than 26 minutes.

## 43.3 The Central Limit Theorem

The normal distribution is the limit distribution of most other kinds of distributions. The *Central Limit Theorem* states:

Let $X_1, X_2, X_3, ...$ be independent variables taken from the same distribution with mean $\mu$ and variance $\sigma^2$. Let $A_n$ be the average of the first $n$ of them.

Then, as $n$ tends to $\infty$, the distribution of $A_n$ tends to $N(\mu, \sigma^2/n)$.

This approximation is especially useful for finding approximations to the Binomial and Poisson distributions and for sample proportions.

When $n$ is large, $B(n,p)$ is approximately $N(np, npq)$.

If $\lambda$ is large, a Poisson distribution with mean $\lambda$ is approximately $N(\lambda, \lambda)$.

Suppose a proportion $\pi$ of a large population has a certain property. A sample of size $n$ is taken, and the sample proportion is $p$. Then, if $n$ is large, $p$ is approximately $N(\pi, \pi(1 - \pi)/n)$.

When using the normal distribution to approximate a discrete distribution, the *continuity correction* is used, as follows:

If $X$ only takes whole number values, then $X > 3$ means the same as $X \geq 4$. So when the normal approximation is applied the compromise $X > 3\frac{1}{2}$ is used.

### 43.3.1 Examples

(1)    The lifetime of a certain brand of battery has mean 12 hours and standard deviation 3 hours. 50 batteries are tested: find the probability that the average lifetime is less than $12\frac{1}{2}$ hours.

Solution    Apply the central limit theorem to the average $A$ of the 50 lifetimes $X_1, X_2, ..., X_{50}$.

$$A \text{ is approximately } N(12, \frac{9}{50}).$$

$$P(A < 12\frac{1}{2}) = \Phi\left( \frac{12\frac{1}{2} - 12}{\sqrt{(\frac{9}{50})}} \right) = \Phi(1.18)$$

**The probability is 0.88**

(2)    $X$ has a Poisson distribution with mean 25. Find the probability that $X$ is greater than 30.

Solution    25 is large enough for the normal approximation to be used. The condition $X > 30$ is equivalent to $X \geq 31$, so apply the continuity correction and use $X > 30\frac{1}{2}$.

$$X \text{ is approximately } N(25, 25)$$

$$P(X > 30\frac{1}{2}) \simeq 1 - \Phi((30\frac{1}{2} - 25)/5)$$

**The probability is approximately 0.14**

(3)    A multiple choice test contains 100 questions, each of which contains 4 possible answers. A candidate answers at random. What is the probability that he scores at least 28?

Solution    Let $X$ be the number of correct answers. $X$ is $B(100, \frac{1}{4})$. The value of $n$ is large enough for the normal approximation to be valid. Applying the continuity correction, find the probability that $X$ is greater than $27\frac{1}{2}$.

$$X \text{ is approximately } N(25, 18\frac{3}{4}).$$

$$P(X > 27\frac{1}{2}) \simeq 1 - \Phi(2\frac{1}{2}/\sqrt{18\frac{3}{4}})$$

**The probability is approximately 0.28**

## 43.3.2 Exercises

(1) The height of a certain species of plant has mean 160 cm and variance 200. 20 plants are measured. Find the probability that the average height is more than 164 cm.

(2) The time that a boy takes to run 200 m has mean 30 seconds and standard deviation $3\frac{1}{2}$. He runs the distance 30 times. Find the probability that his average time is more than 29 seconds.

(3) The weights of a certain grade of egg have mean 50 g and variance 100. 40 eggs are tested. Find the probability that the average weight is more than 48 g.

(4) $X \sim B(60, \frac{1}{4})$. Find the probability that $X$ is more than 20.

(5) $X \sim B(200, 0.4)$. Find the probability that $X$ is less than 75.

(6) $X \sim B(1000, 0.44)$. Find the probability that $X$ is at least 420.

(7) A fair die is rolled 60 times. Find the probability that there are more than 15 sixes.

(8) On average, 2 in 5 potatoes have blemishes. Find the probability that in a batch of 100 potatoes at least 65 have no blemishes.

(9) A fair coin is tossed 200 times. Find the probability of obtaining more than 115 heads.

(10) Four fifths of a sort of tulip bulbs give flowers. If I buy 100, what is the probability that more than 25 fail to give flowers?

(11) It is thought that support for the Conservative Party in a certain town is at 40%. A poll questions 1,000 voters: what is the probability that more than 380 support the Conservative party?

(12) It is thought that 15% of the population are left-handed. What is the probability that the proportion of left-handers in 100 people will be more than 20%?

(13) The proportion of candidates who pass the Driving Test is 0.6. Find the probability that, out of 200 candidates, the proportional pass rate was less than 0.55.

(14) $X$ has a Poisson distribution with mean 40. What is the probability that $X$ is less than 35?

(15) The number of misprints in a page of a newspaper follows a Poisson distribution with mean 4. The newspaper has 20 pages. What is the probability of more than 90 misprints in all?

(16) The number of meteorites which fall in a field each year follows a Poisson distribution with mean 2. What is the probability that over a 15 year period more than 33 meteorites fall?

(17) The number of letters I receive each day follows a Poisson distribution with mean 2. What is the probability that over 30 days I receive less than 50 letters?

(18) A fisherman reckons that the number of fish he catches in a day follows a Poisson distribution with mean $2\frac{1}{2}$. What is the probability that over 12 days he catches no more than 25 fish?

## 43.4 Examination Questions

(1) From a large sample of bars of soap produced by a machine it is found that the mean weight of the bars is 425.1 grams with a standard deviation of 1.6 grams. Assuming that the weights are distributed normally, calculate the percentage of bars of soap produced by the same machine that will weigh

(i)   less than 424 grams;                (ii) not more than 425.5 grams;

(iii)   between 426 grams and 428 grams.

If an adjustment can be made to the machine which alters the mean but leaves the standard deviation unchanged, what should the new mean weight be if it is required that 95% of the bars of soap weigh less than 427 grams?

[*Give all your answers correct to one decimal place.*]

[MEI add]

(2) The length of worms in a certain plot is Normally distributed. About 97% of the worms are found to be under 25 cm long.

a.   How many standard deviations more than the mean, to the nearest tenth, is a 25 cm worm?

b. About 69% of the worms are over 13 cm long. How many standard deviations less than the mean is a 13 cm worm?

c. Hence show that the standard deviation of worm length is about 5 cm and calculate the mean length.

d. Calculate the percentage of the worms which would have length (i) less than 8 cm, (ii) between 18 cm and 19 cm.

[SMP add]

(3) Calculate (a) the mean $\bar{x}$ and (b) the standard deviation $s$ for the following sample of weights, in kilograms, of 11 children. Show all necessary working.

$$37, 38, 38, 42, 42, 44, 46, 46, 48, 50, 53.$$

Find the percentage of the sample lying between $x - s$ and $x + s$.

This sample of 11 was chosen at random from a population of 1000 children of the same age. Estimate how many children from the whole population would have a weight within $s$ of $x$.

[O add]

(4) The times taken by two runners $A$ and $B$ to run 400 m races are independent and normally distributed with means 45.0 s and 45.2 s, and standard deviations 0.5 s and 0.8 s respectively. The two runners are to compete in a 400 m race for which there is a track record of 44.5 s.

i. Calculate, to three decimal places, the probability of runner $A$ breaking the track record.

ii. Show that the probability of runner $B$ breaking the track record is greater than that of runner $A$.

iii. Calculate, to three decimal places, the probability of runner $A$ beating runner $B$.

[JMB]

(5) An analysis of the membership of a large organisation shows that 60% of the members are over 50 years old and 2.5% are under 20 years old.

(i) Using appropriate distributional approximations *when necessary,* calculate the probabilities, correct to three decimal places, that a random sample of 100 members will include

a. 60 or more members over 50 years old,

b. 3 or fewer members under 20 years old,

c. exactly 40 members aged from 20 years to 50 years, inclusive.

(ii) Use a normal approximation to find the smallest number of members that should be sampled at random in order that the probability is at least 0.9 that 55% or more of the sampled members will be over 50 years old.

[W]

(6) $X_i (i = 1, 2, ..., n)$ are $n$ random variables each distributed normally with mean $\mu$ and variance $\sigma^2$. If $Y = X_1 + X_2 + ... + X_n$ state precisely the distribution of $Y$.

A lift can carry with safety a load of no more than 725 kg. The masses of the people using the lift are normally distributed with mean 67.3 kg and standard deviation 7.2 kg. Show that if 9 people enter the lift it is practically certain that the maximum load will not be exceeded. Calculate the probabilities of the maximum load being exceeded when the number of people in the lift is (i) 10 (ii) 11.

A notice is placed in the lift stating the maximum number of passengers, $N$. What should be the value of $N$ in order that with $N$ passengers, the probability of the maximum load being exceeded is less than 1%?

During a certain time of the day the number of passengers in the lift has a Binomial distribution with parameters $N$ and $p$. If $p = 0.8$, calculate the probability that during the journey there will be 9 passengers with a total mass of under 650 kg.

[SUJB]

(7) The random variable $X$ has a rectangular distribution with probability density function $f(x)$, where $f(x) = 1/6$ for $1 \le x \le 7$ and $f(x) = 0$ for all other $x$.

i.   Why is it obvious that the expectation of $X$ is 4? Show by integration that the variance of $X$ is 3. What is the probability that $3.7 < X < 4.3$?

ii.  Use results in (i) to write down the values of the expectation and variance of the mean $\overline{X}_{100}$ of 100 independent observations of $X$. Estimate to 2 decimal places the probability that $3.7 < \overline{X}_{100} < 4.3$.

iii. One observation $x$ of $X$ is made, dividing the interval $[1,7]$ into two segments. For what values of $x$ is the ratio of the length of the shorter segment to that of the longer segment less than $\frac{1}{4}$? What is the probability that this event occurs?

[MEI]

# COMMON ERRORS

## (1) Use of tables

a. Be careful when you solve problems of the form: Find $c$ such that $P(Z < c) = \frac{3}{4}$. You must look through the tables until you find 0.75. Do not look up 0.75 directly.

b. Do not confuse the standard deviation $\sigma$ with the variance $\sigma^2$. When standardizing normal variables, for example, you divide by the standard deviation $\sigma$.

## (2) Sums and Differences

a. If $X$ has variance $\sigma^2$, then $aX$ has variance $a^2\sigma^2$. (Not $a\sigma^2$)

b. If $X$ has variance $\sigma^2$ and $Y$ has variance $\nu^2$, then $X - Y$ has variance $\sigma^2 + \nu^2$. (Not $\sigma^2 - \nu^2$)

## (3) Central Limit Theorem

a. The continuity correction is only used when the original distribution is discrete. Do not use it for continuous distributions.

b. Make sure you go the correct way with the continuity correction. Suppose you are asked to find the probability that $X < 6$; this is equivalent to $X \leq 5$, so compromise by putting $X < 5\frac{1}{2}$.

c. The normal approximation is only valid when $n$ is large. As a rough guide, when approximating the Poisson distribution $\lambda$ must be at least 20. When approximating the Binomial both $np$ and $nq$ must be at least 10.

# 44 Hypothesis Testing

Suppose a sample is taken from a distribution whose mean $\mu$ is not known. The use of the sample to check whether or not $\mu$ has a certain value is a *hypothesis test*.

Suppose we are checking whether or not the parent mean $\mu$ has a certain value $\mu_0$. The *Null Hypothesis* $H_0$ states that it does have the value. The *Alternative Hypothesis* $H_1$ is that it does not.

If $H_1$ is of the form $\mu \neq \mu_0$, then this is a *two-tailed* test.

If $H_1$ is of the form $\mu < \mu_0$ (or $\mu > \mu_0$), then this is a *one-tailed* test.

A two-tailed test is always performed, unless there is prior reason to think that $\mu$ could only be less than $\mu_0$ (or only greater than it).

There is always a chance that $H_0$ is true and yet is rejected by the test. The probability of doing this is the *significance level* of the test.

## 44.1 Tests on the Mean
Throughout it is assumed that the parent distribution is normal.

A *critical value* for the normal distribution is a value of $z$ which cuts off a certain percentage of probability.

For example, the 5% critical value is 1.96.

This means that $P(|Z| > 1.96) = 0.05$.

Critical values can be found in tables.

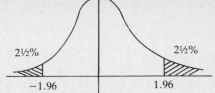

2½%            2½%

−1.96        1.96

### 44.1.1 Examples

(1)     A distribution is thought to be normal with mean 12 and variance 5. A sample of size 10 has sample mean 11. Does this provide evidence at a significance level of 5% to show that the parent mean is not 12?

Solution    There is no prior reason to think that $\mu$ should be greater or less than 12. Hence a two-tailed test is performed.

$$H_0 : \mu = 12$$

$$H_1 : \mu \neq 12$$

Assuming $H_0$, the distribution of the sample mean $\overline{X}$ is $N(12, 5/10)$. The difference between the sample mean and the true mean is 1. Find the probability that the difference between $\overline{X}$ and $\mu$ is as great as this:

$$P(|\overline{X} - 12| \geq 1) = 2(1 - \Phi(1/\sqrt{\tfrac{1}{2}})) = 0.16$$

This is greater than 5%. The null hypothesis is retained.

**We have failed to disprove that the mean is 12**

(2)     A manufacturer of orange juice claims that the volumes of the cartons which his firm produces are normal with mean 1000 *c.c.* and variance 16. A weights and measures inspector tests a sample of 20 cartons and finds that their average volume is 997.5 *c.c.* Is this evidence at a significance level of 1% that the manufacturer is giving short measure?

Solution    The inspector is only interested in showing that $\mu$ is less than 1,000. Hence we do a one-tailed test.

$$H_0 : \mu = 1000$$

$$H_1 : \mu < 1000$$

Assuming $H_0$, the distribution of the sample mean $\overline{X}$ is $N(1000, 16/20)$. Find the probability that $\overline{X}$ is as low as 997.5:

$$P(X \leq 997.5) = 1 - \Phi(2.5/\sqrt{0.8}) = 0.0026$$

This is less than 1%. The alternative hypothesis is proved at this significance level.

### At 1% significance we have proved that the mean is below 1000.

### 44.1.2 Exercises

(1) It is thought that a distribution has mean 2 and variance 0.4. A sample of 8 has sample mean 2.45. Test at the 5% level whether the mean is 2.

(2) Repeat Question 1 for a significance level of 1%.

(3) It is claimed that the mean of $X$ is 40 and its variance 60. It is suspected that the mean might be greater than this, and a sample of size 15 has mean 45. Does this confirm the suspicion, at a level of 5%?

(4) It is thought that a distribution has mean 4. A sample of 10 were as follows:

$$4.1, \ 4.2, \ 4.0, \ 3.9, \ 4.1, \ 4.2, \ 4.3, \ 4.4, \ 4.3, \ 4.1$$

Assuming that the unbiased sample variance is the correct one, test at a 5% significance level whether or not the mean is 4.

(5) The national average mark for a certain exam is 47.5%. the marks of 12 children were:

$$47, \ 46, \ 45, \ 44, \ 49, \ 53, \ 54, \ 44, \ 42, \ 41, \ 42, \ 40$$

Assuming that the unbiased sample variance is the correct one, test at a 5% significance level whether or not the children differ from the average.

(6) A factory produces string which, it is claimed, has a breaking strength of $60N$. A sample of 10 pieces of string had breaking strengths as follows:

$$50, \ 58, \ 64, \ 55, \ 52, \ 53, \ 54, \ 57, \ 50, \ 51$$

Test at the 5% level whether the breaking strength is lower than claimed.

(7) Over the year a man finds that the time it takes him to drive to work has mean 20 minutes and variance 20. A new set of traffic-lights is introduced on his route: for the next ten days his average time of journey was 23 mins. Does this show at a significance level of 2% that the traffic lights have affected his journey time?

(8) A light-bulb manufacturer claims that its bulbs have a mean lifetime of 1000 hours. A sample of 10 were tested, and their lifetimes were:

900, 950, 1100, 800, 700, 850, 930, 900, 920, 940

Is this significant at 5% to show that the average lifetime is less than 1000 hours?

## 44.2 Testing for Differences

Suppose we wish to test whether the means $\mu_1$ and $\mu_2$ of two distributions are the same. Then we test whether the difference $\mu_1 - \mu_2$ is zero.

If there is a natural association between the samples from the two distributions, then the test is a *paired sample test*.

### 44.2.1 Example

The variance of the weight of eggs laid in a farm is 30 $g^2$. The farmer wishes to see whether the addition of a certain ingredient to his hens' diet will increase the weight of their eggs. Ten hens were selected, and the weights of their eggs before and after receiving the ingredient were as follows:

| Hen | A | B | C | D | E | F | G | H | J | K |
|---|---|---|---|---|---|---|---|---|---|---|
| Weight of egg before | 30 | 35 | 40 | 35 | 43 | 39 | 41 | 37 | 49 | 42 |
| Weight of egg after | 33 | 32 | 43 | 36 | 43 | 41 | 44 | 37 | 50 | 44 |

Is this sufficient evidence at 5% to show that the ingredient has increased egg weight?

Solution    The same hens appear in both samples. Hence this is a paired sample test. The farmer is only interested in showing that there has been an increase, hence this is a one tailed test. Write out a table of the differences $D$:

| Hen | A | B | C | D | E | F | G | H | J | K |
|---|---|---|---|---|---|---|---|---|---|---|
| Difference in weight | 3 | -3 | 3 | 1 | 0 | 2 | 3 | 0 | 1 | 2 |

$$H_0 : E(D) = 0$$

$$H_1 : E(D) > 0$$

Assuming $H_0$, the mean difference $\overline{D}$ is $N(0, 30/10 + 30/10)$. The mean sample difference is 1.2.

$$P(D \geq 1.2) = 1 - \Phi(1.2/\sqrt{6}) = 0.31$$

## There is not sufficient evidence to show that the weight has increased

### 44.2.2 Exercises

(1) The variance of the marking for a certain exam is 90. The same scripts for an exam were marked twice by two different examiners. The results were as follows:

| Candidate | A | B | C | D | E | F | G | H | J | K |
|---|---|---|---|---|---|---|---|---|---|---|
| First examiner's mark | 66 | 74 | 59 | 54 | 63 | 72 | 60 | 81 | 71 | 58 |
| Second examiner's mark | 64 | 75 | 53 | 50 | 59 | 67 | 61 | 75 | 68 | 53 |

Is this significant evidence at 5% to show that one examiner is more strict than the other?

(2) Two drivers dispute who is the more economical. They select 9 routes, equal in length, and each drives along them. The results of the petrol consumption for the journeys are:

| Route | A | B | C | D | E | F | G | H | J |
|---|---|---|---|---|---|---|---|---|---|
| M.p.g. for first driver | 35 | 33 | 37 | 48 | 29 | 32 | 34 | 27 | 30 |
| M.p.g. for second driver | 33 | 32 | 37 | 50 | 27 | 30 | 34 | 24 | 28 |

Assuming that the variance for petrol consumption is 4, test at the 5% significance level whether there is any difference between the petrol consumption of the two drivers.

(3) A group of 15 left-handed people had an average I.Q. of 105, while a group of 20 right-handed people had an I.Q. of 99. Assuming that the variance of I.Q is 225, test at a 5% significance level whether left-handers have different intelligence from right-handers.

(4) The I.Q.s of 10 couples of husbands and wives were tested. Find the unbiased sample variance of the differences between their I.Q's. Hence test at a 5% significance level whether there is any difference between their intelligences.

| Couple | A | B | C | D | E | F | G | H | J | K |
|---|---|---|---|---|---|---|---|---|---|---|
| Husband's I.Q. | 103 | 112 | 99 | 107 | 103 | 91 | 88 | 121 | 117 | 102 |
| Wife's I.Q. | 111 | 121 | 103 | 101 | 98 | 99 | 95 | 107 | 110 | 120 |

(5) The scores of 9 golfers were found before and after receiving coaching. Test at a 2% significance level whether or not coaching has improved their performance.

| Golfer | A | B | C | D | E | F | G | H | J |
|---|---|---|---|---|---|---|---|---|---|
| Score before | 103 | 101 | 99 | 97 | 111 | 123 | 88 | 93 | 108 |
| Score after | 96 | 94 | 91 | 92 | 101 | 127 | 86 | 90 | 101 |

## 44.3 Testing Proportion

A proportion of a population has a certain property. Let that proportion be $\pi$. . If a sample of size $n$ is taken, then the number of that sample with the property has a $B(n, \pi)$ distribution.

If $n$ is large then $B(n, \pi)$ is approximately $N(n\pi, n\pi(1 - \pi))$. Here a continuous distribution is used to approximate to a discrete distribution. Hence the continuity correction is used.

Let $p$ be the *proportion* of the sample which has the property. Then $p$ has expected value $\pi$ and variance $\pi(1 - \pi)/n$. If $n$ is large then $p$ is approximately $N(\pi, \pi(1 - \pi)/n)$.

### 44.3.1 Examples

(1) A garden-centre claims that at least 80% of its bulbs will give flowers. When 20 were tested only 12 gave flowers. Is this significant at 5% to discredit the claim?

Solution We are only interested in showing that the proportion is less than 80%. Hence a one-tailed test is used. Let the proportion be $p$.

$$H_0 : p = 0.8$$

$$H_1 : p < 0.8$$

Assuming $H_0$, the number $X$ of flowering bulbs in the sample is $B(20, 0.8)$. This is approximately $N(16, 3.2)$. Using the continuity correction, find the probability that $X$ is less than $12\frac{1}{2}$:

$$P(X < 12\frac{1}{2}) = 1 - \Phi(3\frac{1}{2}/\sqrt{3.2}) = 0.025$$

**At a 5% significance level the claim is false**

(2)  In an opinion poll 100 men and 150 women were asked whether they would vote for the Prosperity Party. The support was 35% and 30% respectively. Is there evidence at 5% significance level that support for the party is different for men and for women?

Solution  Let $p_m$ and $p_w$ be the true proportions of support for men and women respectively.

$$H_0 : p_m = p_w$$

$$H_1 : p_m \neq p_w$$

Assume $H_0$. Estimate the true proportion $p$ by a pooled sample:

$$p \simeq \frac{100 \times 0.35 + 150 \times 0.3}{250} = 0.32$$

The variance of the difference $D$ is $\frac{0.32 \times 0.68}{100} + \frac{0.32 \times 0.68}{150} = 0.0036$

The distribution of the difference $D$ between the sample proportions is $N(0, 0.0036)$. Find the probability that this difference is as high as 0.05.

$$P(|D| \geq 0.05) = 2(1 - \Phi(0.05/\sqrt{0.0036}) = 0.4$$

**There is no evidence to show that the proportions are different**

### 44.3.2 Exercises

(1) A politician claims that 40% of the population will vote for him. A sample of 30 people produced only 10 supporters. Is this significant at 5% to show that he overestimates his support?

(2) In an experiment to verify telepathy a pack of 100 cards is dealt out face down. The pack contains 5 different types of cards, in equal numbers, and a person is asked to guess the type of each card. The person guesses correctly 28 times. Is this significant at 5% to show that the person is telepathic?

(3) Leah claims that she can tell which of the 12 signs of the zodiac a person belongs to. She guesses the sign for 100 people, and gets it right 20 times. Is this significant at 5% to show that her claim is correct?

(4) A multiple choice exam contains 50 questions, each of which has 5 alternative answers. A candidate gets 15 correct. Is this significant at 5% to show that he has not been answering at random?

(5) It is suspected that a coin is biased. It is thrown 100 times, and the proportion of heads is 0.6. Test at whether or not the coin is biased, at (a) 5% (b) at 2%.

(6) It is thought that a die might be weighted. It is rolled 180 times, and the number of sixes was 37. Test at 5% whether or not the die is biased.

(7) There are two driving-schools in a town. In one of them there were 80 pupils, 50 of whom passed at their first test. The other had 120 pupils of whom 100 passed at their first attempt. Is there evidence at 5% that one school is better than the other?

(8) I buy 20 light-bulbs from one shop, and 32 from another shop. 25% of the bulbs from the first shop last less than 6 months, while the corresponding figure for the second shop is $12\frac{1}{2}$%. Is there evidence at 5% to show that one shop sells more reliable bulbs?

(9) A school has 500 pupils. 200 are given an anti-flu jab, and 300 are not. Over the winter 25% of the first group and 30% of the second has flu. Is there evidence at 5% that the jab has some effect?

(10) A rust-proofing process is tested as follows. 40 cars were proofed, and 2 years later 5 had severe rust. 50 similar cars were not proofed, and 2 years later 10 had severe rust. Is there evidence at 5% to show that the process is efficacious?

## 44.4 Confidence Intervals

Suppose a sample of size $n$ is taken from a population with unknown mean $\mu$. A *confidence interval* for $\mu$ is an interval within which $\mu$ is expected to be.

A 95% *confidence interval* is one for which there is a 0.95 probability that it contains $\mu$.

Suppose the sample mean is $\overline{X}$ and the population variance is $\sigma^2$. Assuming that the distribution of $\overline{X}$ is normal, then a 95% confidence interval for $\mu$ is:

$$\overline{X} - 1.96\sigma/\sqrt{n} < \mu < \overline{X} + 1.96\sigma/\sqrt{n}.$$

Figures for other levels of confidence may be found from a table of critical values of the normal distribution.

Suppose a population has a proportion $\pi$ with a particular property. The proportion of a sample of size $n$ with that property is $p$. Provided that $n$ is reasonably large, a 95% confidence interval for $\pi$ is:

$$p - 1.96\sigma < \pi < p + 1.96\sigma, (\text{ where } \sigma^2 = p(1 - p)/n)$$

### 44.4.1 Examples

(1)     A machine produces ball-bearings whose diameter is normally distributed with mean $\mu$ and variance 0.10 mm². A sample of size 10 had mean 11.5 mm. Find a 95% confidence interval for $\mu$.

Solution     Use the formula above. $\overline{X} = 11.5, \sigma = \sqrt{0.1}, n = 10$.

$$11.5 - 1.96(\sqrt{0.01}) < \mu < 11.5 + 1.96(\sqrt{0.01})$$

**The 95% confidence interval is from 11.3 to 11.7**

(2)     Before a general election, a sample of 2,000 voters was asked which party they would support. 800 said they would support the Freedom Party. Find a 99% confidence interval for the true level of support for the Freedom Party.

Solution     Here the sample proportion $p$ is 0.4. Looking up 1% in the table of critical values, we find 2.58. The variance $\sigma^2$ is $0.4 \times 0.6/2000$. The confidence interval is:

$$0.4 - 2.58\sigma < \pi < 0.4 + 2.58\sigma$$

**The 99% confidence interval is from 0.37 to 0.43**

### 44.4.2 Exercises

(1) $X$ has a normal distribution with unknown mean $\mu$ and variance 4. A sample of size 12 has sample mean 13. Find a 95% confidence interval for $\mu$.

(2) A factory produces cartons of orange juice, whose volume is normally distributed with mean $\mu$ and variance 120. A sample of 20 cartons had average volume 995 c.c. Find a 99% confidence interval for $\mu$.

(3) A machine produces bolts, whose weight is normally distributed with variance 0.2 g². A sample of 15 bolts had average weight 12 g. Find a 99% confidence interval for the mean weight of the bolts produced by the machine.

(4) The heights of a certain plant are thought to be normally distributed with variance 12 cm². 10 plants had heights (in cm.):

$$23, 25, 20, 26, 19, 25, 27, 23, 22, 23$$

Find a 95% confidence interval for the mean height of the plants.

(5) The weight of the contents of certain bags of sugar has variance 40 g². 8 bags were weighed as follows:

$$245, 251, 259, 263, 253, 247, 240, 248 \text{ (grams)}$$

Find a 98% confidence interval for the mean weight of the bags.

(6) The diameters of 12 ping-pong balls were (in cm.):

$$3.18, 3.21, 3.25, 3.22, 3.21, 3.22, 3.19, 3.17, 3.20, 3.22, 3.21, 3.19$$

Using the unbiased sample variance find a 95% confidence interval for the mean diameter of a ping-pong ball.

(7) The lifetimes of 10 light-bulbs were as follows (in hours):

$$1034, 1132, 1453, 1234, 1372, 1402, 1362, 1222, 1192, 1365$$

Find a 99% confidence interval for the mean lifetime of the bulbs.

(8) In an investigation to find the proportion of left-handed people in the population, 200 people were asked and 35 said they were left-handed. Find a 95% confidence interval for the proportion of left-handers in the population.

(9) An opinion poll of 1,000 voters found that 30% of the sample would vote for the Magenta Party. Find a 95% confidence interval for the support for the Magenta Party in the population.

(10) Out of 400 households which were investigated 320 were found to contain a pet. Find a 99% confidence interval for the proportion of households in the country which contain pets.

## 44.5 Examination Questions

(1)

a. A news agency wishes to try to predict the result of an election as soon as the polls close. For this purpose they interview a random sample of electors emerging from the polling stations and ask them how they have voted. On a particular occasion 1012 electors were interviewed and 473 of them said they had voted for Party X. Use these figures to calculate an approximate 95% confidence interval for the proportion of the whole electorate supporting Party X.

b. The petrol consumption of a new model of car is being tested. In one trial, 50 cars chosen at random were driven under identical conditions, and the distances, $x$ miles, that were covered on precisely 1 gallon of petrol were recorded. The results gave the following totals: $\sum x = 2685, \sum x^2 = 144,346$. Calculate a 99% confidence interval for the mean petrol consumption, in miles per gallon, of cars of this type.

[C]

(2) The table below summarises the diameters (in mm) of a random sample of 100 rods made at factory $A$.

| Centre of Interval | 5.8 | 6.0 | 6.2 | 6.4 |
|---|---|---|---|---|
| Frequency | 3 | 40 | 50 | 7 |

Find

a. the mean and variance of these measurements,

b. Symmetric 98% confidence limits for the mean diameter of all rods made at factory $A$.

A random sample of 80 similar rods made at factory $B$ had a mean diameter 6.16 mm and a variance 0.024 mm$^2$. Test the hypothesis that the mean diameter of all rods made at $B$ is equal to the mean diameter of all rods made at $A$.

What assumption have you made about the variances of the two underlying populations?

[O&C]

(3) In an examination taken by a very large number of candidates it was found that the mean mark was 43.6 with a standard deviation of 16.8.

200 candidates from centre $A$ had a mean mark of 45.7 and 80 candidates from centre $B$ had a mean mark of 46.4. For each centre test, at the 5% level of significance, whether the examination performance of the candidates was better than that of the population.

If the marks of the candidates from the two centres are combined, find the mean mark of all 280 candidates. Test, at the 5% level of significance, whether the examination performance of these 280 candidates was different from that of the population.

Given that the standard deviations of the marks of the candidates at centres $A$ and $B$ were 14.2 and 16.6 respectively, calculate the variance of the marks of all 280 candidates.

[AEB 1985]

(4) The proportion of the population prepared to vote Conservative on November 1st, 1985 was $p_1$ and to vote Labour was $p_2$. A random sample

of $n$ polled yielded $x_1$ and $x_2$ that said they would vote Conservative and Labour respectively. State the mean and variance of (i) $\hat{p}_1 = x_1/n$ and (ii) $\hat{p}_2 - \hat{p}_1 = (x_2 - x_1)/n$.

Of a sample of 1000 polled 384 said they would vote Conservative and 422 said they would vote Labour. Test the following hypotheses:

(a) $p_1 = 0.42$ (b) $p_1 = p_2$.

[SUJB]

## COMMON ERRORS

### (1) Hypotheses

a. State the null-hypothesis $H_0$ clearly. It must always be definite - that $\mu$ has some fixed value. You cannot have a null-hypothesis of the form $\mu > 3$.

b. If your result is not significant, then do not state: *Hence we have proved $H_0$*. The most that can be said is that: *We have failed to disprove $H_0$*.

c. Only use a one-tailed test if you have *prior* reason to think that a sample mean is less than stated. You cannot look at the figures and then decide to do a one-tailed test.

### (2) Differences

Only use a paired sample test if there is a natural association between the samples. In example 1 of 44.2.1 the same hen was tested. If the farmer had tested two lots of ten different hens then they would not have been paired.

### (3) Proportion

Make sure that you get the continuity correction the right way round. If a result can be written either as $X > 12$ or as $X \geq 13$ then compromise by putting $X > 12\frac{1}{2}$.

### (4) Confidence Intervals

The mean $\mu$ of a population is not a variable, even though it may be unknown. It is better to say: *The confidence interval has probability 0.95 of containing $\mu$* than: *$\mu$ has probability 0.95 of lying within the confidence interval*.

# 45 The t and $\chi^2$ Distributions

## 45.1 The $t$ Distribution

Suppose a sample is taken from a normal distribution, for which the mean and the variance are both unknown. The unbiased sample variance may be inaccurate. The distribution which takes account of this is *Student's t-distribution*.

Suppose a sample of size $n$ is taken from a normal distribution with mean $\mu$. Let $\overline{X}$ be the sample mean and let $\sigma^2$ be the unbiased sample variance. Then:

$$T = \frac{\overline{X} - \mu}{\sqrt{(\sigma^2/n)}} \text{ has a } t\text{-distribution with } n - 1 = \nu \text{ degrees of freedom.}$$

As $n$ tends to infinity the distribution of $T$ tends to the standard normal distribution.

Critical values of $T$ can be found from tables. They are used in exactly the same way as critical values for the normal distribution.

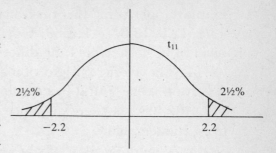

The p.d.f. of the $t$-distribution is flatter than that of the normal. The critical value for 5% cuts off $2\frac{1}{2}$% of the area from each end.

Note that the critical values are given for two-tailed tests. If a one-tailed test at 5% is required, then use the critical value for 10%.

### 45.1.1 Example

An athlete ran a race 9 times, with results (in seconds) as below. Assuming that the underlying distribution is normal, find a 95% confidence interval for his mean time.

20.12, 21.11, 20.96, 20.55, 21.32, 21.65, 20.85, 21.63, 20.45.

Solution  The sample mean and unbiased sample variance are 20.96 and 0.278 respectively. The number of degrees of freedom is 9 - 1 = 8. Look up the critical value of the $t$ distribution, for $v = 8$, at the 95% significance level. The standard deviation of the sample mean is $\sqrt{(0.278/9)} = 0.176$

The confidence interval is $20.96 \pm 2.31 \times 0.176$.

**The confidence interval is $20.55 < \mu < 21.4$**

### 45.1.2 Exercises

(1) The following sets of figures come from normal distributions. Find 95% confidence intervals for the means of those distributions.

a.  1.3, 1.2, 1.25, 1.22, 1.25, 1.27, 1.31
b.  54, 56, 57, 49, 63, 63, 60, 57, 48, 44, 56
c.  —0.3, —0.4, —0.05, 0.0, 1.1, 0.3, 0.5, 0.6, 0.15
d.  150, 162, 166, 143, 169, 171

(2) Find 99% confidence intervals for the figures in Question 1.

(3) The mean time to perform a certain task in a factory is 12 minutes. An employee performs this task 8 times, with the following times (in minutes) : 13.5, 12.5, 13.6, 12.1, 12.9, 11.8, 13.4, 13.5. Is there evidence at a significance level of 95% that his time differs from the average?

(4) The average height of a certain type of plant is 130 cm. 9 plants from a garden were found to have heights (in cm) : 129, 134, 122, 121, 119, 138, 113, 100, 98. Is there evidence, significant at 95%, that these plants differ from the average?

(5) A manufacturer of soup cans claims that the average contents of each can is 500 cm$^3$. An inspector measured 11 cans, and found that the volumes of their contents were 495, 498, 501, 485, 491, 497, 499, 482, 489, 490, 493. Test at a 99% significance level whether or not the manufacturer is giving short measure.

(6) The times taken by 8 employees at a factory to perform a task, before and after lunch, were as given in the table below. Conduct a test on the differences to see whether lunch has made them any slower.

| Employee | A | B | C | D | E | F | G | H |
|---|---|---|---|---|---|---|---|---|
| Before lunch | 12 | 12.6 | 13 | 14 | 13.3 | 14.3 | 12.9 | 16.2 |
| After lunch | 13 | 14 | 16 | 12 | 14.3 | 15.3 | 13.5 | 18.1 |

(7) The mean weight of eggs laid by 7 hens, before and after an additive had been given to their diet, were as in the table below. Has the additive increased the weight of the eggs?

| Hen | A | B | C | D | E | F | G |
|---|---|---|---|---|---|---|---|
| Before additive | 20 | 20.3 | 25.4 | 26.7 | 19.6 | 22.2 | 23.8 |
| After additive | 22.3 | 21.9 | 24.1 | 28.0 | 21.3 | 24.5 | 25.7 |

## 45.2 Testing goodness of fit

Suppose it is suspected that a sample comes from a particular distribution. To find whether or not this is the case a $\chi^2$ test is used.

Divide the sample up into $n$ groups. The frequency in each group is the *observed frequency $f_o$*.

The null Hypothesis is that the figures do come from the suspected distribution. Find the corresponding frequencies for this distribution. These are the *expected frequencies $f_e$*. These frequencies cannot be too small. If any $f_e$ is less than 6 then amalgamate its group with a neighbouring group.

There are $n$ groups. Say there are $m$ restrictions when fitting the distribution. The number of degrees of freedom, $\nu$, is $n - m$. Then:
$$\chi^2(\nu) = \sum \frac{(f_o - f_e)^2}{f_e} \text{ has a } \chi^2 \text{ distribution with } \nu \text{ degrees of freedom.}$$
Critical values of $\chi^2$ are found from tables.
The p.d.f. for $\chi^2(\nu)$ is shown for different
values of $\nu$. The critical value for 5% cuts
off 5% of the area as shown.

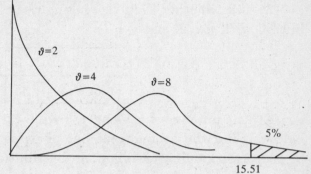

### 45.2.1 Example

A die is rolled 120 times. The results are given in the
table below. Check whether or not it is biased.

| Number | 1 | 2 | 3 | 4 | 5 | 6 |
|--------|----|----|----|----|----|----|
| Frequency | 14 | 13 | 21 | 16 | 27 | 29 |

Solution    These are the observed frequencies. If the die is fair,
then the expected figures are each equal to
$120/6 = 20$. The total of the frequencies must be 120.
This is a restriction. Hence the number of degrees of
freedom is 6 - 1 = 5. Apply the formula:

$$\chi^2(5) = (6^2 + 7^2 + 1^2 + 4^2 + 7^2 + 9^2)/20 = 11.6.$$

Look up the critical value of $\chi^2$ for $\nu = 5$. Notice that
11.6 is between the 5% value and the 1% value.
**At a 5% significance level we have shown that
the die is biased.**

### 45.2.2 Exercises
(1) 100 digits from the random number generator of a calculator are given
by the table below. Test whether or not the digits are all equally likely.

| Number | 0 | 1 | 2 | 3 | 4 | 5 | 6 | 7 | 8 | 9 |
|--------|---|---|---|----|----|---|---|----|----|----|
| Frequency | 6 | 4 | 8 | 13 | 15 | 9 | 7 | 17 | 10 | 11 |

411

(2) It is thought that $X$ might come from a binomial distribution with $n = 3$ and $p = \frac{1}{2}$. 60 values are as below. Find the expected frequencies for $X$, and hence test whether this distribution fits the figures.

| Value of $X$ | 0 | 1 | 2 | 3 |
|---|---|---|---|---|
| Frequency | 6 | 18 | 24 | 12 |

(3) Test whether the following figures could come from a binomial distribution with $n = 2$ and $p = \frac{1}{3}$.

| Value of $X$ | 0 | 1 | 2 |
|---|---|---|---|
| Frequency | 35 | 40 | 15 |

(4) The number of passengers in 100 cars were found to be as in the table below. Find the average number of passengers. Test whether the number of passengers follows a binomial distribution, with the value of $p$ as found. (Note: there is an extra restriction introduced, because the mean is found from the data.)

| No. of passengers | 0 | 1 | 2 | 3 |
|---|---|---|---|---|
| Frequency | 45 | 32 | 15 | 8 |

(5) Test whether the following could have come from a binomial distribution.

| Value of $X$ | 0 | 1 | 2 | 3 | 4 |
|---|---|---|---|---|---|
| Frequency | 10 | 25 | 34 | 48 | 23 |

(6) Test whether the following could have come from a Poisson distribution with mean 1.

| Value of $X$ | 0 | 1 | 2 | 3+ |
|---|---|---|---|---|
| Frequency | 30 | 43 | 17 | 10 |

(7) Test whether the following could have come from a Poisson distribution.

| Value of $X$ | 0 | 1 | 2 | 3 | 4+ |
|---|---|---|---|---|---|
| Frequency | 35 | 45 | 36 | 18 | 16 |

(8) Test whether or not the following could have come from a normal distribution with mean 1 and variance 4.

| Values of $X$ | $X < -2$ | $-2 < X < 1$ | $1 < X < 4$ | $4 < X$ |
|---|---|---|---|---|
| Frequency | 7 | 40 | 38 | 15 |

(9) It is thought that the following figures might come from a normal distribution with variance 25. Find the sample mean, and hence test whether the figures do fit a normal distribution with that mean. (Note: there is an extra restriction introduced, as the mean is found from the data.)

| Values of $X$ | $X < 10$ | $10 < X < 20$ | $20 < X < 30$ | $30 < X < 40$ | $40 < X$ |
|---|---|---|---|---|---|
| Frequency | 10 | 167 | 587 | 195 | 41 |

(10) Find the mean and variance of the following figures. Test whether they come from a normal distribution. (Note: two extra restrictions are introduced, as the mean and variance are found from the figures.)

| Values of $X$ | $0 < X < 5$ | $5 < X < 10$ | $10 < X < 15$ | $15 < X < 20$ | $20 < X$ |
|---|---|---|---|---|---|
| Frequency | 151 | 318 | 345 | 123 | 63 |

## 45.3 Testing Association

The $\chi^2$ distribution can also be used to test whether or not there is a connection between two properties.

A chart which gives the frequencies of the two properties is a *contingency table*. The entries in this table are the observed frequencies.

The null Hypothesis is that there is no association. The chart containing the expected frequencies must have the same row totals and the same column totals as the contingency table.

If the contingency table has $n$ rows and $m$ columns, then the number of degrees of freedom is $\nu = (n-1)(m-1)$.

The value of $\chi^2(\nu)$ is then worked out as in 45.2.

### 45.3.1 Example

It is thought that there is an association between the ages of young candidates for the driving test and whether or not they pass at the first attempt. Analysis of 200 cases gave the following contingency table. Test at a 5% level of significance whether there is an association.

Age

|  | 17 | 18 | 19 | 20 |
|---|---|---|---|---|
| Fail | 21 | 33 | 25 | 1 |
| Pass | 24 | 32 | 55 | 9 |

Solution    These are the observed frequencies. Note that 45 out of 200 were 17 years old, and that 80 out of 200 failed. If there is no association, then the expected number in the top left hand box is $(45/200) \times (80/200) \times 200 = 18$. Fill in the rest of the expected frequencies similarly.

Age

|  | 17 | 18 | 19 | 20 |
|---|---|---|---|---|
| Fail | 18 | 26 | 32 | 4 |
| Pass | 27 | 39 | 48 | 6 |

Note that the top right box has less than 6 terms in it. Amalgamate the 20 column with the 19 column.

Age

|  | 17 | 18 | 19&20 |
|---|---|---|---|
| Fail | 18 | 26 | 36 |
| Pass | 27 | 39 | 54 |

This is now a 3 by 2 table, so the number of degrees of freedom is $(2-1)(3-1) = 2$. The 19 and 20 columns of the observed frequency table are also amalgamated. Evaluate $\chi^2$ as in 45.2.

$$\chi^2 = 3^2/18 + 7^2/26 + 10^2/36 + 3^2/27 + 7^2/39 + 10^2/54 = 8.6$$

This is above the critical figure at 5%. We conclude: **There is an association between age and pass-rate.**

### 45.3.2 Exercises

(1) The following contingency table shows the numbers of men and women in high and low positions in a certain firm. Test whether there is an association.

|         | High | Low |
|---------|------|-----|
| Women   | 16   | 80  |
| Men     | 20   | 28  |

(2) It is thought that there might be a connection between colour of hair and colour of eye. The results of a survey of 80 people are given below. test whether or not there is a connection.

|              | Hair Fair | Dark |
|--------------|-----------|------|
| Eye  Dark    | 28        | 32   |
| Light        | 12        | 8    |

(3) The sixth form of a school contained 300 pupils doing at least one of Maths, Physics, Chemistry. They were asked which was their favourite subject: the results, classified by sex, are given below. Test whether or not there is a connection.

|       | Maths | Physics | Chemistry |
|-------|-------|---------|-----------|
| Girls | 22    | 61      | 37        |
| Boys  | 28    | 89      | 63        |

(4) The connection between A-level passes and television watching was investigated. Group $A$ watched less than 2 hours television a week, Group $B$ watched at least 2 hours. Their exam results are as below:

|         | 0, 1 passes | 2 passes | over 2 passes |
|---------|-------------|----------|---------------|
| Group A | 6           | 6        | 8             |
| Group B | 42          | 48       | 10            |

Is there an association?

(5) A group of people were classified by their age and their political convictions, the results are given below. Is there evidence of an association?

|  | Left | Centre | Right |
|---|---|---|---|
| Young | 16 | 22 | 25 |
| Middle | 16 | 2 | 24 |
| Old | 16 | 24 | 23 |

## 45.4 Examination Questions

(1)

a. Five independent measurements of the diameter of a ball bearing were made using a certain instrument. The results obtained, in millimetres, were 8.9, 9.1, 9.1, 8.9, 8.9.

   i. Given that the true diameter of the ball bearing is 9 mm, calculate unbiased estimates of the mean and variance of the measurement error of the instrument.

   ii. Assuming that the measurement errors are independent and normally distributed, calculate 90% confidence limits for the mean measurement error.

b. The weekly wages received by a random sample of 80 personnel employed in factory $A$ had a mean of £86.40 and a standard deviation of £3.80. Use this information to calculate an approximate 99% confidence interval for the mean weekly wage of all personnel employed in factory $A$.

The weekly wages received by a random sample of 100 personnel employed in factory $B$ had a mean of £87.60 and a standard deviation of £5.20. Calculate an approximate 95% confidence interval for the difference between the mean weekly wages in the two factories. State, with your reason, whether or not your interval discredits the claim that the mean weekly wages in the two factories are equal.

[W]

(2) State the basic assumptions which underlie the use of (i) the paired sample $t$ test, (ii) the independent sample $t$ test.

A tyre manufacturer has produced a new tyre and claims that it wears better than the old tyre. In order to test the claim eight cars were selected at random and fitted with one old tyre and one new tyre on the driving wheels.

The cars were then driven for one month under normal conditions and the amount of wear measured on each of the tyres in mm. The results were as follows:

| Car | A | B | C | D | E | F | G | H |
|---|---|---|---|---|---|---|---|---|
| Old tyre | 3.41 | 2.61 | 0.77 | 1.60 | 0.87 | 2.28 | 1.92 | 3.21 |
| New tyre | 3.19 | 2.36 | 0.47 | 1.28 | 0.93 | 2.05 | 2.04 | 3.11 |

Show that these data do offer evidence that the new tyre wears significantly less than the old. State your null and alternative hypotheses and the best level at which the null hypothesis can be rejected.

Calculate a 90% confidence interval for the difference in mean wear between the new and old tyres.

[SUJB]

(3) In order to determine whether or not the number of books borrowed from a school library depends on the day of the week, the librarian noted the numbers of books borrowed daily during a particular week, with the following results.

| | Mon | Tue | Wed | Thu | Fri |
|---|---|---|---|---|---|
| Number borrowed | 68 | 74 | 78 | 85 | 92 |

Not being a statistician, she concluded that, since the figures were different, the numbers borrowed do depend on the day of the week. Why is the argument incorrect? Perform a significance test at the 5% level to resolve the problem.

During another week the figures were

| Mon | Tue | Wed | Thu | Fri |
|---|---|---|---|---|
| 70 | 80 | 83 | 92 | 98. |

Determine if the extra data alter your conclusion.

[SUJB]

(4) At the end of the first year of a polytechnic course, 105 students sat an examination in statistics. The arithmetic mean and standard deviation of the marks obtained were 46.8 and 12.1 respectively. The marks were then grouped into classes as follows:

| Mark | less than 30 | 30-34 | 35-39 | 40-49 | 50-59 | 60-69 | 70 and over |
|---|---|---|---|---|---|---|---|
| Students numb. | 6 | 11 | 4 | 40 | 26 | 14 | 4 |

a. Use a $\chi^2$ test at a 5% significance level to test whether the normal distribution provides an adequate model for the data.

b. The pass mark is 40 and it is customary to review all scripts which have scored between 35 and 39 to see if it is possible to award any more marks. The marks given in the table have been subject to such a review. Comment on your results in the light of this further information and suggest how the test might be modified.

[AEB 1985]

(5) As part of a survey into transport, the following information was collected on a sample of passenger carrying vehicles arriving in a city.

| | Passenger Transport | | |
| | Privately operated buses | Executive buses | Trains |
| --- | --- | --- | --- |
| Arrived on time | 23 | 62 | 33 |
| Arrived late | 47 | 28 | 7 |

a. Use a $\chi^2$–test to show that the difference between the proportions of late arrivals for the three different forms of transport is significant at the 1% level.

b. A spokeswoman for the private bus company said that the apparent poor performance of their buses was due to the observers using different criteria of lateness for each form of transport. To check this, four observers independently observed the arrivals of a sample of privately operated buses. The resulting contingency table gave a value of 8.12 for $\sum (O - E)^2 / E$. Test, at the 5% significance level, whether there is a difference between observers, and say how this result would affect your previous conclusions (if at all).

c. After further training the four observers were asked to classify the arrivals of a sample of trains as "on time", "slightly late" or "late'. The resulting $4 \times 3$ contingency table gave a value of 9.32 for $\sum (O - E)^2 / E$. Test, at the 5% significance level, whether there is still a difference between observers.

[AEB 1986]

## COMMON ERRORS

(1) Both the $t$–test and the $\chi^2$ test assume that the underlying distribution is normal. Exam questions often ask you to show that you appreciate this.

(2) **t-tests**

a. A $t$–test is used when the variance is estimated from a small sample. If you are told the variance, then an ordinary normal test can be used.

b. You must use the *unbiased* estimate of the variance. But the variance of the sample mean is $\sigma^2/n$, not $\sigma^2/(n-1)$.

c. The critical values for $t$ are given for two-tailed tests. If you are doing a one-tailed test you must allow for this, by using the 10% figure instead of the 5% figure.

(3) $\chi^2$ **tests**

a. It is easy to get wrong the number of degrees of freedom. Think of it as the number of free choices you have when putting numbers into the boxes – this is the number of boxes minus the number of conditions you have to satisfy.

b. Boxes are amalgamated if the *expected* frequency in them is less than 6. It does not matter if the *observed* frequency is small.

# 46 Correlation and Regression

## 46.1 Fitting Straight Lines

Suppose $x$ and $y$ are related variables. Let several pairs of values $(x_i, y_i)$ be found. When they are plotted on a graph they form a *scatter diagram*.

Sometimes these points almost lie on a straight line. Sometimes a change of variables will ensure that the points lie almost on a straight line.

### 46.1.1 Examples

(1)     It is thought that there is a relationship of the form $y = ax^2 + bx$ between the variables $x$ and $y$. The following experimental values were obtained:

| $x$ | 1 | 2 | 3 | 4 | 5 |
|---|---|---|---|---|---|
| $y$ | 8 | 24 | 42 | 76 | 95 |

By a suitable change of variables, put the relationship in a straight line form. Plot the points, and hence find $a$ and $b$.

Solution    Divide by $x$, to obtain $y/x = ax+b$. Write out a new row of the table for the values of $y/x$.

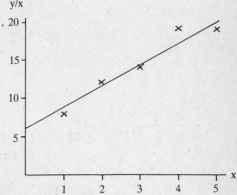

| $x$ | 1 | 2 | 3 | 4 | 5 |
|-----|---|---|---|---|---|
| $y/x$ | 8 | 12 | 14 | 19 | 19 |

Plot these points, obtaining the graph shown.

The graph has a gradient of 2.8, and it crosses the $y/x$−axis at 6.

## The relationship is $y = 2.8x^2 + 6x$

(2)    $r$ and $s$ are related by the formula $r = as^n$. The table below gives experimental values of $r$ and $s$. Re-write the formula so that a straight line can be fitted to the data, and hence find $a$ and $n$.

| $s$ | $\frac{1}{4}$ | $\frac{1}{2}$ | 1 | 2 | 3 | 4 | 5 |
|-----|---------------|---------------|---|---|---|---|---|
| $r$ | 2 | 2.1 | 3 | 3.3 | 3.4 | 3.6 | 3.7 |

Solution    Take logs of both sides. $\ln r = \ln a + n \ln s$. Write out a new table of values of $\ln r$ and $\ln s$.

| $\ln s$ | −1.4 | −0.7 | 0 | 0.7 | 1.1 | 1.4 | 1.6 |
|---------|------|------|---|-----|-----|-----|-----|
| $\ln r$ | 0.7 | 0.74 | 1.1 | 1.2 | 1.2 | 1.3 | 1.3 |

Plot $\ln r$ against $\ln s$, obtaining the graph shown.

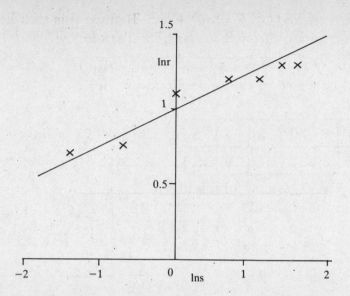

The gradient is $\frac{1}{4}$, and it crosses the $y$-axis at 1.
Hence $n = \frac{1}{4}$ and $\ln a = 1$.

## The relationship is $r = 2.7s^{\frac{1}{4}}$

### 46.1.2 Exercises

(1) $y$ is given in terms of $x$ by $y = ax^2 + b$. By plotting $y$ against $x^2$ for the following figures, find the values of $a$ and $b$.

| $x$ | 1 | 2 | 3 | 4 | 5 |
|---|---|---|---|---|---|
| $y$ | 1.8 | 10.5 | 25 | 45 | 71 |

(2) The relationship between $T$ and $S$ is thought to be of the form $T = a\sqrt{S} + b$. Reduce the equation to a linear form, and hence use the table below to find the values of $a$ and $b$.

| $S$ | 1 | 2 | 3 | 4 | 5 |
|---|---|---|---|---|---|
| $T$ | 45 | 17 | 20 | 22 | 25 |

(3) $x$ and $y$ are related by $y = a/x + b$. Reduce this to a linear form, and use the table below to find the values of $a$ and $b$.

| $x$ | $\frac{1}{4}$ | $\frac{1}{2}$ | 1 | $1\frac{1}{2}$ | 2 |
|---|---|---|---|---|---|
| $y$ | 6 | $-1$ | $-3$ | $-4.5$ | $-5$ |

(4) $F$ and $v$ are related by $F = av^3 + bv^2$. Reduce this to a linear form, and hence find the values of $a$ and $b$, using the data below.

| $v$ | 10 | 20 | 30 | 40 | 50 |
|---|---|---|---|---|---|
| $F$ | 15 | 100 | 320 | 720 | 1400 |

(5) $P$ and $V$ are related by $P = aV^n$. Reduce this to a linear form, and use the data below to find the values of $a$ and $n$.

| $V$ | 1 | 1.2 | 1.4 | 1.6 | 1.8 | 2.0 |
|---|---|---|---|---|---|---|
| $P$ | 4 | 6.2 | 9.4 | 13.5 | 18.6 | 25 |

(6) It is thought that $x$ and $y$ are related by $y = ab^x$. Use the table below to find the values of $a$ and $b$.

| $x$ | 0 | 1 | 2 | 3 | 4 | 5 |
|---|---|---|---|---|---|---|
| $y$ | 0.3 | 0.4 | 0.6 | 0.8 | 1.2 | 1.6 |

(7) $x$ and $y$ are related by $y = ax^n$. One of the values of $y$ in the table below is incorrect. Find which it is, and estimate what the correct value should be.

| $x$ | 1 | 2 | 3 | 4 | 5 |
|---|---|---|---|---|---|
| $y$ | 7 | 94 | 420 | 900 | 8000 |

(8) For the following relationships, find the change of variables which will turn them into a linear form.

(a) $y = ax^3 + b$      (b) $y^2 = ax + b$

(c) $y = a/\sqrt{x} + b$      (d) $y = ax + b/x$

(e) $y = a\sqrt{x} + b/\sqrt{x}$    (f) $y = a/x + b/x^2$

(g) $y = ax^{-n}$          (h) $y = ab^{x^2}$

(i) $y^a = bx$          (j) $(ay)^x = b$

## 46.2 Linear Regression

*Linear regression* of $y$ on $x$ expresses $y$ as a linear function of $x$. Suppose the function is to be found from pairs of values $(x_1, y_1), (x_2, y_2), ..., (x_n, y_n)$. The *Method of Least Squares* finds the equation $y = ax + b$ such that $\sum(y_i - (ax_i + b))^2$ is as small as possible.

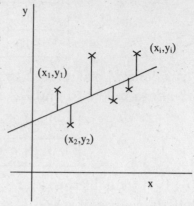

Let $\overline{x}$ and $\overline{y}$ be the sample means of $x$ and $y$ respectively. Let $S_{xx}^2$ be the sample variance of $x$.

Define the *covariance* of $x$ and $y$ as $S_{xy} = (\sum x_i y_i - n\overline{x}\,\overline{y})/n$.

Then the linear relationship is given by:

$y - \overline{y} = a(x - \overline{x})$, where $a = S_{xy}/S_{xx}^2$. $a$ is the *regression coefficient*.

The line goes through the point $(\overline{x}, \overline{y})$. The line of regression of $x$ on $y$ is found by interchanging the rôles of $x$ and $y$. In general, the two lines will not be equal.

Suppose that the values of $x$ are exact but that the values of $y$ are subject to errors with variance $\sigma^2$. Then, in the equation $y = ax + b$, the variances of $a$ and $b$ are approximately $\sigma^2/(nS_{xx}^2)$ and $\sigma^2(1 + (\overline{x}/S_{xx})^2)/n$ respectively.

### 46.2.1 Examples

(1)     10 values of $x$ and $y$ are found. $\sum x = 50, \sum y = 200, \sum x^2 = 300, \sum y^2 = 6000, \sum xy = 1250$. Find the lines of regression of $y$ on $x$ and of $x$ on $y$.

Solution     $\overline{x} = 5, \overline{y} = 20. S_{xx}^2 = 5, S_{yy}^2 = 200$. Use the formula above to show that $S_{xy} = 25$. The regression coefficients can also be found from the formulae. The equations are:

$$y - 20 = 5(x - 5) \text{ and } x - 5 = \frac{1}{8}(y - 20)$$

**The equations are $y = 5x - 5$ and $x = \dfrac{1}{8}y + 2\dfrac{1}{2}$**

(2)    The values of $y$ of Example 1 are subject to errors which are normal with mean zero and variance $\frac{1}{4}$. If $y$ is found from $x$ by the equation $y = ax+b$, find a 95% confidence interval for the true value of $y$ when $x = 0$.

Solution    Putting $x = 0, y = b$. The variance of $b$ is found from the formula above. Put $\sigma^2 = \frac{1}{4}, \bar{x} = 5, S_{xx}^2 = 5, n = 10$ to find that $Var(b) = 0.05$.

The 95% critical value for the standard normal distribution is 1.96. The confidence interval is:

$$-5 \pm 1.96 \times \sqrt{0.05}$$

**The confidence interval for y when x = 0 is −5.44 < y < −4.56**

## 46.2.2 Exercises

(1) Find the line of regression of $y$ on $x$ from the following values:

a.  $n = 5, \sum x = 10, \sum x^2 = 30, \sum y = 13.1, \sum y^2 = 54.41, \sum xy = 40.3$.

b.  $n = 6, \sum x = 15, \sum x^2 = 55, \sum y = 6.4, \sum y^2 = 8.06, \sum xy = 20.4$

c.  $n = 5, \sum x = 20, \sum x^2 = 90, \sum y = 18.7, \sum y^2 = 75.77, \sum xy = 82.3$

d.  $n = 5, \sum x = 15, \sum x^2 = 55, \sum y = 77, \sum y^2 = 1503, \sum xy = 177$.

(2) For each of the situations in Question 1, estimate the value of $y$ when $x = 10$.

(3) For each of the situations in Question 1, find the line of regression of $x$ on $y$.

(4) The following pairs of values of $x$ and $y$ are found. Find (a) the line of regression of $y$ on $x$ (b) the line of regression of $x$ on $y$.

(2.1, 4), (3.3, 8), (4, 10), (5.9, 13.7), (6.4, 14.2), (8.8, 16).

(5) It is thought that there is a relationship of the form $y = ax^2 + b$. Six pairs of values are given below. Use the method of least squares to find the line of regression of $y$ on $x^2$.

(2, 9), (3, 15), (4, 30), (5, 50), (6, 74).

(6) Use the method of least squares to find the line of regression of $y/x$ on $x$ for the figures in Example 1 of 46.1.1.

(7) Use the method of least squares to find the line of regression of $\ln r$ on $\ln s$ for the figures in Example 2 of 46.1.1. Hence find the equation in the form $r = as^n$.

(8) The values of $y$ in Question 1(b) are subject to errors which are normal with mean 0 and variance 0.01. Find a 95% confidence interval for the regression coefficient. Find also a 95% confidence interval for the value of $y$ when $x = 0$.

(9) The values of $y$ in Question 1(a) are subject to errors which are normal with mean 0 and variance 0.0001. Test at a 5% significance level the hypothesis that $y = 0$ when $x = 0$.

(10) 7 pairs of values of $x$ and $y$ are given below. There is a relationship between $y$ and $x$ of the form $y = ax + b$. Find the line of regression of $y$ on $x$. The $y$ values are subject to errors which are normal with mean zero and variance 0.1. Test at the 5% significance level the hypotheses (a) the slope is equal to 2 (b) the line goes through the origin.

$$(1, 2.5)\ (2, 5)\ (3, 7.4)\ (4, 9.3)\ (5, 11.9)\ (6, 14)\ (7, 16)$$

## 46.3 Correlation

Two random variables $X$ and $Y$ are *independent* if for each pair of values $i$ for $X$ and $j$ for $Y$, the events $(X = i)$ and $(Y = j)$ are independent. i.e.:

$$P(X = i\ \&\ Y = j) = P(X = i) \times P(Y = j)$$

If $X$ and $Y$ are not independent, then the correlation coefficient measures the degree to which they are dependent on each other.

The *correlation coefficient* or *product moment correlation coefficient* for two variables $X$ and $Y$ is defined by:

$$\rho_{XY} = \frac{E(XY) - E(X)E(Y)}{\sqrt{(Var(X)Var(Y))}}$$

$\rho$ lies between $-1$ and 1.

If $\rho = 1$ then there is a linear positive relationship between $X$ and $Y$.

If $\rho = -1$ there is a linear negative relationship between $X$ and $Y$.

If $\rho$ is to be estimated from $n$ values $(x_i,\ y_i)$ of $X$ and $Y$, then the estimation is given by:

$$r_{xy} = \frac{\sum x_i y_i - n\bar{x}\,\bar{y}}{\sqrt{((\sum x_i^2 - n\bar{x}^2)(\sum y_i^2 - n\bar{y}^2))}}$$

Suppose that $n$ values of $X$ and $Y$ are found. Let the values be ranked in order. The correlation coefficient between the ranks is *Spearman's coefficient of rank correlation*.

If $d$ represents the difference between the X and Y ranks, then Spearman's coefficient is:

$$r_s = 1 - \frac{6\sum d^2}{n(n^2 - 1)}$$

*Kendall's coefficient of rank correlation* is found by alloting $+1$ to each pair of ranks in the same order, and $-1$ for each pair in the reverse order. The total $S$ is found, and Kendall's coefficient is then:

$$\tau = \frac{S}{\frac{1}{2}n(n-1)}$$

## 46.3.1 Examples

(1) The height and the weight of 10 boys were measured and the results are given by the table below. Find the correlation coefficient between the height and the weight.

| Weight ($kg$) | 38 | 39 | 43 | 44 | 35 | 32 | 31 | 42 | 49 | 41 |
|---|---|---|---|---|---|---|---|---|---|---|
| Height ($cm$) | 150 | 152 | 146 | 158 | 142 | 144 | 135 | 145 | 155 | 150 |

Solution    Letting $X$ be the weight of a randomly selected boy, and $Y$ his height, we have:

$$n = 10 : \overline{x} = 39.4 : \overline{y} = 147.7 : \sum x^2 = 15806 : \sum y^2 = 218559 : \sum xy = 58456.$$

Substitute these values into the formula for correlation.

$$\frac{58456 - 10 \times 39.4 \times 147.7}{\sqrt{((15806 - 10 \times 39.4^2)(218559 - 10 \times 147.7^2))}} = 0.774$$

**The correlation coefficient is 0.774**

(2) Two judges at a diving competition marked the 8 candidates in order as follows. Find Spearman's and Kendall's coefficients for the two orders.

| Candidate | A | B | C | D | E | F | G | H |
|---|---|---|---|---|---|---|---|---|
| First Judge | 4 | 1 | 7 | 8 | 3 | 2 | 6 | 5 |
| Second Judge | 3 | 2 | 8 | 7 | 5 | 1 | 6 | 4 |

Solution    The differences are $1, -1, -1, 1, -2, 1, 0, 1$. $\sum d^2 = 10$. Apply the formula for Spearman's coefficient:

$$\mathbf{r_s = 1 - 6 \times 10/8(8^2 - 1) = 0.88}$$

To find Kendall's coefficient, re-write the table so that the first judge's ranks are in increasing order.

| Candidate | B | F | E | A | H | G | C | D |
|---|---|---|---|---|---|---|---|---|
| First Judge | 1 | 2 | 3 | 4 | 5 | 6 | 7 | 8 |
| Second Judge | 2 | 1 | 5 | 3 | 4 | 6 | 8 | 7 |

Take candidate $B$. In the second judge's row, to the right of $B$, there is 1 rank less than 2 and 6 ranks greater. Hence there is 1 pair in the opposite order to that of the first judge, and 6 pairs in the same order. So allot $-1$ and $+6$.

Repeat this procedure. To avoid counting the same pair twice, consider only the ranks to the right of each term.

$$S = -1 + 6 + 6 - 2 + 3 + 4 + 3 + 2 - 1 = 20$$

**Kendall's coefficient $\tau$ is $20/\frac{1}{2}8(8-1) = 0.71$**

## 46.3.2 Exercises

(1) In each of the following, find the correlation coefficient between $y$ and $x$ from the information given:

|  | $n$ | $\sum x$ | $\sum y$ | $\sum x^2$ | $\sum y^2$ | $\sum xy$ |
|---|---|---|---|---|---|---|
| (a) | 12 | 129 | 63 | 1500 | 800 | 700 |
| (b) | 9 | 56 | 76 | 500 | 830 | 620 |
| (c) | 10 | 69 | 436 | 585 | 31218 | 1858 |

(2) Evaluate the correlation coefficient between $x$ and $y$ for each of the sets of sample pairs given below:

(a)

| Sample | 1 | 2 | 3 | 4 | 5 | 6 | 7 | 8 |
|---|---|---|---|---|---|---|---|---|
| $x$ | 21 | 32 | 39 | 29 | 25 | 31 | 36 | 27 |
| $y$ | 3.1 | 4.3 | 5.7 | 3.8 | 3.0 | 4.1 | 4.8 | 3.2 |

(b)

| Sample | 1 | 2 | 3 | 4 | 5 | 6 | 7 | 8 | 9 |
|--------|-----|-----|-----|-----|-----|-----|-----|-----|-----|
| $x$ | 159 | 190 | 128 | 177 | 155 | 132 | 199 | 207 | 236 |
| $y$ | 163 | 121 | 180 | 111 | 166 | 219 | 98 | 87 | 63 |

(c)

| Sample | 1 | 2 | 3 | 4 | 5 | 6 | 7 |
|--------|-----|-----|-----|-----|-----|-----|-----|
| $x$ | 93 | 88 | 99 | 70 | 105 | 83 | 123 |
| $y$ | 21 | 17 | 16 | 27 | 23 | 34 | 24 |

(3) Select 6 pairs $(x_1, y_1), \ldots, (x_6, y_6)$ on the line $y = 3x + 1$. Check that the correlation coefficient between the $x$ and $y$ values is 1.

(4) Select 6 pairs $(x_1, y_1), \ldots, (x_6, y_6)$ on the line $y = -2x + 3$. Check that the correlation coefficient between the $x$ and $y$ values is $-1$.

(5) Find Spearman's and Kendall's rank correlation coefficients for the rankings given below:

(a)

| Item | A | B | C | D | E | F | G | H |
|------|---|---|---|---|---|---|---|---|
| First rank | 4 | 3 | 8 | 1 | 6 | 5 | 7 | 2 |
| Second rank | 2 | 1 | 7 | 3 | 4 | 6 | 8 | 5 |

(b)

| Item | A | B | C | D | E | F | G | H | I | J |
|------|---|---|---|----|---|---|---|---|---|---|
| First rank | 5 | 3 | 2 | 10 | 8 | 7 | 9 | 1 | 4 | 6 |
| Second rank | 5 | 7 | 10 | 2 | 1 | 3 | 4 | 9 | 6 | 8 |

(c)

| Item | A | B | C | D | E | F | G |
|------|---|---|---|---|---|---|---|
| First rank | 6 | 3 | 5 | 7 | 1 | 2 | 4 |
| Second rank | 1 | 2 | 5 | 7 | 3 | 6 | 4 |

(6) The following marks were obtained by 8 candidates in Maths and English:

| Candidate | A | B | C | D | E | F | G | H |
|---|---|---|---|---|---|---|---|---|
| Maths mark | 63 | 54 | 73 | 88 | 48 | 58 | 74 | 61 |
| English mark | 53 | 39 | 67 | 66 | 42 | 50 | 83 | 51 |

Rank these results and hence find Spearman's and Kendall's rank correlation coefficients between the two sets of results.

(7) For each part of Question 2, find the $x$ and $y$ ranks, and hence find the Spearman and Kendall rank correlation coefficients.

## 46.4 Examination Questions

(1) If experimental readings for $x$ and $y$ obey a formula of the type $y = Ax^B$, where $A$ and $B$ are constants, explain how, by using logarithms, the readings may be plotted to obtain a straight line graph.

For the following pairs of reading construct a suitable table of values to three decimal places and plot such a graph accurately.

$$x \quad 1.20 \quad 1.38 \quad 1.58 \quad 1.85 \quad 2.24 \quad 2.71 \quad 3.09$$

$$y \quad 1.86 \quad 2.29 \quad 2.63 \quad 3.55 \quad 4.74 \quad 6.31 \quad 7.67$$

Show that all but one of the points do lie very close to a straight line. Hence find $A$ and $B$.

State which pair of readings does not obey the formula and, assuming that the value of $x$ is correct, estimate what the value of $y$ should be, either by calculation from the formula or by reading from the graph.

[MEI add]

(2) (a) The table shows experimental values of two variables $x$ and $y$.

| $x$ | 0.2 | 0.6 | 1.0 | 1.4 |
|---|---|---|---|---|
| $y$ | 0.69 | 0.81 | 0.55 | 0.06 |

It is expected that $x$ and $y$ are related by an equation of the form $y = ax\sqrt{x} + b\sqrt{x}$, where $a$ and $b$ are constants. Express this equation in a form suitable for drawing a straight line graph. Draw the graph for the given data and use it to evaluate $a$ and $b$.

(b) It is expected that the variables $x, y$ and $X, Y$ are related by the equations $y = he^{-kx}$ and $Y = p(X + 1)^q$ respectively, where $h, k$ and $p, q$ are unknown constants. Given experimental values of $x, y$ and $X, Y$, (i) determine the variables whose values should be plotted in order to obtain straight line graphs, (ii) explain how these graphs may be used to determine the values of $h, k$ and $p, q$.

[C add]

(3) Two quantities $x$ and $y$ are linearly related. Ten pairs of experimental observations $(x, y)$ were made and the following results were calculated:

$$\sum x = 90, \sum y = 415, \sum x^2 = 3300, \sum xy = 14193$$

Assuming that the observations $x$ are accurate and that the observations $y$ are subject to independent random errors, each normally distributed with mean zero and standard deviation 0.5, determine (i) the least squares estimate for the equation connecting $x$ and $y$, (ii) the 99% confidence interval for the value of $y$ when $x = 0$.

[JMB]

(4) A sample of $n$ pairs $(x_i, y_i)$, $i = 1, 2, ..., n$, is drawn from a bivariate population $(X, Y)$ and a rank correlation coefficient, $r$, calculated.

i. What range of values is it possible for $r$ to have?
ii. What information about the sample does $r$ indicate?
iii. What can be concluded about the sample points when $r = 1$? Can the same be said about the population from which the sample is drawn? Explain your answer.

The table gives the average share rate and average mortgage rate calculated on the first day of the months shown for the years 1976 to 1985.

| Year | 1976 | 1977 | 1978 | 1979 | 1980 | 1981 | 1982 | 1983 | 1984 | 1985 |
|---|---|---|---|---|---|---|---|---|---|---|
| Month | Nov | Nov | Dec | Dec | Jan | Nov | Dec | Jul | Dec | Apr |
| Share% | 7.8 | 6.0 | 8.0 | 10.5 | 10.5 | 9.8 | 6.2 | 7.2 | 6.8 | 8.2 |
| Mortgage% | 12.2 | 9.5 | 11.8 | 11.8 | 15.0 | 15.0 | 10.0 | 11.2 | 11.5 | 14.0 |

Plot a scatter diagram and comment on its implication for $r$. Indicate on your diagram which point appears to be an outlier (i.e. one that is far from the trend line).

Calculate a rank correlation coefficient between share rate and mortage rate.

Under the null hypothesis that the population $r = 0$ against the alternative $r \neq 0$ the following are critical values of Spearman's and Kendall's coefficients for a sample size of 10.

| Significance Level | 10% | 5% | 2% | 1% |
|---|---|---|---|---|
| Spearman's $r$ | 0.564 | 0.648 | 0.745 | 0.794 |
| Kendall's $r$ | 0.467 | 0.511 | 0.600 | 0.644 |

Comment on the significance of your calculated value of $r$.

[SUJB]

## COMMON ERRORS

### (1) Fitting Straight Lines

a. Your equation must be reduced to linear form before you plot points. Do not, for example, plot points of the function $y = ax^2 + b$, and try to fit a parabola. This would have no accuracy at all.

b. The straight line which you fit does not have to go through the origin. It does not have to go through the first and last points.

c. The gradient and intercept must be found from the line which you have drawn. They should not be found from the line joining the first and last points.

### (2) Regression and Correlation

Some calculators can work out regression and correlation coefficients. But do not rely on your calculator - you will get very few marks unless you show that you know the formulae for finding these coefficients.

# Appendix

A-level Mathematics involves a lot of of intricate algebra. Below are some exercises for further practice in algebraic manipulation. Answers are given at the end of the appendix.

## 1. Substitution

*Substitution* involves putting numbers in place of algebraic letters. Be especially careful when the numbers are fractional or negative.

Exercise   Find the values of the following expressions after the substitutions indicated.

1)  $2x - 3y$       (a) $x = 1, y = 3$     (b) $x = -2, y = -7$
                    (c) $x = \frac{1}{3}, y = \frac{1}{4}$

2)  $x^2 - 2x - 2$   (a) $x = 4$       (b) $x = -2$       (c) $x = \frac{1}{2}$

3)  $5/x$            (a) $x = 10$      (b) $x = -2$       (c) $x = \frac{1}{3}$

4)  $1/(x + 2)$      (a) $x = 1$       (b) $x = -3$       (c) $x = -1.5$

5)  $\sqrt{x^2 + 3}$  (a) $x = 1$       (b) $x = -2$       (c) $x = 5$

## 2. Expansion of Brackets

When expanding out brackets, make sure to obtain the correct number of terms. Be careful with negative numbers.

Exercise   Expand the following and simplify as far as possible.

1) $(x + y)(a + b)$    2) $(x + 3)(x - 7)$       3) $(2 - x)(4 - x)$

4) $(x + y)^2$         5) $(a - b)^2$            6) $(2p - 4q)(p + 2q)$

7) $(3x)^2$            8) $(4x^2 y^3)^2$         9) $(x^2 - z)^2$

## 3. Factorization

Factorizing is the opposite operation to expansion. A factorization can therefore be checked by expanding it out again.

Exercise   Factorize the following as far as possible.

1) $x^2 y + y^2 x$        2) $3x^2 y + 9x^3$        3) $x^2 + 4x + 3$

4) $x^2 - 8x + 15$        5) $x^2 - 3x - 28$        6) $x^2 + 5x - 24$

7) $m^2 - n^2$            8) $4p^2 - 9q^2$          9) $3r^2 - 12s^2$

10) $2x^2 - 3x - 5$      11) $2x^2 - 11x + 12$     12) $3x^2 - 8x - 3$

13) $4x^2 - 13x + 3$    14) $xp - yq + yp - xq$   15) $6at + bs - 2sa - 3bt$

## 4. Equations

The basic rule for solving equations is to do the same to the left as to the right. Once a solution has been found it can be checked by substitution back into the original equation.

Exercise   Solve the following equations.

1) $2x - 1 = 3$          2) $7 - 3x = 1$          3) $7 + 2x = 1 - 4x$

4) $\sqrt{x} + 3 = 7$     5) $\sqrt{(x/8)} = 9$     6) $\sqrt{(5/2x)} = 10$

7) $x^2 - 7 = 9$    8) $\dfrac{x + 8}{x} = 2$       9) $\dfrac{3}{x} = \dfrac{4}{x + 1}$

10) $(x + 3)(x + 2) = x(x - 5)$           11) $\dfrac{x}{x - 3} = \dfrac{x - 2}{x}$

12) $x + 3y = 8$      13) $2x - 3y = 4$          14) $3x - 2y = 5$
    $x + 5y = 12$          $5x + 7y = 68$            $7x - 5y = 11$

## 5. Changing the subject

The procedure for changing the subject of a formula is the same as for solving an equation. You must get the new subject by itself on one side of the formula.

If the new subject has more than one occurrence, then all the occurrences must be grouped together and factorized.

Exercise  Make $x$ the subject of the following formulas.

1) $x + a = b$

2) $3x - a = c$

3) $\sqrt{x + p} = q$

4) $q = p + \sqrt{x}$

5) $\dfrac{7}{x} = z$

6) $\dfrac{a}{x + 3} = b$

7) $ax + b = cx$

8) $m - px = n - qx$

9) $x = ax - b$

10) $\dfrac{x + 3}{x} = q$

11) $\dfrac{x + m}{x + n} = p$

12) $\dfrac{x + a}{x + b} = \dfrac{x + c}{x + d}$

13) $a = x^2 + b$

14) $m = \sqrt{4 - x^2}$

15) $7x^3 - p = q$

## 6. Proportion

A proportionality relationship can be written either as $y \propto x^n$ or as $y = kx^n$, where $k$ is a constant called the *constant of proportionality*. If $n$ is a negative number, then the relationship is one of inverse proportionality.

To find the constant $k$, we need a pair of values of $x$ and $y$. To find the power $n$, we need two pairs of values.

Exercise

1) In the following, find the constant of proportionality and the equation giving $y$ in terms of $x$.

(a) $y$ is proportional to $x$. $y = 6$ when $x = 3$.

(b) $y$ is proportional to $x$. $y = 1.5$ when $x = 4.5$.

(c) $y$ is inversely proportional to $x$. $y = 5$ when $x = 4$.

(d) $y$ is inversely proportional to $x$. $y = 0.25$ when $x = 0.5$.

(e) $y$ is proportional to the square of $x$. $y = 40$ when $x = 2$.

(f) $y$ is proportional to the square of $x$. $y = 98$ when $x = 7$.

(g) $y$ is inversely proportional to the square of $x$. $y = 15$ when $x = 2$.

(h) $y$ is inversely proportional to the square of $x$. $y = 40$ when $x = \frac{1}{2}$.

2) In the following, $y$ is proportional to a power of $x$. Describe the proportionality relationship, and express $y$ in terms of $x$.

(a) $y = 2$ when $x = 5$, and $y = 4$ when $x = 10$.

(b) $y = 5$ when $x = 2$, and $y = 45$ when $x = 6$.

(c) $y = 36$ when $x = 3$, and $y = 9$ when $x = 6$.

(d) $y = 4$ when $x = 2$, and $y = 32$ when $x = 4$.

(e) $y = \frac{1}{2}$ when $x = \frac{1}{3}$, and $y = 1$ when $x = \frac{1}{6}$.

## 7. Algebraic fractions

The rules for algebraic fractions are the same as for numerical fractions.

Fractions are unchanged if both top and bottom are multiplied or divided by the same thing.

When fractions are multiplied, multiply the tops and the bottoms.

When one fraction is divided by another, turn the second fraction upside down and then multiply.

When fractions are added or subtracted, they must first be put over a common denominator.

Exercise

1) Simplify the following fractions:

(a) $\dfrac{4x^2}{2xy}$

(b) $\dfrac{x^2 + x}{x^3}$

(c) $\dfrac{x^2 + 4x + 3}{x^2 + 5x + 4}$

(d) $\dfrac{p + q}{1/p + 1/q}$

(e) $\dfrac{a}{1/b}$

(f) $\dfrac{a/b}{b/a}$

2) Write the following as single fractions, simplifying your answers.

(a) $\dfrac{1}{x} \times \dfrac{1}{y}$

(b) $\dfrac{ax}{cy} \times \dfrac{by}{dx}$

(c) $\dfrac{x^2}{y} \times \dfrac{y^2}{x}$

(d) $\dfrac{x + 1}{x + 2} \times \dfrac{x - 1}{x - 2}$

(e) $\dfrac{1}{x + 3} \times \dfrac{1}{x - 4}$

(f) $\dfrac{1}{x} \times \dfrac{x^2 + x}{x + 3}$

(g) $\dfrac{a}{b} \div \dfrac{x}{y}$

(h) $\dfrac{x^2 a}{y^2 b} \div \dfrac{a^2}{b^2}$

(i) $\dfrac{x + 1}{a} \div \dfrac{x^2 - 1}{b}$

(j) $\dfrac{x}{2} + \dfrac{x}{3}$

(k) $\dfrac{x + 3}{3} + \dfrac{x - 7}{4}$

(l) $\dfrac{1}{x} + \dfrac{1}{y}$

(m) $\dfrac{1}{ab} - \dfrac{1}{a}$

(n) $\dfrac{1}{x - 1} - \dfrac{1}{x^2 - 1}$

# Solutions

## Set 1

1) (a) $-7$      (b) 17      (c) $-\frac{1}{12}$
2) (a) 6      (b) 6      (c) $-2.75$
3) (a) ½      (b) $-2\frac{1}{2}$      (c) 15
4) (a) ⅓      (b) $-1$      (c) 2
5) (a) 2      (b) 2.65      (c) 5.29

## Set 2

1) $xa + xb + ya + yb$      2) $x^2 - 4x - 21$

3) $x^2 - 6x + 8$      4) $x^2 + 2xy + y^2$      5) $a^2 - 2ab + b^2$

6) $2p^2 - 8q^2$      7) $9x^2$      8) $16x^4y^6$

9) $x^4 - 2x^2z + z^2$

## Set 3

1) $xy(x + y)$      2) $3x^2(y + 3x)$      3) $(x + 3)(x + 1)$

4) $(x - 5)(x - 3)$      5) $(x - 7)(x + 4)$      6) $(x + 8)(x - 3)$

7) $(m - n)(m + n)$      8) $(2p - 3q)(2p + 3q)$      9) $3(r - 2s)(r + 2s)$

10) $(2x - 5)(x + 1)$      11) $(2x - 3)(x - 4)$      12) $(3x + 1)(x - 3)$

13) $(4x - 1)(x - 3)$      14) $(x + y)(p - q)$      15) $(2a - b)(3t - s)$

## Set 4

1) 2      2) 2      3) $-1$

4) 16      5) 648      6) $\frac{1}{40}$

7) 4      8) 8      9) 3

10) $-0.6$      11) 1.2      12) $x = 2, y = 2$

13) $x = 8, y = 4$      14) $x = 3, y = 2$

## Set 5

1) $b - a$
2) $(c + a)/3$
3) $q^2 - p$
4) $(q - p)^2$
5) $7/z$
6) $(a - 3b)/b$
7) $b/(c - a)$
8) $(m - n)/(p - q)$
9) $b/(a - 1)$
10) $3/(q - 1)$
11) $(m - pn)/(p - 1)$
12) $(ad - bc)/(b + c - a - d)$
13) $\sqrt{a - b}$
14) $\sqrt{4 - m^2}$
15) $\sqrt[3]{(q + p)/7}$

## Set 6

1) (a) 2, $y = 2x$    (b) ⅓, $y = \tfrac{1}{3}x$    (c) 20, $y = 20/x$
   (d) ⅛, $y = 1/(8x)$    (e) 10, $y = 10x^2$    (f) 2, $y = 2x^2$
   (g) 60, $y = 60/x^2$    (h) 10, $y = 10/x^2$

2) (a) direct, $y = 2.5x$    (b) square, $y = 1.25x^2$
   (c) inverse square, $y = 324/x^2$    (d) cube, $y = \tfrac{1}{2}x^3$
   (e) inverse, $y = \tfrac{1}{6}/x$

## Set 7

1) (a) $\dfrac{2x}{y}$    (b) $\dfrac{x + 1}{x^2}$    (c) $\dfrac{x + 3}{x + 5}$

   (d) $pq$    (e) $ba$    (f) $\dfrac{a^2}{b^2}$

2) (a) $\dfrac{1}{xy}$    (b) $\dfrac{ab}{cd}$    (c) $xy$

   (d) $\dfrac{x^2 - 1}{x^2 - 4}$    (e) $\dfrac{1}{(x + 3)(x - 4)}$    (f) $\dfrac{x + 1}{x + 3}$

   (g) $\dfrac{ay}{bx}$    (h) $\dfrac{x^2 b}{y^2 a}$    (i) $\dfrac{b}{a(x - 1)}$

   (j) $\dfrac{5x}{6}$    (k) $\dfrac{7x - 9}{12}$    (l) $\dfrac{y + x}{xy}$

   (m) $\dfrac{1 - b}{ab}$    (n) $\dfrac{x}{x^2 - 1}$

# AS-LEVEL PAPERS

## AS-LEVEL PAPER I. PURE

Time 3 hours. *Answer all the questions*

(1) The first term of a geometric progression is $\frac{3}{4}$ of its sum to infinity. Find the ratio of the second to the fourth term.

[3]

(2) Find the equations of the tangents to $y = \sin 3x$ at $x = 0$ and at $x = \pi/3$. Find where these tangents cross.

[4]

(3) Solve the equation $\sin(x - 45°) = \frac{1}{3}$, giving all the solutions in the range $0 \leq x \leq 360°$.

[4]

(4) $\alpha$ and $\beta$ are the roots of the equation $2x^2 + x + 3 = 0$. Without solving the equation find (i) $\alpha + \beta$ (ii) $\alpha^2 + \beta^2$.

[4]

(5) A vessel is obtained by rotating the curve $y = x^2$, from $y = 0$ to $y = 1$, about the $y$−axis. Distances are measured in inches.
   i.   Find the volume of the vessel.
   ii.  The vessel is gradually filled with water. At the instant when the depth of water in the vessel is $\frac{1}{2}$ in, 0.05 in$^3$ is added. Find the approximate increase in the depth of the water.

[5]

(6) Find the first four terms in the binomial expansion of $(1+x)^{1\frac{1}{2}}$. Hence find an approximation for $109^{1\frac{1}{2}}$.

[5]

(7) Differentiate the following:
   (i) $y = (1 + x)/\sqrt{x}$   (ii) $y = x^2 \cos x$   (iii) $y = \ln(1 + 3x^2)$

[6]

(8) $f$ is defined on the set of all positive numbers by $f : x \to \sqrt{x}$.
$g$ is defined on the set of all numbers by $g : x \to x - 3$.

i.   Find the function $gf$ and state its domain and range.

ii.  Find the function $fg$ and state its domain and range.

[6]

---

(9) Solve the following equations:

(i)   $\log_2 3x - \log_2(x - 1) = 4$   (ii)   $3^{x+2} = 12$.

[6]

---

(10) The figure shows a pyramid $VABCD$, in which $ABCD$ is a square of side 8, and $VA = VB = VC = VD = 12$. Find the following:

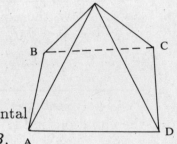

(i) AC   (ii) The height of the pyramid

(iii) The inclination of $VDA$ to the horizontal

(iv) The angle between $VDA$ and $VCB$.

[8]

---

(11) The vector positions of $A$, $B$, $C, D$ are $\mathbf{a}$, $\mathbf{b}$, $\mathbf{c}$ and $\mathbf{d}$ respectively. $\mathbf{c}$ and $\mathbf{d}$ are given by $\mathbf{c} = 3\mathbf{a} + \lambda \mathbf{b}$, $\mathbf{d} = \mu \mathbf{a} - \mathbf{b}$, where $\lambda$ and $\mu$ are scalars.

i.   Find $\lambda$ so that $A$, $B, C$ are collinear.

ii.  With this value of $\lambda$, find $\mu$ so that $CD$ is parallel to $AB$.

[7]

---

(12) Sketch the graph of $y = (1 + x)^{-1}$. Write down the equations of its asymptotes.

Find the area enclosed between the curve and the $x-$axis, for $x$ between 0 and 3.

Find the volume enclosed when this area is rotated about the $x-$axis.

[10]

---

(13) Sketch the graph of $y = x^3 + x - 1$.

Show that there is only one root for this equation.

By use of the Newton-Raphson method find this root to 4 decimal places.

[9]

---

(14) Find the remainders when $4x^3 - 4x^2 - 7x - 2$ is divided by (a) $x - 1$ (b) $x - 2$.

Factorize $4x^3 - 4x^2 - 7x - 2$ completely.

Sketch the graph of $y = 4x^3 - 4x^2 - 7x - 2$, and hence solve the inequality $4x^3 - 4x^2 - 7x - 2 \leq 0$.

[11]

---

(15) Points $P$, $Q$ and $R$ have coordinates $(8,9)$, $(11,3)$ and $(6, -1)$ respectively. The midpoint of $PR$ is $M$.

(a) Write down the coordinates of the point $M$.

(b) Find an equation of the line $QM$.

The perpendicular from $R$ to $PQ$ meets the line $QM$ at point $T$.

(c) Calculate the coordinates of the point $T$.

The point $S$ on the line $RT$ divides $RT$ internally in the ratio 2:5.

(d) Find the coordinates of the point $S$.

[L AS]

[12]

---

## AS-LEVEL PAPER II. PURE AND MECHANICS

Time $2\frac{1}{4}$ hours.

*Answer 5 questions. Throughout take g to be 9.8 m/sec².*

(1) A water trough, 12 metres long, has uniform cross-section in the shape of a semi-circle with horizontal diameter 1 metre. The diagram shows a cross-section of the trough containing water (shaded) to a depth of $x$ metre. The centre of the circle is at $O$ and angle $AOB$ is $\theta$ radians.

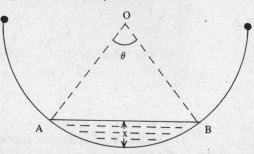

i. Find in terms of $\theta$ an expression for the area of the sector $AOB$.
ii. Use the fact that the area of triangle $AOB$ is $\frac{1}{8}\sin\theta$ m² to obtain an expression for the area of the shaded segment.
iii. Show that if the volume of water in the trough is $V$ m³ then

$$V = \frac{3}{2}(\theta - \sin\theta).$$

iv. A formula for $x$ in terms of $\theta$ is $x = \frac{1}{2}(1 - \cos\frac{1}{2}\theta)$. Find $dx/d\theta$ and hence express $dx/dt$ in terms of $\theta$ and $d\theta/dt$.
v. It may be shown that $dV/dt = \frac{3}{2}(1 - \cos\theta)d\theta/dt$. When $\theta = \frac{1}{3}\pi$ and $d\theta/dt = 0.04$ rad/min, calculate

a. the rate in m³ per min at which the volume of water in the trough is increasing,
b. the rate in metre per min at which the water level is rising.

[SMP add]

---

(2) (a) The point $A(1,2)$ lies on the curve $C$ whose equation is $y = \frac{1}{2}x^2 + x + \frac{1}{2}$. Find
(i) the slope of the tangent to $C$ at $A$,
(ii) the equation of the normal to $C$ at $A$.
This normal intersects $C$ again at $B$. Find

(iii) the coordinates of $B$   (iv) the equation of the tangent to $C$ at $B$.

(b) A rectangular water storage tank, made of material of negligible thickness, is open at the top. The tank is three times as long as it is wide and when it is full it holds 1152 m$^3$ of water. If the width of the tank is $x$ metres

   i. find the length and depth of the tank in terms of $x$, and

  ii. show that the total internal surface area, $A$ m$^2$, is given by

$$A = 3x^2 + 3072/x.$$

 iii. Find the dimensions of the tank so that its surface area, $A$, will be a minimum.                [NI add]

---

(3) (a) Obtain an expression for $\cos^2 x$ in terms of $\cos 2x$ and hence evaluate

$$\int_{\pi/4}^{3\pi/4} 4\cos^2 x\, dx.$$

(b) Find the area of the region bounded by the curve $y = \dfrac{1}{\sqrt{(2x - 1)}}$, the $x$−axis and the lines $x = 1$ and $x = 5$.

Find, to 2 decimal places, the volume obtained when this region is rotated through 360° about the $x$−axis.           [C add]

---

(4) When starting, a train can exert a force of $F$ Newtons. Its mass is $m$ kg and it experiences a resistance of $R$ Newtons. Show that its maximum acceleration up a slope of $\alpha$ is:

$$\frac{F - R - mg \sin \alpha}{m}$$

Suppose $F = 30,000$, $R = 12,000$ and $m = 50,000$. Find the maximum acceleration:

  (i) along a horizontal track     (ii) down a slope of 1°

  (iii) up a slope of $\sin^{-1}(\frac{1}{250})$

Find the steepest slope up which the train can ascend.

---

(5) An elastic string $AB$, of length 1m, is such that a weight of 50 grams will extend it by 10 cm. The string is placed on a smooth horizontal table. $A$ is fixed and $B$ is attached to a mass of 100 grams. The string is stretched to 1.2 m and released.

Letting the length of the string in the subsequent motion be $(1 + x)$ m, find an expression for $d^2x/dt^2$ in terms of $x$.

Find the time taken for the string to become slack.

---

(6) A particle of mass $m$ hangs at the end of a light inextensible string of length $r$. The other end is held fixed, and the particle performs horizontal circles with angular speed $\omega$ radians/sec. Show that $\omega^2 r > g$.

If $m = 0.2$ kg, $r = 1.5$m and $\omega = 4$, find the tension in the string and the angle it makes with the vertical.

---

(7) A particle is thrown horizontally at 5 m/sec from the top of a 19.6 m house. Find (i) its distance from the house when it lands (ii) the angle it makes with the vertical when it lands.

The coefficient of restitution between the particle and the ground is $\frac{3}{4}$. Find (iii) the height it rises to after the first bounce (iv) the total time before the particle strikes the ground for a second time.

## AS-LEVEL PAPER III. PURE AND MECHANICS

Time 3 hours. *Answer all the Questions*

(1) Solve the equation $\cos(2x - \frac{1}{4}\pi) = \frac{1}{2}$, for $-\pi < x < \pi$.
Leave your answers as multiples of $\pi$.

[3]

(2) Solve the equation $e^{2x} + 3e^x - 10 = 0$, giving your answer to 2 decimal places.

[3]

(3) A balloon of total mass 500 kg is floating at a constant height. 20 kg of ballast is thrown out. Find the acceleration with which the balloon starts to ascend.

[3]

(4) Sketch on the same paper the graphs of $y = \sin x$ and $y = \frac{1}{2}x$, for $-\pi \le x \le \pi$. Hence find the approximate solutions of $x = 2\sin x$.

[5]

(5) Find the tangent to $y = 2 - x^2$ at the point $(1,1)$. Find where this tangent crosses the axes. Find the area enclosed by the tangent and the axes.

[6]

(6) A function $f$ is defined by $f : x \to 3/(x - 4)$. What is the domain of $f$? Find $f^{-1}$ in the form of $f^{-1}: x \to$ and state its domain. Find $f \circ f$.

[6]

(7) A body of mass 2 kg is on a horizontal table, attached to a light inextensible string of length 1.6 m, the other end of which is fixed. The body performs horizontal circles at a speed of 3 m/sec. Find the tension in the string.
If the coefficient of friction between the body and the table is $\frac{1}{4}$ find the time it takes to come to rest.

[6]

(8) A body of mass 1,000 kg lies on a slope of $5°$. Find the force parallel to the slope necessary to accelerate it at 1.2 m/sec$^2$, against a resistance of 500 N.

[6]

(9) A particle of mass 0.1 kg travels with velocity vector $3\mathbf{i} - 2\mathbf{j}$. After striking an obstacle it moves with velocity vector $-2\mathbf{i} + \mathbf{j}$.

i.  Find, in vector form, the impulse given to the particle.
ii. Find the magnitude of the impulse.
iii. Find the loss of kinetic energy due to the collision.

[6]

(10) A cylindrical can is to contain 1000 cm$^3$ of liquid. The height of the can is $h$ cm and its base radius is $r$ cm. Find $h$ in terms of $r$.

Find the surface area A of the can in terms of $r$.

Find the ratio of $r$ to $h$ which will ensure that the surface area is as small as possible.

[10]

(11) $A$, $B$, $C$, $D$ are four consecutive posts in a row along the side of a railway track. These posts are 200 m apart. A train, which is known to be moving with constant acceleration, takes 60 seconds to go from $A$ to $B$ and 40 seconds to go from $B$ to $C$. Calculate the acceleration of the train and its velocity at $A$. Deduce the time the train will take to go from $C$ to $D$.

[O&C add]

[11]

(12) A particle of mass $m$ moves under power $P$ and against resistance $kv$, where $v$ is the velocity. Show that its equation of motion is:

$$m\,dv/dt = P/v - kv.$$

Show that the maximum speed is $\sqrt{(P/k)}$. If it starts from rest, show that the time taken to reach half the maximum speed is $\frac{1}{2}(m/k)\ln(1\frac{1}{3})$.

[13]

(13) Differentiate the function $y = e^x(A\cos x + B\sin x)$.

Find $A$ and $B$ such that $dy/dx = e^x\cos x$. Hence find $\int 5e^x\cos x\,dx$.

**Find constants $a$, $b$ and $c$, not all zero, such that:**

$$a\,d^2y/dx^2 + b\,dy/dx + cy = 0.$$

[12]

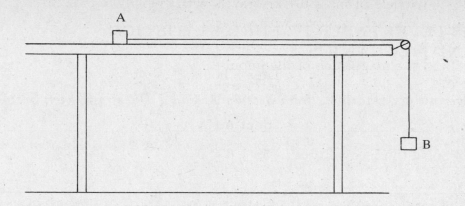

(14) The diagram shows two particles, A of mass $3m$ and B of mass $2m$, connected by a light inextensible string which passes over a smooth fixed pulley at the edge of a horizontal table. Initially A is held at rest on the table and B is hanging freely at a height $h$ above the floor. The particle A is then released and during its motion along the table experiences a retarding force, due to friction with the table, of magnitude $\frac{1}{3}mg$. The particle B strikes the floor before A reaches the edge of the table. Find, in terms of $m$ and $g$, the tension in the string and the acceleration of the particles while they are both moving. Show that the speed of A at the instant when B hits the floor is

$$\sqrt{\left(\frac{2gh}{3}\right)}.$$

When B hits the floor, A continues moving along the table but eventually comes to rest before it reaches the edge. Show that the length of the string must be greater than $4h$.

[JMB AS]

[10]

## AS-LEVEL PAPER IV. PURE, STATISTICS AND MECHANICS

Time 3 hours.

*Answer all the Questions from Section A, and 4 Questions from Section B*

### Section A

(1) Solve the inequality $x^2 - 5x + 6 < 0$

[3]

(2) Find the equation of the tangent to the curve $y = x^2 + x$ at the point $(2,6)$.

[3]

(3) Differentiate (a) $x(1 + x)$      (b) $\sin^2 3x$.

[4]

(4) Solve the equation $4^x + 3(2^x) - 40 = 0$.

[4]

(5) In the circle shown the arc $AB$ subtends $\theta$ radians at the centre $O$. Find the ratio of the area of the sector $AOB$ to the area of the triangle $AOB$.

[4]

(6) The curve $y = e^x$ between $x = 0$ and $x = 1$ is rotated about the $x$-axis. Find the volume of revolution.

[4]

(7)

i. Expand $(1 + 2x)^4$.

ii. Find the term independent of $x$ in $(x - 2/x)^6$.

[5]

(8) Solve the equation $3\sin^2\theta + 2\cos\theta - 1 = 0$, for $0° \leq \theta \leq 180°$.

[5]

(9) Air is being pumped into a spherical balloon at $20$ cm$^3$/sec. At the moment when the radius is $12$ cm, find (i) the rate of change of the radius (ii) the rate of change of the surface area.

[6]

(10) A sheet of cardboard is 10 cm by 20 cm. Squares of side $x$ cm are cut from each corner. The sides are folded over to form a tray.

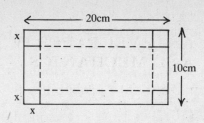

Show that the volume of the tray is $4x^3 - 60x^2 + 200x$. Find the value of $x$ which gives the greatest volume.

[6]

(11) The speed of a point on a cathode ray tube screen is $v = 7\cos 3t$. Given that it starts from the origin find (i) the maximum speed (ii) the maximum displacement. Show that the acceleration is nine times the displacement.

[6]

(12) Find the points of intersection of the curves $y = x^2$ and $y^2 = x$. Find the area enclosed between the curves.

[6]

## Section B. Answer 4 Questions. 11 marks per question

*Throughout take g to be 9.8 m s$^{-2}$*

(13) Three envelopes were addressed for three letters. An incompetent secretary put the letters into the envelopes at random. Show that the probability that each letter is in its correct envelope is $\frac{1}{6}$.

Let $X$ be the number of letters which are in their correct envelopes. Write down a distribution table for $X$. Hence or otherwise find the expectation of $X$.

(14) A test was marked out of 100. 80 pupils took the test, with the following results.

| Mark range | 0-30 | 31-40 | 41-50 | 51-60 | 61-70 | 71-100 |
|---|---|---|---|---|---|---|
| Frequency | 5 | 12 | 17 | 23 | 18 | 5 |

i.  Estimate the mean and standard deviation of these figures.
ii. Draw a cumulative frequency curve, and hence find the interquartile range.

(15) Only 20% of certain silicon chips are satisfactory. In a batch of 10, what is the probability that (i) 3 will be satisfactory (ii) at least two will be satisfactory.

How many chips should a batch contain so that the manufacturer can claim that with probability 95% it contains at least one satisfactory chip?

(16) The time $T$ to complete a certain task is a continuous random variable with p.d.f. $f(x) = k(x - 2)^2$ for $2 \leq x \leq 3$, and $f(x) = 0$ elsewhere.

(i) Find $k$.  (ii) Find the mean time.  (iii) Find the median time.

(17) The school record for the 100 m sprint is 12.3 seconds. The time that $A$ takes to run that distance is normally distributed with mean 13 and variance 0.09, and $B$'s time is also normal with mean 13.2 and variance 0.16. If $A$ and $B$ compete in the same race, find the probabilities that:

(i) $A$ beats the school record   ii) $A$ beats $B$.

(18) An express train approaches a station at a speed of 108 kilometres per hour. When the front of the train is one kilometre from the start of the platform the driver applies the brakes, which cause a constant deceleration. When it reaches the start of the platform it is still travelling at 36 kilometres per hour, and it finally comes to rest 10 metres from the further end of the platform.

a.  Calculate

   i.  the speed on m s$^{-1}$ of the train before the brakes are applied;

   ii.  the uniform deceleration in m s$^{-2}$;

   iii.  the total length of the platform in metres.

b.  From the moment that the brakes are applied, how many seconds elapse before the train comes to rest?

[MEI add]

(19) A horse pulls a barge of mass 50 tonnes, against resistances of $2000 + 1000v$ N, where $v$ is the speed in m s$^{-1}$. The tow-rope makes an angle of 10° with the direction of motion of the barge and horse. The power of the horse is 1200 Watts. Find:

i.  the maximum velocity of the barge
ii.  the tension in the rope at this velocity.

(20) A mass of 2 kg lies on a horizontal table, where the coefficient of friction is $\frac{1}{4}$. A light inextensible string is attached to the mass, and the other end of the string is tied to a mass of 1 kg which hangs over the end of the table. Calculate the acceleration of the system.

After 1 second the string is cut. Find the time which then elapses before the first mass comes to rest, and the total distance it has travelled.

---

(21) Two particles $P$ and $Q$ move in a plane so that at time $t$ seconds, where $t \geq 0$, $P$ and $Q$ have position vectors $\mathbf{r}_P$ and $\mathbf{r}_Q$ respectively, relative to a fixed origin $O$, where

$$\mathbf{r}_P = (3t^2 + 4)\mathbf{i} + (2t - \frac{1}{2})\mathbf{j},$$

$$\mathbf{r}_Q = (t + 6)\mathbf{i} + 1\frac{1}{2}t^2\mathbf{j}.$$

Find

  a.  the velocity vectors of $P$ and $Q$ at time $t$ seconds,
  b.  the *speed* of $P$ when $t = 2$,
  c.  The value of $t$ at the instant when the particles are moving parallel to one another.

Show that the particles collide and find the position vector of their point of collision.

[L add]

---

(22) A shell of mass 0.6 kg is fired into the air at 100 m s$^{-1}$ at an angle of elevation of 60°. Find the greatest height reached.

At its greatest height the shell explodes into two fragments of 0.4 kg and 0.2 kg. The heavier fragment flies vertically upwards at 50 m s$^{-1}$. Find the speed and direction of the lighter fragment. Find the kinetic energy created by the explosion.

---

# A-LEVEL PAPERS

## A-LEVEL PAPER I. PURE

Time $2\frac{1}{2}$ hours. *Answer all the questions*

(1) How many ways can 8 people sit on a bench, if Mr Smith refuses to sit next to Mrs Jones?

[4]

(2) Find the values of $k$ such that $x^2 + 3x + 1 = k$ has no real roots.

[4]

(3) State the periods of (i) $\cos 3x$ (ii) $\sin \frac{1}{2}x$ (iii) $2\cos x + 3\sin x$.

[4]

(4) Express in partial fractions:

$$y = \frac{2}{(x-1)(x+1)}$$

Hence expand $y$ as a series up to the term in $x^2$.

[5]

(5) Differentiate and simplify as far as possible:

(i) $y = \ln \sin 2x$  (ii) $y = \ln \sin x + \ln \cos x$

Show that your answers are the same.

**Give an explanation, not involving calculus, why your answers are the same.**

[9]

(6) Expand $(1 + 2x)^{\frac{1}{2}}$ up to the term in $x^3$. Hence, without the use of a calculator, find the approximate value of $\sqrt{102}$.

[6]

(7) Find the gradient of the normal to the curve $x^2 + xy + 2y^2 = 2$ at the point $(-1,1)$. Hence find the equation of the normal. Where else does the normal cross the curve?

[7]

(8) Show that $\cos 2A = 2\cos^2 A - 1$. Hence or otherwise evaluate the integral:

$$\int \frac{1}{\cos x + 1} dx$$

[7]

---

(9) Show that $x - 1$ is a factor of the cubic $2x^3 + 5x^2 - 4x - 3$. Hence factorize the cubic completely.

Sketch the graph of $y = 2x^3 + 5x^2 - 4x - 3$.
Solve the inequality $2x^3 + 5x^2 - 4x - 3 < 0$.

[7]

---

(10) Suppose that $u_1, u_2, u_3..., u_n$ is a geometric progression. Show that $\log u_1, \log u_2, \log u_3, ..., \log u_n$ is an arithmetic progression.

Give an equation relating the common ratio of the geometric progression with the common difference of the arithmetic progression.

[7]

---

(11) Tabulate the values of $y = \sqrt{(1 + x^3)}$ at intervals of $\frac{1}{2}$ from $x = 0$ to $x = 2$. Apply Simpson's rule to these values to find the approximate value of

$$\int_0^2 \sqrt{(1 + x^3)} dx$$

[8]

---

(12) Write $5\cos\theta + 12\sin\theta$ in the form $A\cos(\theta - \alpha)$, where $A$ and $\alpha$ are to be found. Hence find the greatest and least values of:

$$f(\theta) = \frac{1}{5\cos\theta + 12\sin\theta + 20}$$

[9]

---

(13) The line L passes through the point A(2, -9, 11) and is in the direction of the vector **n**, where

$$\mathbf{n} = \begin{pmatrix} 3 \\ 6 \\ -2 \end{pmatrix}$$

Write down a vector equation for L and show that L passes through the point B(14, 15, 3).

The plane $\Pi$ passes through the point C(4, 7, 13) and is at right angles to **n**. Find an equation for $\Pi$.

Verify that the resolved parts $\underline{AC}$ and $\underline{BC}$ in the direction of **n** have the same magnitude but opposite signs. Give a geometrical interpretation of this result.

[JMB]

[11]

---

(14) A curve is such that its gradient at any point $(x, y)$ is three times its $y$ value. Set up a differential equation for $y$ and find the general solution.

If the curve goes through the point $(1,1)$ find $y$ in terms of $x$.

Sketch the curve for $0 \le x \le 1$, and find the area between the curve and the $x-$axis for this range.

[10]

---

(15)

i.  $2 + i$ is a root of $z^2 + az + b = 0$, where $a$ and $b$ are real. Write down the other root, and hence or otherwise find $a$ and $b$.

ii. Find the modulus and argument of $1 + i$. Hence find the values of $n$ for which $(1+i)^n$ is (a) wholly imaginary (b) real and negative.

[12]

---

# A-LEVEL PAPER II. PURE, MECHANICS, STATISTICS

Time 3 hours. *Answer SEVEN questions*

(1)

a. A bullet of mass 0.02 kg is moving horizontally with speed 505 m s$^{-1}$ when it hits a wooden block of mass 2 kg which is free to move on a smooth horizontal table. Given that the bullet remains embedded in the block, find the loss of kinetic energy.

b. A particle of mass 0.5 kg is moving at constant speed on a rough horizontal table in the direction of the constant unit vector **i**. The particle is acted on by three forces, namely (i) its weight, (ii) an applied force **P**, and (iii) the total reaction of the table **R**. Given that **P** = (3**i** + 8**j**) N, where **j** is a unit vector vertically downwards, and taking $g = 9.8$ m s$^{-2}$, determine **R** in the form **R** = (k**i** + l**j**) N, where $k$ and $l$ are numbers. Hence determine the coefficient of friction between the particle and the table, to 2 decimal places.

[MEI]

---

(2) The gravitational attraction exerted by the planet Xurgon is subject to an inverse *cube* law, so that the force experienced by an object is inversely proportional to the cube of its distance from the planet's centre. The radius of Xurgon is 20,000 km, and the acceleration due to gravity on its surface is 50 m s$^{-2}$.

Find an expression for the acceleration due to gravity $r$ m from the planet's centre.

Find the speed with which a body must be projected from the surface of the planet if it is to escape completely from its gravitational field.

---

(3) A bead of mass $m$ is threaded on a smooth vertical wire, which is bent into the shape of a circle of radius $a$. The bead is attached to a light elastic string of natural length $a$ and modulus of elasticity $4mg$. The other end of the string is attached to the lowest point of the wire. The bead is at the lowest point of the wire, and is given a horizontal speed of $V$.

i. Show that if $V^2 < ag$ the string never becomes taut.

ii. Show that the bead will perform complete circles provided that $V^2 > 8ag$.

iii. Assuming that the bead performs complete circles, find the reaction of the wire on the bead at the top of the circle.

---

460

(4) A smooth particle of mass $m$ rests on a wedge of mass $M$ and angle $\alpha$. The wedge rests on a rough horizontal table where the coefficient of friction is $\mu$. The particle is released, and during the subsequent motion the wedge does not slip on the table.

   i.   Find the acceleration of the particle relative to the wedge.

  ii.   Find the vertical force exerted by the table on the wedge.

iii.   Find, in terms of $m$, $M$ and $\alpha$, the least possible value of $\mu$.

---

(5)        [Throughout this question take $g$ as 10 m s$^{-2}$.]

   i.   A ball is kicked from a point A on level ground and hits a goalpost at a point 4 m above the ground. The goalpost is at a distance of 32 m from A. Initially the velocity of the ball makes an angle $\tan^{-1}\frac{3}{4}$ with the ground. Show that the initial speed of the ball is 20 m s$^{-1}$. Find the speed of the ball when it hits the goalpost.

  ii.   A particle is attached to one end of a light string, the other end of which is fixed. When the particle moves in a horizontal circle with speed 2 m s$^{-1}$ the string makes an angle $\tan^{-1}(\frac{5}{12})$ with the vertical. Show that the length of the string is approximately 2.5 m.

[L]

---

(6) A bag contains 4 red balls and 2 blue balls and balls are withdrawn at random, with replacement. Find the probability that the third ball drawn is the second blue ball to be drawn.

Two additional bags, labelled B and C, are such that bag B contains 3 red balls and 5 blue balls whilst bag C contains 2 red balls and 1 blue ball. One of the three bags is selected at random and a ball is withdrawn from it. Find the probability that

  a.   bag B is selected and a red ball withdrawn,

  b.   A red ball is selected,

  c.   the ball was selected from bag C, given that it is blue.

[L]

---

(7) At a fairground stall the customer has 3 attempts to knock a tin off a shelf. Once the tin is knocked off he wins a prize and has no more attempts. The prize is £5, £3, £1 if he knocks the tin off on the first, second or third attempt respectively.

The chance that a customer will knock the tin off with a single shot is $\frac{1}{20}$. Assuming that each shot is independent, write down the distribution of the amount of prize money the customer wins.

If the stall-holder hopes to gain, on average, 10 p per customer, how much should he charge?

---

(8) The number of flaws in 2 m lengths of material produced by a factory has a Poisson distribution with mean 0.8. If a length has more than 2 flaws then it is not sent out to the shops.

  i.   Find the proportion of lengths which are sent out to the shops.
 ii.   Find the probability that a length on sale in a shop has no flaws.
iii.   Find the average number of flaws in the lengths on sale in the shops.

---

(9) A continuous random variable $X$ has probability density function given by:

$$f(x) = k \sin x, \text{ for } 0 \leq x \leq \pi/2.$$

 (i) Show that $k = 1$.   (ii) find $E(X)$ and $\text{Var}(X)$.

(iii) Find the median value of $x$.

A sample of size 100 is taken from this distribution. Use an appropriate approximation to find the probability that the sample mean is less than 1.05.

---

(10)

I never had a piece of toast

Particularly long and wide

But fell upon the sanded floor

And always on the buttered side.

[James Payn]

To test this poem 80 pieces of toast were dropped, and 52 of them landed on the buttered side. Test the hypothesis that the toast is more likely to land on the buttered side.

From the data give a 95% confidence interval for the probability that a piece of toast will land on its buttered side.

---

(11)

i.   Find the range of values of the function $y = x + 1/x$. Sketch the graph, and find the equations of its asymptotes.

ii.  Sketch the graphs of $y = x(1-x)$ and of $y^2 = x(1-x)$. Find the volume of revolution when the second graph is rotated about the $x-$axis.

---

(12)

i.   Find $|z|$ and arg $z$ for each of the complex numbers $z$ given by

   (a)  12 - 5$i$,   (b)  $(1 + 2i)/(2 - i)$,

   giving the argument in degrees (to the nearest degree) such that $-180° < \arg z \le 180°$.

ii.  By expressing $\sqrt{3} - i$ in modulus-argument form, or otherwise, find the least positive integer $n$ such that $(\sqrt{3} - i)^n$ is real and positive.

iii. The point $P$ in the Argand diagram lies outside or on the circle of radius 4 with centre at $(-1, -1)$. Write down in modulus form the condition satisfied by the complex number $z$ represented by the point $P$.

[L]

---

(13) In the diagram of the graph of $y = 1/x$ for $x > 0$, the shaded area is equal to half the area of the rectangle. Obtain the equation $2 \ln z = z - 1$, and show that $z$ lies between 3 and 4.

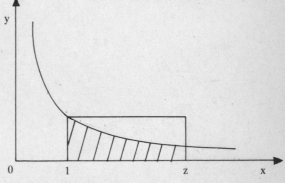

Use the Newton-Raphson method to calculate an approximation to $z$, starting at $z = 3$ and continuing the iteration until successive values differ by less than $10^{-2}$.

[SMP]

---

(14) Solve the differential equation

$$\frac{d^2y}{dx^2} + \frac{dy}{dx} - 2y = 2x - 5$$

given that the solution curve touches the $x$-axis at the origin. Determine the coordinates of any stationary points on the curve and state the nature of any such points.

How many point of inflection are there?

[SUJB]

---

(15) Two lines L and M have equations as follows:

(L) $\quad \dfrac{x+1}{1} = \dfrac{y+1}{-1} = \dfrac{z+2}{-1}$

(M) $\quad \dfrac{x+2}{1} = \dfrac{y-1}{0} = \dfrac{z+\lambda}{1}$

Find the value of $\lambda$ so that the lines intersect.

Find the equation of the plane $\pi$ which includes L and M, in the form **r.n** $= k$.

Find the angle between $\pi$ and the plane $\pi'$, whose equation is $2x + 3y - z = 1$.

Find the angle between L and $\pi'$.

---

# A-LEVEL PAPER III. PURE

Time 3 Hours

*Answer all the questions from Section A,*

*and 3 Questions from Section B*

## Section A

(1) The first three terms of $\sqrt{(1+x)}$ and $(1+ax)/(1+bx)$ are the same. Find $a$ and $b$.

[6]

---

(2) Find the approximate value of $\int_0^2 \sin \sqrt{x} \, dx$, using Simpson's rule with 4 intervals.

[6]

---

(3) Solve the equation $2 \cos x + 3 \sin x = 2\frac{1}{2}$, for $0° \leq x \leq 360°$.

[6]

---

(4) Find the solution of the equation $dy/dx = 2x(y+1)$, for which $y = 0$ when $x = 0$. Sketch the graph of the curve.

[7]

---

(5) The graph of $y = f(x)$ crosses the $y$-axis at $(0,b)$, and touches the $x$-axis at $(a,0)$. A sketch of $y = f(x)$ is shown. On four separate diagrams sketch the graphs of:

(a) $y = f(x) - b$  (b) $y = f(x + a)$

(c) $y = f(-x)$    (d) $y = -f(x)$

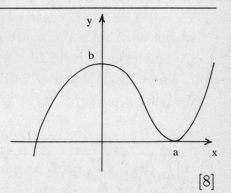

[8]

---

(6) Solve the equations:

(a) $\log_2(x + 1) - \log_2 x = 3$  (b) $e^x + 3 - e^{-x} = 0$.

[8]

---

(7) The fixed circle $C_1$ has equation $x^2 + y^2 = 4$, and the variable circle $C_2$ has equation $x^2 + y^2 - 2kx = 1 - k^2$. Find the two positive values of $k$ for which $C_1$ touches $C_2$, and illustrate both situations.

[9]

---

(8) [In this question $\cos^{-1} x$ and $\tan^{-1} x$ refer to the principal values.]

Show on the same diagram sketches of the graphs of $y = \cos^{-1} x$ and $y = \tan^{-1} x$.

Show that, if $\cos^{-1} x = \tan^{-1} x$, then $x^2(1 + x^2) = 1$, and hence find the value of $x$ such that $\cos^{-1} x = \tan^{-1} x$, giving your answer correct to 3 decimal places.

[C]

[9]

---

## Section B.  Answer three Questions.  16 marks each.

(9) Find the stationary points of $y = x^n e^{-x}$ in the cases (a) $n = 0$, (b) $n = 1$ (c) $n = 2$.

Sketch the graph of the function for (i) $n$ large and odd (ii) $n$ large and even.

Letting $I_n = \int_0^\infty x^n e^{-x} dx$, show that $I_n = n I_{n-1}$.

(10) Three spheres are placed on a horizontal plane in such a way that each sphere is touching the other two. The radii of the spheres are 2 cm, 3 cm and 4 cm; their centres are $A$, $B$, $C$, respectively; the points of contact with the horizontal plane are $P$, $Q$, $R$, respectively.

  i.  Show that $\cos A\hat{C}B = \frac{5}{7}$

  ii.  Show that $PQ = \sqrt{24}$ cm, and find the lengths of $QR$ and $RP$.

  iii.  Show that $\sin P\hat{R}Q = \sqrt{\left(\frac{47}{96}\right)}$.

[C]

---

(11) (a) Show, using the substitution $y = x - 2$, or otherwise, that

$$\int_3^4 \left( \frac{x+2}{x-2} \right)^3 dx = 12 \log_e 2 + 49.$$

(b) Evaluate

$$\int_0^1 \frac{(3x-1)dx}{(x+1)(x^2+1)}$$

giving your answer to 2 decimal places.

(c) Sketch the curve having equation

$$\frac{x^2}{a^2} + \frac{y^2}{b^2} = 1 (a > 0, b > 0).$$

Calculate the volume generated when the region enclosed by the curve and the $x-$axis between the points $(-a, 0)$ and $(a, 0)$ is rotated through 4 right angles about the $x-$axis.

[W]

---

(12)

a. Prove that the points in the Argand diagram representing the complex numbers $2 + 2i$, $-10 + 5i$ and $30 - 5i$ are collinear.

b. Given that $7 + 17i = (1 - i)(a + ib)$ where $a$ and $b$ are real, find the values of $a$ and $b$.
Find the modulus and argument of $\frac{7 + 17i}{1 - i}$.

c. If $z$ is a complex number such that $|z - 3 - 4i| = 6$, describe the possible positions of the point representing $z$ in the Argand diagram. Find the largest value of $|z|$.

[SUJB]

---

(13) The position vectors, with respect to a fixed origin, of the points L, M and N are given by **l**, **m** and **n** respectively, where

$$\mathbf{l} = a(\mathbf{i} + \mathbf{j} + \mathbf{k}), \ \mathbf{m} = a(2\mathbf{i} + \mathbf{j}), \ \mathbf{n} = a(\mathbf{j} + 4\mathbf{k})$$

and $a$ is a non-zero constant. Show that the unit vector **j** is perpendicular to the plane of the triangle LMN.

Find a vector perpendicular to both **j** and $(\mathbf{m} - \mathbf{n})$, and hence, or otherwise, obtain a vector equation of that perpendicular bisector of MN which lies in the plane LMN.

Verify that the point K with position vector $a(5\mathbf{i} + \mathbf{j} + 4\mathbf{k})$ lies on this bisector and show that K is equidistant from L, M and N.

[L]

---

## A-LEVEL PAPER IV. MECHANICS

Time 3 hours. *Answer all the questions*

*Throughout take g to be 9.8 m s$^{-2}$.*

(1) At time $t = 0$ $X$ starts from the origin with constant speed 5 m s$^{-1}$. 2 seconds later $Y$ starts from the origin in the same direction, with zero initial speed and acceleration 1 m s$^{-2}$. Find how long it takes for $Y$ to catch up with $X$.

[5]

(2) A swindler buys and sells diamonds in a lift. When the lift is accelerating down at $2a$ m s$^{-2}$ the diamonds appear to weigh 1.32 grams, and when the lift is accelerating up at $a$ m s$^{-2}$ they appear to weigh 1.41 grams. Calculate the true weight of the diamonds.

[5]

(3) A rough wire joins the points (0,0) and (4,3). A bead is threaded on the wire, and a force of $-2\mathbf{i} + 3\mathbf{j}$ is applied to it, where $\mathbf{i}$ and $\mathbf{j}$ are unit vectors in the $x$ and $y$ directions respectively. Ignoring the effects of gravity find the coefficient of friction if the bead moves at a steady speed.

[6]

(4) A body of mass 5 kg lies on the floor where the coefficient of friction is $\frac{1}{3}$. It is pulled by a light string making $\theta$ with the horizontal. What should $\theta$ be if the force needed to shift the body is as small as possible?

[8]

(5) A body of mass 2 kg lies on a rough horizontal table. It is attached to a light elastic string of modulus 40 and natural length 1 m. The other end is attached to a point which is 1.1 m away horizontally and 0.3 m above the table. If the body does not move find the least coefficient of friction.

[8]

(6) A locomotive of mass M is travelling around a circular bend of radius 1 km. The width of the track is 2 m, and the outer rail is at height $h$ cm above the inner rail. It is found that when the locomotive has speed 20 m s$^{-1}$ there is no sideways pressure on the rails. Show that $h \approx 8$. (Take $g$ as 10 m s$^{-2}$.)

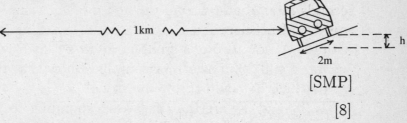

1km

2m

[SMP]

[8]

(7) A uniform lamina $ABCDE$ consists of a square $ABCD$ of side 4 cm with a right-angled triangle $EDA$ affixed to it. $ED = 4$ cm. Find the centre of gravity of the lamina.

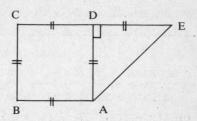

The mass of the lamina is 20 grams. The lamina is placed in a vertical plane with AB on a horizontal plane. Find the greatest weight which can be suspended from E before the lamina topples.

[11]

(8) Two vertical walls meet at right angles, above a smooth horizontal floor. A ball is rolled with speed $u$ towards the corner. It strikes one of the walls at a distance $a$ from the corner, so that its direction makes $\theta$ with the wall. The coefficient of restitution is $e$.

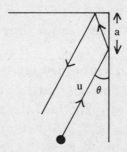

Show that after bouncing off both walls the ball is travelling parallel to its original direction. Find its speed in terms of $u$ and $e$.

If $e = 1$ find the distance between the two lines of motion, in terms of $a$ and $\theta$.

[11]

(9) Two particles of mass 2 kg and 3 kg are connected by a light inextensible string. The string is slung over a smooth peg and the masses are released. Find the acceleration with which the system moves.

After 1 second the heavier mass strikes the floor and is brought instantaneously to rest. Find the speed with which the heavier mass is jerked into motion when the string next becomes taut.

**Describe the subsequent motion of the system until it comes to rest.**

[11]

---

(10) A boy throws a stone at 20 m s$^{-1}$ at a window which is 5 m above his hand and 20 m away horizontally. Show that there are two angles $\theta_1$ and $\theta_2$ at which he could throw the stone.

If T$_1$ and T$_2$ are the times corresponding to the two possible angles of projection, find the ratio T$_1$ : T$_2$.

[11]

---

(11) $ABC$ is a triangle for which $AB = BC = 1$ m, and $A\hat{B}C = 90°$. Forces of 5, $P$ and $Q$ Newtons act along $AB$, $BC$, $CA$ respectively.

i.   If there is no resultant find $P$ and $Q$.

ii.  If $P = 4$ and $Q = 8$ find the magnitude and direction of the resultant force, and find where this force cuts $BC$ produced.

[12]

---

(12) A particle of mass $m$ starts at the origin. The only force it experiences is a force $f(x)$ directed along the $x-$axis towards the origin, given by the formula below:

$$f(x) = 2mx^3 \ \text{ for } x \le a; f(x) = 2\frac{1}{2}mx^4 \text{ for } x > a.$$

The particle is projected away from the origin with speed $u$. Show that if $u < a^2$ then the particle never reaches the point $x = a$.

If $u = \sqrt{2}a^2$ find the greatest distance that the particle reaches.

[14]

---

# A-LEVEL PAPER V. STATISTICS

## Time 3 Hours

*Answer all the questions from Section A and 4 from Section B.*

## Section A

(1) X is a discrete variable with mean 1.55. Its table is given below. Find $a$ and $b$.

| $i$ | 0 | 1 | 2 | 3 |
|---|---|---|---|---|
| $P(X = i)$ | 0.15 | $a$ | $b$ | 0.3 |

[3]

---

(2) Three bags are lettered $A$, $B$ and $C$. Bag $A$ contains 4 red balls, $B$ contains 2 red and 2 blue balls, $C$ contains 4 blue balls. A bag is selected at random and a ball drawn. Find the probabilities that (a) a blue ball is drawn (b) bag $C$ was selected, given that a blue ball was drawn.

[5]

---

(3) A poker hand consists of 5 cards, in any order, from the standard pack. How many possible poker hands are there? What is the probability that a poker hand is a flush? (All cards of the same suit).

[6]

---

(4) $X$ is a continuous random variable with p.d.f. given by $f(x) = -kx$ for $-2 \leq x \leq 0$, $f(x) = kx$ for $0 \leq x \leq 2$, $f(x) = 0$ elsewhere.

(i) Find $k$. (ii) Find $E(X)$ and $Var(X)$. (iii) Find the probability that $X$ lies within one standard deviation of the mean.

[6]

---

(5) The lifetimes of certain batteries are normally distributed. 90% last less than 20 hours, and 5% last less than 14 hours. Find the mean and variance of the lifetime of a battery. What proportion of the batteries last more than 22 hours?

[6]

---

471

(6) 40% of a sample of 1000 claimed that they would vote for the Pragmatic Party. Find a 95% confidence interval for the level of support for the Party throughout the country.

How large must a sample be, if the width of a 95% confidence interval is to be less than 2%?

[7]

---

(7) $A$, $B$ and $C$ are events. Show that:
$$P(A \cup B \cup C) = P(A) + P(B) + P(C) - P(A \cap B) - P(B \cap C) - P(A \cap C) + P(A \cap B \cap C)$$
If $P(A \cap B) = P(A)P(B)$, show that $P(A' \cap B') = P(A')P(B')$

[7]

---

## Section B. 15 marks per Question

(8) The number of appendicitis cases occurring in a year in a town has a Poisson distribution with mean 4. Find the probabilities of:

(i) 3 cases in a year,   (ii) 2 cases in 6 months,

(iii) at least 4 cases in a year, given that there are at least 2,

(iv) 3 cases in a year, given that there was at least one in the first 6 months of that year.

---

(9) $Z$ is a random variable with a standard normal distribution. Find, correct to two decimal places, the five numbers $y_i$ ($i = 1, 2, 3, 4, 5$) defined by $P(Z < y_i) = i/6$.

A botanist attempted to measure the heights in centimetres of five wild saplings. Four of his measurements are given below. The fifth sapling was too tall for his measuring instrument.

$$82, \ 97, \ 88, \ 93.$$

Plot a graph of the $y_i$ (i = 1, 2, 3, 4) against the members of the above sample arranged in a suitable order, and draw by eye a straight line to fit these points.

Assuming that this is a random sample from a normal distribution with mean $\mu$ and variance $\sigma^2$, use your graph to estimate $\mu$ and $\sigma$. Estimate also the height of the fifth sapling.

[O&C]

---

472

(10) An athlete runs the mile 7 times. His results in seconds are:

$$250, \ 245, \ 253, \ 260, \ 248, \ 251, \ 257.$$

Find the mean of these figures and the unbiased sample variance.

Assuming that his time to run a mile is normally distributed, find a 95% confidence interval for his mean time.

If his time has mean 250 and variance 20, how many times would he have to run a mile before he has a 50% chance of doing so in under 4 mins?

---

(11) The radius $R$ of a circle, measured in cm, is uniform in the interval $[0,1]$. Find the cumulative distribution function of $R$.

The area $A$ of the circle is $\pi R^2$. Obtain the c.d.f. of $A$, and hence find the mean and the variance of the area.

If 50 such circles are found, what is the probability that their average area exceeds 1 cm$^2$?

---

(12) The probability that a gun hits a target with a single shot is $\frac{1}{8}$. The gun is fired until the target is hit. Assuming that the shots are independent, find the distribution of the number $X$ of shots.

Find $E(X)$. Find the least number of shots that must be fired, so that the target will be hit with 95% probability.

If the target was hit with at most ten shots, what is the probability that the third bullet struck it?

(You may use without proof the identity $1 + 2x + 3x^2 + \ldots \equiv (1-x)^{-2}$)

---

(13) The distribution table for two variables $X$ and $Y$ is as below.

$X$

|     |   | 0 | 1 | 2 | 3 |
|-----|---|-----|-----|-----|-----|
|     | 0 | 0.1 | 0.2 | 0 | 0 |
| $Y$ | 1 | 0.3 | 0 | 0.2 | 0 |
|     | 2 | 0.1 | 0 | 0 | 0.1 |

  i.   Write down the distribution of $X$.

 ii.   Find $E(X)$ and $E(XY)$.

iii.   Are $X$ and $Y$ independent? Give reasons.

iv.   Find $P(X > Y)$.

 v.   Write down the distribution of $Y$ given that $X = 0$.

---

(14) A man takes a bus which leaves a stop at $X$ minutes past 9 a.m., where $X$ is normal with mean 0 and variance 9. The journey time to a station is also normal, with mean 10 and variance 4. The train leaves the station promptly at 9.17. Ignoring change-over time, what is the probability that the connection is made?

In a working year of 300 days, what is the probability that the connection will be missed more than 10 times?

Another passenger takes the same train, but he drives to the station, taking a time which is normal with mean 20 and variance 12. When should he leave home to be 99% sure of catching the train?

# A-LEVEL PAPER VI. MECHANICS AND STATISTICS

Time 3 Hours. *Answer eight questions*

(1M) A body of mass 240 kg is dropped by parachute with negligible initial speed. Whilst the parachute is opening, the body is subject at time $t$ to a resistance due to the atmosphere of $40v$N, where $v$ is its speed at that time. Show that whilst the parachute is opening, the speed $v$ satisfies

$$6dv/dt = 6g - v.$$

If the parachute is fully open after 6 seconds, prove that its speed will then be $6g(1 - e^{-1})$ms$^{-1}$.

Find an expression for the distance fallen by the body at time $t$ seconds ($t \leq 6$). Show that the body has fallen through a distance $36ge$ m$^{-1}$ whilst the parachute is opening.

Find the distance fallen by the body when the speed is $v$ ms$^{-1}$ where $v < 6g(1 - e^{-1})$. [W]

---

(2M) A uniform ladder of mass 20 kg and length 2 m rests against a smooth wall and on a rough floor. It is at 60° to the horizontal. A man of mass 60 kg can just walk $\frac{3}{4}$ of the way up it. Find the coefficient of friction between the floor and the ladder.

Show that it is impossible for a ladder to rest on a smooth floor and against a rough wall.

---

(3M) The framework shown consists of light rods. The angles are all either 45° or 90°. A load of 40 N is placed at B. Find the forces in the rods, specifying which are thrusts and which are tensions.

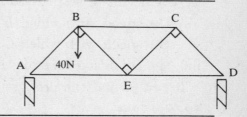

---

(4M) A *Daruma Doll* is a Japanese toy figure, which will return to the upright position when it is knocked.

The doll can be thought of as a solid hemisphere, base radius 2 cm and relative density 11, surmounted by a solid cone of base radius 2 cm, height $h$ cm and relative density 1. Find the distance of the centre of gravity above the base in terms of $h$.

Hence find the values of $h$ for which the toy will rest in stable equilibrium with the cone above the hemisphere.

(The doll is named after Daruma, the founder of Zen Buddhism, who sat for so long in meditation that his legs fell off.)

(5M) A particle moves in a circle of radius $a$ with constant speed $v$. State the magnitude and direction of its acceleration.

A small sphere of mass $m$ is attached to the end $A$ of a light inextensible string of length $2a$ and a similar sphere but of mass $2m$ is attached to the other end, $B$. The mid-point of the string is fixed to a point $O$ of a smooth horizontal table and the spheres lie at rest on the table with each part of the string taut and angle $AOB$ 90°. The coefficient of restitution between the spheres is $e$. The sphere at $A$ is given a speed $u$ along the table in a direction perpendicular to $OA$. Find

 i.  the speeds of the spheres just after the first impact;
 ii.  the ratio of the tensions in $OA$ and $OB$ just after the first impact;
 iii.  the interval of time between the first and second impacts.

What happens to the system ultimately?

[SUJB]

---

(6M) A square $ABCD$ of side 1 m has forces of 4 N, 3 N and 2N acting along $AB$, $AD$ and $DB$ respectively. Find the single force needed to counterbalance these forces, and where along $BC$ it should be applied.

If instead the counterbalancing force is applied at $C$, what extra couple will keep the square in equilibrium?

---

(7M) 3 balls $A$, $B$, $C$ whose masses are in the ratio of $1 : 2 : 3$ lie in that order on a smooth horizontal table. $A$ is projected towards $B$ with speed $u$. The coefficient of restitution is $e$. Find:

 i.  the speed with which $B$ first moves,
 ii.  the speed with which $C$ first moves,
 iii.  the condition on $e$ for there to be only two collisions.

If $e = \frac{3}{4}$, find the proportion of kinetic energy which has been lost after two collisions.

---

(8M) A small bead $B$ of mass $m$ is free to slide on a fixed smooth vertical wire, as indicated in the diagram. One end of a light elastic string, of unstretched length $a$ and modulus of elasticity $2mg$, is attached to $B$.

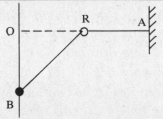

The string passes through a smooth fixed ring $R$ and the other end of the string is attached to the fixed point $A$, $AR$ being horizontal. The point $O$ on the wire is at the same horizontal level as $R$, and $AR = RO = a$.

i. Prove that, in the equilibrium position, $OB = \frac{1}{2} a$.

ii. The bead $B$ is raised to a point $C$ of the wire above $O$, where $OC = a$, and is released from rest. Find the speed of the bead as it passes $O$, and find the greatest depth below $O$ of the bead in the subsequent motion.

[C]

---

(9M) A uniform cylinder of height $L$ and relative density $\rho(\rho < 1)$ floats with its axis vertical in a large lake. Show that a proportion $\rho L$ of the cylinder is submerged.

It is then pushed down vertically by a small amount $\delta$ and released. Show that, if the proportion submerged in the subsequent motion is $\rho L + x$, then $x$ obeys the equation $\ddot{x} = -\omega^2 x$, where $\omega$ is to be found.

Find the greatest speed it reaches and the time taken to achieve this greatest speed.

---

(10M) Ship $A$ is originally 50 km due west of ship $B$. $A$ sails at 15 km h$^{-1}$ on a bearing of 045°. If $B$ can sail at 20 km h$^{-1}$, what course should be set for interception to take place?

If instead $B$ sails on at a bearing of 310°, for how long are the ships within 10 km of each other?

---

(11M) A body at a temperature of 100° is immersed into a large tank containing water at 10°. The rate of temperature loss of the body is proportional to the difference between its temperature $T$ and that of the water, which remains constant throughout.

Find a differential equation giving the rate of change of $T$ in terms of time $t$. Find the general solution of this equation.

If the body cools to 60° in 5 minutes, find (i) the temperature after 10 minutes (ii) the time to cool to 40°.

---

(12S) 3 dice are identical in appearance, but though 2 are fair the third is biased so that the probability of it showing 6 is $\frac{1}{4}$. Two of the three are selected at random and rolled.

i. Write down the distribution of the number of sixes obtained.

ii. If one six was obtained, what is the probability that it was from the biased die?

iii. If 2 sixes were obtained, what is the probability that the biased die was one of the two selected?

---

(13S) A discrete random variable $X$ has the distribution given by:

$$P(X = i) = k(i + 3) \text{ for } i = -2, -1$$

$$P(X = i) = k(4 - i) \text{ for } i = 0, 1, 2, 3.$$

(i) Find $k$.　(ii) Find the expectation and variance of $X$.

(iii) Find the distribution of (a) $|X|$ (b) $X^2$.

---

(14S) The number of buses which pass a stop in an hour has a Poisson distribution with mean 4. Find the probabilities of:

(i) No buses in $\frac{1}{2}$ hour　(ii) No buses in $t$ hours, where $t \geq 0$.

Letting $T$ be the time until the first bus comes, show that T has probability density function $f(t) = 4e^{-4t}$, for $t \geq 0$. Find $E(T)$ and the median value of $T$.

If I have waited for $\frac{1}{2}$ hour, what is the probability that I will have to wait for a further $\frac{1}{2}$ hour?

---

(15S) The weights of coffee in tins used by the catering trade are distributed Normally with standard deviation 0.071 kg.

A random sample of $n$ tins is taken in order to determine a symmetric 99% confidence interval for the mean weight $\mu$ kg of coffee in a tin. How large should $n$ be for the total width of this interval to be less than 0.05 kg?

In a separate investigation a random sample of 36 tins has a mean weight of 0.981 kg. Test at the 1% significance level the null hypothesis $H_0$ that $\mu = 1$, the alternative hypothesis $H_1$ being $\mu < 1$.

Suppose now that it is subsequently discovered that $\mu = 0.950$. Determine the probability that a significance test at the 1% level, using a new random sample of 36 tins and the same $H_0$ and $H_1$ as in the previous paragraph, would give the wrong conclusion, i.e. would lead to the acceptance of $H_0$.

[MEI]

---

(16S) A box contains 20 tokens, of which 10 are numbered 0, 6 are numbered 1, and 4 are numbered 2. Two are drawn from the box without replacement. Let $X$ be the number on the first token and $Y$ the number on the second token. Show that $P(X = 0 \ \& \ Y = 0) = {}^9\!/_{38}$. Complete the table below for the joint probability of $X$ and $Y$.

$$X$$

|   |   | 0 | 1 | 2 |
|---|---|---|---|---|
| | 0 | ${}^9\!/_{38}$ | | |
| $Y$ | 1 | | | |
| | 2 | | | |

Find $E(X)$, $E(Y)$, $E(XY)$. Write out the conditional probability of $X$ given that $Y = 1$.

---

(17S) The proportion of defectives in a large batch is $p$. Two testing schemes are devised.

Method I. Test 10 : reject the batch if there is more than 1 defective.

Method II. Test 5 : accept the batch if there is no defective, and reject if it there is more than 1 defective. If there is 1 defective test a further 10 and reject the batch unless there are no defectives.

For each method, find the probabilities of (i) rejecting the batch if $p = 0.05$ (ii) accepting the batch if $p = 0.3$. Comment on your results.

---

(18S) The four random numbers 3487 are obtained from tables. Use them to obtain:

(i) One observation from $B(10, \frac{1}{3})$  (ii) One observation from $N(5, 4)$

(iii) Two observations from the distribution with p.d.f $2e^{-2x}$, for $x \geq 0$.

---

(19S) It is suspected that a die is biased towards 6. It is rolled 80 times, and the number of 6's is 20. Test at the 5% level whether or not it is biased.

Would your conclusion differ if it was not known which number the die might be biased towards? Give your reasons.

On the basis of the results find a 95% confidence interval for the probability of rolling a 6 with this die.

---

(20S) There are ten adult males in the Smith family. Their heights and masses (where known) are given in the table below.

| | Height (cm) | Mass (kg) | | Height (cm) | Mass (kg) |
|---|---|---|---|---|---|
| Adam | ? | 80 | Fred | 167 | 62 |
| Ben | 170 | ? | George | 184 | 89 |
| Colin | 174 | 83 | Harry | 168 | 90 |
| David | 150 | 55 | Ivor | 173 | 72 |
| Eric | 153 | 63 | John | 159 | 70 |

i. Plot the eight complete pairs on a scatter diagram.

ii. For these eight complete pairs, determine the co-ordinates of the point of intersection of the regression line of mass on height with the regression line of height on mass.

iii. Denoting mass by $m$ and height by $h$, the equation of the regression line of mass on height is $m = -76.1 + 0.898h$, correct to three significant figures. Draw, on the scatter diagram, this regression line. Also draw on the scatter diagram, by eye, the regression line of height on mass, labelling the line clearly.

iv. Use the regression lines to estimate the height of Adam, and to estimate the mass of Ben, showing your methods clearly.

v. For the eight complete pairs of observations, calculate the value of a rank correlation coefficient.

[C]

---

(21S) The following marks were obtained when 100 pupils took an exam.

| Mark range | 0-29 | 30-39 | 40-49 | 50-59 | 60-69 | 70-100 |
|---|---|---|---|---|---|---|
| Frequency | 8 | 15 | 25 | 33 | 14 | 5 |

Find the mean and variance of these figures. Fit an appropriate Normal distribution, and use $\chi^2$ at a 5% significance level to test the goodness of fit.

---

(22S) The time that Alan takes for the 100 m race is normally distributed with mean 11.4 seconds and standard deviation 0.2 sec. Bertram's times are also normal, with mean 11.5 seconds and standard deviation 0.3 seconds. If they race against each other find the probability that Alan wins.

Cedric now challenges Alan. In 10 runs of 100 m his results are summarized by $\sum x = 116$ and $\sum x^2 = 1348$. Is there evidence at a significance level of 5% that he is slower than Alan?

---

# A-LEVEL PAPER VII. PURE, MECHANICS, STATISTICS

## Time 3 Hours

*Answer 6 questions from Section A, and 4 from Section B*

## Section A. 14 marks per Questions

(1) Show that $x^3 + x - 17 = 0$ has a root between $n$ and $n + 1$, where $n$ is to be found. Use linear interpolation between these values to find an approximation for the root.

Use Newton Raphson iteration to find this root to 4 decimal places.

---

(2) The position vectors of $P$ and $Q$ are $3\mathbf{i} + 5\mathbf{j} + \mathbf{k}$ and $4\mathbf{i} - \mathbf{j} - \mathbf{k}$ respectively.

  i.  Find unit vectors parallel to $OP$ and to $OQ$, and hence find the vector equation of the bisector of $P\hat{O}Q$.

 ii.  Find a unit vector $\hat{\mathbf{n}}$, perpendicular to $OP$ and $OQ$. Verify that $\hat{\mathbf{n}}$ is perpendicular to $PQ$.

---

(3) Solve the inequalities:

  (i)  $\dfrac{1}{x+1} \leq \dfrac{1}{x+2}$  (ii)  $\dfrac{1}{x+1} \leq \dfrac{1}{|x+2|}$

  (iii)  $\dfrac{1}{|x+1|} \leq \dfrac{1}{|x+2|}$

---

(4) A sequence $u_1, u_2, ..., u_n$ is defined by $u_1 = 2$ and $u_{n+1} = 2u_n - 1$. Prove by induction that $u_n = 2^{n-1} + 1$.

---

(5) A cone has fixed height $h$ and variable semi-vertical angle $\theta$. If $\theta$ is increasing at a rate $\alpha$ rads/sec, find the rate of increase of (i) the base radius (ii) the volume (iii) the surface area.

---

(6)

  i.  Solve the equation $\cos 2\theta + 3\cos\theta - 1 = 0$, for $0 \leq \theta \leq \pi$.

 ii.  Find the greatest value of the expression $\ln(\cos\theta + 2\sin\theta)$. Find the range of values between $0$ and $2\pi$ for which this function is defined.

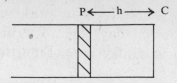

(7) A piston $P$ of mass $M$ is in a smooth long horizontal cylinder. In equilibrium, the distance from the piston to the closed end $C$ of the cylinder is $h$.

If the piston is displaced $x$ towards $C$, then the force acting on the piston away from $C$ is $Mg(x/h)^3$.

Initially the piston is held a distance $\frac{1}{2}h$ away from $C$ and released. Find (a) its speed when it passes the equilibrium point (b) the greatest value of $PC$.

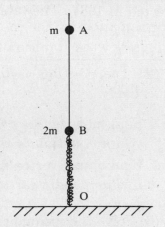

(8) Two small beads $A$ and $B$, of masses $m$ and $2m$ respectively, are threaded on a fixed smooth vertical wire. The bead $A$ can move freely on the wire, but $B$ is attached to the top end of a light elastic spring whose bottom end is fixed at a point $O$ on the wire, as shown in the diagram. The unstretched length of the spring is $a$ and its modulus of elasticity is $8mg$. Find the length of the spring when $B$ rests in equilibrium.

With $B$ resting in equilibrium, $A$ is released from rest at a height $h$ above $B$. When $A$ collides with $B$, the beads stick together and move as a single particle of mass $3m$. Find an expression for the kinetic energy of the combined particle immediately after impact.

In the subsequent motion the greatest height above $O$ reached by the combined particle is $a$. Find $h$ in terms of $a$.

[C]

(9) A small smooth sphere moves on a horizontal table and strikes an identical sphere lying at rest on the table at a distance $d$ from a vertical wall, the impact being along the line of centres and perpendicular to the wall. Prove that the next impact between the spheres will take place at a distance

$$2de^2/(1 + e^2)$$

from the wall, where $e$ is the coefficient of restitution for all the impacts involved.

[L]

(10) If I get to work on time, the probability that I shall be late the following day is $\frac{1}{4}$. If I am late, the probability that I shall be late the following day is $\frac{1}{10}$. Find the probabilities that:

i. I was late on Wednesday, given that I was late on Monday

ii. Letting $p_n$ be the probability that I am late on day $n$, show that $p_{n+1} = \frac{1}{4} - 0.15p_n$. Hence find the long-term proportion of days on which I am late.

---

(11) The records of deaths of those aged 70 or above in a town were collected in 1984. The table shows the number of deaths per quarter from a sample of 100.

|  | Jan-Mar | Apr-Jun | Jul-Sept | Oct-Dec |
|---|---|---|---|---|
| Number | 24 | 16 | 22 | 38 |

i. Perform a test to decide whether the sample data indicate that mortality is independent of quarter.

ii. An accident at a local factory caused atmospheric pollution, during November of that year, and this was thought to increase the number of deaths. Show, by omitting the October-December figure that the data support this belief.

[SUJB]

---

(12) The daily demand for petrol at a certain garage has a normal distribution with mean 3000 gallons and standard deviation 150 gallons. If 3200 gallons are stocked at the beginning of the day, what is the probability of the garage running out?

What should the stock be, if the probability of not running out of petrol is to be at least 95%?

The garage is open for 6 days a week. If instead the garage stocks up at the beginning of the week, what should the stocks be if the probability of not running out is to be over 99%?

---

## Section B 25 marks per question

(13) Two complex numbers $z$ and $w$ are related by $w = z + a^2/z$, where $a$ is a positive real number and $P$, $Q$ are the points representing $z$, $w$ respectively in an Argand diagram.

  i. Show that if $z = 2a(\cos\theta + i\sin\theta)$, then
  $w = (5a/2)\cos\theta + (3a/2)i\sin\theta$.
  Describe the loci of $P$ and $Q$ as $\theta$ varies.

  ii. Show that if $P$ moves along the positive part of the real axis, $w$ is real and has a minimum. Find this minimum value and the position of $P$ when it is attained.

[MEI]

---

(14) A general point $P$ on the parabola $y = x^2$ has coordinates $(t,\ t^2)$, and the point $Q$ below it on the line $y = -1$ has coordinates $(t,\ -1)$. Write down the coordinates of the point $(x,\ y)$ which divides $PQ$ in the ratio $1-k : k$. Find an equation connecting $x$ and $y$ (and also involving $k$, but not involving $t$) for the curve traced out by this point as $t$ varies.

Two such curves, marked $A$ and $B$, are drawn in the diagram. Give the values of $k$ for each of these curves.

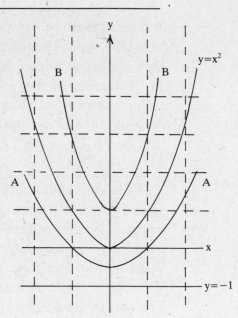

Show that, for all values of $k$, the curves satisfy the differential equation

$$(x^2 + 1)\frac{dy}{dx} = 2x(y + 1).$$

[SMP]

---

484

(15) Throughout this question I is the 2 by 2 identity matrix, and $O$ is the 2 by 2 zero matrix. That is:

$$I = \begin{pmatrix} 1 & 0 \\ 0 & 1 \end{pmatrix} \quad \text{and} \quad O = \begin{pmatrix} 0 & 0 \\ 0 & 0 \end{pmatrix}$$

  i.  Find a non-zero matrix $A$ such that $A^2 = O$.

 ii.  Find 3 different matrices $B$, $C$, $D$ such that $B^2 = C^2 = D^2 = I$.

iii.  Find two matrices $A$ and $B$ such that $AB = O$ but
      $BA \neq O$.

 iv.  Suppose $A$ is such that $A^2 = O$. Show that for all real numbers $k$ the matrix $I + kA$ has an inverse.

---

(16)

  i.  Sketch the graphs of $y = 1/(\cos x + k)$, in the interval $0 \leq x \leq 2\pi$, in the cases (a) $k = 0$ (b) $k = 1$ (c) $k = 2$. In each case state the domain of the function.

 ii.  Evaluate the following integrals:

  (a)  $\int \dfrac{\sin x\, dx}{\sqrt{(1 + \cos x)}}$   (b)  $\int \dfrac{dx}{\sqrt{(1 + \cos x)}}$

  (c)  $\int \cos^{-1} x\, dx$

---

Take $g$ to be 10 m/sec$^2$.

(17) A particle is projected at 100 m/sec, at an angle of elevation of $\theta$. Show that the equation of its trajectory is

$$y = xT - (x^2/2000)(1 + T^2), \quad \text{where } T = \tan\theta.$$

Such a particle is projected from the top of a 20 m tower to a horizontal plane below. Write down the equation relating $T$ and the range $R$. Regarding this equation as a quadratic in $T$ find the condition on $R$ for there to be real roots. Hence find the greatest possible value of $R$.

If a particle is projected at the same speed from the horizontal plane, how close to the base of the tower must the point of projection be if the particle is to reach the top of the tower?

---

(18) Prove that the centre of mass of a uniform solid cone of height $h$ and base radius $b$ is at a height of $\frac{1}{4}h$ above its base.

A uniform solid cone $C_1$ has height $3a$ and base radius $2a$. A smaller cone $C_2$ of height $2a$ and base radius $a$ is contained symmetrically inside $C_1$. The bases of $C_2$ and $C_1$ have a common centre and the axis of $C_2$ is part of the axis of $C_1$. If $C_2$ is removed from $C_1$, show that the centre of mass of the solid remaining is at a distance $11a/5$ from the vertex of $C_1$.

The remaining solid is suspended from a string which is attached to a point on the outer curved surface at a distance of $\frac{1}{3}\sqrt{13}a$ from the vertex of $C_1$. Given that the axis of symmetry is inclined at an angle $\alpha$ to the vertical, find $\tan\alpha$.

[W]

---

(19)

  i. A bag contains N discs, of which $n(\leq N)$ are red. Discs are drawn at random, with replacement, until a red one is obtained. Find the distribution of the number $X$ of drawings.

 ii. Suppose instead that discs are drawn *without* replacement. Show that the probability that it will take $r$ draws before a red disc is found is:

$$P(X = r) = \frac{{}^{N-n}C_{r-1}n}{{}^{N}C_r}$$

Check that your answer is correct in the special cases (a) $n = 0$ (b) $n = N$ (c) $r = 1$.

---

(20) Suppose that $X$ and $Y$ are independent Poisson variables with means $\mu$ and $\lambda$ respectively. Show that $X + Y$ has a Poisson distribution with mean $\mu + \lambda$.

The number of car accidents Mr Smith has in a year follows a Poisson distribution with mean 0.8. The number of car accidents Mrs Smith has is also Poisson, but with mean 0.4. Their accidents are independent of each other.

i. Find the probability that Mr Smith has one accident in a year.

ii. Find the probability that Mrs Smith has no accidents in 6 months.

iii. Find the probability that between them they had 2 accidents in a year.

iv. In 1987 they had one accident between them. What is the probability that it was caused by Mr Smith?

## A-LEVEL PAPER VIII. PURE

Time 3 Hours. *Answer seven questions*

(1) On different graphs sketch the following functions:

(a) $y = \frac{x+1}{x+2}$    (b) $y = \frac{|x+1|}{|x+2|}$    (c) $y^2 = \frac{x+1}{x+2}$

Find the range and domain in each case.

---

(2)

i. $f(x)$ is an *odd* function if $f(-x) = -f(x)$ for all $x$. Show, by graphical means or otherwise, that if $f(x)$ is an odd function then:

$$\int_{-a}^{a} f(x)dx = 0, \text{ for all } a.$$

ii. Show that $\int_0^a f(x)dx = \int_0^a f(a-x)dx$.

Hence show that $\int_0^\pi x\sin^2 xdx = \frac{1}{2}\pi \int_0^\pi \sin^2 xdx$,

and evaluate this integral.

---

(3) Find the equation of the tangent at the point $P(ct, \; c/t)$ on the rectangular hyperbola $xy = c^2$, and prove that the equation of the normal at $P$ is $ty = t^3x + c(1 - t^4)$.

The tangent and normal at $P(t \neq \pm 1)$ meet the line $y = x$ at $T$ and $N$ respectively and the $x$-axis at $L$ and $M$ respectively; $O$ is the origin.

i. Prove that $OP = PN = PL$.

ii. Prove that the product of the lengths of $OT$ and $ON$ is independent of $t$, and determine its value.

iii. Find the area $S$ of triangle $LMP$, showing that $S > \frac{1}{2}c^2$.

[O&C]

---

(4) On the same diagram sketch the curves with equations
(i) $y^2 = 9x$, (ii) $y = x^2(1+x)$, clearly labelling each curve.
Deduce that the equation $x^3(1+x)^2 - 9 = 0$ has exactly one real root.

Denoting this root by $\alpha$, find an integer $n$ such that $n < \alpha < n+1$, and, taking $n$ as a first approximation, use the Newton-Raphson method to find a second approximation to $\alpha$, giving two places of decimals in your answer.

[C]

(5) (a) Find the two complex roots of the equation $z^2 + z + 1 = 0$, and express them in the form $re^{i\theta}$. Show that:

  i.  each root is the square of the other

  ii.  the cube of each root is equal to unity.

(b) By first eliminating $z_2$, or otherwise, solve the simultaneous equations

$$(3 - i)z_1 - iz_2 = 14 + 2i \quad (1 + i)z_1 + 2z_2 = 8 + 10i,$$

giving your answers in the form $x + iy$.

Plot the four points which represent the complex numbers $z_1$, $z_2$, $2 + i$ and $5 + 4i$ on an Argand diagram and show that the four points are the vertices of a rhombus.

[W]

(6)

  i.  Find the series for $(1 + x)^{-\frac{1}{2}}$, up to the $x^3$ term.

  ii.  Hence find the series for $\dfrac{1}{\sqrt{(1 - x^2)}}$, up to the $x^6$ term.

  iii.  Find the series for $\sin^{-1} x$, and use it to estimate $\pi/6$.

(7) The diagram shows a circle with centre $O$ and radius $r$. The three points $A$, $B$, $D$ on the circle are such that $B\hat{A}O = D\hat{A}O = \theta$ radian, and $BCD$ is an arc of the circle with centre $A$ and radius $AB$. The point $E$ lies on the arc $AD$. Find, in terms of $r$ and $\theta$, expressions for

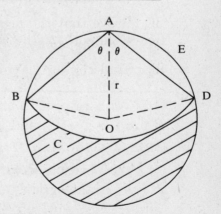

  i.  the length of the straight line $AD$,

  ii.  the area of the sector of the circle (centre $A$) bounded by the lines $AB$ and $AD$ and the arc $BCD$,

  iii.  the area of triangle $OAD$

  iv.  the area of the segment $ADE$.

Hence show that the area of the shaded segment may be expressed as

$$r^2(\sin 2\theta - 2\theta \cos 2\theta).$$

Deduce that, when $\theta = \frac{1}{4}\pi$, this region has an area approximately one third that of the circle with centre $O$.

[C]

---

(8) The pyramid $VABCD$ has a square base $ABCD$ of side 4. The vertex is at $V$, and $VA = VB = VC = VD = 9$. Find the height of the pyramid.
Find the angle between the faces $VBA$ and $VCD$.
Let $E$ be the point on $VA$ such that $AED = 90°$. Find the length of $DE$. Hence or otherwise find the angle between the faces $VBA$ and $VAD$.

---

(9) (a) Show that $\tan 4\theta = \dfrac{4 \tan \theta (1 - \tan^2 \theta)}{\tan^4 \theta - 6 \tan^2 \theta + 1}$.

Hence show that $\tan 22\frac{1}{2}°$ is a root of the equation $t^4 - 6t^2 + 1 = 0$.
Deduce that $\tan 22\frac{1}{2}° = \sqrt{(3 - \sqrt{8})}$, and obtain a similar expression for $\tan 67\frac{1}{2}°$.
Use your results to show that $\sec^2 22\frac{1}{2}° + \sec^2 67\frac{1}{2}° = 8$.
(b) AB is a chord of a circle centre $O$ which subtends an angle $2\theta$ radians at $O(\theta < \frac{1}{2}\pi)$. If $AB$ divides the circle into two regions, one having twice the area of the other, show that $\theta$ satisfies the equation

$$6\theta - 3\sin 2\theta - 2\pi = 0.$$

Hence show that $\theta$ lies between 1.30 and 1.31.

[W]

---

(10) With respect to an origin $O$, the position vectors of $A$ and $B$ are $\mathbf{i} + \mathbf{j} + 2\mathbf{k}$ and $2\mathbf{i} - \mathbf{j} + \mathbf{k}$ respectively, where $\mathbf{i}$, $\mathbf{j}$, $\mathbf{k}$ are perpendicular unit vectors. Find

   i.  the position vector of the point $C$ for which $OACB$ is a parallelogram,

   ii.  the position vector of the midpoint $D$ of $AC$.

Show that $AB$ and $OD$ meet, and find the position vector of their point of intersection.
$F$ is a point such that $OF$ is perpendicular to $OAB$, and $OF = \sqrt{12}$. Find the angle $F\hat{A}B$.

---

# A-LEVEL PAPER IX. PURE, MECHANICS, STATISTICS

Time 3 Hours. *Answer eight questions*

(1)

i. Set up a table of values of the function $y = 3^x$, taking $x$ from 1 to 2 at intervals of 0.2. Give the values to 3 decimal places. Show that the values form a geometric progression, and find its common ratio.

ii. Use the trapezium rule to estimate $\int_1^2 3^x dx$.

iii. Express $3^x$ as $e^{\lambda x}$, where $\lambda$ is to be found. Hence find the exact value of the integral.

iv. Show by graphical means that, however many intervals are taken, the trapezium rule will always result in an overestimate of the integral.

---

(2) The points $O$, $A$, $B$ and $P$ have coordinates $(0,0,0)$, $(2,-1,-3)$, $(1,-1,-2)$ and $(-3,0,-3)$ respectively. Find $\ell$ and $m$ such that the vector $\begin{pmatrix} \ell \\ m \\ 1 \end{pmatrix}$ is perpendicular to both $OA$ and $OB$.

Hence, or otherwise, write down (i) the equation of the plane $OAB$; (ii) the parametric equation of the line through $P$ perpendicular to the plane $OAB$.

Calculate the perpendicular distance from $P$ to the plane.

[SMP]

---

(3) Sketch the curve defined by the parametric equations $x = 4\cos\theta$, $y = 2\sin\theta$, $0 < \theta < \frac{1}{2}\pi$.

Show that the equation of the normal to the curve at the point $P(4\cos\theta, 2\sin\theta)$ is $2x\sin\theta - y\cos\theta = 6\sin\theta\cos\theta$.

This normal meets the $x$-axis at $Q$ and the $y$-axis at $R$. The point $O$ is the origin and the point $S$ is such that $OQSR$ is a rectangle. Find the co-ordinates of $S$. Show the normal at $P$ and the rectangle $OQSR$ on your sketch.

Show that the perimeter $L$ of the rectangle $OQSR$ may be expressed in the form $r\cos(\theta - \alpha)$, where $r > 0$ and $0 < \alpha < \frac{1}{2}\pi$. Give the values, in surd form, of $r$, $\cos\alpha$ and $\sin\alpha$. State the maximum value of $L$ as $\theta$ varies in the interval $0 < \theta < \frac{1}{2}\pi$, and find the coordinates of $S$ when $L$ has this maximum value.

[JMB]

---

(4) (a) Evaluate the following definite integrals:

i. $\int_0^1 (1 + x^3)^2 dx$,

ii. $\int_1^e x^{-\frac{1}{2}} \ln x \, dx$, giving your answer in terms of $e$,

iii. $\int_0^{\pi/2} \frac{\sin 2x}{1 + \sin^2 x} dx$.

(b) Find the area of the region enclosed between the parabola $y^2 = 4x$ and the line $y = x$.

[SUJB]

---

(5)

i. Obtain the first three terms in the expansion in ascending powers of $x$ of

$$\frac{(1 - 2x)^{\frac{1}{2}}}{(1 + x)}, \quad \text{where } |2x| < 1.$$

ii. Express $\dfrac{(3 - x)}{(1 + 2x^2)(1 + 6x)}$ in partial fractions.

Show that

$$\int_0^2 \frac{(3 - x)}{(1 + 2x^2)(1 + 6x)} dx = \frac{1}{2} \ln \left( \frac{13}{3} \right)$$

[L]

---

(6) A bird is 100m due south of its nest. There is a wind of 12 km/hr blowing from 135°.

i. If the bird can fly at 30 km/hr find the direction in which it should fly, and the time it takes to reach its nest.

ii. Show that there are certain speeds $v_0$ and $v_1$, which are to be found, such that if the bird flies at a speed between $v_0$ and $v_1$ then it has a choice of two different directions in which to fly home.

---

(7) A uniform lamina occupies the region enclosed by the positive axes and the curve $y = 1 - x^2$. Find the coordinates of the centre of gravity of the lamina.

The lamina is rotated about the $x$-axis to form a uniform solid of revolution. Find the centre of gravity of this solid.

If this solid is suspended from the point $(0,1)$ find the angle made with the vertical by the flat surface.

---

(8) Prove that the elastic energy of a light spring of natural length $a$ and modulus of elasticity $\lambda$, stretched by an amount $x$, is $\lambda x^2/(2a)$.

A trolley of mass $m$ runs down a smooth track of constant inclination $\pi/6$ to the horizontal, carrying at its front a light spring of natural length $a$ and modulus $mga/c$, where $c$ is constant. When the spring is fully compressed it is of length $a/4$, and it obeys Hooke's law up to this point. After the trolley has travelled a distance $b$ from rest the spring meets a fixed stop. Show that, when the spring has been compressed a distance $x$, where $x < 3a/4$, the speed $v$ of the trolley is given by

$$cv^2/g = c(b + x) - x^2.$$

Given that $c = a/10$ and $b = 2a$, find the total distance covered by the trolley before it momentarily comes to rest for the first time.

[L]

---

(9) A football is kicked with speed $V$ from a point $O$ on level ground. Its initial direction of motion makes an angle $\frac{1}{4}\pi$ with the horizontal. Let $x$ and $y$ be the horizontal and vertical displacements respectively of the ball at time t after being kicked. Write down expressions for $x$ and $y$ in terms of $t$, assuming that air resistance can be neglected. Hence show that

$$y = x - (gx^2/V^2).$$

As the sketch shows, $O$ is 6 m from the foot of a vertical wall $AB$ of height 1.5 m, and 18 m from the foot of a second vertical wall $CD$ also of height 1.5 m. Taking $g$ as 9.8 m s$^{-2}$, show that the ball clears the nearer wall $AB$ when $V = 9$ m s$^{-1}$. Find the minimum value of $V$ which ensures that the ball clears both walls.

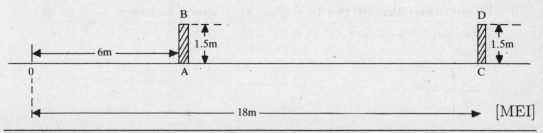

[MEI]

(10) A body moves so that its displacement at time $t$ from the origin is given by $\mathbf{r} = \mathbf{i}(2 - \cos t) + \mathbf{j}(3 + \sin t)$, where $\mathbf{i}$ and $\mathbf{j}$ are unit vectors in the $x$ and $y$ directions respectively.

i. Show that the path is a circle, and find its centre and radius.

ii. Show that the speed of the body is constant.

iii. Find when the velocity is first perpendicular to the displacement, and hence find the greatest distance of the particle from the origin.

iv. Show that the acceleration is always perpendicular to the velocity.

---

(11) Two uniform rods $AB$ and $BC$, each of length $a$ and of masses $m$ and $M$ respectively, are smoothly hinged at $B$. They rest in a vertical plane with $A$ and $C$ in contact with a rough horizontal floor.

i. Find in terms of $m$ and $M$ the vertical reactions from the floor at $A$ and $C$.

ii. If $A\hat{B}C = 90°$ and $m < M$, find in terms of $m$ and $M$ the frictional forces at $A$ and at $C$. Hence find the least possible value of the coefficient of friction $\mu$ if equilibrium is maintained.

---

(12)

a. Events A and B are such that $P(A) = 0.3, P(B) = 0.5$, $P(A \cup B) = 0.7$. Find (i) $P(A \cap B)$, (ii) $P(A|B)$, (iii) $P(A|B')$.

b. A disease afflicts 1% of the population. A test gives positive results for 95% of people with the disease and for 2% of those without the disease. If a test result is positive, what is the probability that the person tested has the disease?

---

(13) A machine produces bolts whose diameters are normally distributed with mean $\mu$ and variance $0.001$ mm$^2$. A sample of 10 bolts is found to have mean diameter 5.34 mm. Find a symmetric 95% confidence interval for $\mu$.

How large should the sample be if the width of the confidence interval is to be less than 0.01 mm?

Samples of 40 each were taken from the production of the machine on two successive days. The average diameters of the samples were 5.31 mm and 5.32 mm. Is this significant at 5% to show that the machine was working differently on the two days?

---

(14) Express $\dfrac{1}{r(r+1)}$ in partial fractions. Hence show that

$$\sum_{r=1}^{r=n} \frac{1}{r(r+1)} = 1 - \frac{1}{n+1}$$

The discrete random variable $X$ has probabilities given by $P(X=r) = \dfrac{k}{r(r+1)}$, where $k$ is a constant.

i.  Suppose $X$ takes the values 1, 2, 3, ... , 10. Find the value of $k$.

ii. Suppose instead that $X$ can take any positive integral value. Find $k$. If $X$ is bigger than 10 find the probability that it is bigger than 20.

# Modular Exam P1

**Time: 1 hour 30 minutes**

**Full marks may be obtained for answers to all the questions.**

1) Show that $(x - 2)$ is a factor of $2x^3 - 9x^2 + 7x + 6$.

   Hence solve the equation $2x^3 - 9x^2 + 7x + 6 = 0$.

   [6]

2) Write down the identity connecting $\cos^2 x$ and $\sin^2 x$. Hence solve the equation:

   $$\cos^2 x + 3 \sin x = 2$$

   giving all the solutions in the range $0° \leqslant x \leqslant 360°$.

   [12]

3) (a) Express $\dfrac{1}{\sqrt{2} - 1} - \dfrac{1}{\sqrt{2} + 1}$ as a single fraction, simplifying your answer as far as possible.

   (b) Write $\dfrac{1}{\sqrt{5} - \sqrt{3}}$ in the form $a\sqrt{5} + b\sqrt{3}$, where $a$ and $b$ are fractions.

   [10]

4) Find the gradient of the curve $y = 2x + \dfrac{4}{x}$ at the point $(2,6)$.

   Hence find the equation of the normal to the curve at this point.

   Find the $x$-coordinate of the point where normal meets the curve again.

   [10]

5) Draw axes on graph paper, using a scale of 1 cm per unit.
   Illustrate the following inequalities on the graph, leaving the required region unshaded.

   $$y \geqslant 0, \ y \leqslant 2x, \ x + y \leqslant 5, \ 3y \geqslant x.$$

   List the integer value points within the region. At which of these points does $3x + 2y$ take its greatest value?

   [9]

496

6) A regular octahedron has eight
faces which are equilateral
triangles.

Suppose each edge of an octahedron
has length 2 cm. Find the distance
between opposite vertices.

Find the angle between adjacent faces of the octahedron.

[12]

7) Find the area enclosed by the $x$-axis, the lines $x = 1$ and $x = 3$, and
the curve $y = 2x^3 + 7x - 3$.

[7]

8) A stone is thrown up in the air. After $t$ seconds its height $h$ in metres
above the ground is given by:

$$h = 2 + 40t - 5t^2$$

By completing the square or otherwise find the greatest height which
the stone reaches.

[8]

9) In a certain country inflation is such that the exchange rate of the Pesta
against the £ doubles every 3 months.

At the beginning of January 1990 there were 250 Pesta to the £. How
many were there at the beginning of October 1990?

Find an expression for the exchange rate $n$ years after January 1990.

[8]

10) (a) The functions $f$ and $g$ are defined by:

$$f(x) = 3x + 2 \qquad g(x) = 2 - 5x.$$

Find $fg(2)$, $gf(2)$, $fg(x)$.

(b) On the right is the graph of
$y = h(x)$. Copy this graph, and on
the same paper sketch the graph of
$y = h^{-1}(x)$.

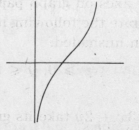

[10]

11) Expand $(1 + x)^{20}$ up to the term in $x^2$.

Hence, without a calculator, find an approximation for
$1.01^{20} - 0.99^{20}$.

[8]

# Modular Exam P2

Time: 1 hour 30 minutes

**Full marks may be obtained by answers to all the questions.**

1) It is thought that there is a relationship between $y$ and $x$ of the form $y = ax^2 + bx$, where $a$ and $b$ are unknown constants.

   Several values of $y$ and $x$ are found. How can the relationship be rewritten so that a linear graph can be drawn?

   [4]

2) (a) Find the binomial expansion of $\sqrt{1 + x}$, up to the term in $x^2$.

   (b) For small values of $x$, $\sin x$ is approximately equal to $x$. Use the relationship $\cos^2 x = 1 - \sin^2 x$ and the result of (a) above to obtain an approximation for $\cos x$, up to the term in $x^2$.

   [10]

3) Solve the following inequalities:

   (a) $|x - 3| < |2x - 1|$     (b) $\dfrac{1}{|x + 1|} < \dfrac{1}{|x + 3|}$

   [10]

4) From the origin O, the points A, B, C have vector positions given by $a(\mathbf{i} + 2\mathbf{j} - 3\mathbf{k})$, $a(3\mathbf{i} + \mathbf{j} + 2\mathbf{k})$, $a(\mathbf{i} - 3\mathbf{j} + 8\mathbf{k})$ respectively.

   (a) Show that BC is parallel to OA.

   (b) Find the angle between OB and OC.

   [8]

5) Express $\dfrac{1}{(x + 1)(x + 2)}$ in partial fractions.

   Use your result to find $\displaystyle\sum_{r = 1}^{n} \dfrac{1}{(r + 1)(r + 2)}$.

   [9]

6) The variables $x$ and $y$ are given in terms of $t$ by $x = 2 \cos t$ and $y = 3 \sin t$.

   Find $dy/dx$ in terms of $t$.

   Sketch the graph of $y$ against $x$, for $t$ between 0 and $\pi$.

   [9]

7) Sketch the curve $y = \sqrt{\sin x}$, of $x$ between 0 and $\pi$.

This curve is rotated about the $x$-axis. Find the volume of revolution generated.

Use the trapezium rule with 6 intervals to find the approximate value of the area between the curve and the $x$-axis.

Is your approximate value an overestimate or an underestimate? Give a justification for your answer.

[14]

8) (a) By considering the expansions of $\sin(A + B)$ and $\sin(A - B)$, show that $\sin X + \sin Y = 2 \sin \frac{1}{2}(X + Y) \cos \frac{1}{2}(X - Y)$.

(b) Solve the equation $\sin(x + 10°) + \sin(x - 40°) = 1.5$, giving solutions between 0° and 360°.

[13]

9) The complex numbers $z$ and $w$ are given by $z = 1 + i$ and $w = 3 + 2i$. Express in the form $a + ib$:

> (i) $zw$      (ii) $1/z$      (iii) $\overline{w}$

Find the modulus and argument of $z$.

Describe the geometrical effect of multiplying a complex number by $z$.

[11]

10) Evaluate the following integrals:

> (i) $\int \sin(3x + 2)\, dx$      (ii) $\int_2^5 \dfrac{dx}{2x - 3}$

> (iii) $\int_0^\infty x\, e^{-2x} dx$

[12]

# Modular Exam M1

**Time: 1 hour 30 minutes**

**Full marks may be obtained by answers to all the questions. Where relevant, take g to be 9.8 m s$^{-2}$.**

1) The vector position **r** of a particle is given by:
$$\mathbf{r} = (t^2 - 10t)\mathbf{i} + (7 - 3t^2)\mathbf{j}$$
Find the expressions of the velocity **v** and the acceleration **a**.

When is **v** perpendicular to **a**?

[6]

2) A ship decelerates constantly from 10 m s$^{-1}$ to 1 m s$^{-1}$. It travels 2,200 m while decelerating.

By means of a speed-time graph or otherwise find the deceleration and the time taken.

[6]

3) Weights of 3 kg and 4 kg are connected by a light inextensible string, which passes over a smooth peg. The system is released from rest. Find the acceleration of the system.

After two seconds the heavier mass strikes the floor and comes to an instantaneous halt. Find the time before the string is again taut.

[8]

4) A solid uniform cylinder has height 6 cm and base radius 2 cm. A cone-shaped hole is carved out from the cylinder: the base of the cone coincides with the base circle of the cylinder, and the apex of the cone is in the middle of the top circle of the cylinder.

Find the centre of mass of the remaining solid.

(The centre of mass of a solid cone is a quarter of the distance from the base to the apex).

[10]

5) A uniform stick AB of mass $m$ and length $2a$ rests with A in contact with a rough horizontal floor. The rod is held at an angle $\theta$ with the ground by a horizontal string attached to B.

Find the tension in the string in terms of $m$, $g$ and $\theta$.

If the rod is about to slip when $\theta = 60°$, find the coefficient of friction $\mu$.

[10]

6) A girl throws a stone at an angle of 45° to the horizontal, at $u$ m/sec. The stone leaves her hand 2 m above the ground, and strikes a bottle on top of a wall which is 3 m high and 20 m away horizontally. Show that $u$ obeys the equation:

$$38 = g \left( \frac{800}{u^2} \right)$$

Solve this equation to find $u$.

The bottle will be knocked off the wall if the speed with which the stone strikes it is greater than 13 m/sec. Will it be knocked off?

[14]

7) The velocity **v** of a ship is given by the vector **v** = 2**i** + 3**j**. On the ship, the wind appears to have velocity −**i** − 4**j**.

What is the true velocity of the wind? What is the speed of the wind?

[8]

8) Suppose a body moves with constant speed $v$ against forces $F$. Show that the power needed is $P = F \times v$.

A vehicle of mass 900 kg can develop a power of 5,400 watts. On level ground its maximum speed is 30 m/sec. If the resistances which it experiences are proportional to its speed, find the constant of proportionality.

The vehicle is driven up a slope of angle $\alpha$, where $\sin \alpha = \frac{1}{70}$. Find its maximum speed up this slope.

[14]

9) Particle A, of mass 1, is moving with velocity vector **i** + 2**j**.
Particle B, of mass 3, is moving with vector −2**i** − 3**j**.

After they collide A is moving at −2**i** − 4**j**. Find the velocity of B. Find the proportion of kinetic energy which has been lost in the collision.

[12]

10) A particle moves in a straight line. It starts with a speed of 21, and experiences an acceleration of $18 - 6t$. Find expressions for its velocity at time $t$ and the distance it has moved.

Find the maximum velocity and the maximum displacement in the subsequent motion.

[12]

501

# Modular Exam S1

Time: 1 hour 30 minutes

**Full marks may be obtained for answers to all the questions.**

1) In a raffle there are 500 tickets, 10 of which will win prizes.

   If I buy 3 tickets, what is the probability that I will win at least one prize?

   [6]

2) Find the mean and the unbiased sample variance for the numbers below.

   2.9, 2.7, 3.1, 3.3, 3.2, 3.0, 2.8, 2.9. 3.0, 2.7

   Assuming that these numbers come from a normal distribution with the mean and variance as found, find the probability that the next number in the series will be over 3.

   [10]

3) The number of flaws in the rugs made by a certain factory follows a Poisson distribution with mean 0.3. If a rug has more than 1 flaw it is rejected.

   Find the proportion of rugs which are rejected.

   If a rug is not rejected, what is the probability it has no flaws?

   [10]

4) The time people take to complete a task testing dexterity follows a normal distribution. 10% of the people completed it in less than 4 minutes, and 25% took over 6 minutes.

   Find the mean and variance of the time taken.

   [10]

5) In a fairground game the customer rolls three dice. If 1 six is obtained, the customer wins £2. If 2 sixes are showing, £3 is won, and if 3 sixes are showing £4 is won.

   Write a distribution table for the amount won by the customer.

   The customer pays £1 to play this game. What is the percentage profit or loss of the stallholder?

   [10]

6) The continuous random variable $X$ has p.d.f. given by:

$$f(x) = \begin{cases} kx^2 \text{ if } 0 \leqslant x \leqslant 2 \\ 0 \text{ otherwise.} \end{cases}$$

(a) Find the value of $k$.

(b) Find the mean of $X$.

(c) Find the probability that $X$ is bigger than the mean.

[12]

7) My journey to work involves a walk then a bus ride. The times for walking, waiting for the bus and for the bus trip are all normally distributed. Their means are 8 minutes, 10 minutes, 7 minutes respectively. Their variances are 1, 5 and 2 respectively.

(a) Find the probability that the total journey takes over 30 minutes.

(b) Find the probability that the time spent waiting at the bus stop is greater than the time spent in the bus.

[10]

8) The probability that a hard disc will still be going after $x$ hours of use is $e^{-0.0001x}$.

Let $X$ be the lifetime of a hard disc. Find the p.d.f. of $X$.

(a) Write down, but do not evaluate, an integral expression for the mean lifetime of the disc.

(b) Find the median lifetime of the disc.

[12]

9) The manufacturers of "Herostratus" matches claim that each box contains 50 matches on average. It is known that the variance of this total is 20.

A sample of 40 boxes were found to contain an average of 48 matches.

Is this significant at 5% to disprove the manufacturers claim?
Show clearly the null and alternative hypotheses you are using.

[10]

10) The lifetime of certain batteries has a standard deviation of $\sqrt{2}$ hours. A sample of 100 of these batteries found that their mean lifetime was 10 hours. Find a 95% confidence interval for the lifetime of these batteries, stating clearly any assumptions that you make.

[10]

# Statistical Tables

## Table I. Cumulative Probability of the Standard Normal Distribution.

This table gives the values of $\Phi(z) = P(Z < z)$, where $Z$ is normal with mean 0 and variance 1.

If $z$ is given to three decimal places, then use linear interpolation. For example:

$\Phi(1.327) \simeq 0.9066 + 0.7 \times 0.0016 \simeq 0.9077$.

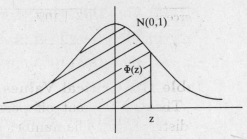

| z | 0.00 | 0.01 | 0.02 | 0.03 | 0.04 | 0.05 | 0.06 | 0.07 | 0.08 | 0.09 |
|---|------|------|------|------|------|------|------|------|------|------|
| 0.0 | 0.5000 | 0.5040 | 0.5080 | 0.5120 | 0.5160 | 0.5199 | 0.5239 | 0.5279 | 0.5139 | 0.5359 |
| 0.1 | 0.5398 | 0.5438 | 0.5478 | 0.5517 | 0.5557 | 0.5596 | 0.5636 | 0.5675 | 0.5714 | 0.5753 |
| 0.2 | 0.5793 | 0.5832 | 0.5871 | 0.5910 | 0.5948 | 0.5987 | 0.6026 | 0.6064 | 0.6103 | 0.6141 |
| 0.3 | 0.6179 | 0.6217 | 0.6255 | 0.6293 | 0.6331 | 0.6368 | 0.6406 | 0.6443 | 0.6480 | 0.6517 |
| 0.4 | 0.6554 | 0.6591 | 0.6628 | 0.6664 | 0.6700 | 0.6736 | 0.6772 | 0.6808 | 0.6844 | 0.6879 |
| 0.5 | 0.6915 | 0.6950 | 0.6985 | 0.7019 | 0.7054 | 0.7088 | 0.7123 | 0.7157 | 0.7190 | 0.7224 |
| 0.6 | 0.7257 | 0.7291 | 0.7324 | 0.7357 | 0.7389 | 0.7422 | 0.7454 | 0.7486 | 0.7517 | 0.7549 |
| 0.7 | 0.7580 | 0.7611 | 0.7642 | 0.7673 | 0.7704 | 0.7734 | 0.7764 | 0.7794 | 0.7823 | 0.7852 |
| 0.8 | 0.7881 | 0.7910 | 0.7939 | 0.7967 | 0.7995 | 0.8023 | 0.8051 | 0.8078 | 0.8106 | 0.8133 |
| 0.9 | 0.8159 | 0.8186 | 0.8212 | 0.8238 | 0.8264 | 0.8289 | 0.8315 | 0.8340 | 0.8365 | 0.8389 |
| 1.0 | 0.8413 | 0.8438 | 0.8461 | 0.8485 | 0.8508 | 0.8531 | 0.8554 | 0.8577 | 0.8599 | 0.8621 |
| 1.1 | 0.8643 | 0.8665 | 0.8686 | 0.8708 | 0.8729 | 0.8749 | 0.8770 | 0.8790 | 0.8810 | 0.8830 |
| 1.2 | 0.8849 | 0.8869 | 0.8888 | 0.8907 | 0.8925 | 0.8944 | 0.8962 | 0.8980 | 0.8997 | 0.9015 |
| 1.3 | 0.9032 | 0.9049 | 0.9066 | 0.9082 | 0.9099 | 0.9115 | 0.9131 | 0.9147 | 0.9162 | 0.9177 |
| 1.4 | 0.9192 | 0.9207 | 0.9222 | 0.9236 | 0.9251 | 0.9265 | 0.9279 | 0.9292 | 0.9306 | 0.9319 |
| 1.5 | 0.9332 | 0.9345 | 0.9357 | 0.9370 | 0.9382 | 0.9394 | 0.9406 | 0.9418 | 0.9429 | 0.9441 |
| 1.6 | 0.9452 | 0.9463 | 0.9474 | 0.9484 | 0.9495 | 0.9505 | 0.9515 | 0.9525 | 0.9535 | 0.9545 |
| 1.7 | 0.9554 | 0.9564 | 0.9573 | 0.9582 | 0.9591 | 0.9599 | 0.9608 | 0.9616 | 0.9625 | 0.9633 |
| 1.8 | 0.9641 | 0.9649 | 0.9656 | 0.9664 | 0.9671 | 0.9678 | 0.9686 | 0.9693 | 0.9699 | 0.9706 |
| 1.9 | 0.9713 | 0.9719 | 0.9726 | 0.9732 | 0.9738 | 0.9744 | 0.9750 | 0.9756 | 0.9761 | 0.9767 |
| 2.0 | 0.9772 | 0.9778 | 0.9783 | 0.9788 | 0.9793 | 0.9798 | 0.9803 | 0.9808 | 0.9812 | 0.9817 |
| 2.1 | 0.9821 | 0.9826 | 0.9830 | 0.9834 | 0.9838 | 0.9842 | 0.9846 | 0.9850 | 0.9854 | 0.9857 |
| 2.2 | 0.9861 | 0.9864 | 0.9868 | 0.9871 | 0.9875 | 0.9878 | 0.9881 | 0.9884 | 0.9887 | 0.9890 |
| 2.3 | 0.9893 | 0.9896 | 0.9898 | 0.9901 | 0.9904 | 0.9906 | 0.9909 | 0.9911 | 0.9913 | 0.9916 |
| 2.4 | 0.9918 | 0.9920 | 0.9922 | 0.9925 | 0.9927 | 0.9929 | 0.9931 | 0.9932 | 0.9934 | 0.9936 |
| 2.5 | 0.9938 | 0.9940 | 0.9941 | 0.9943 | 0.9945 | 0.9946 | 0.9948 | 0.9949 | 0.9951 | 0.9952 |
| 2.6 | 0.9953 | 0.9955 | 0.9956 | 0.9957 | 0.9959 | 0.9960 | 0.9961 | 0.9962 | 0.9963 | 0.9964 |
| 2.7 | 0.9965 | 0.9966 | 0.9967 | 0.9968 | 0.9969 | 0.9970 | 0.9971 | 0.9972 | 0.9973 | 0.9974 |
| 2.8 | 0.9974 | 0.9975 | 0.9976 | 0.9977 | 0.9977 | 0.9978 | 0.9979 | 0.9979 | 0.9980 | 0.9981 |
| 2.9 | 0.9981 | 0.9982 | 0.9982 | 0.9983 | 0.9984 | 0.9984 | 0.9985 | 0.9985 | 0.9986 | 0.9986 |
| 3.0 | 0.9987 | 0.9987 | 0.9987 | 0.9988 | 0.9988 | 0.9989 | 0.9989 | 0.9989 | 0.9990 | 0.9990 |
| 3.1 | 0.9990 | 0.9991 | 0.9991 | 0.9991 | 0.9992 | 0.9992 | 0.9992 | 0.9992 | 0.9993 | 0.9993 |
| 3.2 | 0.9993 | 0.9993 | 0.9994 | 0.9994 | 0.9994 | 0.9994 | 0.9994 | 0.9995 | 0.9994 | 0.9995 |
| 3.3 | 0.9995 | 0.9995 | 0.9995 | 0.9996 | 0.9996 | 0.9996 | 0.9996 | 0.9996 | 0.9996 | 0.9997 |
| 3.4 | 0.9997 | 0.9997 | 0.9997 | 0.9997 | 0.9997 | 0.9997 | 0.9997 | 0.9997 | 0.9997 | 0.9998 |
| 3.5 | 0.9998 | 0.9998 | 0.9998 | 0.9998 | 0.9998 | 0.9998 | 0.9998 | 0.9998 | 0.9998 | 0.9998 |
| 3.6 | 0.9998 | 0.9998 | 0.9999 | 0.9999 | 0.9999 | 0.9999 | 0.9999 | 0.9999 | 0.9999 | 0.9999 |

## Table II. Critical Values for the Standard Normal Distribution.

These values cut off percentages of probability from both tails of the normal distribution. If $a_i$ is the critical value for $i\%$, then:

$$P(|Z| > a_i) = i\%.$$

| Percentage | 20% | 10% | 5% | 2% | 1% |
|---|---|---|---|---|---|
| Critical Value | 1.28 | 1.64 | 1.96 | 2.33 | 2.58 |

## Table III. Critical Values for the $t-$distribution.

These values cut off percentages of probability from both tails of the $t-$distribution. The number of degrees of freedom is $\nu$.

| Percentage | 10% | 5% | 2% | 1% |
|---|---|---|---|---|
| $\nu = 1$ | 6.31 | 12.71 | 31.82 | 63.66 |
| $\nu = 2$ | 2.92 | 4.30 | 6.96 | 9.92 |
| $\nu = 3$ | 2.35 | 3.18 | 4.54 | 5.84 |
| $\nu = 4$ | 2.13 | 2.78 | 3.75 | 4.60 |
| $\nu = 5$ | 2.02 | 2.57 | 3.36 | 4.03 |
| $\nu = 6$ | 1.94 | 2.45 | 3.14 | 3.71 |
| $\nu = 7$ | 1.89 | 2.36 | 3.00 | 3.50 |
| $\nu = 8$ | 1.86 | 2.31 | 2.90 | 3.36 |
| $\nu = 9$ | 1.83 | 2.26 | 2.82 | 3.25 |
| $\nu = 10$ | 1.81 | 2.23 | 2.76 | 3.17 |
| $\nu = 12$ | 1.78 | 2.18 | 2.68 | 3.05 |
| $\nu = 14$ | 1.76 | 2.14 | 2.62 | 2.98 |
| $\nu = 20$ | 1.72 | 2.09 | 2.53 | 2.85 |
| $\nu = \infty$ | 1.64 | 1.96 | 2.33 | 2.58 |

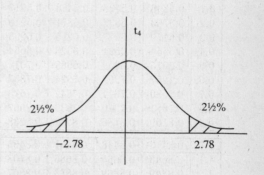

## Table IV. Critical Values of the $\chi^2$ Distribution.

These values cut off percentages of probability from the top tail of the $\chi^2$ distribution. The number of degrees of freedom is $\nu$.

| Percentage | 10% | 5% | 1% | 0.1% |
|---|---|---|---|---|
| $\nu = 1$ | 2.71 | 3.84 | 6.63 | 10.83 |
| $\nu = 2$ | 4.61 | 5.99 | 9.21 | 13.81 |
| $\nu = 3$ | 6.25 | 7.81 | 11.34 | 16.27 |
| $\nu = 4$ | 7.78 | 9.49 | 13.28 | 18.47 |
| $\nu = 5$ | 9.24 | 11.07 | 15.09 | 20.52 |
| $\nu = 6$ | 10.64 | 12.59 | 16.81 | 22.46 |
| $\nu = 7$ | 12.02 | 14.07 | 18.48 | 24.32 |
| $\nu = 8$ | 13.36 | 15.51 | 20.09 | 26.12 |
| $\nu = 9$ | 14.68 | 16.92 | 21.67 | 27.88 |
| $\nu = 10$ | 15.99 | 18.31 | 23.21 | 29.59 |
| $\nu = 12$ | 18.55 | 21.03 | 26.22 | 32.91 |
| $\nu = 14$ | 21.06 | 23.68 | 29.14 | 36.12 |
| $\nu = 20$ | 28.41 | 31.41 | 37.57 | 45.31 |

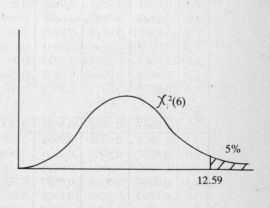

# Solutions to End-of-Chapter Exercises

## Chapter 1

### Exercises 1.1.2  Page 5

(1)  $b,3,$ d,4

(2)  (a) $4x^3 + x - 3$        (b) $2x^5 + 3x^4 - 2x^2 - 3x$

      (c) $x^3 - x^2 + 2x + 5$      (d) $x^7 - x$

(3)  (a) $x^2 + 6x + 25,\ 97$      (b) $x - 4,\ 18x - 3$

      (c) $x^2 - 4x + 18,\ -73$    (d) $2x^3 + 3x^2 + 3x + 4\frac{1}{2}, 14\frac{1}{2}$

(4)  (a) 38                 (b) 29

      (c) 7                  (d) 18

(5)  5                     (6)  $\frac{5}{9}$

(7)  $a = \frac{1}{3}\ b = -\frac{1}{3}$        (8)  $a = -\frac{1}{7},\ b = 1\frac{6}{7}$

(9)  12                (10)  $\frac{1}{2}$

(11)  $a = -10,\ b = 24$      (12)  $a = 2\frac{1}{4},\ b = -4\frac{3}{4}$

(13)  $a = -5,\ b = -4.\ (x - 5)$

(14)  (a) $(x - 1)(x + 1)(x - 2)$      (b) $(x - 2)(x + 2)(x + 3)$

       (c) $(x - 1)(x - 3)(x + 2)$      (d) $(2x + 1)(x + 2)(x + 3)$

       (e) $(2x + 1)(x - 2)(x - 3)$      (f) $(x - 1)(x + 2)(x^2 - x + 2)$

       (g) $(x - 1)^2(x + 1)$         (h) $(x + 1)(x + 2)^2$

(15)  (a) $1, -2, -3$          (b) $-1, 2, 3$

       (c) $\frac{1}{2}, -1, -2$          (d) $1, \frac{1}{2}, \frac{1}{3}$

### Exercises 1.2.2  Page 9

(1)  (a) $\dfrac{2x}{(x + 1)(x + 1)}$      (b) $\dfrac{-x + 3}{x(x + 3)}$

      (c) $\dfrac{2x^2 - x + 2}{x^2(2 - x)}$      (d) $\dfrac{2x^2 - x + 2}{x(x^2 + 1)}$

      (e) $\dfrac{x + 5}{x + 1}$         (f) $\dfrac{-x^2 + 5x + 3}{5 - x}$

(2)  $\dfrac{1}{x - 1} - \dfrac{1}{x + 1}$      (3)  $\dfrac{2}{x - 1} - \dfrac{2}{x + 3}$

(4)  $\dfrac{4}{x - 1} - \dfrac{3}{x}$        (5)  $\dfrac{\frac{3}{4}}{x + 1} + \dfrac{1\frac{1}{4}}{x - 3}$

(6)  $\dfrac{-\frac{2}{3}}{x + 1} + \dfrac{1\frac{1}{3}}{2x - 1}$      (7)  $\dfrac{4/7}{x - 2} + \dfrac{9/7}{3x + 1}$

(8) $\dfrac{-1}{x+1} + \dfrac{x+1}{x^2+1}$

(9) $\dfrac{3}{x} - \dfrac{3x+3}{x^2+x+1}$

(10) $\dfrac{0.6}{x+2} + \dfrac{0.4x-0.8}{x^2+1}$

(11) $\dfrac{1}{x+1} - \dfrac{2x}{2x^2+3}$

(12) $\dfrac{2}{x-1} + \dfrac{2}{(x-2)^2} - \dfrac{2}{x-2}$

(13) $-\dfrac{4}{x+1} - \dfrac{1}{x^2} + \dfrac{4}{x}$

(14) $\dfrac{1/9}{2x-1} - \dfrac{\frac{1}{3}}{(x+1)^2} + \dfrac{4/9}{x+1}$

(15) $\dfrac{5/9}{x-1} - \dfrac{10/3}{(2x+1)^2} - \dfrac{10/9}{2x+1}$

(16) $1 + \dfrac{1}{x-3} - \dfrac{2}{x+4}$

(17) $4 + \dfrac{2}{x-1} - \dfrac{2}{x+1}$

(18) $x + \dfrac{1}{x-1} + \dfrac{3}{x+2}$

(19) $x^2 + 1 + \dfrac{\frac{1}{2}}{x-1} - \dfrac{\frac{1}{2}}{x+1}$

(20) $\dfrac{3}{x-1} - \dfrac{6}{x-2} + \dfrac{3}{x-3}$

(21) $\dfrac{1\frac{1}{2}}{x} + \dfrac{\frac{1}{3}}{x-1} - \dfrac{11/6}{x+2}$

(22) $\dfrac{1}{n} - \dfrac{1}{n+1}$, $1 - \dfrac{1}{n+1}$

(23) $1$

(24) (a) $\dfrac{1}{2} - \dfrac{\frac{1}{2}}{2n+1}$

(b) $\dfrac{1}{4} - \dfrac{1}{4n+4}$

# Chapter 2

## Exercises 2.1.2  Page 13

(1) (a) 31 (b) 53 (c) 6.2 (d) −19
(2) (a) 210 (b) 420 (c) 63.6 (d) −66
(3) (a) $3n-2$, $\frac{1}{2}n(3n-1)$ (b) $4n+9$, $\frac{1}{2}n(4n+22)$
(c) $n/5+4$, $\frac{1}{2}n(8.2+n/5)$ (d) $14-3n$, $\frac{1}{2}n(25-3n)$
(4) (a) $0, 3n-3$ (b) $5, 3n+2$ (c) $1.1, n/5+0.9$ (d) $21, 25-4n$
(5) 3,8
(6) (a) 5,7 (b) 7,4 (c) 1/5, 11/5 (d) −2, 1
(7) 3, 7, 11, 4
(8) (a) 2, 2 (b) 2, −2 (c) 5, 6 (d) $\frac{3}{4}$, $-\frac{1}{2}$
(9) 103 (10) −2, 41
(11) $\frac{1}{2}n(n+1)$ (12) $n^2$ (13) 1365
(14) 5 (15) $43\frac{2}{3}$, $34\frac{1}{3}$

## Exercises 2.2.2  Page 16

(1) (a) 128, 62 (b) 1/16, $7\frac{3}{4}$
(c) 1458, 122 (d) −1/2048, −1.602
(2) (a) $2^n$ (b) $4(\frac{1}{2})^{n-1}$
(c) $2(-3)^{n-1}$ (d) $-2(-\frac{1}{4})^{n-1}$
(3) (a) $2(2^n-1)$ (b) $8(1-\frac{1}{2}^n)$

(c) $\frac{1}{2}(1-(-3)^n)$

(d) $(-8/5)(1-(-\frac{1}{4})^n)$

(4)   $b$, 8   $d$, $-1.6$

(5)   (a) $1\frac{1}{2},2$

(b) 32, $\frac{1}{2}$

(c) $1\frac{1}{4}$, $-2$

(d) 8, $\frac{1}{2}$

(6)   $\pm 5$, $\pm 4/125$

(7) 6

(8)   9

(9) 0.706

(10) $\pm 15$

(11) $-4,2$

(12) (a) 3,4

(b) $\frac{1}{4}$, 3

## Exercises 2.3.2  Page 18

(1)   $d = \frac{1}{4}(y-x)$,  $a = \frac{1}{2}(3x-y)$

(2) 4 or $-1\frac{1}{2}$

(3)   500

(4) £709.6

(5) £13900, £112000

(6)   £12411,  £100,623

(7) 36, 11 bricks high

(8)   40.96 mm, 15 times

(9) $2^{64} - 1$

(10) 12

(11) 4/33

(12) (a) 8/11

(b) 353/1100 (c) 37/999

(d) $23\frac{3139}{9990}$

(13) $1\frac{1}{9}$ seconds.

## Chapter 3

## Exercises 3.1.2  Page 23

(1)   (a) $32 + 80b + 80b^2 + 40b^3 + 10b^4 + b^5$

(b) $1 + 12b + 54b^2 + 108b^3 + 81b^4$

(c) $16x^4 + 96x^3y + 216x^2y^2 + 216xy^3 + 81y^4$

(d) $1 - 12z + 60z^2 - 160z^3 + 240z^4 - 192z^5 + 64z^6$

(e) $128a^7 - 448a^6b + 672a^5b^2 - 560a^4b^3 + 280a^3b^4 - 84a^2b^5 + 14ab^6 - b^7$

(f) $128 - 224x + 168x^2 - 70x^3 + 17\frac{1}{2}x^4 - 2\frac{5}{8}x^5 + 7x^6/32 - x^7/128$

(2)   (a) $56x^3$

(b) $-126y^5$

(c) $180x^8$

(d) $448x^3$

(e) $720y^3$

(f) $-11250x^2$

(g) $4368x^5\, y^{11}$

(h) $6048a^5\, b^2$

(i) $28x^4$

(j) $-672y^{-3}$

(k) $21x^8$

(l) $-84$

(3)   (a) $24310x^9$

(b) $672x^5$

(c) $20412x^6$

(d) $489888x^6$

(4)   416

(5) $1 + 12x + 66x^2 + 220x^3$     (a) 1.26816    (b) 0.61152

(6) (a) 1.083                        (b) 0.698

      (c) 535.5                      (d) 227.2

(7) $a = 3$, $n = 10$             (8) $2/b$

(9) $\sqrt{224}: \sqrt{5}$            (10) $1 + 10x + 55x^2$

(11) (a) $1 - 7x + 28x^2$        (b) $1 + 8x^2 + 28x^4 + 56x^6$

      (c) $1 + 12x + 78x^2$       (d) $128 - 448x + 1568x^2$

## Exercises 3.2.2 Page 25

(1) (a) $1 + \frac{1}{4}x - 3x^2/32$         (b) $1 + 1\frac{1}{2}x - 9/8x^2$

      (c) $1 - 1\frac{1}{2}x + \frac{3}{8}x^2$         (d) $1 - 8x/3 + 8x^2/9$

      (e) $1 - 2x + 3x^2$            (f) $1 - 2x + 4x^2$

      (g) $1 + x^2$                    (h) $3 \neg 3x^2$

(2) $a, c, e, g, h,$      $b, -\frac{1}{3} < x < \frac{1}{3}$      $d, f, -\frac{1}{2} < x < \frac{1}{2}$

      $-1 < x < 1$

(3) (a) 1.0049876       (b) 1.0247           (c) 0.98995

      (d) 0.9798

(4) 1.99997                    (5) 7.07106

(6) (a) 10.04888            (b) 9.8995

      (c) 3.0366                 (d) 3.97906

(7) (a) $1 + 2x + 2x^2$         (b) $1 - 2x + 5x^2$

      (c) $1 - x + 2x^2$          (d) $1 + x - x^2$

(8) $a = 2$, $b = -\frac{1}{4}$       (9) $a = -2$, $b = 1$

## Chapter 4

## Exercises 4.1.2 Page 31

(1) (a) 7, $-11$                 (b) 5, $-1\frac{1}{2}$

      (c) $-0.394$, $-7.61$       (d) 0.4, $-1$

      (e) $\pm 1.618$, $\pm 0.618$     (f) $\pm 1.377$

      (g) $-0.837$, $-1.506$      (h) $\pm 1.272$

      (i) 0.427, $-2.927$         (j) 3, $\frac{1}{2}$

(2) 4.437 ft                   (3) 2.508 cm$^2$

(4) 1.633

509

(5)  (a) $(x+1)^2 - 4 = 0$, 1, -3  (b) $(x - 3\frac{1}{2})^2 - 10\frac{1}{4} = 0$, 6.702, 0.298
(c) $3(x+1)^2 - 2 = 0$,  (d) $2(x - \frac{3}{4})^2 - 9\frac{1}{8} = 0$, 2.886, $-1.386$
$-0.184$, $-1.816$

(6)  (a) (2.562, 3.562) & ($-1.562$,  (b) (3, 3) & ($-0.6$, $-4.2$)
$-0.562$)
(c) $(1\frac{2}{3}, 1\frac{1}{3})$  (d) $(1\frac{1}{2}, \frac{2}{3})$ & (1, 1)

(7)  22.095 & 0.905  (8) ($-0.593$, 1.407) & (0.843, 2.843)

(9)  (2.436, $-1.436$) & ($-1.436$, 2.436)  (10) 12.07 & 4.93

(11) $9x - y = 10$. (1.425, 2.823)
& (0.770, $-3.067$)


## Exercises 4.2.2  Page 32

(1)  (a) 0  (b) 1
(c) 2  (d) 2
(2)  (a) $\lambda \le \frac{1}{3}$  (b) $\lambda \ge -2\frac{1}{4}$
(c) $\lambda \ge 4$ or $\lambda \le -4$  (d) $-\sqrt{\frac{1}{8}} \le \lambda \le \sqrt{\frac{1}{8}}$
(4)  $k = -2$  (6) $\lambda \le -\sqrt{\frac{1}{3}}$ or $\lambda \ge \sqrt{\frac{1}{3}}$
(7)  $\pm\sqrt{8}$  (8) $\pm\sqrt{12}$
(9)  $\pm\sqrt{15}$  (10) $\pm\sqrt{15}$


## Exercises 4.3.2  Page 34

(1)  (a) $1\frac{1}{2}$, $2\frac{1}{2}$  (b) 0, 3
(c) $-5$, 1  (d) $-\frac{1}{3}$, $-1\frac{1}{3}$
(2)  (c) $-0.209$, $-4.791$  (d) 1, $-1\frac{1}{3}$
(3)  (a) $x^2 - 3x + 2 = 0$  (b) $x^2 - 1\frac{1}{2}x - 13\frac{1}{2} = 0$
(c) $x^2 - (k + 1/k)x + 1 = 0$  (d) $x^2 - 4x + 1$
(4)  (a) $-27/4$  (b) $-1/7$
(c) $-27/14$  (d) $-7/4$
(5)  (a) $b^2/a^2 - 2c/a$  (b) $-b/c$
(c) $(b^2 - 2ac)/ca$  (d) $-bc/a^2$
(e) $(3abc - b^3)/a^3$  (f) $b^2/a^2 - 4c/a$
(6)  (a) $cy^2 + by + a = 0$  (b) $ay^2 + (b - 2a)y + a + c - b = 0$
(c) $y^2 - (3abc - b^3)y/a^3$  (d) $y^2 + bcy/a^2 + c^3/a^3 = 0$
$+c^3/a^3 = 0$
(e) $y^2 - b^2/a^2 + 4c/a = 0$
(f) $y^2 + (4 - 2c/a + b/a)y + c^2/a^2$
$- 3c/a - bc/a^2 + 2b/a + 4 = 0$
(7)  $\frac{3}{4}$  (8) 8
(9)  $2b^2 = 9c$

# Chapter 5

## Exercises 5.1.2 **Page 39**

(1)  $x > 1$
(2)  $x \le -\frac{1}{2}$
(3)  $x < 5/3$
(4)  $x \le -9/4$
(5)  $-6 < x < -2$
(6)  $x < -3$ or $x > 6$
(7)  all $x$
(8)  $-2.3 \le x \le 1.3$
(9)  $-2 < x < 1$
(10) $x < -5$ or $x > 7$
(11) $x < -3$ or $-2 < x < -1$
(12) $x < \frac{1}{2}$ or $1\frac{1}{2} < x < 3$
(13) $x \le 1$
(14) $x > -\frac{1}{2}$, $x \ne 0$
(15) $-\frac{1}{2} < x < \frac{1}{2}$
(16) $x < -5$ or $x > -1$
(17) $x \le -\frac{1}{2}$
(18) $x \le -1$ or $x \ge \frac{1}{3}$
(19) $x < -3$ or $-2 < x < 1$
(20) $-3 < x < -2$, $-2 < x < \frac{1}{2}$
(21) $x < -5$ or $0 < x < 2$
(22) $\frac{1}{2} < x < 2$
(23) $x < -6$ or $0 < x < 6$
(24) $x < 0$
(25) $x < 0$
(26) $x > 0$
(27) $-\frac{1}{3} \le x \le 1$
(28) $x \ge 2$ or $x \le -2$

## Exercises 5.2.2 **Page 40**

(4)  (a) 6  (b) 4
(5) (a) $3\frac{1}{9}$  (b) 4
(6)  (a) 4  (b) $-1\frac{1}{2}$
(7) (a) $-1.75$ to $3.2$  (b) $-1.4$ to $3$

# Chapter 6

## Exercises 6.1.2 **Page 45**

(1)  (a) 4
     (b) 1000
     (c) 16
     (d) 16
     (e) 25
     (f) 3
(2)  (a) $x^{-4}$
     (b) $y^3$
     (c) $5^{9x}$
     (d) $2^{20n}$
(3)  (a) $4 = \log_2 16$
     (b) $3 = \log_{10} 1000$
     (c) $1\frac{1}{2} = \log_9 27$
     (d) $-\frac{1}{2} = \log_{25} \frac{1}{5}$
     (e) $\ln 7.34 = 2$
     (f) $\ln 10 = 2.0258$
(4)  (a) $2^3 = 8$
     (b) $9^{\frac{1}{2}} = 3$
     (c) $10^{-1} = 0.1$
     (d) $16^{\frac{3}{4}} = 8$
     (e) $e^{1.792} = 6$
     (f) $e^{2.5} = 12.18$
(5)  (a) 4
     (b) 3
     (c) $\frac{1}{2}$
     (d) $-3$
     (e) $-3$
     (f) 1
     (g) 2
     (h) $-\frac{1}{2}$

(6)   (a) 1.585                 (b) 1.585

      (c) 0.431                (d) $-5.657$

(7)   (a) $\log 2x$            (b) $\log_2 \frac{1}{3}$

      (c) $\log_2 x^4$           (d) $\log 9x^3$

      (e) $\log 10x$          (f) $\log_2 4x$

(8)   (a) 1.585                 (b) 0.778

      (c) 0.262                (d) $\frac{3}{8}$

      (e) 1 or 1.585        f) 3.15

      (g) 0.672               (h) 0.898

      (i) 1.609 or 0.693      (j) $\pm 1.317$

(9)   (a) $y = 10^{1000 - \log x}$     (b) $y = {}^3\sqrt{x}$

(10)  (a) 128                  (b) 2 or $-3$

      (c) 200/99               (d) 15.59

      (e) 81                   (f) 1.3195

      (g) 20.09                (h) 0.135

(11) 22.5 years           (12) 5.93 years

(13) 3.1 years            (14) 0.083, 26.6 years

## Chapter 7

### Exercises 7.1.2 Page 51

(1)   (a) 6.32     (b) 5.39     (c) 3.61     (d) 11.7

      (e) 5        (f) 7.62

(3)   6.5

(4)   (a) (3, 4)     (b) $(1, 2\frac{1}{2})$     (c) $(3, 7\frac{1}{2})$     (d) $(0, 2\frac{1}{2})$

      (e) $(-1, -3\frac{1}{2})$   (f) $(-1\frac{1}{2}, -4\frac{1}{2})$

(5)   (a) $(1\frac{1}{4}, 4)$     (b) (3.2, 7.6)     (c) (1.4, 4.4)     (d) (8/11, $-39/11$)

    (7) No.   (10) $(\frac{1}{2}(x_2 + x_3), \frac{1}{2}(y_2 + y_3))$, $(\frac{1}{3}(x_1 + x_2 + x_3), \frac{1}{3}(y_1 + y_2 + y_3))$

### Exercises 7.2.2 Page 53

(1)   (a) $y = 4x - 3$     (b) $3y = x + 10$     (c) $y = -2x + 7$

      (d) $4y + 3x = 30$     (e) $y = 2x - 2$     (f) $2y = x$

      (g) $y = -3x + 8$     (h) $4y + 3x = -9$     (i) $y = 4x - 5$

      (j) $y = 3 - x$     (k) $y = 12 - x$     (l) $2y + x = -4$

(2)   (a) 1.66         (b) 7.07         (c) 1.34

      (d) 0.277

(5)   No                        (6) (2,2), $\sqrt{5}$

(7) $y = 4x - 5, 3y = 4x - 7, y = 3 : 4y + x = 16, 4y + 3x = 18, x = 1.$

Meet at $(1, 3\frac{3}{4})$     (8) $y = 2x + 1$

## Exercises 7.3.2 **Page 55**

(1)  (a) $(x-1)^2 + (y-2)^2 = 25$     (b) $(x-1)^2 + (y+3)^2 = 64$
(2)  (a) $(-2,1), \sqrt{8}$     (b) $(1\frac{1}{2}, \frac{1}{2}), \sqrt{1\frac{1}{2}}$
     (c) $(0,3), \sqrt{7}$     (d) $(-1\frac{1}{2}, 0), 1\frac{1}{2}$
(3)  $(x-1)^2 + (y-3)^2 = 17$     (4) $(x+1)^2 + (y-5)^2 = 5$
(5)  $0.6, (x-1)^2 + (y+1)^2 = 0.6^2$     (6) $(x-2)^2 + (y-3)^2 = 0.4$
(7)  $y = x$     (8) $(1,0)$ & $(2,0)$. $2y = x - 1, 2y = 2 - x$
(9)  $(-1,-1)$ & $(-\frac{1}{2}, -\frac{1}{2}).2y = x - 1,$ (10) $(4,-12), \sqrt{40}$
     $y = 2x + \frac{1}{2}$
(11) $(x-3)^2 + (y-3)^2 = 9$     (12) $(3,1), \sqrt{17}$
(13) $(3,1), \sqrt{33}$     (14) 5, outside, 4.
(15) $m = 5/12$     (16) $k = -2 \pm \sqrt{14}$

## Exercises 7.4.2 **Page 57**

(1)  (a) $x^3 = y^2$     (b) $xy = 5$
     (c) $y = 3x - 5$     (d) $y + 1 = (\frac{1}{2}x)^2$
     (e) $xy^3 = 1$     (f) $x = (1/y - 1)^2$
     (g) $x^2 - y^2 = 1$     (h) $x + 2y = 1$
(2)  $pqy + 3x = 3(p+q)$
(3)  $4y = (p+2)x - 8p, \ y = x - 4$     (4) $(\frac{1}{2},0), \frac{1}{2}$

## Chapter 8

## Exercises 8.1.2 **Page 62**

(1)  (a) 52     (b) 50
     (c) $7 - 15x$     (d) $(2 - x)/5$
(2)  (a) $-17$     (b) $-7$
     (c) $6x - 5$     (d) $6x + 5$
     (e) $(x - 3)/2$     (f) $(x + 4)/3$
     (g) $(x + 5)/6$     (h) $(x - 5)/6$
     (i) $(x - 5)/6$     (j) $(x + 5)/6$
(4)  $\{y : y \geq 7\}$     (5) $(x - 2)/5$. Dom. $\{x : x \geq 7\}$,
     Range $\{y : y \geq 1\}$

513

(6)    (a) $\{-1 \le x \le 1\}$        (b) $\{x : x \ge 0)$
      (c) $\{2 \le x \le 4\}$         (d) $\{x > 0\}$
      (e) $\{-3 \le x \le 1\}$       (f) $\{5 \le x\}$
      (g) $\{-3 \le x\}$          (h) all $x$.

(7)    (a) No. restrict to $\{x \ge 0\}$     (b) yes. $(x+4)/3$
      (c) yes. $\sqrt[3]{x}$                (d) no. $\{-180° \le x \le 180°\}$
      (e) no. $\{x \ge 1\}$            (f) yes. $\sqrt[3]{x} - 1$.

## Exercises 8.2.2 **Page 67**

(3)    (a) $x = 0$, $y = 0$      (b) $x = 1$, $y = 0$      (c) $x = 1$, $y = 0$
      (d) $x = 0$, $y = 3$      (e) $x = -3$, $y = 2$     (f) $x = -2$, $y = 1$

(4)    inverses of each other.

(6)    (a) $x = 0$            (b) $x = 0$             (c) $x = 2$
      (d) $x = -2$        (e) $x = 1\frac{1}{2}$         (f) $x = -1/6$

(7)    (a) $b = 0$, $c = 1$      (b) $b = -2$, $c = 0$      (c) $b = 2$, $c = 1$

(8)    (a) $b = 2$, $c = 1$      (b) $b = 0$, $c = -1$      (c) $b = -2$, $c = 0$

(9)    (a) $b = 0$, $a = 1$      (b) $a = 0$, $b = -2$      (c) $a = -1$, $b = 1$

(11)   (a) $x = 0$, $y = 1$      (b) $y = 0$, $x = 2$      (c) $x = -1$, $y = -1$

(12)   0.47                                   (13) $-0.39$

(14)   90°, 270°, 30°, 150°              (15) 51°

(16)   (a) 27°, 207°                   (b) 0.44
      (c) 66°                            (d) 0°, 60°

(17)   (a) even    (b) odd      (c) odd, periodic,
                                  period 360°.

      (d) even, periodic, 360°(e) odd         (f) even, periodic, 180°

      (h) odd, periodic, 180° (j) odd, periodic, 60°

      (k) odd, periodic, 720° (l) periodic, 180°

## Chapter 9

## Exercises 9.1.2 **Page 75**

(1)    (a) 11.3                       (b) 9.43

(2)    (a) 50.5                       (b) 4.85

(3)    (a) 136.5°                   (b) 129°

(4)    (a) 44.4° or 135.6°        (b) 124.5° or 5.47°.

(5)    4.22 & 3.60               (6) $\hat{A} = 70.7°$ or 109.3°, $\hat{B} = 55.3°$
                                            or 16.7°

(7)   2807 m

(8) 29.8 km

(9)   54 m

(10) 075° or 174°. 3.03 km
or 0.25 km

(11) (a) 3.88

(b) 7.30

(12) (a) 46.6°

(b) 134.6°

(13) 65.6°, 63.0°, 51.3°

(14) 25.1

(15) 81.8 miles

(16) 5.35 km

(17) 12.6 cm

(18) 126.6°,  6.89

(19) 6.4°

(20) (a) 76°

(b) 92.8°

(21) (a) 3.86

(b) 80.3

(22) 33.8°

(23) 36.9°

(24) 4.25

(25) 27.9° or 7.29

(26) 45.5

(28) 14.4 cm

## Exercises 9.2.2 Page 79

| | | | | |
|---|---|---|---|---|
| (1) | (a) 45° | (b) 90° | (c) 60° | (d) 54.7° |
| (2) | (a) 45° | (b) 45° | (c) 35.3° | (d) 0° |
| (3) | (a) 45° | (b) 54.7° | (c) 35.3° | (d) 90° |
| (4) | (a) 71° | (b) 61.5° | (c) 34.9° | (d) 81.2° |
| (5) | (a) 38.9° | (b) 70.5° | (c) 61.9° | (d) 69.3° |
| (6) | (a) 45° | **(b) 47.1°** | (c) 15.8° | (d) 21.8° |
| (7) | (a) 54.7° | (b) 70.5° | | |

## Chapter 10

### Exercises 10.1.2 Page 83

(2)   5/3, 4/5, 3/4

(3) $\sqrt{5}$, $1/\sqrt{5}$, $2/\sqrt{5}$

(4)   $(1 - t^2)/(1 + t^2)$, $2t/(1 - t^2)$

(5)   (a) $\sin^2 x$

(b) $2 \sec^2 x$

(c) $\cos x \sin x$

(d) $\sin x \cos x$

(7)   (a) $x^2 + y^2 = 9$

(b) $x^2/4 + y^2/9 = 1$

(c) $y^2 - x^2 = 1$

(d) $y^2/4 - 4x^2 = 1$

(e) $(x - 1)^2 + (y - 2)^2 = 1$

(f) $((x - 3)/2)^2 + ((y - 2)/3)^2 = 1$

(g) $x^2 + y^2 = 2$

(h) $xy = 1$

### Exercises 10.2.2 Page 85

(1)   (a) $\sin 24°$

(b) $- \cos 40°$

(c) $- \tan 35°$

(d) $- \cot 50°$

(2)　(a) 35°, 325°　　　　　　　　　(b) 36°, 126°, 216°, 306°
　　　(c) 103°, 317°　　　　　　　　(d) 86°, 314°
　　　(e) 76°, 284°　　　　　　　　　(f) 92°, 188°
　　　(g) 44°　　　　　　　　　　　　(h) 215°
　　　(i) 24°, 216°　　　　　　　　　(j) 168°, 348°
(3)　143°　　　　　　　　　　　　　　(4) 247°
(5)　−15/17　　　　　　　　　　　　　(6) 25/7
(7)　(a) 45°, 135°　　　　(b) 60°, 120°　　　　(c) 55°, 125°
　　　(d) 55°, 125°　　　　(e) 79°　　　　　　　(f) 0°, 180°
　　　(g) 60°, 71°　　　　　(h) 60°　　　　　　　(i) 45°

## Exercises 10.3.2  Page 86

(1)　(a) $\sin 20°$　　　　　　　(b) $\cos 20°$　　　　　(c) $- \cot 40°$
　　　(d) $- \sec 70°$　　　　　(e) $\tan 20°$　　　　　(f) $- \operatorname{cosec} 80°$
(2)　(a) $60° + n360°$, $300 + n360°$　　　　(b) $45° + n180°$
　　　(c) $90° + n360°$
(3)　(a) $33° + n180°$, $147° + n180°$　　　　(b) $10° + n120°$, $50° + n120°$
　　　(c) $5° + n90°$　　　　　　　　　　　　　(d) $k + n360°$, $180° - k + n360°$
　　　(e) $k/2 + n180°$, $180° - k/2 + n180°$　　　　(f) $k/2 + 15° + n90°$

## Exercises 10.4.2  Page 88

(1)　(a) $\sin 40°$　　　　　　　　　(b) $\cos 20°$
　　　(c) $- \sin A$　　　　　　　　　(d) $\cos 4A$
(2)　(a) $\frac{1}{2} \sin 80°$　　　　　　　(b) $\tan 40°$
(3)　(a) $\sin(\theta + \alpha)$　　　　　　(b) $\cos(\theta - \alpha)$
(4)　(a) $1/\sqrt{2}(\frac{1}{2}\sqrt{3} + \frac{1}{2})$　　　(b) $1/\sqrt{2}(\frac{1}{2}\sqrt{3} - \frac{1}{2})$
　　　(c) $1/\sqrt{2}(\frac{1}{2}\sqrt{3} - \frac{1}{2})$　　　(d) $(\sqrt{3} - 1)/(\sqrt{3} + 1)$
　　　(e) $\sqrt{(\frac{1}{2}(1/\sqrt{2} + 1))}$　　　(f) $\sqrt{2} - 1$
(5)　$\frac{1}{2}$
(6)　(a) 56/65　　　　　　　　　　　(b) 16/65
　　　(c) 63/65　　　　　　　　　　　(d) 56/33
(7)　(a) 0°, 180° 32°　　　　　　　　(b) 39°
　　　(c) all angles　　　　　　　　　(d) 45°
　　　(e) 0°, 180°, 30°, 150°　　　　(f) no solutions
(10) (a) 65°, 175°　　　　　　　　　(b) 90°, 45°, 135°
　　　(c) 45°, 135°, 10°, 50°,　　　 (d) 75°
　　　130°, 170°
　　　(e) 60°, 120°　　　　　　　　　(f) 90°, $22\frac{1}{2}°$, $112\frac{1}{2}°$
(11) $4 \cos^3 A - 3 \cos A$　　　　　　(12) $3 \sin A - 4 \sin^3 A$

## Exercises 10.5.2 Page 90

(1)  (a) 5, 53.1°     (b) $\sqrt{41}$, $-51°$    (c) $\sqrt{45}$, 117°
    (d) $\sqrt{2}$, $-45°$    (b) $\sqrt{(5/16)}$, 27°    (f) $\sqrt{(145/64)}$, $-5°$

(2)  (a) 5, 37°    (b) $\sqrt{41}$, 141°    (c) $\sqrt{45}$, $-27°$
    (d) $\sqrt{2}$, 135°    (e) $\sqrt{(5/16)}$, 63°    (f) $\sqrt{(145/64)}$, 95°

(3)  (a) $-5 < f < 5$    (b) $-\sqrt{41} < f < \sqrt{41}$   (c) $-\sqrt{45} < f < \sqrt{45}$
    (d) $-\sqrt{2} < f < \sqrt{2}$    (e) $-0.559 < f < 0.559$ (f) $-1.5052 < f < 1.5052$

(4)  (a) $-40°$, 108°    (b) 79°, $-157°$
    (c) 9°, 73°                        (d) 96°, 170°

(5) $r = 5, \alpha = 53.1°$. $s = 5$, $\beta = 36.9°$. $x = -23°$, 97°.

## Chapter 11

## Exercises 11.1.2 Page 94

(1)  (a) $\pi$                         (b) $\pi/3$
    (c) $4\pi/3$                     (d) $\pi/6$
    (e) $\pi/18$

(2)  (a) 60°                      (b) 74.5°
    (c) 212°                     (d) 720°
    (e) 45°

(3)  5.24                       (4) 191

(5)  $1.75 \times 10^{-3}$, $1.45 \times 10^{-4}$

(6)  70 m/s                  (7) 8.9

(8)  (a) $7.27 \times 10^{-5}$        (b) $1.99 \times 10^{-7}$

(9)  2 cm, 5 cm$^2$           (10) 1/5

(11) 4.55 cm              (12) 13.1, 439

(13) 45.3                   (14) $\frac{1}{2}$ ra

(15) (a) 0.201, 2.940        (b) 1.982, 4.301
    (c) 1.107, 4.249        (d) 2.034, 5.176
    (e) 0, $\pi$, $\frac{3}{4}\pi$, $1\frac{3}{4}\pi$      (f) 0.685, 2.457, 3.826, 5.598
    (g) 1.994, 5.336        (h) 0.507, 3.649
    (i) $\frac{1}{2}\pi$, 6.12, 3.31

## Exercises 11.2.2 Page 95

(1)  (a) 1                        (b) 2
    (c) $\frac{1}{2}$                      (d) $\frac{1}{2}$
    (e) 4/9                   (f) $(1 + \theta)/(1 - \theta)$
    (g) $(1 + 2\theta)/(1 - 2\theta)$

(2)  2                        (3) $\frac{1}{2} + \frac{1}{2}\sqrt{3}\theta$

(4)  $-\frac{1}{2}\sqrt{3}$             (5) $1 - \frac{1}{2}(\pi/90)^2$

## Chapter 12

### Exercises 12.1.2 Page 100

(1)  $a, c$

(2)  (a) 5

(c) $\sqrt{10}$

(b) $\sqrt{54}$

(d) $\sqrt{19\frac{1}{4}}$

(3)  (a) (1,2)

(c) $(p - x, \; q - y)$

(b) $(-1, \; -5, \; -1)$

(d) $(1 - x, \; 2y - 3, \; z)$

(4)  $\frac{1}{2}(\mathbf{b} - \mathbf{a})$

(6) $\mathbf{a} + \mathbf{c}, \; \frac{1}{2}(\mathbf{a} + \mathbf{c})$

(7) $\frac{1}{2}(\mathbf{a}+\mathbf{b})$, $\frac{1}{2}(\mathbf{b}+\mathbf{c})$, $\frac{1}{2}(\mathbf{c}+\mathbf{d})$, $\frac{1}{2}(\mathbf{d}+\mathbf{a})$. $\frac{1}{2}(\mathbf{c}-\mathbf{a})$, $\frac{1}{2}(\mathbf{d}-\mathbf{b})$, $\frac{1}{2}(\mathbf{c}-\mathbf{a})$, $\frac{1}{2}(\mathbf{d}-\mathbf{b})$

Parallelogram.

(8)  $\frac{1}{2}(\mathbf{b}+\mathbf{c})$

(9) $2\mathbf{a}-\mathbf{b}$

(10) 0.6

(11) $\mathbf{b}$, $\mathbf{a} - \mathbf{b}$, $-\mathbf{b}$, $2\mathbf{a} - 2\mathbf{b}$

### Exercises 12.2.2 Page 102

(1)  (a) 11

(c) 9

(b) 18

(d) $-7$

(2)  (a) 10.3°

(c) 47.9°

(b) 55.3°

(d) 112.4°

(3)  $-1$

(4) $(7, -2)$

(5)  $(24/25, -7/25)$

(6)  $x = -9/5, \; y = -5.1$

(7) $(3, -4, -1)$

(8)  $(1/\sqrt{2}, -1/\sqrt{2}, 0)$

(9) $\sqrt{10}$

(10) $3/\sqrt{10}$

(16) $(-0.72, 0.96)$, 1.2

(17) $(-2.8, -0.6)$, 8.

### 13.1.2 Page 108

(1)  (a) $3x^2$

(d) $-2 + 20x^4$

(g) $2x^{-\frac{1}{2}}$

(j) $-2x^{-2} + 24x^{-4}$

(m) $10x^4 + 30x^{-7} - 7x^{-1\frac{1}{4}}/4$

(b) $35x^4$

(e) $-6x^{-4}$

(h) $-9x^{-4} - x^{-1\frac{1}{2}}$

(k) $\frac{1}{2}x^{-\frac{1}{2}}$

(c) $6x + 2$

(f) $2 + 12x^{-5}$

(i) $-21x^{-4}$

(l) $1\frac{1}{2}x^{-\frac{1}{2}} + 3\frac{1}{2}x^{-1\frac{1}{2}}$

(n) $-x^{-1\frac{1}{2}} + 9x^{-2}$

(2)    (a) $2x - 3$      (b) $2x - 5$      (c) $-15x^4 + 6x^2 - 24x$

      (d) $2 - 6x^{-3} - 9x^{-4}$    (e) $2x + 4$      (f) $24x + 16x^3$

      (g) $-12x^{-2} - 18x^{-3}$    (h) $18x - 32x^{-3}$    (i) $1\frac{1}{2}x^{\frac{1}{2}} - 2x^{-\frac{1}{2}}$

      (j) $1 - \frac{1}{2}x^{-\frac{1}{2}}$      (k) $-3x^{-4} - 68x^{-5}$    (l) $2 - x^{-2}$

      (m) $\frac{1}{2}x^{-\frac{1}{2}} - 4x^{-1\frac{1}{2}}$                    (n) $-x^{\frac{-7}{6}}/6 + \frac{1}{4}x^{-1\frac{1}{4}} - 1\frac{1}{2}x^{-1\frac{1}{2}}$

(3) (a) $6x$                                    (b) 4

      (c) $12x^2 - 24x$                    (d) $-\frac{3}{4}x^{-1\frac{1}{2}} - 12x^{-4}$

## 13.2.2 Page 109

(1)    (a) $y = 4x - 4$                 (b) $y = x - 2$

      (c) $y = -13x - 1$            (d) $y = \frac{1}{8}x$

(2)    (a) $y = -\frac{1}{4}x + 4\frac{1}{2}$        (b) $y = -x$

      (c) $13y = x + 157$           (d) $y = -8x + 32\frac{1}{2}$

(3)    $x = -\frac{2}{3}$        (4) $\pm\sqrt{\frac{1}{3}}$         (6) $7\frac{1}{4}$

## 13.3.2 Page 111

(1)    (a) $(1,-1)$ min               (b) $(2,6)$ max

      (c) $(1,-2)$ min, $(-1,2)$ max      (d) $(2,24)$ max, $(3,23)$ min

      (e) $(1,2)$ min, $(-1,-2)$ max      (f) $(2,3)$ min

(2)    6                                    (3) a $= -\frac{3}{4}$, b $= 3$

(4)    11.7 cm          (5) 12.6 cm       (6) 10 cm

(7)    4.3 cm           (8) 7.69 cm      (9) 25 m by 50 m

(11) 7 cm                              (12) $(0, 2-m)$, $(1 - 2/m, 0)$,

                                                $m = \pm 2$

# Chapter 14

## 14.1.2 Page 116

(1)    (a) $(x^2 + 7x - 3) + x(2x + 7)$      (b) $(2x^3 + 6x) + (x + 3)(6x^2 + 6)$

      (c) $2x(3x^5 - 3x^2 + x) + x^2(15x^4$    (d) $2x(x^2 + 1) + 2x(x^2 - 1)$

      $-6x + 1)$

(2)    (a) $((x + 3) - x)/(x + 3)^2$       (b) $((2x + 7)(x^2 + 3) - 2x(x^2 + 7x - 2))$

                                         $/(x^2 + 3)^2$

      (c) $(6x(x - 17) - 3x^2)/(x - 17)^2$    (d) $-1/(x + 3)^2$

(3)    $y = 4$

(4)    (a) $(0,0)$ max, $(2,4)$ min        (b) $(0.414,0.828)$ min,

                                         $(-2.414,-4.828)$ max

      (c) $(0,1)$ max                   (d) $(-2, 1/5)$ max

Solutions

## 14.2.2 Page 117

(1) (a) $1\frac{1}{2}(3x+7)^{-\frac{1}{2}}$ (b) $-10x(2-x^2)^4$
(c) $2x(1+2x^2)^{-\frac{1}{2}}$ (d) $-\frac{1}{2}(1+x)^{-1\frac{1}{2}}$
(e) $\frac{1}{2}(2x+1)(1+x+x^2)^{-\frac{1}{2}}$ (f) $200x(1+x^2)^{99}$
(2) (a) $(1+2x)^{\frac{1}{2}}+x(1+2x)^{-\frac{1}{2}}$ (b) $(x-17)^{21}+21(x+3)(x-17)^{20}$
(c) $(\sqrt{(x^2+1)}-x(x+4)(x^2+1)^{-\frac{1}{2}})/(x^2+1)$
(d) $(\frac{1}{2}x^{-\frac{1}{2}}(\sqrt{x}+1)-\frac{1}{2})/(\sqrt{x}+1)^2$

## 14.3.2 Page 118

(1) (a) $3\cos 3x$ (b) $-4\sin 4x$ (c) $2e^{2x-1}$
(d) $5\sec^2(5x-3)$ (e) $-15\cos 3x-8\cos 4x$
(f) $-\sin x e^{\cos x}$ (g) $2/(2x-3)$ (h) $-\tan x$
(i) $\cos x - x\sin x$ (j) $2x\sin x + x^2\cos x$
(k) $e^x(\tan x + \sec^2 x)$ (l) $\ln x + 1$
(m) $e^x\ln x + e^x/x$ (n) $-e^{-x}\sin 2x + 2e^{-x}\cos 2x$

(o) $-3\sin 3x\sin 2x + 2\cos 3x\cos 2x$ (p) $-2x\sin(1+x^2)$
(q) $\sin(1+3x^2)+6x^2\cos(1+3x^2)$ (r) $-2\cos x\sin x$
(s) $9\cos 3x\sin^2 3x$ (t) $(\cos x + x\sin x)/\cos^2 x$
(u) $(2x(\cos x +\sin x) - x^2(\cos x - \sin x))$
(v) $(-2\cos x\sin x\ln x - (\cos^2 x)/x)/(\ln x)^2$
(w) $-x(x^2+3)^{-\frac{1}{2}}\sin\sqrt{(x^2+3)}$
(x) $-2e^x\sin x$
(y) $0$ (z) $1$
(3) $-\text{cosec }^2 x,\ \sec x$
   $\tan x, -\cot x$ $\text{cosec } x$
(4) $(\ln 10)10^x$ (5) $1/(x\ln 10)$ (6) $(\ln a)a^x, 1/(x\ln a)$

520

**14.4.2 Page 120**

(1) (a) $-\frac{1}{2}$      (b) $\frac{1}{2}$      (c) $-\frac{1}{4}$

     (d) $\infty$      (e) 3      (f) $-1\frac{1}{3}$

     (g) $-\frac{1}{2}$      (h) -10

(2) (a) $-x/y$      (b) $(3 - 2x)/(3y^2 + 1)$

     (c) $(2x + 4y)/(2y - 4x)$      (d) $-(2x + 9yx^2)/(3x^2 + 4)$

(4) $y = 1\frac{1}{4}x - \frac{1}{4}$      (5) $\pm 2/\sqrt{3}$

(6) $\pm 2/\sqrt{3}$

(7) (a) 3t      (b) $-2t(1 + t)^2$

     (c) $(2t - 3t^2)/(1 + 4t)$      (d) $(2t(1 + t)^2)/(1 + t^2)^2$

     (e) $1/t$      (f) $-1/t^2$      (g) $-\cot t$

     (h) $-\frac{2}{3}\cot t$      (i) $(e^t + e^{-t})/(e^t - e^{-t})$ (j) $1\frac{1}{2}\sin t$

(8) $3y + 4x = 12\sqrt{2}$      (9) $3y + x = 26$

(10) $0.4 \text{ cm}^2$      (11) $0.27 \text{ cm}^3$      (12) $3.2 \times 10^{-4}$

(13) $95 \text{ cm}^3$      (14) $8.6 \times 10^{-3}$, 0.58

(15) 2%      (16) 2%      (17) $15 \text{ cm}^2/s$

(18) $3 \text{ cm}^2/s$, $9 \text{ cm}^3/s$      (19) 0.07 cm/s      (20) 0.014 cm/s

(21) $\frac{1}{16}$ cm/s, $3 \text{ cm}^2/s$      (22) 0.293 m/s

# Chapter 15

**15.1.2 Page 127**

(1) (a) $y = x^2 + 1$      (b) $y = x^3 + \frac{1}{2}x^2 - \frac{1}{2}$

     (c) $y = \frac{1}{3}x^3 + \frac{1}{2}x^2 + x + 7/6$      (d) $y = 2 - 1/x$

     (e) $y = x^{2\frac{1}{2}}/2\frac{1}{2} - 11.8$      (f) $y = 6\sqrt{x} - 20$

     (g) $y = \frac{1}{4}x^4 + \frac{1}{2}x^2 - \frac{3}{4}$      (h) $y = x^{2\frac{1}{2}}/2\frac{1}{2} + 6\sqrt{x} - 21.8$

(2) (a) $x^2 + c$      (b) $x^3 + x^2 + x + c$

     (c) $\frac{1}{3}x^3 + \frac{1}{2}x^4 + 5x + c$      (d) $\frac{1}{3}x^6 - 5/16x^8 + c$

     (e) $x^{2\frac{1}{2}}/2\frac{1}{2} + c$      (f) $3x - x^{1\frac{1}{2}}/1\frac{1}{2} + c$

     (g) $c - 1/2x^{-2}$      (h) $-2/x - 3\frac{1}{2}/x^2 + 2x + c$

     (i) $\frac{3}{4}x^4 + 3\frac{1}{2}x^2 + c$      (j) $\frac{1}{4}x^4 - \frac{1}{3}x^3 - 3x^2 + c$

     (k) $x^4 - 2x^5/5 + c$      (l) $x^{5\frac{1}{2}}/5\frac{1}{2} + x^{4\frac{1}{2}}/4\frac{1}{2} - 2x^{1\frac{1}{2}} - 6x^{\frac{1}{2}} + c$

**15.2.2 Page 129**

(1) (a) 36      (b) 0.283      (c) $14\frac{2}{3}$

     (d) $43\frac{1}{2}$      (e) 10.4      (f) 45.43

(2) (a) $8\frac{2}{3}$      (b) 0.95      (c) 6

     (d) $-\frac{1}{4}$

(3)  $10\frac{2}{3}$

(4) (a) $\frac{1}{4}$  (b) $-\frac{1}{4}$

(5) (a) 1/6  (b) 7/6

(6)  12

(7) 0.15625, -32.15625

(8)  (a) 64

(b) 1.5

(c) $5\frac{1}{3}$

(d) 4

(9) 4/15

## 15.3.2 Page 130

(1)  (a) 175.3

(b) 14.1

(c) 2.83

(d)  64.9

(e) 490

(f) 37.7

(2)  4, 12, 603

(4) Sphere.  4.189

(5)  $y = x + 1,\ 27.2$

(6) $2\frac{2}{3}a^2, 2\pi a^3$

## Chapter 16

### 16.1.2 Page 135

(1)  (a) $-\frac{1}{2}\cos 2x + c$

(b) $2\sin\frac{1}{2}x + c$

(c) $-\frac{1}{3}\cos(3x - 1) + c$

(d) $2\sin(2x + 3) + c$

(e) $\frac{1}{3}e^{3x} + c$

(f) $\frac{1}{2}e^{2x+1} + c$

(g) $\ln(x + 3) + c$

(h) $\frac{1}{2}\ln(2x - 5) + c$

(2)  1/5

(3) 23

(4) 3.37

(5) 25.9

(6) 0.649

(7) $\frac{1}{2}\ln(1+a)$

(8)  0.693

(9) 0.847

(10)  $(2/9)(x^3 + 4)^{1\frac{1}{2}} + c$

(11) $2\sin\sqrt{x} + c$

(12)  $\frac{1}{4}\tan^4 x + c$

(13) $\ln(\ln x) + c$

(14)  $0.4(x + 3)^{2\frac{1}{2}} - 2(x + 3)^{1\frac{1}{2}} + c$

(15) $(4/27)(1 + 3x)^{1\frac{1}{2}}$
$-(4/9)(1 + 3x)^{\frac{1}{2}} + c$

(16)  $(2/7)(1 + x)^{3\frac{1}{2}} - 0.8(1 + x)^{2\frac{1}{2}} + c$

(17) $-(1/6)/(3x - 1)^2 + c$

(18)  $(1 + 4x)^{16}/256-$
$(1 + 4x)^{15}/240 + c$

(19)  $(x + 2)^{14}/14 - (5/13)(x + 2)^{13} + c$

(20) $\sin x - \frac{1}{3}\sin^3 x + c$

(21)  $-\cos x + \frac{2}{3}\cos^3 x-$
$0.2\cos^5 x + c$

(22) $\ln(1 - e^{-x}) + c$

(23)  $\frac{1}{2}x + \frac{1}{4}\sin 2x + c$

(24) $\frac{1}{2}x - \frac{1}{12}\sin 6x + c$

(25)  $1/(1 + x) - 1/(2 + x).\ \ln(1 + x) - \ln(2 + x) + c$

(26)  (a) $\ln(3 + x) + \ln(2 + x) + c$

(b) $1/2 \ln(1 + 2x) - 1/3 \ln(1 - 3x) + c$

(c) $2\ln(2 + x) - 2\ln(1 + x) - 3/(1 + x) + c$

**16.2.2 Page 137**

(1) 0.730

(2) $2\frac{1}{2}\pi$

(3) $\pi$

(4) 0.927

(5) $3\sin^{-1}\frac{1}{3}x + c$

(6) $\frac{1}{6}\tan^{-1}1\frac{1}{2}x + c$

(7) $\sin^{-1}(x+1) + c$

(8) $\frac{1}{2}\tan^{-1}\frac{1}{2}(x-3) + c$

(9) $\frac{3}{2}\sin^{-1}(x+\frac{1}{2}) + c$

(10) $\frac{7}{12}\tan^{-1}1\frac{1}{3}(x-3) + c$

(11) $\ln x + 1/2 \tan^{-1}x/2 + c$

**16.3.2 Page 138**

(1) $-xe^{-x} - e^{-x} + c$

(2) $x\sin x + \cos x + c$

(3) $-x\cos x + \sin x + c$

(4) $\frac{1}{2}x^2\ln x - \frac{1}{4}x^2 + c$

(5) $\frac{1}{3}x^3\ln x - x^3/9 + c$

(6) $x^{n+1}/(n+1)\ln x - x^{n+1}/(n+1)^2 + c$

(7) $x\sin^{-1}x + \sqrt{(1-x^2)} + c$

(8) $x\tan^{-1}x - \frac{1}{2}\ln(1+x^2) + c$

(9) $x^2e^x - 2xe^x + 2e^x + c$

(10) $x^2e^{ax}/a - 2xe^{ax}/a^2 + 2e^{ax}/a^3 + c$

(11) $\frac{1}{3}x^2\sin 3x + 2x/9\cos 3x - \frac{2}{27}\sin 3x + c$

(12) $xe^x - 4e^x + c$

(13) $-x^2/a\cos ax + 2x/a^2\sin ax + 2/a^3\cos ax + c$

(14) $-\ln(x)/x - 1/x + c$

**Chapter 17**

**17.1.2 Page 145**

(1) -0.2

(2) -0.166796

(3) $2, 3, 2\frac{1}{3}$

(4) 2.48558

(5) 0.442854

(6) 0.510973

(7) 1.132268

(8) 0.739

(9) 0.682

**17.2.2 Page 147**

(1) 2.135

(2) 0.6295

(3) 10.6875

(4) 2.129875

(5) 0.63746

(6) 10.66667

(7) (a) 1, (b) 0.987, (c) 1.000135

(8) 0.74682

(9) 316

(10) 0.806

(11) 0.8013

(12) 28.65, 74.625

(13) 5.74, 79.28

(14) 0.4488

# Chapter 18

### 18.1.2 Page 153

(1) (a) $1 - 2x^2 + \frac{2}{3}x^4$      (b) $3x - 4\frac{1}{2}x^3 + 81x^5/40$

     (c) $1 + 3x + 4\frac{1}{2}x^2$      (d) $1 - 2x + 2x^2$

     (e) $x + x^2 + \frac{1}{3}x^3$      (f) $1 - x + \frac{1}{3}x^3$

     (g) $2x - 2x^2 + 2\frac{2}{3}x^3$      (h) $-x^2 - \frac{1}{2}x^4 - \frac{1}{3}x^6$

(2) (a) 1.646      (b) 0.969

     (c) 0.0998      (d) 0.366

     (e) 0.0954      (f) -0.223

(3) $x - \frac{2}{3}x^3$      (4) $1 - x^2 + \frac{1}{3}x^4$

(5) $x - \frac{1}{2}x^2 + \frac{1}{3}x^3 - \dots$      (6) $\ln 2 + \frac{1}{2}x - \frac{1}{8}x^2 + x^3/24 - \dots$

(7) $\frac{1}{2}$      (8) (a) $\frac{1}{2}$   (b) 0   (c) 1   (d) 2

(9) $1 + x \ln 2 + (x \ln 2)^2/2! + (x \ln 2)^3/3! + \dots$

(10) $(\ln 2)/(\ln 3)$      (11) $1 - x + \frac{1}{2}x^2 . x = 0.59$

(12) (a) 0.32   (b) 0.

### 18.2.2 Page 154

(3) (a) $x + \frac{1}{6}x^3$      (b) $\frac{1}{2}\pi - x - x^3/6$

     (c) $1 + \frac{1}{2}x^2$      (d) $1 + x + \frac{1}{2}x^2 + \frac{1}{2}x^3$

(5) $\frac{1}{2} - \frac{1}{2}\sqrt{3}x - \frac{1}{4}x^2$

# Chapter 19

### 19.1.2 Page 162

(1) (a) 2, 5      (b) -3, 7      (c) 0.3, -0.7   (d) -2, -0.1

(2) (a) 2-5i      (b) -3-7i      (c) 0.3+0.7i   (d) -2+0.1i

(3) (a) 3-2i      (b) 1+8i      (c) 17-7i      (d) $-\frac{1}{2} + \frac{1}{2}i$

     (e) -1-i      (f) -5+12i

(4) (a) 2+i      (b) -8-5i      (c) -9-19i      (d) -21/34-i/34

     (e) -21/13 + i/13      (f) 5+12i

(5) (a) $-1 \pm 3i$      (b) $2 \pm 4i$      (c) $-\frac{1}{2} \pm i\frac{1}{2}\sqrt{3}$

     (d) $\frac{1}{4} \pm i\frac{1}{4}\sqrt{23}$      (e) $1, -\frac{1}{2} \pm i\frac{1}{2}\sqrt{3}$

     (f) $\pm 1, \pm i$

(6) $-\frac{1}{2} - i\frac{1}{2}\sqrt{3}, 1, 1$      (7) $\frac{1}{2}i, -\frac{1}{4} + \frac{1}{4}i, -\frac{1}{4}, \frac{1}{16}$

(8) $\pm(2 + i)$      (9) $\pm(3 - 2i)$

(10) (a) $2\frac{2}{3} - \frac{2}{3}i$      (b) 3-4i      (c) -1-2i      (d) -1-2i

(11) a=-4, b=5, 2-i      (12) a=-9, b=43, 3-4i, 3

## 19.2.2 Page 164

(1)  (a) 6.4, 51.3°       (b) 8.06, 82.9°       (c) 3.61, −56.3°
     (d) 5.83, 239°       (e) 0.5, 36.9°        (f) 0.90, 124°
(2)  (a) 2.24, 63°        (b) 3.61, 56.3°       (c) 8.06, 120°
     (d) 5.83, 59°        (e) 5, 127°           (f) 0.62, 7.1°
(3)  (a) 2.24, −26.6°     (b) 2.24, 26.6°       (c) 5, 0°
     (d) 4, 0°            (e) 5, −53°           (f) 1, −53°
(4)  (a) $\frac{1}{2}$ + i0.866   (b) 1 + i     (c) -2 + i3.46
     (d) -1.08 - i2.97    (e) 0.29 - 0.08i      (f) 4.19 - 2.72i
(5)  (a) 1.1 + i0.46                            (b) 0.71 + i0.71
     (c) 2.10 + i1.19                           (d) 1.43 + i2.46
(6)  (a) -0.29 + 0.71i,   (b) $-\frac{1}{2}i \pm \frac{1}{2}\sqrt{11}$   (9), 6, 4
     -1.71 - 0.71i

## 19.3.2 Page 166

(1)  (a) $\sqrt{5}e^{i1.11}$               (b) $5e^{i2.21}$
     (c) $2e^{-i\frac{1}{4}\pi}$           (d) $\sqrt{34}e^{-2.11i}$
(2)  (a) -2                                (b) -2.12+2.12i
     (c) -4                                (d) 0.54+0.84i
(3)  (a) 1                                 (b) 1
     (c) 32768i                            (d) -1
     (e) $e^{i3\theta}$                    (f) $e^{-11\theta i}$
(4)  $3\sin\theta - 4\sin^3\theta$
(5)  $16\cos^5\theta - 20\cos^3\theta + 5\cos\theta$,
     $16\sin^5\theta - 20\sin^3\theta + 5\sin\theta$
(6)  (a) $e^{i\pi/6}$, $e^{i5\pi/6}$, $e^{i3\pi/2}$   (b) $2.245\,e^{i\theta}$, for $\theta$ =-2.6, 1.83, 3.93
(8)  $\frac{1}{32}(\cos 6\theta + 6\cos 4\theta + 15$
     $\cos 2\theta + 10)$

## 19.4.2 Page 168

(1)  (a) $\sqrt{8}$, 45°                   (b) 5, 90°
     (c) 2, 60°                            (d) $\sqrt{8}$, 150°
(2)  (a) $(4/\sqrt{2},\ 4/\sqrt{2})$       (b) (-2.6, 1.5)
     (c) (-3, 0)                           (d) $(\sqrt{2}, -\sqrt{2})$
(3)  (a) r = 6                             (b) $\theta = 45°$ or 225°
     (c) $r^2 \sin\theta\cos\theta = 3$    (d) $r^2\cos 2\theta = 1$

(4)   (a) $x^2 + y^2 = 4$                  (b) $y = \sqrt{3}x$
     (c) $x = 1$                           (d) $x^2 + y^2 = 2y$

(5)   (2,0), 2           (7) 3              (8) $4\frac{1}{2}\pi$

# Chapter 20

## 20.1.2 Page 173

(1)   (a) $y = Ae^{x^2}$            (b) $y = \sqrt{(x^2 + c)}$     (c) $y = Ae^{\frac{1}{2}x^2}$ - 1
     (d) $y = \cos^{-1}(c - \sin x)$ (e) $y = Ax/(1 - Ax)$   (f) $y = -\ln(-\ln Ax)$

(2)   (a) $y = e^{\frac{1}{2}(x^2-1)}$        (b) $y = 1\frac{1}{3}x$            (c) $y = -1/(\ln e(1 + x))$
     (d) $y = e^{-\cos x}$                                 (e) $y = -\ln(-\ln x/e)$

(3)   $h = 6 \times 2^{-t/12}$                         (4) $M = M_0 e^{-t/1000}$. 693

(5) $y = Ae^x - 1 - x$

(6)   (a) $y = \tan(x + c) - x$                  (b) $y = Ae^{\frac{1}{2}}x - x$

(7)   (a) $y = 1 - Ae^{-x} - x$               (b) $y = Ae^{2x} - \frac{3}{4} - 1\frac{1}{2}x$

(8)   (a) $y = x \ln x + cx$                  (b) $y = x \tan(\ln x + c)$
     (c) $y = x \sin(\ln z + c)$

## 20.2.2 Page 175

(1)   $a, d, f$

(2)   (a) $\frac{3}{4}x^3 + c/x$                    (b) $\frac{1}{4}x + c/x^3$
     (c) $cx^3 - x$                         (d) $2\tan x + c\sec x$
     (e) $x^2 e^{-x} + ce^{-x}$                 (f) $(3x + \frac{3}{2}x^2 + c)/(1 + x)$
     (g) $-x - 1 + ce^x$               (h) $e^{-x^2}(x + c)$

(3)   (a) $\frac{1}{3}x^2 - 6/x$      (b) $5x^3 - x$       (c) $-x - 1 + 2e^x$
     (d) $-x - 1 + 3e^x$    (e) $\sqrt{2}/\sin x - \cot x$   (f) $1/a + (1 - 1/a)e^{-ax}$

## 20.3.2 Page 177

(1)   (a) $Ae^{-2x} + Be^{-3x}$           (b) $Ae^{2x} + Be^{4x}$
     (c) $Ae^{-4x} + Be^{3x}$            (d) $Ae^{5x} + Be^{-3x}$
     (e) $e^{-2x}(A\cos 3x + B\sin 3x)$   (f) $e^x(A\cos x + B\sin x)$
     (g) $A\cos 3x + B\sin 3x$         (h) $Ae^{\frac{2}{3}x} + Be^{-\frac{2}{3}x}$

(2)   (a) $Ae^{-2x} + Be^{-3x} + \frac{1}{2}$      (b) $Ae^{2x} + Be^{4x} + 2x + 1$
     (c) $Ae^{-4x} + Be^{3x} + x^2 + 2x - 1$  (d) $Ae^{5x} + Be^{-3x} - 3e^{2x}$
     (e) $e^{-2x}(A\cos 3x + B\sin 3x)$   (f) $e^x(A\cos x + B\sin x) + 2e^{-x}$
     $+ \cos x$
     (g) $A\cos 3x + B\sin 3x + 2x/$   (h) $Ae^{-\frac{2}{3}x} + Be^{-\frac{2}{3}x} - e^{-\frac{1}{3}x}$
     $9 - 1/9$

(3)  (a) $-\frac{1}{2}e^{-2x} + \frac{1}{2}$  (b) $e^{2x} + e^{4x} + 2x + 1$
   (c) $e^{-4x} - e^{3x} + x^2 + 2x - 1$  (d) $0.007\,(e^{5x} - e^{-3x}) - 3e^{2x}$
   (e) $2e^{-2x}\sin 3x + \cos x$  (f) $-2e^{-\pi}e^x \sin x + 2e^{-x}$
   (g) $(10/9)\cos 3x + 2.99\sin$
       $3x + 2x/9 - 1/9$
   (h) $e^{-\frac{2}{3}x} - e^{-\frac{1}{3}x}$

## Chapter 21

### 21.1.2  Page 182

(1)  (a) $(1,1,2) + \lambda\,(2,1,7)$  (b) $(1,0,3) + \lambda\,(4,2,0)$
   (c) $(1,3,1) + \lambda\,(1,2,1)$  (d) $(1,2,-1) + \lambda\,(0,-4,2)$
(2)  (a) $(x-1)/2 = (y-1)/1 =$  (b) $(x-1)/4 = y/2 = (z-3)/0$
       $(z-2)/7$
   (c) $(x-1)/1 = (y-3)/2$  (d) $(x-1)/0 = (y-2)/-4 = (z+1)/2$
       $= (z-1)/1$
(3)  (a) $t = 3$  (b) $t = -2$  (4) (a) $40.5°$  (b) $98°$
(5)  (a) $(1,2,3) + \lambda\,(1,1,1) + \mu\,(1,0,1)$ (b) $(1,2,1) + \lambda\,(1,-1,2) + \mu\,(0,3,0)$
(6)  (a) $r.(2,1,-1) = 3$  (b) $r.(0,0,1) = 4$
   (c) $r.(1,-1,0) = 0$  (d) $r.(1,1,1) = 5$
(7)  (a) $25°$  (b) $14°$
   (c) $17°$
(8)  (a) $60°$  (b) $50°$
   (c) $60°$
(9)  (a) $0.816$  (b) $1.67$
(10) $(3,1,-1).\ 79°$  (11) $(\frac{1}{2},1,-1).47°$

### 21.2.2  Page 185

(1)  (a) $\begin{pmatrix} 1 & -\frac{1}{2} \\ 0 & \frac{1}{2} \end{pmatrix}$  (b) $\begin{pmatrix} -1 & 2 \\ \frac{1}{2} & -\frac{1}{2} \end{pmatrix}$  (c) $\begin{pmatrix} 0.3 & 0.1 \\ -0.1 & 0.3 \end{pmatrix}$

(2)  (a) $\begin{pmatrix} 2 & 6 \\ 2 & 4 \end{pmatrix}$  (b) $\begin{pmatrix} 1 & 9 \\ 1 & 5 \end{pmatrix}$  (c) $\begin{pmatrix} -5 & 20 \\ 5 & -20 \end{pmatrix}$

   (d) $\begin{pmatrix} 1 & 3 \\ 0 & 4 \end{pmatrix}$  (e) $\begin{pmatrix} 1 & 7 \\ 0 & 8 \end{pmatrix}$  (f) $\begin{pmatrix} 9 & -36 \\ -18 & 72 \end{pmatrix}$

(3)  (a) $\{(x, 0)\}$           (b) $(0,0)$
     (c) $(0,0)$             (d) $(0,0)$

(4)  (a) $y = 0$ and $y = x$       (b) $y = 0.64x$ and $y = -0.39x$
     (c) none               (d) $y = \frac{1}{4}x$ and $y = -2x$

(5)  $y = -2x$                 (6) $4y = x$

(7)  $y = 2x,\ 2y = -x$        (8) $\{(x,0)\},\quad y = 0$

(9)  $b\mathbf{i} + d\mathbf{j}$

(10)  $\begin{pmatrix} 2 & 2 \\ 1 & -1 \end{pmatrix}.$     $(0,0).\ y = 0.28x,\quad y = -1.78x$

(11)  $\begin{pmatrix} 1 & -1 \\ -2 & 2 \end{pmatrix}.$     $y = -2x,\quad y = x.$

# Chapter 22

## 22.1.2 Page 196

(1)  4 m/s,  10 m      (2) 1.5 m/s, 75 m     (3) 10 s

(4)  0.02 s           (5) 5/9 m/s$^2$,  $6\frac{2}{3}$ m/s (6) 11.4 s

(7)  75 m            (8) 4 s           (9) 0.8 m/s$^2$, 5 s

(10) 3.194 s, 31.3 m/s                   (11) 2.33 s, 32.86 m/s

(12) 11.48 m, 5.35 s,      (13) 15 s, $6\frac{2}{3}$ m/s
     37.43 m/s

(14) 40.65 m         (15) $1\frac{1}{3}$ m/s$^2$       (16) $13\frac{1}{8}$ s

(17) 30 s, 1.5 m/s$^2$

## 22.2.2 Page 198

(1)  6, -126

(2)  (a) 4           (b) 4             (c) 0.71 s
     (d) 1.09

(3)  4, 5, 4.5 m      (4) 3, 22.5        (5) 4,  $5\frac{1}{3}$, 6 s,  $10\frac{2}{3}$

(6)  164 m/s, 95 m     (7) (a) 121 m/s      (b) 1764 m
     (c) 32 s, 362 m/s

(8)  (a) 2.73 s,  6.13 m     (b) 4.37 s,  8.37 m/s    (9) 6 s, 21 m/s.

## 22.3.2 Page 200

(1)  (a) $3\mathbf{i} + 14t\mathbf{j}$  (b) $3t^2\mathbf{i} - 4t\mathbf{j}$
     (c) $-\sin t\mathbf{i} + \cos t\mathbf{j}$  (d) $2\cos 2t\mathbf{i} - 6\sin 2t\mathbf{j} + \mathbf{k}$

(2)  (a) $\sqrt{(9 + 196t^2)}$  (b) $\sqrt{(9t^4 + 16t^2)}$
     (c) 1  (d) $\sqrt{(4\cos^2 2t + 36\sin^2 2t + 1)}$

(3)  (a) $14\mathbf{j}$  (b) $6t\mathbf{i} - 4\mathbf{j}$
     (c) $-\cos t\mathbf{i} - \sin t\mathbf{j}$  (d) $-4\sin 2t\mathbf{i} - 12\cos 2t\mathbf{j}$

(4)  (a) $3t\mathbf{i} + 5t\mathbf{j}$  (b) $\frac{1}{2}t^2\mathbf{i} + 1\frac{1}{2}t^2\mathbf{j} - 2\frac{1}{2}t^2\mathbf{k}$
     (c) $\frac{1}{2}\sin 2t\mathbf{i} + (\frac{1}{3}\cos 3t - \frac{1}{3})\mathbf{j}$  (d) $(e^t - 1)\mathbf{i} - (1\frac{1}{2}e^{2t} - 1\frac{1}{2})\mathbf{j}$

(6)  (a) $t = \frac{1}{2}$  (b) $t = 2$

(7)  $-\mathbf{i} + \mathbf{j}.\ t = 3$  (8)  $\mathbf{i} + (2t + 1)\mathbf{j}.\ t = 2$

## Chapter 23

## 23.1.2 Page 206

(1)  49 N  (2) 30 N  (3) 24 N
(4)  $\frac{1}{3}$ kg  (5) 3 m/s²  (6) 4000 N
(7)  950 N  (8) 100.8 N  (9) 10000 N
(10) 50000N  (11) 980 N  (12) 2.95 N
(13) 0.3 m/s²  (14) 0.976 kg  (15) 4.8 m/s²
(16) 653 N 3.27 m/s²  (17) 78.93 kg  (18) 0.588 m/s²
(19) 69.87 kg  (20) 1.25 kg  (21) 2.45 m/s²
(22) 8.93 kg  (23) $1\frac{1}{2}\mathbf{i} + \mathbf{j}$  (24) $(4 + 4t)\mathbf{i} + 48\mathbf{j}$
(25) $4t\mathbf{i} + 10t^2\mathbf{j}.\quad \mathbf{v} = 2t^2\mathbf{i} + 3\frac{1}{3}t^3\mathbf{j}.\quad \mathbf{s} = \frac{2}{3}t^3\mathbf{i} + \frac{5}{6}t^4\mathbf{j}$
(26) $2\frac{1}{2}\cos t\mathbf{i} + 2\frac{1}{2}\sin t\mathbf{j}.\quad \mathbf{v} = 2\frac{1}{2}\sin t\mathbf{i} + (2\frac{1}{2} - 2\frac{1}{2}\cos t)\mathbf{j}$
     $\mathbf{s} = (-2\frac{1}{2}\cos t + 3\frac{1}{2})\mathbf{i} + (2\frac{1}{2}t - 2\frac{1}{2}\sin t)\mathbf{j}$

## 23.2.2 Page 209

(1)  3250 N,  1150 N  (2) 24000 N & 12000 N
(3)  20000 N & 40000 N  (4) 2.45 m/s², 36.75 N, 73.5 N
(5)  3.27 m/s², $65\frac{1}{3}$ N, $130\frac{2}{3}$ N  (7) 3.675 m/s², 18.375 N
(8)  3.267 m/s², $32\frac{2}{3}$ N  (10) 1.4 m/s², 42 N, 33.6 N
(11) 31 N  (12) 9.6 N

## 24.1.2 Page 214

(1)   6.2 N,  23.2 N

(2)   (a) 9.8 N                    (b) 0

(c) 0.018                    (d) -25.4

(3)   7.3 N,  227°

(4)   (a) 24.8 N,  133.4°          (b) 5N, 336.9°

(c) 69.3 N,  181.4°          (d) 17 N,  186.6°

(5)   15 N,  225°                  (6) (a) 34.2 N,  2.2°

(b) 2.1 N,  141.3°           (c) 48.3 N, 162.5°

(7)   1 m s$^{-2}$, 24°             (8) 2 m s$^{-2}$, 346.6°

(9)   20.7 N                        (10) 144.9 N

(11) 0.35 m s$^{-2}$

(12) 195 N                          (13) 0.19 m s$^{-2}$

## 24.2.2 Page 217

(1)   5.62 m s$^{-2}$                            (3) 92.1 N

(4)   82.8 N                  (5) 1.45 m s$^{-1}$     (6) 0.38 m s$^{-2}$

(7)   1.63 m s$^{-2}$, 32.7 N   (8) 8 kg          (9) 2.9 kg

(10) 2.1 kg                   (11) 2.67 m s$^{-2}$   (12) 3.54 kg

(13) 14.3 kg                  (14) 63 N,  21.4°    (15) 12.5 N

(16) 27.7 N                   (17) 46.5 N, 38°     (18) 32 N, 49.3 N

(19) 46.9 N & 36.5 N                              (20) 29.4°

(21) 46.4 N, 26°                                  (22) 45°, 37.4°

## Chapter 25

## 25.1.2 Page 223

(1)   29.4 N               (2) 0.57            (3) 2.55 m

(4)   24 N                 (5) 0.46            (6) 1.57 m s$^{-2}$

(7)   34.4 N               (8) 0.235           (9) 26.6°

(12) 8.33 N, 21.1 N

(13) (a) 1.7 s             (b) 1.96 s          (c) 1.613 s

(14) (a) 112.7 N           (b) 100.8 N         (c) 103.6 N

(15) (a) 183.75 N          (b) 198.4 N         (c) 215.1 N

(16) 6.85 N,  13.42 N

(17) 5.39 m s$^{-2}$          (18) 0.184          (19) 4.1 m s$^{-2}$

# Chapter 26

## 26.1.2 Page 228

(1)  (a) 16 N                    (b) 300 N                   (c) 14 N
(2)  (a) $1\frac{1}{3}$ m        (b) $3\frac{1}{3}$ N        (c) 10.8 N
(3)  $1\frac{1}{3}$ m from centre   (4) 50 kg                (5) 0.7 m from one end
(6)  2.5 kg                      (7) 12.5 kg                 (8) 8 kg
(9)  6 kg                        (10) 1.6 m from hinge       (11) 23.5g N, 26.5g N
(12) $1\frac{1}{8}$ m from one end   (13) 280g N, 210g N,    (14) 0.3g N, 0.35g N

## 26.2.2 Page 231

(1)  (a) 10 N                    (b) 9.4 N                   (c) 13.5 N
(2)  (a) 3.62                    (b) 0.23                    (c) 1.47
(3)  (a) 50.3°                   (b) 53.1°                   (c) 81.8°
(4)  2.31 N                      (5) 22.6 N                  (6) 5 N
(7)  17°                         (8) 6.1g N                  (9) 45.6°
(10) 0.182                       (11) 170 N                  (12) 44 N
(13) 26.6°                                                   (14) 29.2 N, 0.6

# Chapter 27

## 27.1.2 Page 237

(1)  x=5                         (2) $(\frac{2}{3}, 0)$         (3) $\frac{2}{3}$ kg
(4)  $(-8\frac{1}{2}, 0)$        (5) 18.53 cm from base        (6) 1.23 m from base
(7)  $4\frac{1}{3}$             (8) $\frac{1}{11}$ m from centre   (9) $\frac{2}{11}$ m from centre
(10) $11\frac{2}{3}$ from bottom  (11) 3.35 cm from base      (12) 7.71 cm from base
(13) 3.37 cm                     (14) $\frac{1}{33}$ cm from centre   (15) $\frac{1}{333}$ from centre

## 27.2.2 Page 239

(1)  (1.3, 0.4)                  (2) 5 kg
(3)  $(8, 11\frac{3}{4})$        (4) (a) (5, 3)
     (b) (2.86, 3.82)                (c) (2.93, 3.91)
(5)  $(1\frac{1}{4}, 1\frac{1}{4})$   (6) (2.042, 1.042)
(7)  (4.73, 1.13) (12 cm on x-axis)
(8)  $(2\frac{1}{2}, \frac{3}{4}, 2\frac{11}{12})$   (9) (29, 65, 85)

## 27.3.2 Page 241

(1) $(\frac{3}{4}, 0.3)$        (2) $(\frac{5}{6}, 0)$

(3) $(0.4, 0.43)$      (4) $(1.39, 0.29)$

(5) $(1.29, 0)$       (6) $(1\frac{1}{8}, 3.6)$

(7) $(0, 3)$         (8) $(\frac{15}{16}, 0)$

       (11) $(0, 0.424a)$     (12) $(0, \frac{3}{8} a)$

## 27.4.2 Page 242

(1) $36.9°$         (2) 4.2 cm

(3) $51.5°$        (4) $60.2°$

(5) $10.8°$        (6) $45°$

(7) 11 cm      (8) 4.2 cm

# Chapter 28

## 28.1.2 Page 247

(1) (a) 1 Nm      (b) 2 Nm      (c) 1.126 Nm

(2) (a) 3, 1 Nm    (b) $2\sqrt{2}$, 1.6 Nm    (c) -3, 5.2 Nm

(3) 4.12 N, 7.12 N, 6 Nm    (4) 15 Nm       (5) 1.2 Nm

(6) 3.73 Nm        (7) 4.22 N        (8) 17.9 N

## 28.2.2 Page 249

(1) (a) 7.21 N, 56.3° to AB, $\frac{1}{6}$ m from A along BA produced

      (b) 8.32 N, 70° to AB, 0.74 from A along AB

(2) 9.97 N, 49° to AB, 1.06 m from A

(3) $5\mathbf{i} + 4\mathbf{j}$, $(3, 0)$

(4) 9.79 N, 41° to BC, 2.29 from B

(5) 8.06 N, 83° to AB, 18 cm from A, 0.24 Nm

(6) $3\mathbf{i} + \mathbf{j}$, $(0, -2\frac{2}{3})$, 8

## 28.3.2 Page 250

(1) 1.17 m from one end    (2) 30°         (3) 70° to vertical

(4) $\sqrt{3}$                 (5) 16° to vert.    (6) 18.4° to vert

(7) 30°             (8) 0.166       (9) 0.83 m from one end

(10) 15°            (11) 0.42       (12) 45°

(13) 69% of way up.

## 28.4.2 Page 252

(1)  BC: $W\sqrt{2}$, tension 　　　　CD: W thrust
　　　BD: $W\sqrt{2}$ thrust 　　　　AB: 2W tension
(2)  AB: $W\sqrt{2}$, tension 　　　　DB: W thrust
　　　BC: W tension 　　　　　　　DC: 0
(3)  AC & BC: $W/\sqrt{2}$, thrust 　AB: $\frac{1}{2}$ W, tension
(4)  CA: $\frac{1}{2}\sqrt{3}W$, thrust 　　　CB: $\frac{1}{2}$ W, thrust
　　　AB: $\frac{1}{4}\sqrt{3}W$, tension
(5)  CA: $2\frac{1}{2}/\sqrt{3}W$, thrust 　　DB: $3\frac{1}{2}/\sqrt{3}W$, thrust
　　　AE: $1\frac{1}{4}/\sqrt{3}W$ tension 　BE: $1\frac{3}{4}/\sqrt{3}W$ tension
　　　CE: $\frac{1}{2}/\sqrt{3}W$ tension 　　DE: $\frac{1}{2}/\sqrt{3}W$ thrust
　　　CD: $\frac{1}{2}\sqrt{3}W$ thrust

## Chapter 29

### 29.1.2 Page 256

(1)  60 J 　　　　　　　　　　(2) 10 m
(3)  3 N 　　　　　　　　　　　(4) (a) 196 J
　　　(b) 24.5 J 　　　　　　　　(c) 0.00353 J
　　　(d) -98 J 　　　　　　　　(5) (a) 9 J
　　　(b) 225,000 J 　　　　　　(6) 1.6875 N
(7)  6.125 m 　　　　　　　　　(8) 312.5 N
(9)  1500 N 　　　　　　　　　(10) 25 m s$^{-1}$
(11) 14 m s$^{-1}$ 　　　　　　　　(12) 3.66 m s$^{-1}$
(13) 6.53 m 　　　　　　　　　(14) 11.9 m s$^{-1}$
(15) 0.41 m 　　　　　　　　　(16) 7.25 m
(17) 16.1 m s$^{-1}$ 　　　　　　　(18) 6.26 m s$^{-1}$
(19) 1.19 m s$^{-1}$ 　　　　　　　(20) 0.013 m, 9.2°
(21) 19 　　　　　　　　　　　(22) 13
(23) 3.74

### 29.2.2 Page 258

(1)  400 W 　　　　(2) 2 m s$^{-1}$ 　　　　(3) 58.8 W
(4)  343 W 　　　　(5) 980 W 　　　　　(6) 245 W
(7)  14.1 m s$^{-1}$ 　　(8) 596 W 　　　　　(9) 5.9 m s$^{-1}$
(10) 16 m s$^{-1}$, 0.625 m s$^{-2}$ 　(11) 7.64 m s$^{-1}$ 　　(12) 6.1°
(13) 8000 W 　　　(14) 13.2 m s$^{-1}$ 　　　(15) 35.2 m s$^{-1}$
(16) 1.5 m s$^{-2}$ 　　(17) 3 m s$^{-2}$ 　　　　(18) $4\frac{2}{3}$ W
(19) 6.26 W

## Chapter 30

### 30.1.2 Page 263

(1)  2.24,  26.6°

(2) 5.1,  78.7°

(3)  -i - 9j, 9.1,  84° with i

(4) 8.6 km hr$^{-1}$, 122°

(5)  782 km hr$^{-1}$,  118°

(6) 2.3 km hr$^{-1}$,  352°

(7)  14.1 km hr$^{-1}$, from 89°

(8) 1432 km hr$^{-1}$, from 094°

(9)  60 m

(10) 20.5 km hr$^{-1}$,  293°

(11) 11.1 km hr$^{-1}$,  331°

(12) 42° to line across. 89 secs.

(13) 010°, 1.86 hr

(14) 81.2°, 3.58 hr

### 30.2.2 Page 265

(1)  222°,  1.34 min

(2) 287°,  1.11 hr

(3)  42° with -ve x-axis, 3.09i + 6.18j

(4)  30° with y-axis, 7.52i + 10.03j

(5) 300.1°

(6)  72° with touch line. 2.62 s

(7) 36.7° to line of wickets

### 30.3.2 Page 266

(1)  12.8 m, after 72 s

(2) 5.55 m,  4.6 m

(3)  2.77

(4) 1, $-\frac{1}{3}$ i + j

(5)  212 km, after 20.5 min

(6) 34 km

## Chapter 31

### 31.1.2 Page 271

(1)  44.1 m,  60 m

(2) 3.78 s,  56.7 m

(3)  0.553 s,  0.553 m

(4) 0.11 m

(5)  1.225 m

(6) 1980 m s$^{-1}$

(7)  1.24 m

(8) 40.1 m s$^{-1}$, 38.6° to vert

(9)  13.7 m s$^{-1}$ at 18.8° to horiz.

(10) 7423 m, 386 m s$^{-1}$, 39° to horiz.

### 31.2.2 Page 273

(1)  161 m, 5.25 s, 33.7 m

(2) 34.4 m, 2.65 s

(3)  17,720 m

(4) 23.78 m, 24.7° to horiz

(5)  17.59 m, 2.05 m

(6) 18 m s$^{-1}$, 16.4 to horiz,
after 0.38 s

534

(7)  43° to horiz, 1.74 s

(8) 5.05 s, 77.4 m, 67.3° to horiz

(9)  10.6 m, at 47° to wall

(10) 105 m

(11) 1676 m

## 31.3.2 Page 274

(1)  18.9° & 71.1°

(2) 23.7° & 66.3°

(3)  80° & 17.6°

(4) 75° & 14.7°

(5)  85.89° & 25.9°

(6) 28.3°, 38°

(7)  67.5° or −9.5°

## Chapter 32

## 32.1.2 Page 280

(1)  (a) 10000 Ns

(b) 0.5 Ns

(2)  4 m s$^{-1}$

(3) 8 m s$^{-1}$

(4)  2.4 Ns

(5) 9 Ns

(6)  5.4 Ns

(7) $5\frac{5}{9}$ m s$^{-1}$, 11111J

(8)  17.3 m s$^{-1}$

(9) 400 kg

(10) 0.494 m s$^{-1}$, 39.5 J, 13170 N

(11) 10 m s$^{-1}$, 150 N

(12) 10 m s$^{-1}$, 7794 N

(13) 1 m s$^{-1}$, 6 J

(14) 1.25 m s$^{-2}$, $10\frac{1}{2}$ Ns

(15) 29.1 Ns

(16) $4\mathbf{i} + 6\frac{1}{2}\,\mathbf{j}$, $45\frac{1}{4}$ J

(17) $\mathbf{i}/7 + 4\mathbf{j}/7$, $\pm(4\frac{2}{7}\mathbf{i} + 7\frac{1}{7}\mathbf{j})$

(18) 1.59 m s$^{-1}$, at 9° to original line
     of motion

(19) 0.84, at 27° to original line of motion

(20) 2 m s$^{-1}$, 3208 J

(21) 400 m s$^{-1}$, 400000J

(22) 4.23 Ns, at 56.3° to line of wickets

(23) 1.45 Ns at 25° to line of wickets

(24) 6.16 Ns

(25) 32 m s$^{-1}$ at 51.3 to line of wickets

(26) 25.1 m s$^{-1}$

## 32.2.2 Page 284

| | | |
|---|---|---|
| (1)  1.914 m | (2) $\frac{1}{2}$ | (3) 2 & 3 |
| (4)  0.6 m s$^{-1}$, 0.4 m s$^{-1}$ | (5) $\frac{1}{5}$ | (6) $\frac{1}{4}$ |
| (7)  $\frac{7}{16}$ | (8) 0 | (9) $\frac{1}{2}$ |
| (10) 0 | (11) $\frac{49}{32}$ | (12) $2\frac{1}{24}$ |
| (13) 2.45 | (14) $\frac{49}{60}$ | (15) 50.5° |
| (16) 0.834 | (17) 8.83, 7.07 Ns | |

## Chapter 33

### 33.1.2 Page 291

| | | |
|---|---|---|
| (1)  196 m s$^{-1}$ | (2) 7.67 m s$^{-1}$ | (3) 25 m s$^{-1}$ |
| (4)  42.5 m s$^{-1}$ | (5) 1.96 | (6) 0.383 |
| (7)  171 | (8) 0.05 s | (9) 1 |
| (10) 2.4 | (11) 2, 0.693 | (12) 1.52 |
| (13) 3 | | (14) 2.565 |

### 33.2.2 Page 293

| | | |
|---|---|---|
| (1)  17.32 m s$^{-1}$ | (2) 1.45 | (3) 0.284 m |
| (4)  17 m | | (5) 1.63 m s$^{-1}$ |
| (6)  (a) 2 m s$^{-1}$ | (b) $1\frac{1}{6}$ s | |
| (8)  495000 m | | (9) 11200 m s$^{-1}$ |

## Chapter 34

### 34.1.2 Page 298

| | |
|---|---|
| (1)  (a) 151 | (b) 8.06 |
| (c) 0.262 | (d) 0.0048 |
| (2)  (a) $1.45 \times 10^{-4}$ | (b) $1.75 \times 10^{-3}$ |
| (c) $7.27 \times 10^{-5}$ | (d) $1.99 \times 10^{-7}$ |
| (3)  8 m s$^{-1}$ | (4) 1.68 m s$^{-1}$ |
| (5)  0.524 m s$^{-1}$ | (6) 360 m s$^{-1}$, 1080 N |
| (7)  4.44 m | (8) 2.63 |
| (9)  1.225 m | (10) 0.215 |
| (11) 8.57 | (12) (a) 21 m s$^{-1}$ |
| (b) 45.4 m | (13) 1.42 |
| (14) 4.43 m s$^{-1}$ | (15) 0.98 |

## 34.2.2  Page 300

| | | |
|---|---|---|
| (1)  25° | (2) 3.07 | (3) 16.3 m |
| (4)  2.86 | (5) 5.875 N | (6) 4.95 |
| (7)  2.71 | (8) 16.8 m s$^{-1}$ | (9) 35.4 m s$^{-1}$ |
| (10) 0.932 | (11) 99.2 m | (12) 20° |
| (13) 1.21 m s$^{-1}$ | | (14) 0.95 m |

## 34.3.2  Page 302

| | |
|---|---|
| (1)  5.42 m s$^{-1}$ | (2) 0.735 |
| (3)  3.13 m s$^{-1}$ | (4) 22.1 m s$^{-1}$ |
| (5)  (a) 17.9 m s$^{-1}$, | (b) 302 N |
| (6)  19 m s$^{-1}$,  361 N | (7) (a) 15.5° |
| (b) 10.25 N | |
| (8)  2.32 m s$^{-1}$, 0.05 N | (9) 0.204 m, 0.59 N |

## Chapter 35

## 35.1.2  Page 308

| | | |
|---|---|---|
| (1)  1.47 m | (2) 6.125 N | (3) 32$\frac{2}{3}$ N |
| (4)  0.75 m | (5) 19.6 N | (6) 4900 N |
| (7)  0.8 m, 78.4 N | (8) 1.95 m | (9) 0.4875 |
| (10) 1.375 m | (11) 0.098 J | (12) 17.64 J |
| (13) 11.1 m s$^{-1}$ | (14) 51 m s$^{-1}$ | (15) 0.226 m |
| (16) 3.43 m | | (17) 0.8 m, 0.29 m |
| (18) (a) 29.6 m | (b) 18 m s$^{-1}$ | (c) 18.6 m |
| (19) 0.08 m, 0.22 m s$^{-1}$ | | |

## 35.2.2 Page 310

| | | |
|---|---|---|
| (1)  (a) 3, $\pi$, 1 | (b) 4, 4$\pi$, -2 | (c) 5, 2$\pi$, 0.64 |
| (d) 13, $\frac{2}{3}\pi$, -1.18 | (e) 2, $\frac{2}{3}\pi$, $\frac{1}{4}\pi$ | (f) $\sqrt{5}$, 4$\pi$, 0.987 |
| (2)  1$\frac{1}{2}$ | (3) 10 sin 6t | (4) $\frac{2}{3}\pi$ |
| (5)  0.212 | (6) 0.262 | (7) 6.97 cm |
| (8)  36 s | (9) 9.978 cm | (10) 10 cm s$^{-1}$, 0.823 s |

### 35.3.2 Page 312

(1)   2.84 s              (2) 6.2 m              (3) 6.58 m s$^{-2}$
(4)   $\frac{1}{2}$%              (5) 0.16 m              (6) 0.065 m s$^{-1}$
(7)   0.705              (8) 0.562, 0.0018       (9) 0.281, 0.224 m s$^{-1}$
(10)  $\sqrt{(g/a)}/2\pi$                     (11) $2\pi\sqrt{(\rho a/g)}$

## Chapter 36

### 36.1.2 Page 320

(1)   (a) 1/36              (b) 1/36
      (c) 1/6               (d) 5/12
      (e) 1/6               (f) 11/36
(2)   (a) $\frac{1}{4}$               (b) 1/17
      (c) 13/204            (d) 4/663
(3)   (a) 5/18              (b) 4/9
      (c) 5/6               (d) 4/9
(4)   (a) 20/171            (b) 31/57
      (c) 91/171
(5)   (a) 1/36              (b) 11/36
(6)   (a) 1/9               (b) 4/9
(7)   (a) 1/6               (b) 5/36
      (c) 25/216            (d) 125/216
(8)   (a) 1/80              (b) 567/6400

### 36.2.2 Page 322

(1)   A & C, A & D, B & C, B & D    (2) A & C, A & D
(3)   A & B                        (4) A & D
(5)   (a) 4/51                     (b) 13/51
(6)   (a) 1/5                      (b) 1/6
(7)   (a) 1/6                      (b) 0
(8)   (a) $\frac{1}{4}$                     (b) $\frac{3}{4}$
(9)   6/10                         (10) (a) 35/68
      (b) $\frac{5}{8}$                     (c) $\frac{1}{2}$
(11)  (a) 1/100                    (b) 612/625
      (c) 25/52
(12)  (a) 0.9712                   (b) 0.3125
      (c) 0.999
(13)  $\frac{7}{8}$                        (14) 4/9

# Chapter 37

## 37.1.2 Page 329

(1)   (a) 720
     (c) 39916800
     (e) 11880
     (g) 15

     (b) 3628800
     (d) 20
     (f) 1860480
     (h) 792

(2)   (a) 120
     (c) 1
     (e) 500500

     (b) 94109400
     (d) 500500

(5)   No

(6) 120

(7)   210

(8) 15!

(9)   60

(10) 840

(11) 2184

(12) 13800

(13) 40320

(14) 330

(15) 220

(16) 36

(17) 3003
     $6.35 \times 10^{11}$

(18) 3003, 360360

(20) 210

(21) 126

## 37.2.2  Page 331

(1)   (a) 60
     (c) 120
     (e) $5.28 \times 10^{13}$

     (b) 5040
     (d) 60

(2)   120

(3) 240

(4)   240

(5) 72

(6)   6885

(7) 1800

(8)   203212800
     (b) 5760
     (d) 2880

(9) (a) 362880
     (c) 14400

(10) 2401

(11) 729

(12) 50

(13) 225

(14) 132
     (b) 175760000

(15) (a) 78624000
(16) 33

(17) 6

(18) (a) $365!/(338! \times 365^{27}) = 0.373$
     (b) 0.627

(19) $5.364 \times 10^{28}$

(20) (a) 0.0088
     (b) 0.035

(21)  0.68
    (b) 31680

(22) (a) 5760

(23)  (a) 35

    (b) $\frac{1}{2}$ n(n-3)

(24)  40

## Chapter 38

### 38.1.2 Page 338

(1)   (a) 15.1

    (c) $63\frac{2}{3}$

(b) 1.36

(d) 118.5

(2)   (a) 14

    (c) $63\frac{1}{2}$

(b) 1.3

(d) 117

(3)   (a) 14.7

    (c) 63.5

(b) 1.32

(d) 117.9

(4)   (a) 12.1, 3.48

    (c) 20.6, 4.53

(b) 0.0984, 0.314

(d) 138, 11.74

(5)   (a) 153, 1210

    (c) 639, 2058

(b) 15.6, 9.84

(d) 1187, 13793

(6)   6.2, 0.96

(7) 3.633, 0.875

(8)   21.1, 8.8, 21.6

(9) 1.55, 1.5, 0.63

(10) 14.2

    (b) 60

    (d) 40, 50

(11) (a) 50

(c) 20

(12) 38 + 0.2x

### 38.2.2 Page 341

(6)   4.3, 0.71

(7) 1.24, 14.3 secs

(8)   10.8, 3%

(9) over 3.4 kg

## Chapter 39

### 39.1.2 Page 346

(1)   0.4

(2) 7/60

(3)   0.1

(4) 0.05

(5)   0.175

(6)

| $i$ | 1 | 2 | 3 | 4 | 5 | 6 |
|-----|---|---|---|---|---|---|
| $P(X = i)$ | 1/6 | 1/6 | 1/6 | 1/6 | 1/6 | 1/6 |

(7)

| $i$ | 2 | 3 | 4 | 5 | 6 | 7 | 8 | 9 | 10 | 11 | 12 |
|-----|---|---|---|---|---|---|---|---|----|----|----|
| $P(X = i)$ | 1/36 | 2/36 | 3/36 | 4/36 | 5/36 | 6/36 | 5/36 | 4/36 | 3/36 | 2/36 | 1/36 |

(8)

| $i$ | 1 | 2 | 3 | 4 | 5 | 6 |
|-----|---|---|---|---|---|---|
| $P(X = i)$ | 1/36 | 3/36 | 5/36 | 7/36 | 9/36 | 11/36 |

(9)

| $i$ | 1 | 2 | 3 | 4 |
|-----|---|---|---|---|
| $P(X = i)$ | 1/10 | 2/10 | 3/10 | 4/10 |

(10)

| $i$ | 0 | 1 | 2 |
|-----|---|---|---|
| $P(X = i)$ | 1/7 | 4/7 | 2/7 |

### 39.2.2 Page 348

(1)  $2\frac{7}{8}$       (2) 12.2       (3) 2.7
(4)  $1\frac{1}{2}$       (5) 1.3       (6) 4
(7)  2       (8) 3.5       (9) 2.75
(10) $3\frac{1}{2}$       (11) 7       (12) 161/36
(13) 3       (14) 8/7       (15) $3\frac{1}{3}$
(16) a = 0.4,  b = 0.3       (17) 37/13       (18) 7/6
(19) £20,  £100       (20) £17

### 39.3.2 Page 350

(1)  1.243       (2) 1.45       (3) 0.81
(4)  0.75       (5) a = 4,  b = 6       (6) 4/5,  32/75
(7)  $3\frac{1}{2}$,  $2\frac{11}{12}$,  7,  $5\frac{5}{6}$       (8) 0,  $5\frac{5}{6}$

# Chapter 40

## 40.1.2 **Page 356**

| | | | |
|---|---|---|---|
| (1) | (a) 0.297 | (b) 0.0044 | (c) 0.822 | (d) 0.995 |
| (2) | (a) 0.238 | (b) 0.191 | (c) 0.181 | (d) 0.946 |
| (3) | (a) 0.190 | (b) 0.122 | (c) 0.878 | (d) 0.392 |
| (4) | (a) 0.056 | (b) 0.282 | (c) 0.244 | |
| (5) | (a) 0.0115 | (b) $1 \times 10^{-14}$ | (c) 0.218 | (d) 0.931 |
| (6) | (a) 0.354 | (b) 0.114 | | (7) 2, 1.8 |
| (8) | $7\frac{1}{2}$, $1\frac{7}{8}$ | (9) 4, 3.2 | (10) 0.6, 0.54 | |
| (11) | 18 | (12) 9 | (13) 4/5 | (14) 1/10 |

## 40.2.2 **Page 359**

| | | | |
|---|---|---|---|
| (1) | (a) 0.126 | (b) 0.223 | (c) 0.809 | (d) 0.442 |
| (2) | (a) 0.14 | (b) 0.260 | (c) 0.125 | (d) 0.960 |
| (3) | (a) 0.168 | (b) 0.161 | (4) (a) 0.076 | (b) 0.779 |
| (5) | (a) 0.104 | (b) 0.092 | (c) 0.865 | |
| (6) | (a) 0.224 | (b) 0.223 | | |
| (7) | (a) 0.195 | (b) 0.122 | (c) 0.368 | (d) 0.865 |
| (8) | (a) 0.693 | (b) 0.120 | (9) 1.386, 0.085 | |
| (10) | 0.168 | (11) 0.0164 | (12) 0.271 | (13) 0.037 |
| (14) | (a) 0.219 | (b) 0.217 | | |

# Chapter 41

## 41.1.2 **Page 366**

| | | |
|---|---|---|
| (1) | (b) 15/16 | (c) 5/16 |
| | (d) 1/4096 | |
| (2) | (c) 1/16 | (d) 0.5525 |
| (3) | (c) 0.75 | (d) 1/9 |
| (4) | 2 | (5) 2 |
| (6) | 2 | (7) $^3\sqrt{3}$ |
| (8) | 1.56 | (9) (a) 4/5 |
| | (b) 0.0267 | (c) 0.841 |
| (10) | (a) $\frac{2}{3}$ | (b) 2/9 |
| | (c) 0.586 | |

(11)  2, $\sqrt{2}$

(13)  1/(b-a), for $a \leq x \leq b$

(15)  (b) $\frac{1}{3}$

     (d) $\frac{2}{3}$

(12) $\frac{1}{3}$ for $2 \leq x \leq 5$

(14) 9

(c) 0.854

(e) 0.722

## 41.2.2 Page 369

(1)  (a) $x^4$ for $0 \leq x \leq 1$

    (c) $1 - \cos x$ for $0 \leq x \leq \frac{1}{2}\pi$

(2)  (a) $\frac{1}{2} + x$ for $0 \leq x \leq 1$

    (c) $2 \cos 2x$ for $0 \leq x \leq \frac{1}{4}\pi$

(3)  $x^4$ for $0 \leq x \leq 1$

(5)  $1 - 1/x^2$ for $x \geq 1$

(7)  $\frac{1}{4}$

(9)  2/5

    (b) 15 min

    (d) 0.368

(11)  $(x - a)/(b - a)$ for $a \leq x \leq b$.

    $\frac{1}{2}(a + b).(b - a)^2/12$

(b) $x - \frac{1}{4}x^2$ for $0 \leq x \leq 2$

(d) $1 - 1/x$ for $x \geq 1$

(b) $8/x^3$ for $x \geq 2$

(d) $3e^{-3x}$ for $x \geq 0$

(4) $x - \frac{1}{4}x^2$ for $0 \leq x \leq 2$

(6) 0.732

(8) 1/6

(10) (a) $e^{-x/15}/15$

(c) 10.4 min

## Chapter 42

### 42.1.2 Page 375

(1)  (a) 6

    (d) -4

(2)  (a) 8

    (d) 5

    (g) 69

(3)  a=2,  b=0

(6)  a=3,  b=-3

(b) 45

(e) 20

(b) 5

(e) 35

(h) 9

(4) $\frac{1}{8}$, -1

(c) 14

(f) 21

(c) 45

(f) 25

(5) $1/\sigma$, $-\mu/\sigma$

(7) 210, 18.  170, 38

### 42.2.2 Page 377

(1)  23,  1.49

(4)  94g

(7)  0.26

(10)  1.2

(2) 3.07, 0.038

(5) 0.03

(8) 0.8

(3) 72

(6) 1/7

(9) 0.64

(11) (a) a = 4/5, b = 1/5

## 42.3.2 Page 380

(1)  (a) $2\frac{2}{9}$, 2.5          (b) 90.2,  103.1
     (c) $1.18 \times 10^{-5}$, $1.38 \times 10^{-5}$   (d) 0.5189,  0.577
(2)  (a) 1.157,  1.197          (b) 0.950, 0.969
     (c) 1.002,  1.013
(3)  7/30               (4) (a) 1250   (b) $1\frac{23}{30}$

## 42.4.2 Page 381

(1)  (a) 0.472               (b) 0.4, 0.6, 1.2
(2)  0.93785               (b) 0.9365, 0.7614
     (c) 0.92, 1.90, 0.40
(3)  (a) 2                (b) 1
(4)  (a) 0.4252, 0.0942          (b) 0.425, 0, 1.43
(5)  (a) 2                (b) 1, 3
(6)  31                 (7) (a) 5
     (b) 5, 3              (c) 5, 2, 5, 2, 5, 4

## Chapter 43

### 43.1.2 Page 386

(1)  (a) 0.994               (b) 0.067
     (c) 0.081               (d) 0.9965
     (e) 0.301               (f) 0.464
(2)  (a) 0.842               (b) 0.524
     (c) -0.1                (d) -1.175
(3)  (a) 0.6915               (b) 0.105
     (c) 0.599               (d) 0.266
(4)  4.022 & -0.022            (5) 6.24
(6)  (a) 87.82               (b) 82.39
     (c) 65.46               (d) 54.46
(7)  15.6                (8) 60
(9)  3.75                (10) 81.8
(11) 1001.6 cc, 26.3           (12) 1.9975 cm
(13) 31.2 m

## 43.2.2  Page 388

(1)  (a) 0.5           (b) 0.6915        (c) 0.909
     (d) 0.553        (e) 0.47          (f) 0.159
     (g) 0.32         (h) 0.37
(2)  (a) 43.9         (b) 5.51         (c) 112
     (d) 35            (e) 48.7         (f) 100.2
(3)  0.0295         (4) 0.29          (5) 0.987
(6)  0.69
(7)  (a) 0.76         (b) 0.998       (c) 0.52
     (d) 0.455        (e) 0.223       (f) 0.135
(8)  (a) 49.5         (b) 45.9         (c) 3.41
     (d) 2.71         (e) 0.41         (f) 0.35
(9)  (a) 0.057       (b) 0.376       (10) (a) 0.02
     (b) 0.02

## 43.3.2  Page 391

(1)  0.103         (2) 0.94          (3) 0.9
(4)  0.05           (5) 0.214       (6) 0.904
(7)  0.0285        (8) 0.18         (9) 0.014
(10) 0.085        (11) 0.896     (12) 0.08
(13) 0.07          (14) 0.19       (15) 0.12
(16) 0.262        (17) 0.088     (18) 0.206

## Chapter 44

## 44.1.2 Page 398

(1)  $z = 2.01$ sig.     (2) not sig.         (3) $z = 2.5$ sig.
(4)  $z = 3.36$ no     (5) $z = 1.48$ not sig.  (6) $z = 4.07$ yes
(7)  $z = 2.12$ no     (8) $z = 3.1$ yes.

## 44.2.2 Page 400

(1)  $z = 0.78$ no     (2) $z = 1.18$ no     (3) $z = 1.17$ no
(4)  $z = 0.71$ no     (5) $z = 3.6$ yes

## 44.3.2 Page 402

(1)   $z = 0.56$ no   (2) $z = 1.875$ yes   (3) $z = 4$ yes
(4)   $z = 1.59$ no   (5) $z = 1.9$   (a) no
      (b) no
(6)   $z = 1.3$ no   (7) $z = 3.3$ yes   (8) $z = 1.16$ no
(9)   $z = 1.22$ no   (10) $z = 0.95$ no.

## 44.4.2 Page 404

(1)   $11.9 < \mu < 14.1$   (2) $989 < \mu < 1001$   (3) $11.7 < \mu < 12.3$
(4)   $21.2 < \mu < 25.4$   (5) $245.5 < \mu < 256$   (6) $3.19 < \mu < 3.22$
(7)   $1170 < \mu < 1390$   (8) $12\% < p < 23\%$   (9) $27\% < p < 33\%$
(10) $75\% < p < 85\%$

## Chapter 45

## 45.1.2 Page 409

(1)   (a) $1.26 \pm 0.037$   (b) $55.2 \pm 4.09$
      (c) $0.21 \pm 0.36$   (d) $160.2 \pm 11.8$
(2)   (a) $1.26 \pm 0.056$   (b) $55.2 \pm 5.81$
      (c) $0.21 \pm 0.53$   (d) $160.2 \pm 18.5$
(3)   $t_7 = 3.67$. Sig.   (4) $t_8 = 2.31$. (Just) sig. at 5%
(5)   $t_{10} = 4.03$ sig.   (6) $t_7 = 1.97$ sig at 5%
(7)   $t_6 = 2.98$ sig at 5%

## 45.2.2 Page 411

(1)   $\chi^2 (9) = 15$. Not sig.   (2) $\chi^2(3) = 4$. Good fit
(3)   $\chi^2 (2) = 3.125$. Good fit   (4) p = 0.287. $\chi^2 (1) = 5.71$. Not good fit
(5)   $\chi^2 (2) = 9.36$. Not good fit   (6) $\chi^2 (3) = 2.85$. Good fit
(7)   $\chi^2 (3) = 1.37$. Good fit   (8) $\chi^2 (3) = 9$. Not good fit.
(9)   $\mu = 26$. $\chi^2 (1) = 44$. Not good fit
(10) 10.8, 33. $\chi^2 (2) = 31$. Not good fit.

## 45.3.2 Page 415

(1)  $\chi^2$ (1) = 10.7. Sig   (2) $\chi^2$ (1) = 1. Not sig.
(3)  $\chi^2$ (2) = 0.74. Not sig.   (4) $\chi^2$(1) = 1. Not sig.
(5)  $\chi^2$ (4) = 15.7. Sig.

## Chapter 46

## 46.1.2 Page 422

(1)  3, -1          (2) -13, 50          (3) 3, -6.5
(4)  0.01, 0.05     (5) 4, 2.5           (6) 0.3, 1.4
(7)  (5, 2300)
(8)  (a) $X = x^3$, $Y = y$   (b) $X = x$, $Y = y^2$   (c) $X = 1/\sqrt{x}, Y = y$
     (d) $X = x^2$, $Y = yx$   (e) $X = x$, $Y = y\sqrt{x}$   (f) $X = x$, $Y = yx^2$
     (g) $X = \ln x$, $Y = \ln y$ (h) $X = x^2$, $Y = \ln y$  (i) $X = \ln x$, $Y = \ln y$
     (j) $X = 1/x$, $Y = \ln y$

## 46.2.2 Page 425

(1)  (a) $y = 1.41x - 0.2$          (b) $y = 0.25x + 0.44$
     (c) $y = 0.75x + 0.74$         (d) $y = -5.4x + 31.6$
(2)  (a) 13.9                       (b) 2.95
     (c) 8.24                       (d) -22.4
(3)  (a) $x = 0.7y + 0.16$          (b) $x = 3.6y - 1.3$
     (c) $x = 1.28y - 0.8$          (d) $x = -0.17y + 5.6$
(4)  (a) $y = 1.78x + 1.96$         (b) $x = 0.52y - 0.58$
(5)  $y = 2.08x^2 - 1.86$           (6) $y/x = 2.9x + 5.7$
(7)  $r = 2.7s^{0.22}$              (8) $0.2 < a < 0.3.\ 0.3 < b < 0.58$
(9)  Reject                         (10) $y = 2.25x + 0.44$
     (a) Reject.                    (b) Accept.

## 46.3.2 Page 428

(1)  (a) 0.1              (b) 0.87           (c) -0.998
(2)  (a) 0.956           (b) -0.957          (c) -0.297
(5)  (a) $\frac{2}{3}$, 0.5    (b) -0.85, -0.69    (c) 0.18, 0.14
(6)  0.9, 0.79
(7)  (a) 0.98, 0.93      (b) -0.97, -0.9     (c) -0.36, -0.14

# Solutions to End-of-Chapter Examination Questions

These solutions are the responsibility of the author, and have neither been supplied nor approved by the examination boards.

If a method is suggested for the solution of a question, then that method is not necessarily the best or the only way to solve the question.

## 1.3 Page 10

(1)   (i) $x + 4$ is a factor.
The factors are $(x + 4)$, $(x + 3)$, $(x + 2)$.
The coefficient of $x^2$ is 9.

    $a=3$, $b=2$, $r=7$.                   (By long division)

(2)   (a) 6 (Put $x=1$)
(b) 0
(c) $x(x\text{-}3)(2x+1)(3x\text{-}4)$       (Divide by $x(x\text{-}3)$)
(d) $x = 0, 3, -\frac{1}{2}, 1\frac{1}{3}$.

(3)   (a) $a = \text{-}21$, $b = \text{-}54$       (Put $x=3$ and -2)
(b) $x = 2$ or $\frac{1}{2}$ or 1       (First solve $2u^2 - 9u + 10 = 0$)

(4)   $f(x) = \frac{1}{2}/(x + 1) - \frac{1}{2}/(x + 3)$
$1/6 - \frac{1}{2}/(2n + 3)$

(Expand each term of the series, and cancel all but the first and last.)

## 2.4 Page 19

(1)   $-\frac{1}{3}$ or $-\frac{2}{3}$            (Use the equation $1 + r + r^2 = 7/9$)

(2)   (i) 25                 (Use the formula for the sum of an AP)

(ii) $r = \pm 1/6$. $a = \pm 12$.

(iii) 12.

Series is 12, 2, $\frac{1}{3}$, 1/18 or
$-12$, 2, $-\frac{1}{3}$, 1/18.
(Must have $4^n > 6000001$)

(3)  (i) By 1.12. 1.76. 76%.
(ii) £(25n - 5). £$\frac{1}{2}n$ (15 + 25n)
9 years.

(When $\frac{1}{2}n(15 + 25n) > 1000$)

(4)  $S_{n-1} = \frac{1}{4}(5n^2 + n - 6)$
$u_n = 2\frac{1}{2}n + 1\frac{1}{2}$
$a = 4$, $d = 2\frac{1}{2}$.

(Take $S_n - S_{n-1}$)

(5)



$n$ is at least 44.

(Common ratio is $1 - x/10$.
This is between -1 and 1.)
(The sum is $100/x$)
(Sum is $100(1 - 0.9^n)$)

**3.3 Page 25**

(1)  (i) $1 - 15x + 90x^2$
(ii) $16 + 32x + 24x^2$.
Coeff. = 984

(2)  (i) $1 - 5x + 10x^2 - 10x^3$
$+5x^4 - x^5$
$x^3$ term is $-40x^3$.
(ii) 0.9225. The $x^3$ term is
0.00004, which does not
affect the answer.

(Multiply together).

(3)  $1 - 8x + 28x^2 - 56x^3 + 70x^4$
$-56x^5 + 28x^6 - 8x^7 + x^8$.
0.663.
6.63 m.

(Height = $10 \times (0.95)^8$)

(4)  (a) 495
(b) $1 - x - 1\frac{1}{2}x^2 + 2\frac{1}{2}x^3$.
Valid for $-\frac{1}{2} < x < \frac{1}{2}$.

($^{12}C_4 x^8 (1/x^2)^4$)

(5)  q = 0.45, p = 0.55.

(Expand both series, and equate coeffs.)

(Write $33^{0.1} = (32+1)^{0.1}$.

Put $x = 1/32$ in the result above.)

(6)  (a) 1/(1+x) - 1/(2+x)

(Refer to 1.2)
(Write $1/(2+x)$ as $\frac{1}{2}/(1+\frac{1}{2}x)$)

(b) Next term = $\frac{1}{6}(1/n^4)$
0.98952.

(Put n = 10)

(7)  $1 - \frac{1}{4}x - 3x^2/32 - 7x^3/128$.
1.49535.
$x^3$ term $< 10^{-7}$,
hence need not be included.

## 4.4 Page 35

(1)  $3(x+2)^2 + 5$.

(a) Both terms are positive.

(b) Least value is 5.

(c) -1.2 and -2.8.

(d)

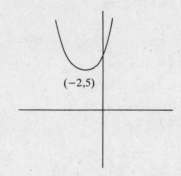

(-2,5)

(2)  (a) 3 and $-\frac{3}{4}$.

(The discriminant must be 0.)

(b) $m > 4$ or $m < -4$.

(Discriminant must be positive.)

(3)

$(n\beta^2 = c/a, (n+1)\beta = -b/a$.  Eliminate $\beta$)

(4)  $p^2 - 4$
$y^2 - 1\frac{1}{2}(p^2 - 4)y + 9 = 0$.

(Find the sum and product of the new roots).

## 5.3 Page 41

(1)  (a) $-4 < x < 1\frac{1}{2}$

(b) $x < -1$ or $x > 2$

(Subtract 1 from both sides.)

(2)  (a) $(x-3)(x^2+4x+4)$
 (b) $(x+2)^2$
 (c) $x > 3$.                     (As $g(x)$ is positive, it does
                                   not affect the answer.)

(3)  $2y - 3x$ is greatest at $(0,3)$
 Area $= 3$                        (The triangle is right-angled)

(4)  (a) (i) $x < 2$ or $x > 4$
 (ii) $\frac{2}{5} < x < 1$         (Subtract 2 from both sides)

 (b) $(5,3)$

(5)  (i) $x < 1$ or $x > 1\frac{2}{3}$       (Subtract 4 from both sides)
 (ii) $|x| > 1\frac{2}{3}$ or $|x| < 1$   (Consider the cases $|x| > 1$
                                    and $|x| < 1$)
 (iii) $x < \frac{3}{5}$ or $x > 1\frac{2}{3}$   (Square both sides)

(6)  (a) $0 \leq x \leq 4$, $3 \leq y \leq 12$.
 (b) $x < 2$ or $3 < x < 5$        (Collect both terms on one side.)

## 6.2 Page 47

(1)  (i) $2^{\frac{2}{3}}$. 8
 (ii) $z/x^2$.
 (iii) 2.

(2)  (i) $\log_{10} \frac{4}{5}$.
 (ii) 1 or -1.585                   (Consider it as a quadratic in $2^x$)

(3)  (a) $2^{-4}$, $2^{6a}$, $2^{3b-2c}$
 (b) $\sqrt{30}$, 27000.
 (c) 0.774.

(4)  (a) $x=6$ (and -9).            (Regard 1 as $\log_3 3$)
 (b) (i) k-1,   (ii) $\frac{1}{2}(1 + 1/k)$

                                    (Note: $\log_9 x = \frac{1}{2}\log_3 x$.
                                    Also $\log_a b = 1/\log_b a$)

(5) (i) $1/(\ln a - 2)$
(ii) $\sqrt{(\frac{1}{4}ea)}$

(6) (i) $5050 \ln 2$     (Refer to 2.1)
(ii) $(\ln 2)/(1 - \ln 2)$     (Refer to 2.2)

## 7.5 Page 57

(1) Gradient $\frac{2}{3}$ $E(2,3)$
$2y + 3x = 12$. $B(0,6)$
$4y = 7x - 28$. $D(4,0)$.

(2) (i) $B(5,0)$     (Put $y = 0$ in the equation of $BC$)
(ii) $D(-1,3)$     (From B, go $1\frac{1}{2}$ of the way
from $B$ to $M$.)
(iii) $A(-2,0)$     (Find the equation of $AD$.)
    $C(7,6)$     (Find where $AM$ and $BC$ intersect)
(iv) $E(-9,0)$     (Where $CD$ crosses the $x$−axis.)
(v) $31\frac{1}{2}$.     (Find $\Delta EBC - \Delta EAD$).

(3) $A(a,0)$ $B(0,b)$
(i) $G(\frac{1}{2}a, \frac{1}{2}b)$
(ii) $H(0.6a, 0.4b)$
(iii) Centre $(0,0)$, radius 5.     (Put $x = \frac{1}{2}a$, $y = \frac{1}{2}b$)
(iv)     (Put $x = 0.6a$, $y = 0.4b$)

(4) $P(0,\lambda)$

(5) $x = \pm 3/\sqrt{2}, y = 2 \pm 3/\sqrt{2}$.

(Centre is $(0,2)$, radius is 3)
(Find the radii and the
distance apart of the centres.)

(6) (a) $C_1(-1, 2)$. $C_2(1, 3)$. Radii
$\sqrt{10}$ and $\sqrt{5}$.
$A(0, 5)$, $B(2, 1)$.

(Gradient $AB = -2$, Gradient
$C_1C_2 = \frac{1}{2}$)

(b)
$R(\frac{1}{2}a(p^2 + 1/p^2),\ a(p - 1/p))$.

(Gradient of $PQ$ is $2/(q + p)$)

(Put $x = \frac{1}{2}a(p^2 + 1/p^2)$,
$y = a(p - 1/p)$).

## 8.3 Page 69

(1) (i) (a) $x^2 + 3$, (b) $(x + 3)^2$.
(ii) $\{x : x \geq 3\}$
(iii) No. $gf(1) = gf(-1)$.

(2) (a) (i) $f^{-1} : x \to (x + 3)/(2 - x)$
for $x \neq 2$
$ff : x \to (x - 9)/(3x - 2)$ for $x \neq \frac{2}{3}$.
(ii) $x^2 - x + 3$ has no roots.
(b) $a = 5$.

(Use the discriminant.
Refer to 4.2)

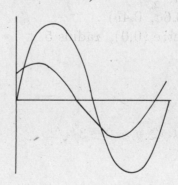

(3) (a) $24°$, $204°$

(b) $0 \leq x \leq 24°$, $204° \leq x \leq 360°$

(4)

(a)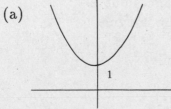

(b)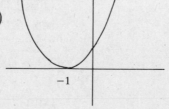

(c)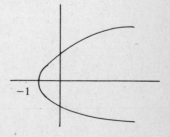

(5)   $x < 0$ or $x > 1$.

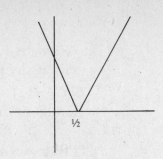

(6)   $2[(x-3)^2 - 4\frac{1}{2}]$.
(a) Shift 3 to right.   (b) Shift down by $4\frac{1}{2}$. (c) Stretch by 2, parallel to $y-$axis.

$f^{-1} : x \rightarrow \sqrt{(\frac{1}{2}x + 4\frac{1}{2})} + 3$. Range $\{x : x \geq 3\}$ Domain $\{x : x \geq -9\}$

(7)

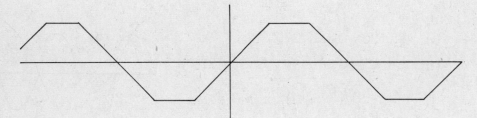

$a = 1\frac{1}{2}$.

(8)

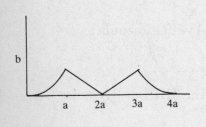
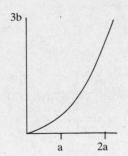
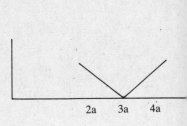

## 9.3 Page 80

(1)   3.386 knots.  003°

(Find the distances out to sea, and use the cos rule.)

(2)   (a)                            (Use the cos rule)

(b) 10.4 cm$^2$

(c) 71.5°                          $(\tan^{-1}(PA/AB))$

(d) 74°                            (Find the distance from $A$ to $BC$).

554

(3)  48.2°, 21.7$m^2$.

(4)  $AF = 2.08$ m  (First find $AD$, then find $DF$.)
     60°.  (Find the distance from $F$ to $AC$.)

## 10.6 Page 90

(1)  (Put over a common denominator.)

(2)  (i) 35°, 145°, 215°, 325°
     (ii) 76°, 256°, 135°, 315°  (Regard as a quadratic in $\tan x$)
     (iii) 90°, 37°, 143°  (Use $\cos^2 x = 1 - \sin^2 x$)

(3)  (i)

     (ii) 49°, 90°, 131°, 270°.

     (iii) 49° $\leq x \leq$ 90°, 131° $\leq x \leq$ 270°.

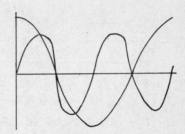

(4)  (i) (a) $\frac{1}{2}$  ($\sin 30°$)
     (b) $\frac{1}{2}$  ($\sin 30°$)
     (c) $1/\sqrt{3}$  ($\tan 30°$)
     (ii) 23.8°, 203.8°  (Use the $\cos(A - B)$ formula)

(5)  0°, 45°, 90°, 135°, 180°, 60°, 120°
(Either $\sin 4x = 0$ or $\cos 4x = \cos x \cos 3x$. Write the RHS as $\frac{1}{2}(\cos 4x + \cos 2x)$.)
(6)  15°, 75°, 90°, 135°.  (Use the factor formulae.)

(7)  $5\cos(x - 53.1°)$

     Max. = 5, at $x = 53.1°$.

     Min. -5, at $x = 233.1°$.

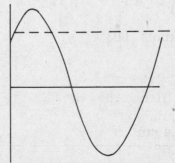

     (i) 98.7°, 7.6°.    (ii) 0 $\leq x <$ 7.6 & 98.7 $< x \leq$ 360°.

## 11.3 Page 96

(1)  (i) $60\frac{1}{2}\theta^2$
(ii) $37\frac{1}{2}\theta^2$
(iii) 0.894
(iv) 28.4 cm.

(2) (a)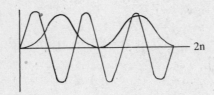

(d) 0, 0.848, 2.29, 3.14, 4,71.
(e) 27%                            (Between 0 & 0.848, and
                                   between 2.29 & 3.14)

(3)  (i) $-\frac{1}{2}\pi$   (ii) $\frac{1}{3}\pi$      (iii) $\frac{1}{2}\pi$

(4)  (a) (i) $r = 25$, $\theta = 1.287$.
(ii) 25, for $\theta = 2.858$.
(iii) Least Positive value 1/30,
for $\theta = 2.858$.
(b) (ii)

                                   (Let the radius be $r$. Express
                                   the angles in terms of $r$ and $x$.)

(5)  0.27

## 12.3 Page 103

(1)  2i - j, 5i - 5j, 2i - 2j, 5i - j - i - 2j
(a) $5\lambda$ i - $\lambda$ j
(b) $(3 - \mu)$i + $(1-2\mu)$j.
$\lambda = 5/11$,  $\mu = 8/11$.          (Equate i and j coefficients).

(2)  (i) m = 19,  n = -3
(ii) 0. Hence they are
perpendicular.
(iii) 33.7°.

(3)                                            $(\underline{BN} = \underline{AB})$

$(2 - q : 1 = q : p)$

$\quad$ $LM : LN = 1{:}4$

$\quad$ $\frac{6}{7}\,\mathbf{i} + \frac{9}{7}\,\mathbf{j} + \frac{18}{7}\mathbf{k}.$

(4)$\quad$ ( i ) $\mathbf{r} = 2\mathbf{i} - \frac{1}{3}\,\mathbf{j} + 2\mathbf{k} + t\,(\mathbf{i} - \frac{2}{3}\,\mathbf{j} + 2\mathbf{k})$

$\quad$ (ii) $3\mathbf{i} - \mathbf{j} + 4\mathbf{k}.$

(5)$\quad$ (i) $4\mathbf{i} + 18\mathbf{j} - 12\mathbf{k}$ and $4\mathbf{i} + 6\mathbf{j}.$

$\quad$ (ii) $4\mathbf{i} + 6\mathbf{j} + t(\mathbf{j} - \mathbf{k})$

$\quad$ (iii) $4\mathbf{i} + 2\mathbf{j} + 4\mathbf{k}.$

$\quad$ (iv) $88°.$

(6)$\quad$ $(0.6, 0.8)$ and $(0.8, -0.6).$

$\quad$ $r = t(1.4, 0.2)$ $\qquad$ (The line goes through $(0,0)$.)

$\quad$ $r = (13, 13) + t(1.4, 0.2)$ $\qquad$ (The line goes through $(13,13)$.)

## 13.4 Page 112

(1)$\quad$ (i) $3x^2 - 3x^{-4}$

$\quad$ (ii) $3x^2 - 4x + 1$

$\quad$ (iii) $-1/162$

$\quad$ (iv) $\frac{3}{4}$

(2)$\quad$ (a) $y = x + 10\frac{2}{3}$

$\quad$ (b) $x = 6$

$\quad$ (c) $\qquad$ (The equation $x^2 - 8x + 16$ has only one root)

(3)$\quad$ $6\frac{2}{3}$

(4)$\quad$ (ii) $h = 1000/\pi r^2$

$\quad$ (ii) Area $= 2000/r + 8/r^2$

$\quad$ $r = 5$, $h = 12.7$, cost $= 6$p

(5)$\quad$ At $(4a, 4a)$

$\quad$ $y = 2x - 4a$, $x = 2y - 4a$

$\qquad$ (Gradients are 2 and $\frac{1}{2}$. Use the $\tan(A - B)$ formula of 10.3)

(6)　(a)

$(AC = y/t.\ AB = 2(x + y/t).$
Height $= tx + y$
(Differentiate with respect to $t$)

　　(b)

$(tx + y = \ell \sin \theta)$
$(S = 2xy)$
(Differentiate with respect to $x$)


**14.5 Page 122**

(1)　(a) (i) $3/(3x+1)$

　　(ii) $\cos 2x - 2x \sin 2x$

　　(b) $7y = x - 11$

　　(c) $-2xy/(x^2 + 2y)$


(2)　(a)

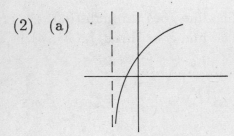

　　(b) $1/e$　　　　　　　　(The curve goes through $(e\text{-}3, 0)$)


(3)　(a) 0.19 cm/s　　　　　$(r = 3.385,\ dA/dr = 8\pi r)$

　　(b) 27　　　　　　　　$(dV/dr = 4\pi r^2)$

　　3.4 cm$^3$　　　　　　(First find $\delta r$)


(4)　$5/(x\text{-}3) - 2/(3x+2)$　　(Refer to 1.2)

　　-4.90625


(5)　(a) $(y - 3x^2)/(3y^2 - x)$

　　　　　　　　　　　　(Put $x = 3y^2$. Show that the
　　　　　　　　　　　　original equation has no root).

　　(b)　　　　　　　　　(For $x = 0$, $y = 1$. The
　　　　　　　　　　　　**derivative is** $>0$.)


(6)　(a) $5y - x = 7\frac{1}{4}a$

　　(b) $(a + y - x)/(y - x - a)$

　　(c) 0.33

(7)   0.02

$(d(\tan x)/dx = \sec^2 x$. Put $x = \frac{1}{4}\pi$

(8)

Gradient $(-b\cos\theta)/(a\sin\theta)$

$U(0, b/\sin\theta), T(a/\cos\theta, 0)$

$M(((a^2-b^2)\cos\theta)/a, 0), N(0, ((b^2-a^2)\sin\theta)/b)$

Product of gradients = -1.

$Q(\frac{1}{2}a/\cos\theta, \frac{1}{2}b/\sin\theta)$

$(a/2x)^2 + (b/2y)^2 = 1$

(Put $x = \frac{1}{2}a/\cos\theta$, $y = \frac{1}{2}b/\sin\theta$, eliminate $\theta$)

### 15.4 Page 131

(1)   (a) (i) $\frac{1}{3}x^3 - x^{2\frac{1}{2}}/2\frac{1}{2} + c$
       (ii) $x^5/5 - \frac{2}{3}x^3 + x + c$
       (b) $y = \frac{2}{3}x^{1\frac{1}{2}} + 3x - 43$,
       $y = 6x - 52$

(2)   $\frac{16\pi}{15}$

(Crosses at $x = 0$ and $x = 2$

(3)   (a)

      (b)

      (c) 95 m³

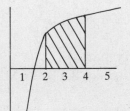

(Integrate $20(3 - 5/t^2)$
from 2 to 4)

(4)

(Integrate $\pi x^2$ with respect to
$y$, from 3 to $3 + h$)

(a) 6.28 secs
(b) (i) 0.354 cm/s
    (ii) 10 cm²/sec

(Put $h = 6$ : divide V by 30)
(Use $dV/dt = dV/dh \times dh/dt$)
(Use $A = \pi x^2$)

(5)

8/15           (Integrate between $t = 0$
and $t = 1$)

(6)

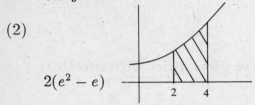

5/6

## 16.4 Page 138

(1)   (a) (i) $-\frac{1}{4}\cos 4x + c$
       (ii) $\sin(\frac{1}{2}x + \frac{1}{2}) + c$
    (b) $\frac{1}{9}\ln 10$

(2)

$2(e^2 - e)$

(3)   $1/(1 + 2x) + (1 - 2x)/(1 + 4x^2)$   (Refer to 1.2)
    0.566

(4)   (i) $e^{2x}(1\frac{1}{2}x + 1\frac{1}{4}) + c$           (By parts)
     (ii) 0.0803                (Use $\cos 2A = 2\cos^2 A - 1$)

(5)   $\frac{1}{2}\pi$                       (Use $\cos 2A = 2\cos^2 A - 1$)

(6)

Domain $\{x : -a \leq x \leq a\}$,
Range $\{-\frac{1}{2}\pi \leq x \leq \frac{1}{2}\pi\}$

                            (Substitute $u = x + 1$)

**17.3 Page 148**

(1) (i) 18

(ii)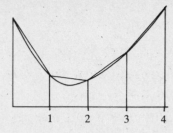

(The trapezia enclose the area)

(2) Tables: 1, 1.41, 3, 5.29, 8.06, 11.22, 14.73
36.53

(3)

(ii) Converges to 1.926

$(dy/dx = 3x^2 + 2 > 0$ for all $x)$

(4)

(Refer to 17.1)

0.33

(5)

(Use parts, twice. Refer to 16.3)

Trapezium rule gives 0.7454

(The trapezium enclose the area.)

(6) (i) 3.79       (Linear interpolation)

(ii) 1.54      (Linear interpolation)

(iii) 3.3593

**18.4 Page 157**

(1) (i) $x^3 - \frac{1}{2}x^5$

(ii) $\frac{1}{2}x^3 - x^5/24$

2

(2) $a = -\frac{1}{2}$, $b = \frac{1}{2}$

(Expand and equate coefficients)

(3)    $x - \frac{1}{2}x^2 + \frac{1}{3}x^3 - \frac{1}{4}x^4 + x^5/5$          $(\log a/b = \log a - \log b)$

Valid for $-1 < x < 1$

Put $x = 1/(2\text{n-}1)$

In $(n/(n - 1)) = 2(1/(2n - 1))$

$+ \frac{2}{3}(1/(2n - 1))^2 + \frac{2}{5}(1/(2n - 1))^5$

Valid for $n > 1$ or $n < 0$

$k = 2$

                           (Put $n = 9$ and $n = 6$)

$\log_e 1.62 \simeq 0.48243$

(4)    $y = 1 + x + \frac{1}{2}x^2 - x^3/6 - 7x^4/24$

                           (Differentiate $(1 + x^2)dy/dx = y$, and put $x = 0$)

(5)    (a)                               (Add the $k+1$th term)

        (b)                               (Add the $k+1$th term)

        (c)                               (Subtract the $k$th term from the $k+1$th).

(6)    $u_1 = 2, u_2 = 4, u_3 = 8$

$\alpha = 2$

## 19.5 Page 168

(1)    1 - 2i

$(x^2 - 2x + 5)(x + 2)$

(2)    $1\frac{1}{2} + i1\frac{1}{2}$ or $\frac{1}{2} + i1\frac{1}{2}$

                           (Substitute $z = x + iy$, equate real and imaginary parts).

(3)    (a) $-2 + 2i$, $\sqrt{8}e^{i2.36}$

        (b)                               (Disc, centre $-\frac{1}{2}$, radius 1)

(4)  (a) $y + 3 = k(x + 1)$
Centre $-3 - i$, radius $\sqrt{8}$

(Equate real and imaginary parts.)
(Eliminate $k$)
circle, centre 3, radius 5

(b) (i)

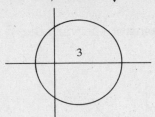

(ii)

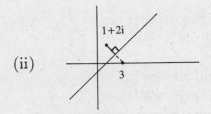

(Perp.bisector of line
from 3 to 1+2i)

(5)  $\tan 5\theta = (t^5 - 10t^3 + 5t)/$
$(5t^4 - 10t^2 + 1)$
$\theta = 0, \pm\pi/5, \pm 2\pi/5,$

(Divide by $c^5$)

(Find the smallest positive root
of $t^5 - 10t^3 + 5t = 0$)

(6)

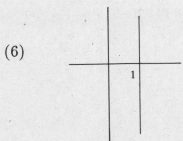

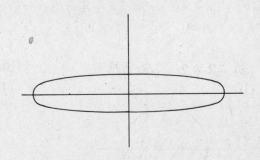

(7) (a)

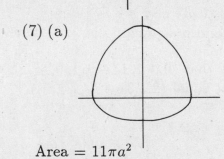

Area $= 11\pi a^2$
(b) $x^2/25 + y^2 = a^2$.

## 20.4 Page 178

(1)  $x = \tan(\frac{1}{2}y^2 + y + \frac{1}{4}\pi)$     (Separate the variables)

(2)  (i) $y = (1+x)^2 e^{-x}$     (Separate the variables)
     (ii) $y^2 = 2x$

(3)  (a) $y = (\frac{1}{2}e^{-x} + c)^2$
     (b) $\frac{2}{3}\cos 3x - \frac{2}{3}\sin 3x$

(4)  (a) $y = kx^2$

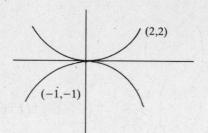
(2,2)
(−1,−1)

     (b) $3e^{-2x} + 2e^{-3x} + x - 1$

(5)  $y = e^{2x^2 - 2}$     $(dy/dx = 4xy)$

## 21.3 Page 186

(1)  (i)                    (Put $s = -2$, $t = 4$)
     (ii) B(5, 8, -6)       (For $s = 2$)
     (iii)                  (No value of $t$)
     (iv) 0.529, 32°

(2)  (a) $a(-4, 4, -1) + \lambda(3, -2, 4)$
     (b) $\mathbf{r} = \lambda(5, -1, -3) + \mu(-4, 4, -1)$
     (c) 0.618
     (d) $\mathbf{r}.(3,-2,4) = 5a$
     $3x - 2y + 4z = 5a. (x + 4a)/3$
     $= (y - 4a)/-2 = (z + a)/4$

(3)                          (Show that $(0, -1, 1) + \lambda(1, 0, 1)$
                             cannot equal $(2,1,3) + \mu(1,-1,2)$)

     (i) (1,-1,-1)
     (ii) 19.5°              $(\underline{AB} = (2,2,2))$
     (iii) $x - y - z = 0$
     (iv) $|AB| = 2\sqrt{3}$.  From $B$ to $\pi =$
     $2/\sqrt{3} = \frac{1}{3}|AB|$.

                             $((\text{ii}) = \sin^{-1}\frac{1}{3})$

(4)

(a) $\begin{pmatrix} 0 & 0 \\ 0 & 0 \end{pmatrix}$ (b) $\begin{pmatrix} 6 & 2 \\ -18 & -6 \end{pmatrix}$ (c) $\begin{pmatrix} 5 & 7 \\ 4 & -8 \end{pmatrix}$ (d) $\begin{pmatrix} -7 & 17 \\ -7 & 17 \end{pmatrix}$

$e = c$ (Disributive) $f = d$(Associative) (i) $A$ contracts the plane to the line $y = x$ (ii) $C$ is a shear parallel to the $x-$axis.

(5)  $M_1^{-1} = \frac{1}{3} \begin{pmatrix} 2 & 5 \\ 1 & 4 \end{pmatrix}$

(i) $\begin{pmatrix} 17 & -16 \\ 13 & -14 \end{pmatrix}$  (Premultiply by $M_1^{-1}$)

(ii) $\begin{pmatrix} 4 & 13 \\ 2 & -1 \end{pmatrix}$  (Post multiply by $M_1^{-1}$)

Area = 60  (Multiply by the determinant)

(6)  (i) $y = 2x$
(ii) $3x + ay = 0$
(iii)  (Put $a = -1\frac{1}{2}$)
(iv)  Take $(x, (d - 3x)/a)$ on the line $3x + ay = d$)

**22.4 Page 200**

(1)  (a) 38 m/s  (b) 16 s
(c) 230 m  (d) 380 m

(2)  (a) $t = 1.2$ s  (b) $10\frac{2}{3}$ m

(3)  30 m/s
3i - 14j  (Put the **i** velocity equal to 0)
1 second. 54i - 108j

(4)  (a) $3\frac{1}{3}$ m/s$^2$  (Find time at constant velocity)
(b) $t = 8$ and $t = 14$  (Find the distances at time $t$.)
72, 210

(5) (i) (a) $t = \frac{1}{4}\pi$           (When the velocity vectors are parallel)

     (b) $t = \frac{3}{4}\pi$

     (ii) $(t+1)e^{-t} - 2\cos t + 1$      (Integrate twice)

(6)   $\mathbf{v} = -\omega a \sin \omega t \mathbf{i} + \omega a \cos \omega t\, \mathbf{j} + b\mathbf{k}$

    $\mathbf{a} = -\omega^2 a \cos \omega t \mathbf{i} - \omega^2 a \sin \omega t\, \mathbf{j}$

    speed $= \sqrt{(\omega^2 a^2 + b^2)}$

    $|\mathbf{a}| = \omega^2 a$

    Particle moves in a spiral with constant speed,

## 23.3 Page 210

(1)   6000 N & 3800 N

    10500 N & 4500 N

(2)   $p = $ -6               (Net force must be $(k, k)$)

                        (Acceleration = (-30, -30))

    -58i - 52 **j**

(3)   (a) 1.4 m/s$^2$             (b) 3.36 N

(4)   $R = 200$ N            $T_1 = 40$ N

(5)   10M

                        (Acc. down is 1 m/s$^2$)

                        (Find the new mass; the upthrust is unchanged)

    (a) $p = 0.2$             (Use $0 = u^2 - 2as$)

    (b) 30 secs            (Find the acceleration of the balloon)

(6)                          (Forces are 16 **i**-2 **j** + 8 **k** and $(6\text{-}t)(\text{-}2\mathbf{i}+2\mathbf{j} - \mathbf{k})$)

                         (Integrate the acceleration)

    At $t = 6$,  $\mathbf{v} = 32\mathbf{i} + 12\mathbf{j} + 15\mathbf{k}$

**24.3 Page 219**

(1)   (a) 5.66 N, 2.83 N

(b) 49°

(2)   $T_1 = 1.47$ N
$T_2 = 2.55$ N
$x = 0.79$ N                          (Along $AB$ the $T$'s cancel out)

(3)   $T = 10.4$ N                          (Resolve at $A$ and and $B$)
$a = 4.606$ m s$^{-1}$
Distance $= 15\frac{2}{3}$ m                (Find the speed when B hits
the floor)

(4)   310 N
0.33 m s$^{-2}$

(5)   $\sqrt{7}$                          (Draw a triangle of forces:
use the cos rule)

**25.2 Page 225**

(1)   $P = 55$,  $Q = 27.5$                (Resolve horiz. and vert.)

(2)   (a) 2 m s$^{-2}$, 36 N, 40 N        (Resolve at A, B and C)
(b) 1 m s$^{-2}$, 33 N, 45 N

(3)   (i)                              (Show that the force down the
plane is greater than friction)

(ii)

(Resolve along and perp. to the plane. Write $\mu = \tan \lambda = \sin \lambda / \cos \lambda$)
Least $P = W \sin(\alpha - \lambda)$, when $\beta = \frac{1}{2}\pi + \lambda - \alpha$

(iii) Least $= W \sin(\alpha + \lambda)$, when $\beta = \frac{1}{2}\pi - \lambda - \alpha$ (Repeat part (ii), with
friction acting down the plane)

567

## 26.3 Page 233

(1)  (a) 3 kg                          (Moments about D)
     (b) C: 10g N, D:5g N

(2)  3.6 m up the ladder              (Resolve and take moments
                                       about the base)

(3)                                    (Resolve and take moments
                                       about the base)

(4)  (a)                               (Note that $\triangle APB$ is isosceles)
     $F = Mg \cot \theta$              (Resolve at B)

     (b)                               (Resolve at B)
     $S = 1\frac{1}{3} Mg \cot \theta$  (Take moments about $A$)
     (c) 3M                            (T is now Mg/$\sin \theta$. Resolve at $B$)

(5)  (i) $2W/\sqrt{3}$, $W/\sqrt{3}$   (Resolve horiz. and vert.
                                       for the disc)
     (ii) $1\frac{1}{3}$ W             (Take moments about $A$ for the rod)
     (iii) 2.4 W, 14° to vertical      (Resolve horiz. and vert. for rod)

## 27.5 Page 243

(1)  (a)                               (Moments about $AB$ and $BC$)
     (b) 23°

(2)  $\frac{1}{4} h (1 + k)$
     $k = \frac{1}{3}$

(3)  $((0.385a, a/6)$
     $1\frac{5}{6}$

                                       (Take moments about C: split the
                                       weight into $x$ and $y$ components)

    (4) (Split the shell up into rings subtending $d\theta$ at the centre. Integrate
from $\theta = 0$ to $\theta = \frac{1}{2}\pi$)

                                       (Take moments about base)

(5)

$\bar{y} = 4b/3\pi$
$\tan \theta = b/a$

(Write $y$ in terms of $x$)
(Use $\cos 2A = 2\cos^2 A - 1$)
(By symmetry)

## 28.5 Page 253

(1)   0.49 Nm                    (Moments about A)

(2)   (a) 8.22 N,  18° to OA
      (b) $y = -\frac{1}{3}x$            (Gradient of line $= -\tan 18°$)
      (c) 13.4 Nm, anticlockwise

(3)   2 N, 60° to AC, 2 from C
      2 N, 60° to AC, 6.93 Nm,
      anticlockwise (if $ABC$ is
      lettered clockwise).

(4)   (i) P = 5                   (Moments about midpoint)
      (ii) 8.94 N
      (iii) $\frac{1}{2}a$
      $2\frac{2}{3}a$                    (Moments about $A$)
      8a Nm, anticlockwise (if $ABCD$
      is lettered clockwise).

## 29.3 Page 259

(1)   4650 J

(2)   (a) 3.265, 8 m s$^{-1}$
      (b) 10000 N
      (i) 3.39 m s$^{-2}$           (ii) 12.1 m s$^{-1}$

(3)   (i) 1000 N                  (Convert to m s$^{-1}$)
      (ii) 1.21 m s$^{-2}$
      (iii) 300 kg

(4)

$14 \text{ m s}^{-1}$
$\mathbf{F_1} = 6\mathbf{i} + 4\mathbf{j} - 12\mathbf{k}$

$\mathbf{F_2} = -4\mathbf{i} - 12\mathbf{j} - 6\mathbf{k}$

$\mathbf{R} = \mathbf{F_2}$

(5)

$3.8\text{gk m s}^{-1}$

(6)  (a)

(b)
Work done $= (7\frac{1}{2}\sin\theta)/$
$(\sin\theta - 0.3\cos\theta)$

(Use scalar product)

(Find a unit vector parallel
to $AB$)
(Subtract $\mathbf{F_1}$ from $\mathbf{F}$)

(Obtain two expressions for $P$,
and eliminate $\sin\alpha$)
(Find the net force at this speed)

(Resolve horiz. and vert. for
the ring)
(T must be positive)

(Distance travelled $= 2\frac{1}{2}$ m.
Use "work = force $\times$ distance")

## 30.4 Page 267

(1)  (a) (i) 93.8°
 (ii) 36 mins
 (b) 26 km hr$^{-1}$,  067.3°

(2)  187 km hr$^{-1}$, at 202°

 4.96 secs

 375 m

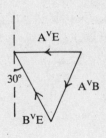

(3)  (i) 43.3 km hr$^{-1}$, 050°

 (ii) 25.7 km, 42.8 min

 199°

(4)  $u_1 = 1$
 $u_2 = 4\sqrt{3}$
 $\sqrt{3}\mathbf{i} + 3\mathbf{j}$

(Let the wind velocity be $x\mathbf{i} + y\mathbf{j}$)

(5)   $\sin \beta = W/V \sin \alpha$

      (The resultant velocity is $u_1 \mathbf{i}$)
(Use $\cos^2 A = 1 - \sin^2 A$)

$U_2 = -W \cos \alpha +$
$\sqrt{(V^2 - W^2 \sin^2 \alpha)}$

(Time is $a/U_2 - a/U_1$)

(6)   (i) $t = 4$ hr,  dist. $= 20$ km

      (Find the position vectors
of A and C)

   (ii) $\lambda = 3$
     $\mu = 6$
   $10/\sqrt{2}$

      (Find $_B\mathbf{v}_A$: the $\mathbf{i}$ component is 0.)
($_C\mathbf{v}_A$ is parallel to $\mathbf{i} + \mathbf{j}$)

## 31.4  Page 274

(1)   (i) 11.6 m
   (iii) 4.08 s
   (v) 141.4 m

      (ii) 37 m s$^{-1}$,  20.8°
(iv) 20.4 m

(2)   (a) 80 m
   (b) 5.8 s
   (c) $5[18.25 - (1\frac{1}{2} - t)^2 ]$
   (d) at $t = 1\frac{1}{2}$ s, 91.25 m
   (e) 88.8 m, 1.4 s

      (Put $t = 0$)
(Put $h = 0$)
(Refer to 4.1)

(3)   (i)
   (ii) 6.4 m
   (iii) 48 m

      (Find horiz. and vert. speeds)

(Use the range formula)

(4)   $H = V^2/2g$
   (a) $\theta = 15°$ or $75°$. 0.0034
   $V^2$, 0.048 $V^2$
   (b) $\theta = 45°$, $R = V^2/9.8$

      (Use $R = V^2 \sin 2\theta/g$)

(5)   (a) 11 cm
   (b) 16.6 m s$^{-1}$

   (i) 15.2°

      (Horiz. speed $= 16$. Find the
vert. speed)
(ii) 4.1°

(6)  (a) $x = (u \cos \alpha)t$, $y =$
$(u \sin \alpha)t - \frac{1}{2}gt^2$
(b) (i)                                                   (Write $\tan \beta = \sin \beta / \cos \beta$)
(ii) $R = (2u^2 \cos \alpha \sin(\alpha - \beta))/$
$g \cos^2 \beta$.                                         ($R \cos \beta = x$)
(iii)                                                     ($y$−speed$/x$−speed $= -\cot \beta$)

## 32.3 Page 285

(1)  5.89 m s$^{-1}$, 45390 J
1.12 m s$^{-1}$, 627.2

(2)  7 m s$^{-1}$, 6 m s$^{-1}$
$R$ - 3500g
$R = 160300$ N

(3)  (a) 250 m s$^{-1}$ and 4 m s$^{-1}$
(b) 1000 N      (c) 4 m

(4)  (a) 4.33 Ns, 26.5° to new line
(b) $7.6 \times 10^6$, at 19° to
original line

(5)  1.5 m s$^{-1}$ 19°
8.2 Ns                                                    (Change of momentum of arrow
and target)

(6)  $\sqrt{(d/g)}(\sqrt{5} - \sqrt{3})$ sec.                    (Speed at floor $= \sqrt{(5gd)}$)
$e = \sqrt{0.8}$
$1\frac{1}{2}d$ high, speed $= \sqrt{(gd)}$

(7)  After first collision: $A$ at
u/5, $B$ at 6a/5
After second collision: $B$
at 2u/5, $C$ at 8u/5.
$B$ is faster than $A$.

(8)   $A$'s speed $= u/6$ in other
      direction.
      (i) Both move at $\frac{1}{3}u$
      (ii) Impulse $= \frac{1}{2}mu$ Ns
      (iii) Time $= 4a/3u$
      (iv) $\frac{1}{3}mu^2$ lost

(9)   (a) (i) $\frac{1}{2}u$   (ii) $\frac{1}{3}$        (iii) $\frac{5}{6}mu^2$
      (b) (i) $\frac{3}{8}v$   (ii) $1\frac{7}{8}mv$        (iii) $0.9375$ mv$^2$

## 33.3 Page 294

(1)   6.93 m                   (First find the constant of
      proportionality)

(2)   u/9                    (Find $v$ in terms of $x$ and $u$)
      (Find the constant of
      proportionality)

(3)   (i)                     (Write $d(\frac{1}{2}v^2)/dx = -4/x^3$,
      and integrate)

      (ii)                   (Write $dx/dt = 2/x$, and integrate)
      Loss $= 0.17778$

      (Work done $= \int F\,dx$)

(4)   $F = 8000$ N, $b = 5$         (Power $=$ force $\times$ velocity)
      (i) 832 secs             ($Mdv/dt = F - 40(100 + bv)$)
      4636 m                 ($Mvdv/ds = F - 40(100 + bv)$)

(5)   (a) 0.231 s            (Integrate $dv/dt = 6e^{-3t}$)
      3 m s$^{-1}$
      (b)                    (Use $vdv/dx = -n^2x$,
      and integrate)

      $\sqrt{3\frac{1}{2}}na$            (Use $vdv/dx = -n^2x^3/a^2$,
      and integrate)

(6)   $v = \sqrt{(8ak - 6a^2k/x - 2kx)}$
      $x = a$ (min), $x = 3a$ (max)    (Put $v = 0$)
      (Write $v = dx/dt$ as $dt = dx/v$
      and integrate)
      457.5 sec.             (Refer to 17.2)

### 34.4 Page 303

(1)  (a) 6.13 N,  2.87 N                (Radius of circle is 0.4 m. Resolve at $B$)

(b) 5.72                                (Lower tension = 0)

(2)  $v^2/r$
speed $= \sqrt{(GM/(R+h))}$          (Length of orbit $= 2\pi(R+h)$)

(3)  (a)                                (Tension $=$ mg.  Resolve at $P$)
(b)                                     (Resolve at $P$)

(4)  $mg(2 + 3\cos\theta)$             (Initial speed $= 2\sqrt{(ag)}$)

(Find the speed at $\theta$.   Resolve perpendicular to the wire) $d\theta/dt = 2\sqrt{(g/a)}\cos\frac{1}{2}\theta$ (Use $v = ad\theta/dt$, and $\cos 2A = 2\cos^2 A - 1$) (Integrate from $\theta = 0$ to $\theta = \frac{1}{2}\pi$. $\int secxdx = \ln(\sec x + \tan x) + c$)

(5)  $v^2 = u^2 - 2ag\cos\theta$        (By energy)
$T = mu^2/a - 3mg\cos\theta$           (Resolve along the string)
                                        (Put T = 0)

(Find the velocity when $\theta = 30°$. Show that the trajectory goes through $(1\frac{1}{2}a, -\frac{1}{2}\sqrt{3}a)$. Refer to 31.3)

### 35.4 Page 312

(1)  (a) $\frac{1}{3}$ m               (Refer to 34.1. The string provides the centripetal force)

(b) $\theta = 60°$, $v = 1.732$.       (Find the tension, and resolve at the particle. Refer to 34.2)

(2)                                     (Take moments about $A$)
$\tan\theta = \frac{3}{4}$             (Resolve horiz. and vert. Normal force $=$ weight, frictional force $=$ tension in string))

(3)                                     ($ABC$ is equilateral)
(i)                                     (Find the tension $T$. Take moments about $A$)

(ii)                                    (Resolve horiz. and vert.)
$3\sqrt{3}\lambda$, at 30° to vertical

(4)  (i) 2.1 m s$^{-1}$                         (First find $\omega$)
     (ii) 0.872 m
     (iii) 0.022 N
     3 secs                                     (Power = force × velocity)

(5)  $A = -3$, $B = 4$, $c = 2$, $n = 3$     (Refer to 20.3)
                                              (Refer to 10.4)

     (i) -1, 7
     (ii) 12, 15

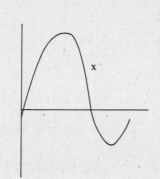   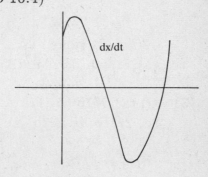

(6)  (i)                                       (Use $dv/dt = v\,dv/dx$.
                                               Refer to 33.1)
     (ii)                                      (Refer to 20.3)
     $a = 5$, $\omega = 2$                     (Use (i))
     Time = 0.142 sec                          (Use (ii))
     Slides.                                   (Greatest acceleration
                                               = 20 m s$^{-2}$ > $\mu g$)

(7)  $\lambda = 140$ Newtons
     Speed = 1.67 m s$^{-1}$                   ($\omega = \sqrt{70}$)
     Height = 0.413 m.

## 36.3 Page 324

(1)  (a) True  (b) True  (c) False
     (d) False                                 (If $B \cap C$, then $A$)
     (e) False                                 (LHS = $\frac{1}{4}$, RHS = $\frac{1}{8}$)

(2)

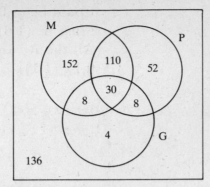

136 study none.
(a) 11/50   (b) 39/125   (c) 37/75

(3)   (i) (a) 2/15 (b) 1/5
(c) 2/15   (d) 2/5   (e) 3/5          (Write out a 6 by 6 table)

(ii)  (a) 1/75                        ($X$ must draw 12 then 13, or
                                      13 then 12, or 13 then 13)

(b) 74/75²                            ($P(X$ does not win$) = 179/180$)

(4)   (a)  (i) 0.855
(ii) 0.145                            ( (ii) = 1 - (i))
(iii) 0.14

(b) (i) 0.266                         (WWL or WLW or LWW)
(ii) 0.578                            (1 - P(WWW)
Most likely WWW, least
likely LWL

(5)   (i) $P(A \cup B) \neq P(A) + P(B)$
$P(A \cap B) = 0.17 \neq P(A) \times P(B)$
(ii) 0.138, 0.19

(6)   (i) 1/50
(ii) 9/50                             (P(Both red) - P(Both red and
                                      maggot-free))
(iii) 27/95                           ( (ii) ÷ P(Both red))
(iv) 0.655

(7)  (a) (i) 9/100                    (Could be (1,0), 2,1), ... (9,8))
     (ii) 1/100                       (Must be (1,0))
     (iii) 3/25                       (All the R cases, and (0,0),
                                      (0,1), (1,1))


     (b) (i) 0.074
     (ii) 0.0811
     (iii) 0.0093


## 37.3 Page 333

(1)  (a) 5040                         $(^{10}P_4)$
     (b) 10000                        $(10^4)$
     (c) 0.496                        $(1 - a)/ (b))$
     (d) 0.9                          $(^{10}P_2 \times 10^2/(b))$

(2)  720                              (6!)
     72                               $(2 \times 3! \times 3!)$
     144                              $(^4P_3 \times 3!)$

(3)  (a) $2 \times 9!$
     (b) (i) 56                       $(^8C_3)$
     (ii) 252                         $(2 \times^9 C_4)$
     (iii) 196                        $(^{10}C_5 -^8 C_5)$

(4)  (i) (a) 302400                   (10!/3!2!)
     (b) 5040                         (7!)
     (ii) (a) 1/12                    $(^5C_3/^{10}C_3)$
     (b) 1/40                         (2E's and 1 L must be taken)

(5) 50400(10!/3!3!2!)
    98


(2 ways in which all are the same, 36 ways with 2 the same, $^5P_3$ ways
with all different) 0.295 (Consider the cases for the first draw: (i) 2S's or 2

T's (ii) 1 S or 1 T, and one A, I or C (iii) 2 A, I or C's)

## 38.3 Page 342

(1)  (i) 14   (ii) 12
(iii) 5.5   (iv) 41
(v) 12.6

(2)  $p = 3$ and $q = -40$          $(50 = 30p + q$ and $15 = 5p)$
38

(3)  For Smith: 111.3.
For Jones: 110.92
116 and 106

(Let the values be $x$ and $y$.
Find two simultaneous equations).

(4)  (a) (i) 2.6,   (ii) 46%
100.4 to 106.4

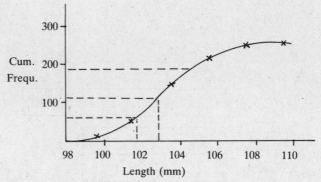

Cum. Frequ. / Length (mm)

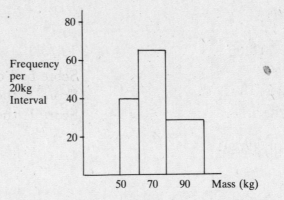

Frequency per 20kg Interval / Mass (kg)

(b) (i)
(ii) 68.4                          (By linear interpolation)

**39.4 Page 351**

(1)

|   | 0 | 1 | 2 | 3 |
|---|---|---|---|---|
| 0 | 0 | 0 | 0 | 0 |
| 1 | 0 | 1 | 2 | 3 |
| 2 | 0 | 2 | 4 | 6 |
| 3 | 0 | 3 | 6 | 9 |

| $i$ | 0 | 1 | 2 | 3 | 4 | 6 | 9 |
|---|---|---|---|---|---|---|---|
| $P(X = i)$ | 7/16 | 1/16 | $\frac{1}{8}$ | $\frac{1}{8}$ | 1/16 | $\frac{1}{8}$ | 1/16 |

$E(X) = 2.25$. Loss of 75 p.

(2)

(i)

| $n$ | 1 | 2 | 3 | 4 |
|---|---|---|---|---|
| $P(X = n)$ | 2/5 | 3/10 | 2/10 | 1/10 |

| m | 1 | 2 | 3 |
|---|---|---|---|
| $P(Y = m)$ | 7/15 | 4/15 | 4/15 |

$E(Y) = 1\frac{4}{5}$

(3)  (i) $\frac{5}{8}$                (Score 5, 4 or 3)
      (ii) 15/64            (Score 1, then 5, 4 or 3)
      (iii) 9/64             (Score 1, then 1)
      $E(X) = 1\frac{33}{64}$, $E(X^2) = 2\frac{53}{64}$,
      $\mathrm{Var}(X) = 0.531$

      (iv) $\frac{3}{4}$
      (v) 3/16
      (vi) 1/16
      $E(Y) = 1\frac{5}{16}$, $E(Y^2) = 2\frac{1}{16}$,
      $\mathrm{Var}(Y) = 0.34$
      $B$ better and more consistent.

(4)  (i)
  (a) $A$, $A'$  (b) $A$,not $A$, $A$          (c) $ABC$ (in any order) then $A$)
  or not $A$, $A$, $A$
  (ii) (a) 1/16,  (b) 3/32,                     (c) 3/64
  (iii) Most likely = 3                         $(P(X = 1) = \frac{1}{4} + 1/16 + 1/16$ etc)
  $E(X) = 2\frac{13}{16}$


(5)  0.619                                       (Find the ways in which $A$
                                                 could win. Use the sum of a
                                                 G.P. Refer to 2.2)

  $B$, with probability 0.52.


  ($P(A$ wins the first non-drawn game) = 0.692. $A$ wins the series if $A$
wins the first two non-drawn games, with probability $0.692^2 < \frac{1}{2}$)

## 40.3 Page 360

(1)                                              ($X$ = number right. $X \sim B$ $(5, \frac{1}{3})$)
        0.373                                    ($Y$ = number who pass. $Y \sim B$ $(4, \frac{131}{243})$)


(2)  (i) 0.165                                   ($X \sim B$ $(5, \frac{1}{3})$)
  (ii) 0.79
        0.738                                    ($Y \sim B$ $(4, \frac{3}{4})$. Find P(Y = 4 or 3))


(3)  (i) 0.346                                   ($X \sim B$ $(4, 0.4)$)
  (ii) 0.04

                                                 $(0.8 \times 0.6 + 0.4 \times 0.9 \times 0.3)$
        0.4736                                   (Wins either 3 or 2 of his
                                                 good first serves)


(4)                                              (Use the series for $e^a$.
                                                 Refer to 18.1)
        2                                        (Let $X$ = demand. Find $P(X = 1)$
                                                 & $P(X = 2)$ & $P(X = 3)$)
  (i) 45.6%                                      ($P(X > 2)$)
  (ii) 0.191
  (Either 1 refusal on both days,
  or 2 refusals on one day
  and none on the other)
  (iii) 0.185                                    ($P(X = 0) + \frac{1}{2}P(X = 1)$)

(5)  (i) (a)                  ($X$ is Poisson, mean $\frac{1}{4}$)
       (b) $1\frac{1}{2}$             ($X$ is Poisson, mean $1\frac{1}{2}$)
       (ii) 0.577         ($X$ is Poisson, mean 3)
       (iii) 0.025

(6)  (i) 0.11               ($P(X = 0)$)
       (ii) 0.181
       (iii) 5 days        (If n days, (i)$^n$ < 0.0001)
       0.369              ($Y$ = number of days. $Y \sim B$
                                (7, 0.181))

## 41.3  Page 370

(1)  (i)
       (ii) 1.75, 0.5375

(2)  11/128
       $E(X) = \frac{3}{4}$, Var$(X)$ = 19/80

(3)  $P(X \le t) = 2kt - \frac{1}{2}kt^2$        (Integrate)
       $\frac{1}{2}$

(4)  (i) A = 3
       (ii) $1\frac{1}{2}$, $\frac{3}{4}$
       (iii) 3/125

                                 (Find$P(X < n + 1 | X > n)$)

(5)  (i) $\frac{2}{3}$  (ii) $\frac{2}{3}$  (iii) $\frac{1}{3}x$

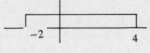

       (iv) $x/6 + \frac{1}{3}$        (Consider the areas of rectangles)
       (v) 1

       $\frac{1}{3}$ for $0 \le t \le 2$
       $f(t) = 1/6$ for $2 \le t \le 4$        (Find the c.d.f.)
       0 elsewhere
       $E(|X|) = 1\frac{2}{3}$

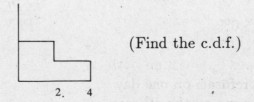

(6)                                          (By integration)

$a = 92.2, \quad A = 1/92.2$

(i) 0.114                                     (Use the c.d.f.)

(ii) 0.338                                    $(P(T > 300|T > 200))$

(iii) 0.202                                   $(2 \times P(T > 200) \times P(T < 200))$

## 42.5 Page 382

(1)   $V(X) = \int x^2 f(x)dx - (\int x f(x)dx)^2$
      $V(X)$ is also $\int (x - \mu)^2 f(x)dx$
      $Var(Y) = \frac{7}{9}$                  $(E(X_1) = E(X_2) = 1/6, Var(X_1)$
                                              $= Var(X_2) = 7/180)$

      $Y$ goes from -2 to 4

(2)   $np, np(1 - p)$                         (Refer to 40.1)
                                              $(X \sim B(20, \theta))$
                                              $(Y \sim B(10, 2\theta))$

      $Var(P_1) = \theta(1 - \theta)/20$
      $Var(P_2) = \theta(1 - 2\theta)/20$
      Choose Method 2.                        (Variance is smaller)

(3)   (i) 7.55, 7.95
      7.55, 8.37
      (ii) 2.75, 2.3125
      (a) 0.5, 9.25
      (b) 0, 4.625

(4)   $Var(X) = 0.8$

| $i$ | 0 | $\frac{1}{2}$ | 2 |
|---|---|---|---|
| $P(X = i)$ | 0.36 | 0.32 | 0.32 |

$((X_1 - X_2)^2$ can only be 0, 1 or 4)

$E(T) = 0.8$

**43.4 Page 392**

(1)  (i) 0.2  (ii) 0.6  (iii) 0.3
424.4 grams

(2)  (a) 1.881                    ($\Phi$ (1.881) = 0.97)
(b) 0.496                    ($\Phi$ (0.496) = 0.69)
(c) 15.6                     ((25-13)/(1.881+0.496) = 5)
(d) (i) 0.0644  (ii) 0.067            ($\mu$ = 15.6)

(3)  (a) 44  (b) 4.954
54.5%,  68.3%                (Assuming that it is normal)

(4)  (i) 0.159
(ii)                        ($B$'s prob. = 0.19)
(iii) 0.584                  ($B - A \sim N$ (0.2, 0.89))

(5)  (i) (a) $\frac{1}{2}$
(b) 0.759                   (B(100, 0.025))
(c) 0.072                   (B(100, 0.375) $\simeq$ N(37.5, 23.44))
(ii) 158

(Sample proportion $\zeta \simeq$ N(0.6, 0.24/n).  Require 1.282 $\times \sqrt{(0.24/n)} <$ 0.05)

(6)  $Y \sim N(n\mu, n\sigma^2)$
(If $n = 9, P(Y > 725 = 1 - \Phi(5.5))$)

(i) 0.0111
(ii) 0.739
By above, N = 9
0.132                       ($0.8^9 \times 0.9798$)

(7)  (i)                        (By symmetry)
0.1                        (Area of rectangle)
(ii) 4, 3/100
0.92                       ($\overline{X} \sim N(4, 3/100)$)
(iii) $1 \leq x \leq 2.2$ or $5.8 \leq x \leq 7$
Prob. = 0.4

**44.5 Page 405**

(1)  (a) $0.44 < p < 0.5$
(b) $53 < \mu < 54.4$                    (Find the unbiased sample
variance)

(2)  (a) 6.122, 0.0175
(b) $6.091 < \mu < 6.153$                (Using the figures in (a))
$z = 1.74$. No sig. difference at 5%.

(The variance of the difference
of the sample means is
$4.77 \times 10^{-4}$)

It is assumed that the
populations are normal.

(3)  For $A$ : $z = 1.77$.
Significantly better.                (A 1-tailed test)
For $B$ : $z = 1.49$.
Not significant.
Total mean $= 45.9$
$z = 2.29$. Significantly
better.
Variance $= 223$                     (Find $\sum X^2$ for $A$ and $B$.
Combine these)

(4)  (i) $E(\hat{p}_1) = p_1$, $\mathrm{Var}(\hat{p}_1) = p_1$
$(1 - p_1)/n$
(ii) $E(\hat{p}_2 - \hat{p}_1) = p_2 - p_1$,
$\mathrm{Var}(\hat{p}_2 - \hat{p}_1) = (p_1(1 - p_1)$
$+ p_2(1 - p_2))/n$
(a) $z = 2.31$. Significantly wrong
at 5%.
(b) $z = 1.73$. Not significantly
wrong at 5%.

(If $p_1 = p_2$, estimate $p_1$ as 0.403)

**45.4 Page 416**

(1)   (a) (i) 0.02, 0.012

(ii) $-0.08 < \mu < 0.12$                (Using a $t_4$ distribution)

(b) $£85.3 < \mu < £87.5$

$-£0.1 < D < £2.5$

$£0$ is included in the interval.

Hence the claim is not disproved.

(2) For a paired sample test, there must be a natural association between the members of each pair.

$H_0$ : no difference

$H_1$ : old tyres wear more

$t_7 = 2.65$. Reject $H_0$ at 5%

$0.044 < D < 0.266$

(3)   The differences might be
due to chance.

$\chi^2 (4) = 4.42$. Not significant.

$\chi^2 (4) = 9.94$. Significant at 5%.   (Combine the figures)

(4)   (a) $\chi^2 (3) = 9.5$. Significant at
5%. Not a good fit.

(b) The odd group is 35-39

It would be fairer to combine
this group with the 40-49 group.

(5)   (a) $\chi^2 (2) = 32.5$. Significant.

(b) $\nu = (4\text{-}1)(2\text{-}1) = 3$

8.12 is significant at 5%.

There is a difference.

(c) $\nu = 6$. 9.32 is not significant.

No proved difference.

## 46.4 **Page 430**

(1)  $\ln y = \ln A + B \ln x$ . Plot $\ln y$ against $\ln x$ .

| $\ln x$ | .182 | .322 | .457 | .615 | .806 | .997 | 1.128 |
|---|---|---|---|---|---|---|---|
| $\ln y$ | .621 | .829 | .967 | 1.267 | 1.556 | 1.842 | 2.037 |

$B = 1.5,\quad A = 1.41$

3rd term should be (1.58, 2.807)

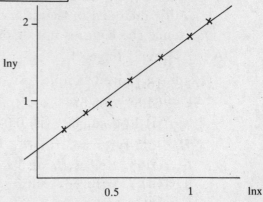

(2) (a) $y/\sqrt{x} = ax + b$
$a = -1.25,\ b = 1.8$
(b) (i) $\ln y$ against $x$
$\ln Y$ against $\ln(X+1)$
(ii) gradient $= -k$. Intercept $= \ln h$.
gradient $= q$. Intercept $= \ln p$.

(3) $(i) y = 4.2x + 3.7$
(ii) Var $(b) = \frac{1}{2}^2 (1 + 81/249)/10$
Interval $= 3.7 \pm 0.47$

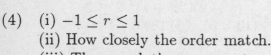

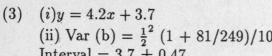

(4) (i) $-1 \le r \le 1$
(ii) How closely the order match.
(iii) The populations may not
necessarily be correlated.

(10.5, 11.8) is far from the line.
Spearman's coefficient $= 0.85$
(For tied ranks, at 9 say, allot $9\frac{1}{2}$
each)
This is significant at 1% to show that
there is a correlation.

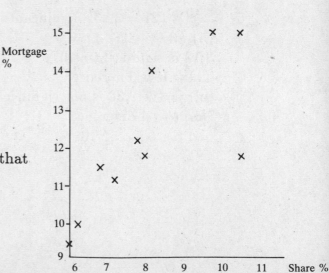

# Solutions to Test Papers

## AS Paper I  Page 441

(1)  16:1

(2) $y = 3x,\ y = -3x + \pi(\pi/6, \pi/2)$

(3)  64.5°, 205.5°

(4) (i) $-\frac{1}{2}$, (ii) $-2\frac{3}{4}$

(5)  (i) 1.57 cu. in.  (ii) 0.032 in

(6)  $1 + 1\frac{1}{2}x + \frac{3}{8}x^2 - \frac{1}{16}x^3$. 1138

(7)  (i) $-\frac{1}{2}x^{-1\frac{1}{2}} + \frac{1}{2}x^{-\frac{1}{2}}$

(ii) $2x\cos x - x^2\sin x$

(iii) $6x/(1 + 3x^2)$

(8)  (i) $\sqrt{x} - 3.\ \{x : x \geq 0\},\ \{y : y \geq -3\}$

(ii) $\sqrt{(x - 3)}.\ \{x : x \geq 3\},\ \{y : y \geq 0\}$

(9)  (i) 16/13  (ii) 0.262

(10)  (i) 11.3

(ii) 10.58

(iii) 69.3°

(iv) 41.4°

(11)  (i) $\lambda = -2$

(ii) $\mu = 2$

(12)  $x = -1,\ y = 0.\ 1.39.\ 2.36.$

(13) 0.6823

(14)  (a) -9  (b) 0

$(x - 2)(2x + 1)^2\ x \leq 2$

(15)  (a) (7,4)  (b) $4y + x = 23$  (c) (13,2.5)  (d) (8,0)

## AS Paper II  Page 444

(1)  (i) $\frac{1}{8}\theta$

(ii) $\frac{1}{8}(\theta - \sin\theta)$

(iv) $dx/d\theta = \frac{1}{4}\sin\frac{1}{2}\theta$

$dx/dt = \frac{1}{4}\sin\frac{1}{2}\theta\, d\theta/dt$

(v) (a) 0.03

(b) 0.005

(2)  (a) (i) 2

(ii) $y = -\frac{1}{2}x + 2\frac{1}{2}$

(iii) $(-4, 4\frac{1}{2})$

(iv) $y = -3x - 7\frac{1}{2}$

(b) (i) 3x, $1152/(3x^2)$

(ii) $8 \times 24 \times 6$

(3)  (a) $\cos^2 x = \frac{1}{2}(\cos 2x + 1), \pi - 2$

(b) 2, 3.45

(4)  (i) 0.36 m s$^{-2}$

(ii) 0.53 m s$^{-2}$

(iii) 0.32 m s$^{-2}$  2.1°

(5)  $d^2x/dt^2 = -49x.\ 0.224$ sec

(6) Tension $= 4.8$ N. 66°

(7)  (i) 10 m

(ii) 14.3°

(iii) 11 m

(iv) 5 sec

## AS Paper III Page 447

(1)  $7\pi/24,\ -\pi/24,\ 23\pi/24,\ -17\pi/24$     (2) 0.69

(3)  0.41 m s$^{-2}$     (4) $x = 0$ or $\pm 1.9$

(5)  $y = -2x + 3.(1\frac{1}{2}, 0), (0, 3).2\frac{1}{4}$

(6)  $\{x : x \neq 4\}\ f^{-1} : x \to (3 + 4x)/x.$    $f°f : x \to (3x - 12)/(19 - 4x)$

     Domain $\{x : x \neq 0\}$

(7)  11.25 N. 1.22 secs.    (8) 2554 N

(9)  (i) -0.5$\mathbf{i}$ + 0.3$\mathbf{j}$   (ii) 0.583    (iii) 0.4 J

(10  $h = 1000/\pi r^2.$

     $A = 2\pi r^2 + 2000/r.$  1:2

(11)  $a = 1/30$ m s$^{-2}.$   $2\frac{1}{3}$ m s$^{-1}$     32 sec

(13)  $e^x(A\cos x - A\sin x + B\sin$      $A = B = \frac{1}{2}$

     $x + B\cos x)$

     $\int 5e^x \cos x\, dx = 2\frac{1}{2}e^x$      $a = 1,\ b = -2,\ c = 2.$

     $(\cos x + \sin x)$

(14)  $T = 1\frac{1}{3}$ mg, $a = \frac{1}{3}g$

## AS Paper IV Page 450

(1)  $2 < x < 3$    (2) $y = 5x - 4$

(3)  (a) $1 + 2x$    (b) $6\sin 3x \cos 3x$

(4)  3    (5) $\theta : \sin\theta$

(6)  10.04    (7) (i) $1 + 8x + 24x^2 + 32x^3 + 16x^4$

     (ii) -160    (8) 123°

(9)  (i) 0.011 cm/sec    (ii) $3\frac{1}{3}cm^2/\sec$

(10) 2.11 cm    (11) (i) 7   (ii) $2\frac{1}{3}$

(12) (0,0),  (1,1), $\frac{1}{3}$

(13)

| $i$ | 0 | 1 | 2 | 3 |
|-----|---|---|---|---|
| $P(X = i)$ | $\frac{1}{3}$ | $\frac{1}{2}$ | 0 | 1/6 |

$E(X) = 1$

(14) (i) 51.97, 15.8    (ii) 26

(15) (i) 0.201    (ii) 0.624.  14

(16) (i) $k = 3$   (ii) $2\frac{3}{4}$    (iii) 2.79

(17) (i) 0.01    (ii) 0.655

(18) (a) (i) 30 m s$^{-1}$    (ii) 0.4 m s$^{-2}$

     (iii) 115 m    (b) 75 sec

(19) (i) 0.483 m s$^{-1}$    (ii) 2520 N

(20) 1.63 m s$^{-2}$. $\frac{2}{3}$ sec. 1.361 m

(21) (a) $v_p = 6t\mathbf{i} + 2\mathbf{j}$,      $v_q = \mathbf{i} + 3t\mathbf{j}$

    (b) $\sqrt{148}$      (c) $t = \frac{1}{3}$

    For $t = 1$, $\mathbf{r}_p = \mathbf{r}_q = 7\mathbf{i} + 1\frac{1}{2}\mathbf{j}$

(22) 383 m. 180 m s$^{-1}$, at 33.7°
    to horiz. 3000 J

## A Paper I Page 457

(1)   30240          (2) $k < 4/9$

(3)   (i) $\frac{2}{3}\pi$          (ii) $4\pi$

    (iii) $2\pi$

(4)   1/(x-1) - 1/(x+1). -2 - $2x^2$

(5)   (i) $(2\cos 2x)/(\sin 2x)$      (ii) $\cos x/\sin x - \sin x/\cos x$

(6)   $1 + x - \frac{1}{2}x^2 + \frac{1}{2}x^3$.   10.099505

(7)   $-3. y = -3x - 2. (-\frac{3}{8}, -\frac{7}{8})$      (8) $\tan\frac{1}{2}x + c$

(9)   $(x - 1)(2x + 1)(x + 3). x < -3$

    and $-\frac{1}{2} < x < 1$

(10) Common difference = log

    (common ratio)          (11) 3.24

(12) $13\cos(\theta - 67.4°)$. Max 1/7,
    min 1/33

(13) $\mathbf{r} = 2\mathbf{i} - 9\mathbf{j} + 11\mathbf{k} + \lambda$

(3$\mathbf{i}$ + 6$\mathbf{j}$ - 2$\mathbf{k}$). Put $\lambda$=4. $\mathbf{r}$ is at B.
    $3x + 6y - 2z = 28$. B is the
    reflection of $A$ in $\Pi$.

(14) $dy/dx = 3y. y = Ae^{3x}$.
    $y = e^{3x-3}$.   0.317

(15) (i) 2 - i.   $a$=-4, $b$=5

    (ii) $\sqrt{2}$, 45°   (a) $n = 2, 6, 10$ etc   (b) $n = 4, 12, 20$ etc

## A Paper II Page 460

(1)   (a) 2525 J          $R = -3\mathbf{i} - 12.9\mathbf{j}$. $\mu = 0.23$

(2)   $50 (2 \times 10^7/r)^3$.          31,600 m s$^{-1}$

(3)   (iii) $mV^2/a - 13\,mg$

(4)   (i) $g\sin\alpha$          (ii) $g(M + m\cos^2\alpha)$

    (iii) $(m\,\sin\alpha\,\cos\alpha)/(M + m\,\cos^2\alpha)$

(5)   (i) 17.89 m s$^{-1}$

(6)   2/15   (a) $\frac{1}{8}$          (b) 41/72   (c) 8/31

(7)

| Gain | £5 | £3 | £1 | £0 | |
|------|-----|--------|--------|------------|------|
| Prob. | $1/20$ | $19/20^2$ | $19^2/20^3$ | $(19/20)^3$ | 54 p |

(8) (i) 0.95          (ii) 0.472
    (iii) 0.679

(9) (ii) 1, 0.142        (iii) $\frac{1}{3}\pi$
    (iv) 0.91

(10) Sig. evidence at 1%. $0.65 \pm 0.1$

(11) (i) $y \geq 2$ or $y \leq -2$.   $x = 0$, $y = x$(ii) $\pi/6$

(12) (i) (a) 13, $-23°$   (b) 1, $90°$     (ii) 12   (iii) $|z + 1 + i| \geq 4$

(13) 3.513                (14) $y = -x + 2 - e^x - e^{-2x}$.
                                   Max at (0,0). None.

(15) $\lambda = -1$.            $\mathbf{r}.(\mathbf{i} + 2\mathbf{j} - \mathbf{k}) = -1$.   $11°$, $0°$

## A Paper III Page 465

(1) $b = \frac{1}{4}$, $a = \frac{3}{4}$          (2) 1.505

(3) $102°$ and $10.2°$        (4) $y = e^{x^2} - 1$

(6) (a) 1/7   (b) -1.19      (7) 1, 3    (8) 0.786

(9) (a) none   (b) $(1, e^{-1})$, max.     (c) (0,0) min., $(2, 4e^{-2})$ max.

(10) (ii) $\sqrt{48}$, $\sqrt{32}$      (11) (b) 0.09   (c) $1\frac{1}{3}\pi ab^2$

(12) (b) -5, 12. 13, $112.6°$      (c) circle, centre 3+4i, radius
                                   6. Max = 11

(13) $2\mathbf{i} + \mathbf{k}$. $a(\mathbf{i} + \mathbf{j} + 2\mathbf{k}) + \lambda(2\mathbf{i} + \mathbf{k})$

## A Paper IV Page 468

(1) 11.7 sec          (2) 1.38g

(3) 0.056            (4) $18.4°$

(5) 0.3               (7) At $(3\frac{1}{9}, 2\frac{2}{9})$
                             (B as origin). $4\frac{4}{9}$

(8) $eu.2a\sin\theta$        (9) 1.96 m s$^{-2}$. 0.784 m s$^{-1}$

(10) 1:0.32

(11) (i) $Q = 5\sqrt{2}, P = 5$.   (ii) 1.782 N, at 22° to BC.
7.6 m from C.

(12) $^5\sqrt{(a^4 + a^5)}$

## A Paper V Page 471

(1)   a = 0.45, b = 0.1   (2) (a) $\frac{1}{2}$  (b) $\frac{2}{3}$
(3)   2598960, 0.002   (4) (i) $\frac{1}{4}$  (ii) 0, 2  (iii) $\frac{1}{2}$
(5)   17.37, 4.202, 0.012   (6) $37\% < p < 43\%$. 9220
(8)   (i) 0.195   (ii) 0.271
      (iii) 0.624   (iv) 0.198
(9)   -0.97, -0.43, 0, 0.43, 0.97.   93, 11, 103 cm.
(10)  252, $26\frac{2}{3}$. $2.47 < \mu < 2.57$.
      55 times

(11)

$$F_R(x) = \begin{cases} 0 & \text{for} \quad x \leq 0 \\ x & \text{for} \quad 0 \leq x \leq 1 \\ 1 & \text{for} \quad x \geq 1 \end{cases} \quad F_A(x) = \begin{cases} 0 & \text{for} \quad x \leq 0 \\ \sqrt{(x/\pi)} & \text{for} \quad 0 \leq x \leq \pi \\ 1 & \text{for} \quad x \geq \pi \end{cases}$$

$E(A) = \frac{1}{3}\pi$, Var(A) $= 4\pi^2/45$. 0.64

(12) $P(X = i) = \frac{1}{8} \times \frac{7}{8}^{i-1}$, for i = 1, 2, 3,
.... $E(X) = 8$. 23 shots. 0.13

(13)

(i)

| $i$ | 0 | 1 | 2 | 3 |
|---|---|---|---|---|
| $P(X = i)$ | 0.5 | 0.2 | 0.2 | 0.1 |

(ii) 0.9, 1

(iii) No. $P(X = 2 \& Y = 0) \neq P(X = 2) \times P(Y = 0)$

(iv) 0.5

(v)

| $j$ | 0 | 1 | 2 |
|---|---|---|---|
| $P(Y = j)$ | 0.2 | 0.6 | 0.2 |

(14)   0.974      0.167      11 minutes to 9

## A Paper VI Page 475

(1)   $s = 6gt - 36g + 36ge^{-t/6}$          $s = -6v - 36g \ln(1 - v/6g)$

(2)   0.397

(3)   $AB : 30\sqrt{2}th, CD : 10\sqrt{2}th.$
$AE : 30te. DE : 10te. BE : 10\sqrt{2}th.$
$CE : 10\sqrt{2}te. BC : 20th.$

(4)   $(220 + 8h + h^2)/(176 + 4h).$
$h < 11.5$

(5)   $v^2/a$, towards the centre.
(i) $\frac{1}{3}u(1 - 2e)$, $\frac{1}{3}u(1 + e)$          (ii) $(1 - 2e)^2 : 2(1 + e)^2$
(iii) $2\pi a/eu$
Ultimately the masses go round
together at $\frac{1}{3}u$.

(6)   5.64 N at 16° to $AB$. 0.55 m
from B. 2.414 Nm

(7)   (i) $\frac{1}{3}u(1 + e)$  (ii) $\frac{2}{15}u(1 + e)^2$          (iii) $e \geq 0.382$.   0.47

(8)   (ii) $2\sqrt{(ga)}$. $2a$          (9) $\omega^2 = \sqrt{(g/\rho L)}$, $\delta\sqrt{(g/\rho L)}$,
$\frac{1}{2}\pi\sqrt{(\rho L/g)}$

(10)  302°.   0.693 hrs.

(11)  $dT/dt = -\lambda(T - 10)$.          (i) 37.8°  (ii) 9.35 min
$T = Ae^{-\lambda t} + 10$.

(12)

(i)

| $i$ | 0 | 1 | 2 |
|---|---|---|---|
| $P(X = i)$ | 0.648 | 0.315 | 0.037 |

(ii)   0.441    (iii) 0.75

(13)  (i) 1/13    (ii) 6/13    (iii) 1.787

(iii)

| $i$ | 0 | 1 | 2 | 3 |
|---|---|---|---|---|
| $P(|X| = i)$ | 4/13 | 5/13 | 3/13 | 1/13 |

(12)

| $i$ | 0 | 1 | 4 | 9 |
|---|---|---|---|---|
| $P(X^2 = i)$ | 4/13 | 5/13 | 3/13 | 1/13 |

(14)   (i) 0.135   (ii) $e^{-4t}$. $E(T) = \frac{1}{4}$.   Median = 0.173 hr.   0.135

(15)   54 tins. $z = 1.6$, not significant. 0.0287

(16)

$$X$$

|     |   | 0 | 1 | 2 |
|-----|---|------|------|------|
|     | 0 | 9/38 | 3/19 | 2/19 |
| $Y$ | 1 | 3/19 | 3/38 | 6/95 |
|     | 2 | 2/19 | 6/95 | 3/95 |

$E(X) = E(Y) = 0.7$

$E(XY) = 87/190$

(v)

| $i$ | 0 | 1 | 2 |
|-----|------|------|------|
| $P(X = i)$ | 10/19 | 5/19 | 4/19 |

(17)   (i) Method 1: 0.086, Method 2: 0.104

  (ii) Method 1: 0.149,  Method 2: 0.178

  Method 1 better.

(18) (i) 3  (ii) 4.218          (iii) 0.21, 1.02

(19) $z = 1.85$. Sig. Yes.

  $0.155 < p < 0.345$

(20) (ii) (166, 73)          (iv) 171 cm, 76.6 kg

  (v) Spearman = 0.786

(21) 48.725, 240. $\chi^2$ (3) = 6.3. Good fit(22) 0.61. $t_9 = 1.225$. Not sig.


## A Paper VII Page 481

(1)   $n=2$. 2.35. 2.4418

(2)   (i) $(1/\sqrt{35})$ $(3\mathbf{i} + 5\mathbf{j} + \mathbf{k})$,

  $(1/\sqrt{18})$ $(4\mathbf{i} - \mathbf{j} - \mathbf{k})$

  $\mathbf{r} = \lambda$ $(1.45\mathbf{i} + 0.61\mathbf{j} - 0.07\mathbf{k}$          (ii) $(1/\sqrt{594})$ $(-4\mathbf{i} + 7\mathbf{j} - 23\mathbf{k})$

(3)   (i) $-2 < x < -1$          (ii) $x < -1$  (iii) $x \le -1\frac{1}{2}$

(5)   (i) $\alpha h \sec^2 \theta$          (ii) $\frac{2}{3}\alpha\pi h^3 \tan\theta \sec^2\theta$

  (iii) $2\pi\alpha h^2 \tan\theta \sec^2\theta + \alpha\pi h^2 \sec^3\theta$

  $+\alpha\pi h^2 \sec\theta \tan^2\theta$

(6)   (i) $\frac{1}{3}\pi$          (ii) $\frac{1}{2}\ln 5$. $\theta < 2.68$ and $\theta > 5.82$

(7)  (a) $\sqrt{(gh/32)}$

( b) $1\frac{1}{2}h$

(8)  $\frac{3}{4}a. \frac{1}{3}$ mgh.  $h = 1\frac{1}{2}a$

(10) (i) 47/200  (ii) 0.217

(11) (i) $\chi^2$ (3) = 10.4 sig.

(ii) $\chi^2$ (2) = 1.68 not sig.

(12) 0.0915. 3247 galls. 18855 galls.

(13) (i) P: circle, radius 2a,
centre origin. Q: ellipse,
axes of length 5a and 3a.

(ii) min. $w = 2a$,  at $z = a$

(14) $(t, kt^2 + k - 1).y = kx^2 + k - 1. A : k = \frac{1}{2}. B : k = 2.$

(15) (i)

$$\begin{pmatrix} 0 & 1 \\ 0 & 0 \end{pmatrix} \quad \text{(Many others)}$$

$(ii)$ $\begin{pmatrix} 0 & 1 \\ 1 & 0 \end{pmatrix}$ $\begin{pmatrix} -1 & 0 \\ 0 & -1 \end{pmatrix}$ $\begin{pmatrix} -1 & 0 \\ 0 & 1 \end{pmatrix}$  (Many others)

$(iii)$  $A = \begin{pmatrix} 0 & 1 \\ 0 & 0 \end{pmatrix}$  $B = \begin{pmatrix} 1 & 0 \\ 0 & 0 \end{pmatrix}$  (Many others)

(16) (i) (a) $\left\{x : x \neq \frac{1}{2}\pi \text{ or } 1\frac{1}{2}\pi\right\}$

(b) $\{x : x \neq \pi\}$  (c) all $x$.

(ii) (a) $-2(1 + \cos x)^{\frac{1}{2}} + c$

(b) $\sqrt{2} \ln (\sec \frac{1}{2}x + \tan \frac{1}{2}x) + c$

(c) $x \cos^{-1} x - (1 - x^2)^{\frac{1}{2}} + c$

(17) $-20 = RT - (R^2/2000)(1 + T^2)$.  $R^2 > 4 \times (R^2/2000)(R^2/2000 - 20)$
1019.8 m. 979.8 m.

(18) $\tan \alpha = 5/9$

(19) (i) $P(X = i) = (n/N)((N - n)/N)^{i-1}$

(20) (i) 0.359  (ii) 0.819

(iii) 0.217  (iv) $\frac{2}{3}$

## A Paper VIII Page 488

(1) (a) $\{y : y \neq 1\}$, $\{x : x \neq -2\}$    (b) $\{y : y \geq 0\}$, $\{x : x \neq -2\}$
(c) $\{y : y \neq \pm 1\}$, $\{x : x < -2 \text{ or } x \geq -1\}$

(2) (i) $\frac{1}{4}\pi^2$                  (3) $t^2 y + x = 2ct$. (ii) $4c^2$
(iii) $s = \frac{1}{2}c^2(1 + t^{-4})$

(4) n=1. 1.31

(5) (a) $-\frac{1}{2} \pm i\frac{1}{2}\sqrt{3}, e^{i\frac{2}{3}\pi}, e^{i1\frac{1}{3}\pi}$.    (b) $z_1 = 3 + 3i$, $z_2 = 4 + 2i$

(6) (i) $1 - \frac{1}{2}x + \frac{3}{8}x^4 - \frac{5}{16}x^3$    (ii) $1 + \frac{1}{2}x^2 + \frac{3}{8}x^4 + \frac{5}{16}x^6$
(iii) $x + \frac{1}{6}x^3 + \frac{3}{40}x^5 + \frac{5}{112}x^7$. 0.524

(7) (i) $2r\cos\theta$                  (ii) $4\theta r^2 \cos^2\theta$
(iii) $\frac{1}{2}r^2 \sin 2\theta$            (iv) $\frac{1}{2}r^2(\pi - 2\theta - \sin 2\theta)$

(8) 8.544. 26.3°. $DE = 3.9$. 93°    (9) (a) $\sqrt{(3 + \sqrt{8})}$

(10) (i) $3\mathbf{i} + 3\mathbf{k}$ (ii) $2\mathbf{i} + \frac{1}{2}\mathbf{j} + 2\frac{1}{2}\mathbf{k}$   $1\frac{1}{3}\mathbf{i} + \frac{1}{3}\mathbf{j} + 1\frac{2}{3}\mathbf{k}$. 73.2°

## A Paper IX Page 491

(1) (i) 1.25                (ii) 5.48
(iii) $\lambda = \ln 3$. 5.46

(2) $\ell = 1$, $m = -1$         (i) $x - y + z = 0$.
(ii) $x = -3 + \lambda$, $y = -\lambda$,
$z = -3 + \lambda$. $2\sqrt{3}$.

(3) $S(3\cos\theta, -6\sin\theta).r = \sqrt{180}$,
$\cos\alpha = 6/\sqrt{180}, \sin\alpha = 12/\sqrt{180}$
Max. $= \sqrt{180}$, for S at
$(18/\sqrt{180}, -72/\sqrt{180})$

(4) (a) (i) $1\frac{9}{14}$      (ii) $4 - 2\sqrt{e}$      (iii) $\ln 2$ (b) $2\frac{2}{3}$

(5) (i) $1 - 2x + 1\frac{1}{2}x^2$      (ii) $3/(1 + 6x) - x/(1 + 2x^2)$

(6) At 016°.9.66secs.$v_0 = 8.49$
km hr$^{-1}$. $v_1 = 12$ km hr$^{-1}$.

(7) $(\frac{3}{8}, \frac{2}{5})$, $(\frac{5}{16}, 0)$, 17.4°      (8) $2\frac{1}{2}a$

(9) $x = vt/\sqrt{2}, y = vt/\sqrt{2} - \frac{1}{2}gt^2$.
13.9 m s$^{-1}$

(10) (i) centre (2,3), radius 1.      (iii) 2.16, 4.61

(11) (i) $\frac{1}{4}(3m + M)$, $\frac{1}{4}(m + 3M)$      (ii) $\frac{1}{4}(m + M).(m + M)/(3m + M)$

(12) (a) (i) 0.1 (ii) $\frac{1}{5}$      (iii) $\frac{2}{5}$ (b) 0.324

(13) $5.32 < \mu < 5.36$. At least 154.
$z = 1.41$, not sig.

(14) 1/r - 1/(r+1).      (i) $k = \frac{11}{10}$ (ii) $k = 1.\frac{11}{21}$

## Modular Paper P1 Page 496

(1) $x = 2, 3, -\frac{1}{2}$      (2) $\cos^2 x + \sin^2 x = 1.$ $x = 22.5°, 157.5°$

(3) (a) 2      (b) $\frac{1}{2}\sqrt{5} + \frac{1}{2}\sqrt{3}$      (4) 1. $y = -x + 8.$ $x = \frac{2}{3}$

(5) (0,0), (1,1), (1,2), (2,1), (2,2), (2,3), (3,1), (3,2). At (3,2)

(6) 2.83 cm. 109.5°      (7) 62      (8) 82 m

(9) 2,000. $250 \times 2^{4n}$      (10) (a) $-22, -38, 8 - 15x$

(11) $1 + 20x + 190x^2.$ 0.4

## Modular Paper P2 Page 498

(1) $y/x = ax + b$      (2) $1 + \frac{1}{2}x - \frac{1}{8}x^2.$ $1 - \frac{1}{2}x^2$

(3) (a) $x < -2$ or $x > \frac{4}{3}$ (b) $x < -2$      (4) 60.2°

(5) $1/(x + 1) - 1/(x + 2).$ $\frac{1}{2} - 1/(n + 2)$      (6) $-3 \cos t/2 \sin t$

(7) $2\pi.$ 2.24. Underestimate      (8) 71°, 139°

(9) (i) $1 + 5i$      (ii) $\frac{1}{2}(1 - i)$      (iii) $3 - 2i.$

$\sqrt{2}$, 45°. Lengthen by $\sqrt{2}$. Turn through 45° anticlockwise

(10) (i) $-\frac{1}{3} \cos (3x + 2) + c$      (ii) 0.973      (iii) $\frac{1}{4}$

## Modular Paper M1 Page 500

(1) $\mathbf{v} = (2t - 10)\mathbf{i} - 6t\mathbf{j}$    $\mathbf{a} = 2\mathbf{i} - 6\mathbf{j}$    $t = \frac{1}{2}$

(2) $0.0225$ m/s$^2$. 400 secs.      (3) 1.4 m/s$^2$    $\frac{4}{7}$ sec

(4) 3.75 cm from base      (5) $mg/2 \cot \theta$      0.289

(6) 14.4 m/sec. Yes      (7) $\theta \mathbf{i} - \mathbf{j}.$ $\sqrt{2}$

(8) $k = 6.$ 21.3 m/sec      (9) $-\mathbf{i} - \mathbf{j}.$ $\frac{9}{22}$

(10) $v = 21 + 18t - 3t^2.$ $d = 21t + 9t^2 - t^3.$ 48. 245

## Modular Paper S1 Page 502

(1) 0.0589      (2) 2.96, 0.0404, 0.42      (3) 0.037, 0.77

(4) $\mu = 5.31,$ $\sigma^2 = 1.05$

(5) Probs. of 0, 2, 3, 4 are $\frac{125}{216}, \frac{25}{72}, \frac{5}{72}, \frac{1}{216}.$ 7.9% profit

(6) (a) $\frac{3}{8}$      (b) $1\frac{1}{2}$      (c) 0.578125

(7) (a) 0.04      (b) 0.87

(8) $0.0001e^{-0.0001x}$ for $x \geqslant 0.$      $\int_0^\infty x\, e^{-0.0001x} dx$      (c) 6931 hours

(9) $H_0$: $\mu = 50.$ $H_1$ : $\mu < 50.$ $z = 2.83.$ Yes.

(10) Assume normality. $9.7 < \mu < 10.3$

# Index

*Note – always consult the common error section at the end of the chapter in addition to reference given here.*